THE BOOK OF

PISTOLS AND REVOLVERS

The W.H.B. SMITH Classic

Book of
PISTOLS

HARRISBURG, PA.

and
REVOLVERS

completely up-dated by Joseph E. Smith

CASTLE BOOKS
New York

BOOK OF PISTOLS AND REVOLVERS

Printed in the U. S. A.

Foreword

In this edition, readers will notice some changes in format and a considerable change in content. Although the section of the book which deals with pre-World War II and World War II handguns remains essentially the same, the post-war section has been redone with change in emphasis. The material furnished in the past three editions by the late Kent Bellah has been combined in a different format with additional material. The post-war handguns are broken down by country of origin; service handguns are covered first. Sporting and target arms follow in the order of their caliber, ranging from the smaller to the larger.

In order to present additional material on military pistols, it was necessary to compress some of the excellent material of Kent Bellah to keep the book within reasonable size. Thus we have only one chapter on post-war handgun ammunition. There is some coverage on weapons which, technically speaking, are World War II types, but which before were not adequately covered owing to the earlier unavailability of many details.

We live in the age of the specialist; there are excellent books for the specialist on the outstanding pistols—the Colt Peacemaker, the Colt Automatic, the Luger, the Walther, the Savage, the Mauser, etc. Such books cover *specific* pistols in far greater detail than this book can. This book covers all pistols, however, and those which are significant are covered in detail. The genius of W. H. B. Smith and his successor on this book, Kent Bellah, who to the loss of those of us who enjoy guns, died an untimely death in 1966, was that they could and did cover the broad panorama of all pistols.

I do not mean to downgrade in any respect the specialist. It is the specialist who has disinterred ancient bones and killed ancient legends. I freely admit that I have leaned heavily on specialists for much of my data and am proud to number some of them among my close friends. I think we help each other considerably. At least I feel that way; I hope they do. In this age of gun specialization, there are sure to be many differences of opinion. This is a healthy proposition because at this time, as never before in history, there are enough people around to be knowledgeable about pistols and have an opinion.

I do not subscribe to the idea that the field of pistol, rifle, machine gun, etc. development should be the preserve of the "Holy Few." I subscribe to the conviction that all of the good ideas, new principles, new applications, etc., are not necessarily found among those whose paid profession is arms development. There are many people who earn their living by delivering milk, pleading cases in court, preserving our wildlife, upholding the law or serving in our Armed Forces who have the spark that will speed our developments.

This book is aimed at those having a general interest in the field of handguns and who want to broaden their knowledge, whether for business or pleasure. I believe that this book will be of value to the professional arms designer and others connected with the manufacture and sale of arms, the law officer who encounters them in the course of his duties, the pistol shooter who enjoys—and long may he enjoy it—the thrill of putting 5's in the center of the black, and the Serviceman who may have to use these—innocuous in themselves—pieces of machinery to protect himself and these United States of America.

JOSEPH E. SMITH
Vienna, Virginia

Acknowledgments

I would like to thank the following individuals who have assisted in one way or another in the preparation of this edition.

Gen. Frank S. Besson, Jr., Dr. Fred H. Carten, Mr. A. C. Bonkemeyer, Mr. T. E. Cosgrove and Mr. Joe Penton of the U.S. Army Materiel Command, Col. G. Stevens, Col. G. M. Payne, Mr. J. J. Reen, Mr. Harold Johnson, Mr. Phillip Valentini, Mr. C. J. Hamasaki and Mr. L. C. Burden of the U.S. Army Foreign Science and Technology Center, Mr. Tom Wallace of Springfield Armory, Mr. R. C. Maguire of U.S. Army Weapons Command, Rock Island, Ill., Mr. Howard Johnson of Aberdeen Proving Ground and Col. G. B. Jarrett, USAR Ret'd, formerly of that installation, Mr. Donald Bady of New York City, Mr. Tom Nelson of Alexandria, Va., Mr. Daniel D. Musgrave of Cabin· John, Md., Mr. Fred Dardick, Mr. I. J. Osacar of Buenos Aires, Argentina, Mr. Fred Datig of Neuhausen am Rheinfalls, Switzerland, Mr. Jack Krcma of the Institut De Medecine Légale et de Police Scientifique, Montreal, Canada, Maj. R. French of the Ministry of Defence, London, Mr. H. L. Visser of Nederlandsche Wapen en Munitiefabriek S'Hertogenbosch, the Netherlands.

The following firms have been very helpful: Colt Industries Inc., Firearms Div.; Smith & Wesson, Springfield, Mass.; Sturm Ruger & Co., Southport, Conn.; Harrington & Richardson, Worcester, Mass.; Thompson Center Arms, Rochester, N. Y.; Interarmco, Alexandria, Va.; Firearms International, Washington, D. C.; Hammerli, Lenzburg, Switzerland; P. Beretta, Gardone, Italy; Heckler & Koch A. G., Oberndorf; Carl Walther, Ulm, A/D, W. Germany; Astra Unceta y Compania, Guernica, Spain; V. Bernardelli, Gardone, V. T. Italy; Llama-Gabilondo y Compania, Vitorio, Spain; Iver Johnson Arms & Cycle Works, Fitchburg, Mass.; MAB, Bayonne, France; Manufrance, St. Etienne, France; Miroku Firearms Mfg. Co. Ltd., Inari-Cho Kochi, Japan; SIG, Neuhausen am Rheinfalls, Switzerland; Star, Bonifacio Echeverria, S. A. Eibar, Spain; Armas "Trejo" S. A. Zacattan Pue. Mexico; Manufacture D'Armes des Pyrénées Françaises, Hendaye France; Amadeo Rossi & Cia, Rio Grande do Sul, Brazil.

I must also gratefully acknowledge the assistance of many people and organizations, most named above, but some possibly—and I apologize herewith for my neglect—not mentioned who have assisted both actively and sympathetically with this work. None has, however, suffered as much as my wife and family who have again had to live with a littered house and a somewhat "abstract" husband and father during the period of my labors on this edition.

J. E. S.

Contents

PART I. HANDGUNS TO INCLUDE WORLD WAR II
BY W. H. B. SMITH

CONTENTS

xiii

CONTENTS

General Note on Ballistic Data of Cartridges

The ballistic data on U. S. handgun cartridges in Part I was prepared for this book by Western Cartridge Company.

Ballistic data on foreign and obsolescent cartridges was prepared for this book by the H. P. White Company, Ordnance Engineers, of Bel Air, Maryland.

In Part II, ballistics are supplied by Winchester-Western, Remington-Peters, Norma-Precision, Shooters Service, and Kent Bellah. The designations following the caliber are the trade names used by the various makers. Similar loads giving approximately the same results are generally sold by other standard ammunition manufacturers under their individual trade designations.

General and explanatory notes on the various cartridges in Part I are from the files of the late Walter H. B. Smith, while those in Part II are from the files of Kent Bellah and Joseph E. Smith.

It must be emphasized that all ballistic data refers to the specific cartridges examined or tested. Velocities, pressures, energies and penetration figures vary slightly not only with manufacturers but even with different loadings by the same manufacturer. This is particularly true of foreign loads. The date provided herein is included to serve as a guide only; and is subject to change with manufacturing practice.

The only safe practice is to use ammunition made by reputable companies and guaranteed by them for use in your particular weapon. Handloads are safe and accurate when assembled with the proper components for pressure in a safe range.

Theoretically all U. S. ammunition made for foreign handguns is the same regardless of the manufacturer. Members of the Sporting Arms and Ammunition Manufacturers Institute are all supposed to work to the same specifications. In actual practice there are still enough manufacturing variables involved that various brands should be tested in individual arms. Foreign pistols which will not properly chamber one U. S. brand may function perfectly with another.

PART I: Handguns To Include World War II

By W. H. B. SMITH

Preface to the Early Edition

THE STORY OF PISTOLS AND REVOLVERS

The story of the inventions and developments of pistols, revolvers, and automatic pistols, from their earliest forms to the present day, is a complex one. It is really a part of many other stories: *Of ammunition,* from the crudest black powder to the most modern brass—and steel-cased center-fire rimless cartridges with smokeless propellants. *Of ignition systems,* from the primitive touching of a lighted match to powder over a simple priming hole in the barrel to the most advanced flying firing pins striking swiftly at the metal primer cup to crush the priming mixture and flash fire into the propelling charge. *Of mechanical developments,* from the simple hollow metal tube fastened to a stick which formed the early cannon-locks, to the present finely machined double-action automatic pistols which, once loaded, require only successive pulls on the trigger to discharge their magazines. *Of metallurgy,* from the crude iron which would stand the blast of the weak early powders, to the high-tensile metals which permit the use of today's charges developing pressures in the tens of thousands of pounds.

It is part and parcel, too, of the rise of the common man. The development of firearms as cheap and readily produced instruments of force gradually brought home to the robber barons of early days the necessity for easing social conditions which could stir up armed strife in which the serf was a match for his lord in combat.

Their story reaches deep into the history of art, of sport, and of the military sciences. Theirs is indeed a complex story.

This book tells in words, statistics, photographs, and drawings such parts of that story as have a direct bearing on modern, successful pistols, revolvers, and automatic pistols. This is a book fashioned directly from existing weapons and from the records and tools and blueprints of those who make or made them.

The drawings and photographs, all originally planned and designed to tell what mere words alone cannot tell, have the further feature of being an art form rather than a series of mechanical drawings or blueprints. Understanding them requires no special knowledge. The book has a utilitarian, definite purpose: To present in the most graphic manner, every weapon and every operating principle and mechanical development thus far produced which has proven sound in practice; or which occurs frequently enough that its merit makes it worthy of attention or further research.

1

Because this book is intended to cover, primarily, modern weapons we will deal but briefly with the past. Histories must always deal in conjecture, in opinion, and in the finding of earlier writers, researchers, and historians. If we remember that firearms were in general use in Europe for two centuries or so before the introduction of printing there, it becomes immediately apparent that trustworthy accounts of early arms developments are difficult to unearth; the more so when it is realized that inventions very often appear simultaneously in widely separated parts of the world, and that only the Church had facilities for communication in the Middle Ages. Developments in Germany and Italy of those days seem to have followed so closely that it is often impossible to ascribe a new design either to a given year or a given country.

Many histories seek to establish that pistols and gunpowder first made their appearance in the Far East and came to Europe through Arabia. My own study and research among museums, manuscripts, and contemporary tapestries throughout Europe leads me to believe that such histories have been influenced too much by legends, technically incorrect translations, and ambiguous accounts. Lieutenant Colonel H. W. L. Hime published in London, in 1915, *The Origin of Artillery*, unquestionably the most exhaustive work the world has yet seen dealing with the invention of gunpowder. Weighing all the evidence presented in previous books, showing in detail the misapprehensions which arose when authors dealt with languages, sciences, periods, and customs with which they were not thoroughly familiar, Colonel Hime concluded that true gunpowder (as distinguished from "Greek fire" preparations) should be ascribed to Europe in the Middle Ages.

It advanced through but few elementary stages from its first specific mention by Roger Bacon in 1249, until the 16th century. In 1540 a treatise was published in Venice, Italy, under the title *De la Pirotechnia*, by Vanucchio Biringuccio. In 1546 one of the most remarkable research manuscripts in the long history of explosives made its appearance under the title *Questi e Inventioni Diversi*. This work marks Tartaglia, the author, as one of the true scientists of recorded history, little though his name is known. In an earlier book, *Nuova Scienzia*, published in Venice in 1537, he first applied abstract mathematical reasoning to the use of artillery, establishing among other things that no portion of a projectile's flight is ever in a straight line. He was probably the discoverer of the gunner's quadrant.

However, Tartaglia's most amazing sections in the 1540 book are those dealing with actual gunpowder formulae. He gives twenty-five detailed, specific compositions covering all types of powders from those giving a faint squib action, through priming powders, to types entirely too powerful to be used in ordinary weapons. At this period, when knowledge of chemistry was just developing, Tartaglia employed an inspired combination of deductive reasoning and routine trial-and-error methods to develop these formulae.

While the scientist himself is little known, his formulae are well known because, ironically enough, Nicola Machiavelli in *The Arte of Warre* (English Whithorne translation, 1588) copies them exactly—and without credit to Tartaglia.

Just when or where originated the idea of loading powder and ball together

2

in a piece of paper or linen so the entire barrel charge could be loaded down the muzzle speedily and easily, again is not clear. However, as early as 1590, Sir John Smythe, in his *Certain Discourses Concerning the Formes and Effects of Divers Sorts of Weapons,* makes specific mention of musketeers loading with a single operation by the use of "cartages" containing both powder and ball.

Even today, incorrect ideas about weapons reach the public and become records which some future researcher accepts in good faith, only to be entirely in error in his findings. In a book once distributed by the hundreds of thousands of copies, Sergeant Bill Mauldin, one of the finest living depictors of army life, a soldier who fought with courage and honor against the Germans in Africa and Europe, who faced all German equipment and handled much of it—a man in short whom any future writer might reasonably accept as an authority to quote—says, "The P-38 (German pistol) is the mass production model of the Luger." In actual fact, the Luger (as we call it in this country) was patented in Germany by George Luger in 1902, was adopted by the German Army in caliber 9 mm. in 1908, and was officially known in Germany as the "P-08"—pistol adopted in 1908. It is a distinctive striker-fired weapon with a toggle-locked breech. The "P-38," or official German pistol adopted in 1938, is an entirely different arm invented by Karl Walther about 1937. It has an external hammer, is double action, and has an entirely different type of rising-block breech. The only thing the Luger and the P-38 have in common is that they use the same cartridge! Here is the result of a statement of a good soldier who has handled the weapon, but whose background in weapons did not qualify him as an observer.

But Sergeant Mauldin is hardly to be blamed, since official British Intelligence publications as late as 1942 would give only sketchy descriptions of the P-38, which was classed as something of a mystery weapon, illustrated with a sketchy line drawing later borrowed for use in official United States and British handbooks. Any future researcher encountering reports from such sources might reasonably assume that the P-38 was something hitherto unknown. But was it? As a matter of cold fact, it was given an entire page of description, with excellent photographs, in the 1939 catalog of the Stoeger Arms Company of New York City, importers who actually sold the pistol in the United States before the outbreak of the war! It is evident, therefore, that even trained intelligence organizations are not necessarily reliable as sources of information.

Even today writers with a knowledge of foreign languages are unable to analyze foreign arms (or any other) technical developments without a thorough knowledge of the subject itself. The best general translator available cannot make intelligible a handbook on German or Russian arms unless it happens to be so well illustrated that the drawings fill in the gaps in the word translations. This applies particularly to the German arms which by and large have been the most highly developed during the past thirty years. As they developed new designs and refinements, the Germans coined new words. Hence, even an arms expert might be unable to visualize a new development from a correctly translated description of it. Consider the German term "Scheintot Pistol." Literally translated it means "Appearance-of-Death Pistol." This is a variety of pistol intended to shoot gas cartridges. When of standard pistol size, it

3

usually has a barrel constricted enough to prevent the passage of a bullet. The name developed from the fact that the gas it projects will produce unconsciousness—"the appearance of death"—when used at close quarters. Unless one has a very close acquaintance with German arms, or has an opportunity to examine and use both the ammunition and the pistol, it would take a vivid imagination indeed to identify and classify this weapon.

To prevent such errors in the body of the present work, I have not written about any weapon without personally examining and using it. While I have had recourse to all the published literature in French, Italian, Spanish, Portuguese, German, Swedish, and English, as well as to some in Russian and Japanese, and have in every modern instance examined the manufacturer's literature on the weapons described, such recourse has been utilized only to check and amplify my own findings. In the Russian, Japanese, and Swedish books and pamphlets I have had the translating cooperation of men who knew weapons as well as the languages.

While technical data on United States and British weapons were taken directly from the manufacturers' records, then checked against representative samples of the arms, all foreign data were developed from several samples of each arm, then checked against the best foreign data available. All technical data, all photographs, all drawings, all explanations of operation, construction and disassembly were worked out from actual weapons. Every conceivable step was taken to make this *a source book*. Any variations found from American data indicate experimental arms or altered arms of which the manufacturer has no record. In foreign arms, any variations indicate at least weapons not widely manufactured, since great pains have been taken to feature those types most widely issued.

Differences of terminology and unusual conditions of manufacture all through history to the present day have also led to honest but fundamental errors by many writers. In the United States during World War I, the service automatic pistol was made by Colt, Remington and Springfield Armory. All look alike but have different stampings. In World War II, the very slightly modified version of this pistol may be encountered stamped only US&S; and some future collector might feel he has stumbled on an exceptional weapon, rather than the standard pistol made by the Union Switch & Signal Company. Or he may find it stamped *Ithaca*—or even *Singer*, for the Singer Sewing Machine Company. All these organizations, as well as Colt's, turned out standard .45 automatics for the Army. Meanwhile, imitations of this design perfect in every exterior detail but bearing no manufacturers name have been made of pot metal in Spain and of second class workmanship in South America. An excellent very close imitation has been made in Sweden. The possibilities for a future researcher with limited facilities making very serious errors are quite apparent.

Yet another factor difficult for any researcher to evaluate except in unusual cases is what constitutes a really "qualified source." Personally I have found that catalogs of the present are not necessarily reliable; hence I have hesitated to use too often the catalogs of the past. If, as has happened, manufacturers and government sources have published and widely distributed data and drawings which are inaccurate, and have failed to check and correct them over the

4

years, it is clear that care must be taken to check even these sources before accepting their material.

Research in the United States has not nearly come into its own; and so we find our manufacturers complacently turning out good arms and smugly assuring all and sundry that they are the very best. As a matter of cold fact, no arms manufacturer in the United States in the year 1945 had either a complete collection of foreign types or an adequate weapons library to enable him to do intelligent research! Within the past month I have had brought to me for inspection a very fine advanced form of automatic pistol which the manufacturer's designers pioneered. A very casual inspection of the arm showed that they had worked and experimented to develop a form of slide mounting and barrel removal which had been worked out in detail in England years ago and had been marketed in the United States by a rival manufacturer; while their trigger bar, sear and hammer actions had been in general use in Germany and Czechoslovakia for years. The point here is not that the American weapon is not a fine, advanced form. It definitely is. The point is that if intelligent research had preceded the development, time and effort and money could all have been saved while achieving the same end.

This book seeks to be more than the bare Story of Revolvers and Pistols. It seeks to be a pattern for beginners of a new approach to research in all mechanical fields. When facts as divorced from opinions can be marshalled and presented properly buttressed by easily grasped drawings and photographs, and when all that is reliably known about a given field can be thereby made available not only to the designer and manufacturer and enthusiast, but also to the amateur and the coming generation; when tomorrow's scientists can readily avail themselves of the labors of those who have preceded them, and can start where their predecessors halted—then and only then will research, both pure and specific, be utilized to the full.

New York   W. H. B. Smith.
December 1945.   ————————

Chapter 1

The Evolution of the One-Hand Gun

Since the earliest times the means of firing a weapon has been called the "lock." The earliest one-hand guns were miniature cannon, elementary tubes of wrought iron fastened to a frame or grip with metal bands or leather thongs.

Like the first cannon, they were loaded with powder, wad, and ball from the muzzle. A hole in the top of the tube at the rear or breech end gave access to the powder charge. A small charge of priming powder was placed over this hole. While the weapon was thrust forward with one hand to "aim" it, a lighted match or a hot wire or iron was applied to the priming powder over the "touch-hole." The ignited priming powder flashed fire down into the main charge in the barrel to discharge the piece.

These early "cannon-locks" are very rare. In view of the very inefficient powders of those early days, as well as the crude method of ignition and aiming, it is obvious that accuracy was out of the question, and that the arm had very little use other than the psychological one of noise-making.

Just when or where the earliest handguns were used is impossible to determine accurately. While W. W. Greener, in *The Gun and Its Development* (London, 1881), cites a number of instances of the reported use of cannon in Spain between 1247 and 1311, the earliest record we can authenticate concerning their introduction is in the chronicles of the city of Ghent, Belgium. Among the records listed for the year 1313 is one which states that in that year the use of cannon was discovered in Germany. In 1314 the same chronicles list shipments of gunpowder and cannon to England. Just how soon after the introduction of cannon the hand versions were used cannot be definitely determined, as recorded items seldom distinguish between heavy portable cannon and small one-hand types which were the forerunners of true pistols.

However, in Grazzini's Chronicle in *Archivio Storico Italiano* we have the authenticated record of an order by the town of Perugia, Italy, for 500 portable bombards of only a span's length. It is noted that they are to be fired from the hand. The Roman "span" then in use was equivalent to 7½" in length.

It would appear that such short arms were in common use at the time, as the town order does not indicate that the items are unusual in any respect. In fact, the Chronicles of Modena, Italy, for the year 1364 list "Four little *scioppi* for the hand" as being among the town's possessions. The term *scioppi*, it may be noted, finally emerged as *sclopetum*, the authorized Latin word for pistol.

Possibly these early arms were generally used fastened to pikes or staffs, but they were obviously capable of use from the hand in pistol fashion.

One of the very few authentic illustrations of a very early short hand gun is to be found in the fresco in the Palazzo Publico at Sienna, Italy, which pictures the battle of Poggibonzi, where the Duke of Calabria defeated the Florentines in the fifteenth century.

Auguste Demmin, whose *Die Kriegswaffen* is a monumental if not always too-well-documented coverage of early arms and armor (an English edition, Black's translation, under the title, *An Illustrated History of Arms and Armour* was published in London in 1877) attributes the earliest use of hand firearms to the Flemings. However, his statements that the town of Liege had made several experiments in manufacturing *knallbuschen* or hand cannon, while probably correct in the face of the known early history of that city, have never been documented.

The first use of the term "handgun" thus far authenticated appears in English records in the year 1386 when one Ralph Hatton sent three to the Chamberlain of Berwick. (See *14th Century Art*, in the 1911 *English Historical Review*).

The first recorded use of the cannon lock as a cavalry weapon is that of the so-called *petronel*, whose barrel was usually about seven inches long and was attached to a wooden staff or welded to an iron rod. The *Mss. of Marianus Jacobus*, written and illustrated in 1449, shows a mounted soldier ready to fire a *petronel*. The barrel is supported by a forked rest attached to the front of the saddle. The stock is held with the left hand while its tip rests against the man's chest. In his right hand he holds a lighted slow match ready to apply it to the touch-hole. The German black knights, the Reiters (also known as Ritters, Raitres) used these against French infantrymen, to their great surprise. While the German records list them only as *knallbuchen* (literally, pop-guns), the French named them *poitrinal*, indicating "fired from the chest" a term probably later corrupted into "petronel." This seems a more logical derivation than that advanced by some writers who have thought petronel was derived from an early Spanish term "pedernal," meaning a firearm.

Combinations of the one-hand cannon with the war mace and the battle axe were common early in the 16th century. Indeed the most reliable museum specimens of the cannon-lock for one hand use are of this variety.

An English development of which many museum specimens of known authenticity exist is the "Holy Water Sprinkler." This instrument is a heavy mace whose front end or head consists of four or more short barrels resembling an over-sized revolver cylinder. These barrels were loaded with powder, ball and wad. Pushing back a cover to the rear of the barrels exposed a cavity leading to a single touchhole. Priming powder was placed in the cavity and, when the weapon was pointed with one hand and a lighted match was thrust down into the priming powder, fire was flashed to all barrels, discharging them simultaneously. This is the earliest authenticated attempt at developing a multi-shot one-hand gun; it is also liberally studded with spikes.

PHASE II—THE MATCHLOCK

The first great advance in pistols, as in all small firearms, came with the introduction of the Matchlock, which made it possible to fire the weapon

7

with one hand and hence gave some opportunity to aim it. In this type of arm the barrel was still loaded with powder, ball and wad rammed down the muzzle, and priming powder was placed over the small touchhole near the breech end of the barrel, or in a shallow pan near the hole.

The very earliest Matchlock as Thierbach copied it from the Glockenton manuscript is merely a curved hook screwed to the right side of the stock. This "serpentine" as it was called (it developed into the "cock" which was roughly equivalent to the "hammer" in a modern revolver) was split at the end to receive a "match" as the prepared slow-burning cord was named. There was no trigger section to this first serpentine. It was merely pushed or pulled to drop the lighted match on the priming powder. The second step appears to have been merely to lengthen the serpentine so a lower arm acted as a trigger to pivot the upper end down into the priming. This was an adaptation of the string release then in use on crossbows. The third step was to provide a slot in the stock and mount the serpentine on a cross-pin which served as a pivot. The use of springs to retain the head of the serpentine in safety and to withdraw it as the weapon fired were the next developments.

While some writers have ascribed the Matchlock development to Liege about 1375, the earliest form of serpentine of which there is satisfactory documentation appears in an early 15th century illustration, now at Vienna, Codex Manuscript 3,069; and it is shown attached to a handgun.

While literally scores of variations of the Matchlock are recognized, they fall into two general classes. One: Those in which pressure on the trigger end of the serpentine merely pivots the upper end to bring the lighted match down into the powder pan. This is the pressure type. Two: Those of later date—generally towards the end of the 15th century—in which a trigger and spring-rebound action drop the lighted match quickly into the priming powder, permitting better aiming and ignition. This is the snapping type.

Probably the most exhaustive study of Matchlocks ever presented is that published in Dresden in 1899 by Thierbach in his work, *Die Geschichtliche Entwickelung der Handfeurwaffen*. No English translation exists.

During the era of the Matchlock dependable English records appear. Under Henry the VIII, for instance, who reigned from 1509 to 1547, we find that many cavalry were armed with early forms of pistols. It is on record, too, that Henry induced Peter Bawd and Peter Van Collen to move from Flanders, where Henry's earliest firearms were made, to London where he set them up in the business of gun making.

In the Ashmolean Museum at Oxford University in England are three pistol barrels of the Matchlock era fastened together to form a single unit revolving on a pin attached to the stock. Each barrel has a separate flash-pan fitted with a sliding cover. This unit formed a three-barreled pistol with a single serpentine. The barrels were loaded from the muzzle in regular fashion; then the pan covers were opened and priming powder placed in each pan, over which the cover was then drawn. In firing, a pan cover was slid forward; the trigger end of the serpentine was pulled to drop the lighted match into the primer pan to fire the first barrel. The barrels were turned by hand to bring the second one in line with the serpentine and the process repeated. Here we have the forerunner of the American "pepperbox" of the 19th century!

The pans and covers on these barrels (which, by the way, are usually credited to the 15th century) resemble very closely those employed on the famous multi-chambered, single-barreled true revolver-type arquebus believed to have belonged to Henry VIII, now in the Tower of London.

It has a single brass barrel, a brass cylinder with eight chambers which was revolved by hand to bring each chamber successively in line with the barrel, and individual priming pans and touch-holes for each chamber. While the lock itself is missing, the construction makes it evident that it was fired with a single-serpentine Matchlock. A Tudor rose is embossed on the pommel. Another early Matchlock revolver, which seems to be of 17th century origin is now part of the Pitt-Rivers Collection at Oxford.

The Matchlock, as in the case of every other advance, persisted long after more efficient systems had been developed. In quite recent years it has been encountered in Mongolia and in Korea.

The Matchlock, of course, suffered from the major defect that it required a lighted slowmatch to fire it, thus rendering it practically useless in surprise attack or for hunting, and making its use in damp or rainy weather very impracticable. It was not until the turn of the 16th century that human ingenuity found a partial answer in the next evolutionary step.

PHASE III—THE WHEEL LOCK

This development completely revolutionized the art of war. It resulted in new tactics which for a time made cavalry supreme on the field of battle. It made ambush with firearms possible for the first time, since it did away with the necessity for the lighted match; and this same feature also made practicable the use of firearms in hunting. Both directly and indirectly it produced economic and military advances of epochal stature.

And what was this startling development? Just a complicated forerunner of our modern pocket lighter!

In its simplest forms it consists of a steel wheel mounted on the side of the weapon at the rear of the barrel. The circumference of this wheel is grooved, roughened or notched. An axle protrudes from the side of the wheel and a spanner or wrench is provided to fit over this protrusion. Inside the lockplate a chain is attached to the inner axle of the wheel at its forward end and to a spring at its rear on the principle of a watch drum. Thus when the wheel is turned with the spanner, the chain is wound around the inner axle and the spring is tensioned. A bar in the lockwork drops into a notch in the wheel, acting as a sear to keep the wheel from revolving and thereby relieving the spring.

Part of the wheel edge projects into the flash pan which communicates with the touchhole in the breech of the barrel. The pan is usually covered, and the cover must be pushed forward when the arm is made ready for firing. The serpentine is pivoted on the side of the lockplate just ahead of the flash pan, where it is held by a powerful spring. The jaws of the serpentine open to the rear and are really a small vise. A piece of pyrites (originally used instead of flint because it would not wear the wheel rapidly) is clamped securely in the jaws and the serpentine is pulled down until the pyrites is in contact with the wheel. Pressing the trigger pulls the stop pin out of the notch in the wheel and frees the spring to unwind the chain. This action of course spins the wheel rapidly on its axle. The edge of the steel wheel strikes sparks from the pyrites and showers them down into the priming powder, igniting it to flash through the touchhole into the barrel charge.

Where did the wheel lock originate? While some writers have ascribed it to Italy, there is weighty evidence to indicate that the wheel lock originated in Nuremberg, Germany, in 1515 or 1517. Records of Germany and of the Low Countries, which even then were hives of activity as arms centers, link the names of Kaspar Rechmagel and Georg Kuhfuss to improvements of the system. But another Nuremberg gunmaker, Johann Kiefuss, is generally credited as the direct inventor.

The Wheel lock made possible the first reasonably satisfactory pistol—more particularly the military cavalry pistol. The Germans, whose Black Knights had already shocked the French by the surprise use of the petronel in Cannon-lock days, speedily applied the Wheel lock to long-barrelled all-steel pistols carried in holsters swung across the pommels of their saddles, each man carrying two or four.

The Century Dictionary and Encyclopedia states that the Ritters made common use of pistols in 1520. Whether they were armed widely with Wheel locks at that time is not certain; but in 1544, at the battle of Renty, they introduced against the French King Henry II an entirely new maneuver using pistols as their main arm.

While the French waited in formation for the charge, the Ritters galloped in rank formation almost to the French lines, discharged their pistols into the massed men, then wheeled their horses out of line to reload while their next rank rode up to continue pouring demoralizing fire from their pistols. This manuever, afterwards named "caracole," was adopted by the French. Henry shortly afterwards hired the Ritters (who were paid mercenaries, the Hessians of those early days) to join his army. Henry of France called these troops "Pistoleers."

And here develops one of the puzzles of firearms history: *Why is a pistol called a pistol?*

Most dictionaries and encyclopedias repeat the early explanation that the pistol was invented by one Camillio Vettelli in Pistoia, Italy, about 1540. So far as I have ever been able to determine, no satisfactory documentation exists for that statement. Vettelli as a gunmaker may have lived, though even that has not been clearly established.

As indicated above, short guns of the pistol type existed long before the date ascribed to Vettelli; and in view of the development and use of Wheel lock pistols in Germany, France, Belgium, Holland, and even England—records of the time of King Henry VIII of England show that some of his cavalry were armed with clumsy Wheel lock pistols by 1545—it is difficult to believe that all Europe, in less than five years, in those days of slow travel and poor communication, would have evolved the term "pistol" or "pistole" from the name of the town of Pistoia.

Could "pistol" have evolved from the fact that the general caliber of the arm was about that of a coin called "pistole," as has also been offered as a derivation? It is rather far fetched, particularly in view of the fact that no two guns were of the same caliber in those days.

Why, then, did Henry II of France name his pistol-carrying troopers "pistoleers?"

There is a third solution, already suggested by Demmin and other researchers whose backgrounds in languages, knowledge of arms, and opportunity to check early European records qualify them as expert witnesses. It seems most likely that the term derived from the fact that those original pistols, commonly associated with the cavalry, were invariably *carried in holsters swung across the pistallo* (or pommel) of the saddle.

The French assigned the name *petronel* quite evidently to a hand weapon hung across the *poitrine*—the chest, and rested against it when firing. What is more logical, then, that a later French king and army should link the name with the method of carrying? Certainly, "pistole" would represent a closer approach to "pistallo," a word any French cavalryman of the day would associate with the pommel of the saddle, than it would to the name of a distant city in Italy which by no stretch of the imagination could have been the source of the surprise mass of weapons the Ritters used against the French at Renty!

The Wheel locks which have come down to us in original condition, and there are thousands of them, are nearly all rich man's weapons. Very few are plain and unornamented. Even the cheapest were far too expensive for the average citizen or for general issue to all soldiers. Other drawbacks were that it took considerable time to wind the spring. If kept wound ready for action, it soon lost its strength, since the steels of those days were not suited for spring purposes. In the heat of battle or the hunting chase the all important spanner might be lost. A cheaper and simpler ignition system was needed.

While the wheel lock pistol reached an advanced stage of evolution in Germany, Belgium, France, and Italy towards the close of the 16th century, it was not widely manufactured in England. The English showed little interest in pistols until the introduction of the flintlock.

One development of this era which has a most important bearing on the use of pistols and all firearms is unfortunately shrouded in mystery. It is the employment of rifling to give better accuracy. The earliest English patent records dealing with rifling are dated 1635. It was employed on the Continent long before that date, Augustin Kotter of Nuremberg being known for star-shaped rifling as early as 1520. Yet in a novel, *Jewel House,* written by Sir Hugh Plat and first published in 1594, there is an account of a *rifled pistol!*

While the Wheel lock was widely manufactured as late as 1640, by the turn of the 17th century it was gradually making way for its successor.

PHASE IV—THE FLINTLOCK

The elementary principle of the Flintlock is that of fastening a piece of flint in the head of the "cock" or hammer, so that when the trigger is pulled the hammer spring will drive the flint down to strike a glancing blow against a piece of case-hardened steel so placed that the resulting sparks shower down into the priming pan.

The evolution of the true Flintlock was long. Just when or just where it first appeared, no man can say positively. The standard way of lighting fires in the day of the early Matchlock was to strike flint against steel. Why, then, the long use of the complicated Wheel lock? Even in our own day we find cheap and simple forms of weapons failing to get attention or acceptance because the military or the manufacturers, for reasons peculiar to them, resist change and simplification. That may have had something to do with the delayed general appearance of the Flintlock. Then, too, the Flintlock made possible the arming of the common man with cheap, dependable weapons, an undesirable factor to those who controlled the policies of those early days.

While isolated examples of the use of some form of Flintlock may be traced, with necessarily foggy documentation, to the early 16th century, its first wide use cannot be established with acceptable proof until the beginning of the 17th century.

Writers in the 17th century listed all flint-and-steel ignition weapons generally as "snaphaunces." It should be noted that this type of ignition differed in the various countries of its manufacture. In an early form in Germany it actually was a steel-and-pyrites system of the type found in the "Monk's Gun" in the Dresden Museum. Pyrites was not satisfactory, however, because it was highly friable. A lock using it had to provide a scraping, rasping effect to produce sparks. This type of lock, though authenticated, is little known.

Modern writers generally distinguish the varieties of flintlocks as follows:

The Snaphaunce. Mechanism and mainspring covered by lock-plate. Cock (hammer) has a miniature vise in its head to hold the flint. Flash-pan opposite touch-hole holds priming powder. A pan-cover, which *must be manually pushed back* in some models before the weapon can be fired, protects the priming. The steel against which the flint is struck, usually works on a hinged arm and was variously called "frizzen," "battery," "hen" or "hammer." The steel is separate from the pan cover.

The derivation of the word "Snaphaunce" is a matter about which experts have quarrelled for centuries. It may be from the Dutch *schnapp-hahn,* indicating a pecking cock (the "cock" or hammer falling and pecking at the "hen" or steel); it may be from the Dutch *snaap-haans,* meaning chicken thieves. (Some of the earliest reported uses of cheap flint-type weapons indicate their employment by poachers). It has been corrupted in both English and French usage and spelling in many ways.

The Miquelet Lock. Mainspring on outside of lock-plate. Steel "frizzen" and pan-cover are *in one piece.* Thus when the cock is driven forward by the mainspring, it strikes the flint against the upright steel piece and, as the sparks shower down, the frizzen is rocked back so its pan-cover section exposes the powder in the priming pan to be ignited by the sparks.

"Miquelet" is said to derive from the Spanish or Portuguese raiders, called *miguelitos,* who first achieved attention for their use of this form of arm. This form of lock is common to all types and qualities of small arms made in Spain at the Flintlock period. Its manufacture was continued well into the 18th century.

The true Flintlock, sometimes called "French Flintlock." Essentially the same as the Snaphaunce except that it uses the Miquelet principle of a combined pan-cover and frizzen. This unit is mounted on a pivot and is spring-supported. The weapon being loaded both in the barrel and in the priming pan, and cocked, pressure on the trigger releases the cock to strike the flint a glancing blow at the upright steel piece. The frizzen, thus rocked back on its pivot as sparks are produced, carries the pan-cover section away from the priming, permitting ignition. These weapons have a half-cock position which serves as a safety. England, Holland, Sweden, and Scotland all produced variations with individual characteristics.

The Flintlock, which survived for over 200 years and is even today made and used in some far corners of the world, appeared at various times in practically every form of one-hand weapon known today, with the sole exception of the automatic pistol! A revolver dating from the period of King Charles I (1625-1647) is in the Tower Collection in London. It is unusual in early revolver types in that the cylinder is automatically revolved as the hammer is raised. A patent was granted the Marquis of Worcester for a revolver in 1661. In *Pepy's Diary* under entry of the 3rd of July, 1662, mention is made of a "gun to discharge seven times," which Mr. Pepys found reliable. On the 3d of March, 1664, patent office specifications were filed by Abraham Hill for a gun or pistol to carry seven or eight charges in the stock. Hill was also granted a patent for a breech-loading gun or pistol "which hath a hole at the upper end of the breech to receive the charge, which hole is opened or stopped by a piece of iron or steel that lies alongside the side of the piece which is movable."

Magnificent Flintlock pistols, with hinged-frame, drop-down barrels very similar to those of the present day, were manufactured in Italy. Many of these were supplied with steel inserts which were carried loaded and were dropped into the breech end of the barrel for quick loading. Side loaders, screw-plug breeches, three and four-barreled pistols, magazine pistols of the "Cookson" type, seven-barrelled pistols revolving around a spindle in the manner of the later "pepperbox" pistols, over-and-under pistols, removable-barrel types—these are but a few of the varieties known and authenticated.

And what about America during the Flintlock period? Of the period before 1680, not much is known. Some very fine examples of pocket-type snaphaunces now in the Smithsonian Institution have come down from the families of early Dutch settlers. Some few gunsmiths came to New England with the twenty-odd thousand souls who came between 1630 and 1640. However, there is no early record of their making pistols. Later, when it was customary to import the locks (which were difficult to make), pistols with those locks were made by numerous gunsmiths.

The records of the Massachusetts Bay Company show the importation of snaphaunce weapons for their soldiers in 1628 and 1629; while early records of the same Company also indicate that about that same time Indians residing near the villages were well supplied with both pistols and bullet molds. The Dutch in those early years did a tremendous business with the Indians in firearms—a business which led to the eventual loss of their American colony. The "bosch-lopers" or woods runners dealing with the Indians as agents of the wealthy patroons found arms and powder the best trading units for fine furs.

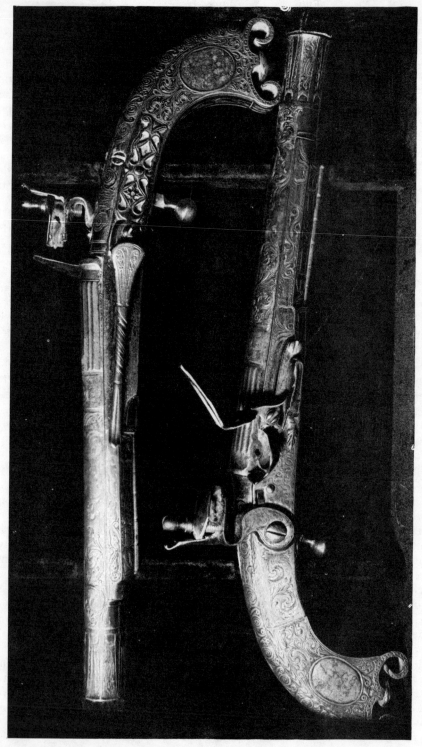

Highlander flintlock pistols carried by the British Commander, Major Pitcairn, at the historic battle on Lexington Common. One of these pistols may have fired the "Shot Heard 'Round the World" which precipitated the battle. These pistols are now in the Museum of the Historical Society at Lexington, Massachusetts.

Pistols are seldom mentioned in the first half of the 17th century in America. The Rev. Wm. Hubbard, of Ipswich, Mass., in his story of the Pequot Wars written in 1677, tells of "pieces laden with ten or twelve pistol bullets" being fired at close range into the Pequots. Bodge, in his *Soldiers in King Phillip's War*, tells how Capt. John Gallup, of Boston Harbor, attacked a boat the Indians had stolen. "Gallup," he writes, "was armed with two guns and two pistols and with buckshot for bullets."

With the start of the French and Indian Wars, however, the picture grows clearer. Pistols now are, for the most part, those manufactured in England or whose locks were made there. The extent to which pistols were in use in the Colonies as the day of the American Revolution drew near may be grasped from the account in Frothingham's contemporaneous *Siege of Boston,* wherein he lists 634 pistols as having been turned in by Boston householders when the British General Gage assured them they might leave the city if the arms were surrendered. (As a matter of further record, General Gage broke his promise.)

And here we reach another milestone in the history, the always-too-obscure history, of firearms: Was "The shot heard round the world" fired from a pistol?

Paul Revere, in his *Letter,* states that a pistol was fired to start the Battle of Lexington. *The Essex Gazette,* Vol. III, No. 352, dated the 25th of April, 1775, makes the same statement. Parson Stiles, an eye witness, in his *Diary* states that British Major Pitcairn, after cursing the Colonists and ordering them to lay down their arms and retreat, when they did not obey, "Rushed forward and discharged his pistol."

If, as might very well have been the case, Major Pitcairn did fire that world-shattering shot, it came from one of two Highlander Flintlock pistols now reposing in the battered little old Hancock Clark House which serves as a Museum at Lexington, Massachusetts. In common with many officers of his day, Pitcairn took great pride in his pair of beautiful all-metal Scotch made pistols whose distinctive grips, magnificent workmanship and quality are still a wonder to every lover of fine hand-guns. These pistols—lineal descendants of the all-metal Wheel lock pistols of the long-dead German Ritters—were carried like their earlier counterparts in holsters swung across the pommel of the saddle, the "pistallo" of an earlier day. As the British retreated from the Common, shots fired from ambush hit Pitcairn's horse, throwing the rider. The wounded horse bolted and was captured, with the pistols hung from the pommel, by Minute Men. The pistols were offered to General Washington, who declined to accept them. It is an interesting sidelight on Washington that, except for presentation pistols, all weapons we can trace definitely to him have been plain, unornamented arms intended strictly for field use.

Pitcairn's pistols were carried throughout the War by Captain Parker, and were later donated to the little Museum where they now rest, little known and less seen—a strange commentary on the interest the average man has in the people and the things which paved the way for his present liberties.

As an evidence of the extent to which the Flintlock pistol contributed to later American history, consider the fact that some 70,000 men shipped out of New England ports alone aboard privateersmen during the War of 1812, and that it was customary for such men to carry at least two heavy belt pistols, as close-quarter arms for boarding ships. Yet today only a handful of pistols of this type are in the hands of collectors. Such is the way with weapons of use—as opposed to ornamented weapons—at the close of each war.

As the 18th century drew to a close, experience had shown that, with flint-lock ignition, only the single and the double-barrelled pistols were truly prac-tical. While authorized pistols were made in America during the Revolutionary period by the Committee of Safety's orders, the first official pistol contract let by the United States Government was not until 1799 when Simeon North fur-nished 500 North and Cheney pistols.

Early in the 19th century attempts were again made to apply the multishot ideas to the Flintlock. "Pepper-box" Flintlocks similar to the somewhat earlier Twigg and Ketland types; "volley guns" of the Nock type in which several barrels are fired simultaneously by a single flint; magazine weapons of the Mortimer type in which two motions of a lever loaded the barrel, primed the pistol and cocked the arm for firing—these and scores of other types were tried.

In 1818, Elisha H. Collier, of Boston, Massachusetts, was granted an English patent on a Flintlock revolver of unusual design. The first of Collier's revolv-ers was developed in the United States by Artemus Wheeler who obtained a patent in 1818. Specimens of Collier's revolver exist with four-inch barrels and an overall length of about eleven and one-half inches; also with six and one-eighth-inch barrel, longer (one and seven-eighths inch) cylinders, and overall length of about fourteen inches.

An automatic primer holding enough priming powder for about ten charges was mounted on top of the pan cover. The cylinder, which contained five chambers, was rotated to bring each chamber in line with the barrel for firing. The truly original feature of the Collier, however, was the gas-check cylinder which was used in principle in the Russian Nagant Service revolver, and which may possibly be further developed. The rear or breech end of the barrel was cone-shaped, and the chambers in the cylinder had countersunk mouths. The cylinder was normally thrust forward by a spiral flat spring working on a center pivot, and was supported when firing by a trigger-actuated sliding bolt. In its forward position the chamber ready for firing was thrust over the tapered end of the barrel, thus assuring positive alignment of barrel and cylinder (the most important feature in revolver design), and also hold-ing to a minimum the escape of gas between cylinder and barrel, thereby as-suring the utmost use of the power of the discharge and reducing the danger of fire from one chamber setting off the charges in the other chambers. The cylinder had to be drawn back about one-eighth of an inch against spring tension before it could be revolved on its center pin. While a few samples of the Collier were known later for use with percussion powder, the patent granted covered use of the Flintlock system of ignition.

By now the era of the Flintlock was drawing to a close. Where all major evolutionary steps had heretofore been the result of mechanical changes in ignition systems, chemistry now entered the field.

16

PHASE V—THE PERCUSSION LOCK

"I do make use of some one of the compounds of combustible matter, such as sulphur or sulphur and charcoal, with an oxymuriatic salt; . . . . or of fulminating metallic compounds, as fulminate of mercury . . . . Instead of permitting the touch-hole, or vent, of the species of artillery, fire-arms, mines, etc., to communicate with the open air, and instead of giving fire by lighted match, or flint and steel, or by any other matter in a state of actual combustion applied to a priming in an open pan, I do so close the touch-hole, or vent, by means of a plug or sliding piece so as to exclude the open air . . . .; and, as much as possible to force the said priming to go in the direction of the charge and to set fire to the same . . . ."

Those direct quotations from the letters patent of the Rev. Alexander John Forsyth, LL.D., (for fifty-two years minister of Belhelvie, Scotland), dated the 11th of April, 1807, mark the accepted legal proof of the application of a revolutionary principle for exploding gunpowder—the percussion principle. Heretofore it had been necessary to produce fire to explode the charge. Now the priming could be done by a blow delivered directly by the hammer. With the development of this principle, the successful revolver was at last to become an actuality.

Forsyth did not discover the fulminating mixtures. Even before 1700 a German scientist, Johann Von Lowenstern, is known to have conducted inquiries into this field. Nicholas Lemery gives notices in the reports of the Royal Academy of Sciences of experiments in 1712 and again in 1714. The first important authenticated discovery, however, is that of Louis XV's Chief Army Physician, Dr. Bayen, who reported fulminate of mercury and told of its explosive properties. As in the case of Roger Bacon, who, in 1249, described gunpowder without apparent thought to its application to firearms, Bayen overlooked the application of mecuric fulminate to weapons. Berthollet, in 1788, was injured doing experimental work which resulted in the ultra-sensitive silver fulminate. In 1800, "Howard's powder," a mixture of mercuric fulminate and saltpeter, was developed in England as an outgrowth of the inventor's study of earlier French researches.

But first official *application* of the principle is credited to the Rev. Forsyth.

From 1807 to 1845 a tremendous range of systems for applying the percussion principle was developed, as well as of weapons to use these systems. In 1812, a Swiss gunmaker, Pauly, then working in Paris, patented a paper cap in which fulminate was enclosed. This was fired by a needle driven through the paper when the trigger was pulled. Somewhat later, the priming mixture came in pellets and resulted in the development of "pill-lock" pistols, many of most ingenious design. Egg, Manton, and other famous gunmakers, as well as dozens of lesser known figures, claimed to have invented the most successful percussion system—that of the metal cap in which the fulminate was housed so that the cap could be placed over the nipple of the touch-hole and fired when the falling hammer crushed the cap.

However, the earliest instance of use duly credited seems to be that of an Englishman, Joshua Shaw, then working in Philadelphia, Pa. In 1814, he employed a steel cap, which could be reloaded. In 1815, he used pewter and,

17

in 1816, developed the copper cap used through the American Civil War period.

The Maynard tape primer was invented in the United States in 1845. It fed fulminate, held between strips of paper as in children's cap pistols, into position to be struck by the hammer. Variations were copper strip primers on the general principle of the tape, and disc primers. All met with some temporary success.

Of all systems, that of the copper cup which could be placed over the nipple was by far the best. Although its application was made to both breech and muzzle loading arms, it was truly successful only in the latter, since escape of gas at the breech was not fully controllable in early breech-loaders.

In the United States, Deringer of Philadelphia was the first to develop a pistol to use the new percussion cap. The first models were very small compact muzzle loaders of .51 caliber shooting a half-ounce ball. These arms were widely used during the great American era of the Ohio and Mississippi steamboats. It was with one of them that John Wilkes Booth killed President Lincoln; and it is a strange comment on the history of mankind that the publicity given the Deringer as a result of Lincoln's assassination resulted in such a huge demand for the arm that imitators of the pistol sprang up overnight and plagued the original maker for years by unfair competition.

In 1845, Ethan Allen patented the arm which was one of the principal weapons of the "49-ers"—the Allen & Thurber pepperbox. At the age of twenty-one, Allen, then living at North Grafton, Massachusetts, had manufactured cane guns for a Dr. Lambert. At twenty-three he was turning out rifled pistols with saw-handle grips. It is possible that he was the real inventor of the "double-action lock," in which simple pressure on the trigger acts both to cock and drop the hammer. In England, pepperboxes are thought to have been introduced some time before the Allen. However, the record is not clear, and it is probable that the invention had parallel development in several countries. Clustered barrel arms, similar to the pepperbox, appeared as early as the mid-16th Century, but Allen's was the first to have a double-action lock.

In the case of the Allen, both patents and weapons definitely establish that Ethan Allen actually manufactured them for general sale. The pepperbox is essentially a series of barrels—usually six—either gathered together around a central axis pin or bored from a single block of metal. This design, obviously, results in a very heavy weapon for any caliber employed. The weapon was loaded from the muzzle and percussion caps were placed over the individual nipples at the breech. They were held on by an enclosing metal band at the breech. The lockwork is timed so that, as the trigger is pressed, it raises the hammer and turns the barrel assembly. At each fall of the hammer a barrel is in line to have its percussion cap crushed to fire that barrel, the entire barrel assembly being momentarily locked by mechanical action.

The Pepperbox cannot be fired with any degree of accuracy because of the heavy trigger pull required. However, as a dependable, close-quarters weapon —both as a firearm and as a club in emergency—it was quite successful in its day

One other specimen of pepperbox is worthy of American note: the almost unknown "Blunt & Syms." Unlike the Allen, which had a top hammer, this arm had an underhammer. Blunt & Syms, of 44 Chatham Street, New York City, were among the largest gun dealers in the country in the 1830's and for the following two decades. One of their employees, John Zettler, who came to the United States from Marburg, Germany, in 1837, manufactured a model of a pepperbox for an inventor whose name is lost to record. He never made an appearance to claim his model, and Blunt & Syms took out patents on it and put it into manufacture. Naturally, they sold their own arm wherever possible, and large quantities went to California in the period of 1849. These pistols usually had six barrels, each about five and one-half inches long. The bullets used were distinctive, being .368 in diameter and .430 inch long. These egg-shaped bullets would turn end-on-end at ten yards; but what they lacked in accuracy they made up in close-quarters stopping power.

The Belgian "Mariette" pepperbox system used on the Continent was patented in Belgium in 1837. This was an underhammer weapon operated by trigger pull. The barrels had to be unscrewed from the frame to permit the priming powder to be loaded in. The nipples were in line with the axis of the barrels, thus varying from the standard vertical type.

All these were merely transitional arms, however; for, with the coming of percussion caps, Samuel Colt had found the way to provide a rifled, multishot arm in which a single action would cock the hammer and revolve and lock the cylinder; an arm which would combine accuracy, sturdiness, simplicity, and dependability, and which, having only one barrel, was lighter than the pepper-boxes of comparable power.

The First Successful Revolver

In the long history of pistols and revolvers, no name stands out as clearly as that of Samuel Colt. "Colt" has become synomymous with revolver. Yet Colt did not invent the revolver as such, and never claimed he did.

As we have seen, the principle of the true "revolver"—a weapon with a revolving cylinder containing a number of firing chambers which may be successively lined up with and discharged through a single barrel—was known in very early times. Perhaps the most famous early revolver is that mentioned in General Norton's *American Breech Loading Small Arms,* published in 1872. This is a Snaphaunce revolver of the days of King Charles I of England, and is still to be seen in the Royal United Service Museum in Whitehall. The date of manufacture is prior to 1650.

This early revolver, astonishingly enough, is practically identical with the action covered in Colt's first patents and still used in that most famous of all Colt's, the Single Action Army or "Frontier" Model! A ratchet with six teeth is cut into the head of the cylinder. As the hammer is thumbed back, a metal hand attached to the front of the hammer thrusts up against the ratchet to turn the cylinder the distance of one chamber. A spring catch engages in a notch in the cylinder to lock it at that point. This early revolver is a brass-barrelled, brass cylindered giant of .500 caliber with a nine and one-half-inch barrel. It is nearly twenty-two inches long and weighs about six and one-quarter pounds. The barrel is badly worn, but seems to have the remains of rifling in it. Ignition and metallurgy were not far enough advanced when it was designed to make it a success, but it is strange indeed that its revolving system should have been overlooked for centuries.

Samuel Colt's original patent was granted in England—then the seat of small-arms manufacture in the world—in 1835. While it dealt with the revolving of the cylinder by action of the hammer-attached hand acting on the cylinder ratchet when the hammer was cocked, it specified in great detail the feature of center-fire ignition through horizontal nipples which were separated by partitions to prevent the accidental firing of chambers adjoining the one in line with the barrel. It also dealt specifically with the lockwork. It was first patented in the United States on the 25th of February, 1836.

The first model Colt had made for him by Anson Chase of East Hartford, Connecticut, blew up because it lacked partitions between the nipples. The discharge of the first chamber set off the others. His next one, now in the Colt Museum at Hartford and known as the "Anson Chase Model," from the name of the gunsmith who made it, bears in general appearance and in weights and measurements an astonishingly close resemblance to the Single Action Army model still in manufacture.

Colt's patents were so ironclad, and he fought so hard to protect them, that nothing but freak revolvers were developed from 1840 to 1850, either in the United States or in Europe. Colt's first production revolvers were made at Paterson, N. J. That company went bankrupt. Six years later, at the outbreak of the Mexican War, Colt with the help of Eli Whitney—one of the earliest of the assembly-line-production geniuses—and with suggestions from Captain Walker of the Texas Rangers, was back in production at Whitneyville. Shortly afterward, Colt was able to finance his own orders, and he started at Hartford the plant which was to become the best-known revolver manufactory in history.

By 1850, Colt was exporting to Europe. In 1853, he opened a plant in London, using trained men brought from the United States as foremen.

The only British competition Colt received during these years was from the Deane-Adams revolver patented in 1851. This was the first successful, solid-frame revolver. The barrel and the frame were a single forging, providing a weapon which was actually stronger than the Colt of that period. This was a double-action revolver in which a pull on the trigger rotated the cylinder, cocked and dropped the hammer. While others were made—notably the Lang and the Witton & Daw—they were too expensive to compete with the mass-production Colts.

In February, 1855, the Beaumont selective double-action system was patented in England. This was a real advance in lockwork, as it permitted the revolver to be thumb cocked, then fired by trigger pressure—or fired double action by pulling through on the trigger to raise and drop the hammer. This Beaumont action was incorporated in the Adams revolver. Later, when Adams sold out to the London Armoury Company and that company was awarded a government contract for the double-action Adams as the British service revolver, Colt saw the writing on the wall and, in 1857, shut down the London factory. Tranter, Webley, Kerr, Daw and Westley Richards all made percussion revolvers in England, none of which had the success of the Adams. In Europe Comblain of Liege, Belgium developed a single action weapon in 1854,

Amangeot of Brussels developed a double action system; but in general nothing of particular merit emerged.

In the United States, when the Colt patents expired, a wide variety of revolvers flooded the market. Of those used during the Civil War, the best is the Remington—a standard design percussion cap revolver. Another type, the Starr, had a double trigger. Pressure on the first trigger raised the hammer and revolved the cylinder. Continued rearward pressure forced the second trigger to trip the hammer. The Pettingill was a massive .44 caliber hammerless (enclosed hammer design) and had a quick-removable cylinder. The Savage, patented by H. S. North in 1865, was single-action and had a ring trigger and a spur-type trigger. Like the earlier Collier flintlock revolver, the Savage employed the principle of the chambered cylinder. Action of the trigger-guard lever forced the mouth of the cut-back chamber over the breech end of the barrel to make a gas-seal.

But again a new phase was underway, a new era beginning. In France, experiments with breech-loading arms were underway, and the end of muzzle-loading revolvers was in sight.

PHASE VI—THE METALLIC CARTRIDGE

The Pinfire

The Pauly cartridge already mentioned paved the way for the Lefaucheux Pinfire cartridge, which in its original form closely resembled the modern shotgun cartridge. Its base was a brass cap, its body a pasteboard tube carrying the powder, ball, and percussion cap. A pin through the side of the case rested on the percussion cap. This system made it possible to confine the gases in the chamber at the instant of firing, as the brass expanded momentarily and provided a positive breech seal.

Lefaucheux Pinfire revolvers in various types of 5 mm., 7 mm., 9 mm., 12 mm., and 15mm calibers are still widely found in Europe and South America, the cartridges being standard manufacture there before the outbreak of World War II. In this type of revolver the cylinder is notched at the side of each chamber at the breech end. The cylinder, instead of being solid except for the touch-hole, as required in percussion types, is bored through with chambers so that the complete cartridge can be inserted in the chamber through the breech. The pin projecting from the side of the cartridge case (which is now made of copper or brass), drops into the notch prepared for it. It will be seen that this requires the cartridge to be loaded in the chamber in just one way. That is, if the pin is not opposite its notch, the cartridge cannot enter the chamber fully.

In a Pinfire revolver, when the trigger is pressed and the hammer falls, the hammer strikes the projecting pin and drives it down inside the case to explode the primer which sets off the powder charge. The expansion of the gas inside the cartridge case swells the case to grip momentarily against the chamber wall as the bullet is driven out of the chamber. Thus any rearward escape of gas is impossible—unless, as happens on occasion, the head of the case is weak. Even then, little harm can result. The projecting pin can be used to lift the empty case out of its chamber.

21

Rimfire

With the introduction of the Rimfire cartridges, however, the true story of the modern revolver begins. The honor of its initial development belongs to a Paris gunsmith, Flobert, who produced it as early as 1847, and who exhibited it at the Great International Exhibition in London in 1851. How Colt, whose revolvers achieved great attention and renown at that same Exhibition, ever missed the potentialities of the metallic cartridges, is another of the mysteries of the history of revolvers. Flobert's invention is in use today. We know it as the "BB Cap"—the bulleted breech-cap. As originally issued it contained no powder. It was designed for indoor target service, and the fulminate under the rim provided all the power necessary to drive the bullet out. The Rimfire cartridge has a relatively soft copper case with a hollow rim in which is the priming mixture. The rim rests on the cylinder metal around the chamber. When the hammer falls, its nose (or a special firing pin, as the revolver design requires) hits the rim of the cartridge case, crushing it and thus detonating the priming mixture.

In 1857, Smith & Wesson produced the first revolver to fire rimfire cartridges; a hinged-frame revolver of .22 caliber in which the barrel was tipped up on a hinge at the top of the standing breech. This permitted the cylinder to be removed for loading and unloading. Smith & Wesson had previously patented a center-fire cartridge and had worked on the idea of a revolver to use it. They found that a patent for the necessary type of cylinder, bored through to permit insertion of cartridges through the breech end, had been granted to Rollin White on April 3, 1855. Their purchase of those patents gave them a monopoly on the device needed to use metallic cartridges until 1869. Where Colt had formerly strangled development, Smith & Wesson now were able to do the same.

Colt introduced the "Thuer Alteration" which made possible the use of either percussion or a special metallic ammunition inserted from the front of the cylinder. This and dozens of other hybrids were produced while the arms makers sat back and waited for the S&W patents to expire; just as previously they had had to wait for Colt's to expire.

The Civil War was fought almost entirely with Percussion-lock revolvers, but the arms most highly prized by the few who could get them were Smith & Wesson's of .22 and .32 rim-fire caliber. The Colt Model of 1860, a .44 caliber six shooter was the most widely used revolver in that War, over 100,000 having been made.

In 1871 and 1872 Colt's purchased patents covering an alteration which permitted loading rimmed cartridges from the rear. It again was a series of freaks. In 1872 an open top .44 was introduced, which paved the way for the most famous revolver in all history—the solid frame Single Action Army which was issued in 1873.

With the passing of the Smith & Wesson patents, a flood of breech loading arms in calibers from .22 to .50 were marketed. This era saw the introduction of the counterbored or recessed-head cylinder, where the entire cartridge head is below the outer circumference of the cylinder to prevent injury from a blownout cartridge case head—a feature used also in Europe about the same time, and which appeared in the 20th century as a "modern" development. The Colt House Pistol, the Remington Elliot, and the Italian Glisenti were just a few to employ it.

General Norton, writing in 1872, states that the Union Metallic Cartridge Company at Bridgeport, Connecticut was then the largest and best known cartridge company in the United States. He lists the sale of .22 Smith & Wesson (the .22 short) cartridges as being then 30,000,000 per year. Truly the era of the revolver had arrived.

In Europe and in England numerous experiments were underway, though few were put into general production, and fewer had any real merit. Except for the beginning of the Webley firm as arms manufacturers of quality in England, there were few developments of interest.

The day of the Rimfire, except for the super-accurate .22, was on the way out, as was the copper cartridge case associated with the Rimfires. They continued to be manufactured until well into the present century; but today only the .22 remains—a monument to the original cartridge design Smith & Wesson developed from the Flobert cap.

The Center-Fire

With the development of the Center-fire cartridge another great milestone was reached. Only the primer cup needed to be made soft enough to be crushed by the firing pin. The cartridge case could be made of heavy metal which would act as a safe gas seal for pressures much higher than were permissible with the soft copper Rimfire case. The fired primer cups could be punched out and a new primer inserted so that the sturdy brass case could be reloaded many times. "Rimless" cases could be designed for better functioning through the magazines of repeating arms. Through the years, the Center-fire cartridge has undergone hundreds of modifications which cannot be recounted here. But with its coming the reliability of the revolver was greatly enhanced.

The various types of weapons using these cartridges are so numerous that only a few observations on types are required here.

The Colt S.A. Army Model 1873 was the first heavy-caliber Colt with top strap and spring-loaded ejector. While the principle of the self-extracting or automatic-ejecting revolver has been often credited to the Belgian Galand revolver, the weight of evidence seems to show that it was really developed in the United States. From 1860 to 1871, over 500 patents for breech-loading firearms were recorded in the U. S. Patent Office. When it is known that less than 200 were filed in all the history of the Office prior to that date, the interest in development is at once seen.

Apparently W. W. Greener was the first person to ascribe (without any attempt at documentation) the honor to Galand, whose principle was that of sliding forward the barrel and cylinder while the cartridge cases were held by the extractor until clear of the chambers. W. C. Dodge, an examiner in the U. S. Patent Office, conceived the idea of a hinged-frame weapon in which the act of bending down the barrel and cylinder assemblies on the hinge would automatically raise the extractor and eject the empty cartridge cases. The law did not permit a Patent Office employee to acquire an interest in a patent, and not until he retired did Dodge seek patents. They were granted on January 17 and 24, 1865, and were assigned to Smith & Wesson, who proceeded to use the system in their revolvers. On May 1, 1872, Dodge wrote a bitter letter, later published by General Norton, the outstanding arms writer of that day, complaining about Greener's statement. He claimed to have invented his principle three years before the appearance of the Galand. Dodge also complained, and with a good deal of grounds, of treatment he had received at the hands of the British Patent Office. Under a technicality (the boat carrying a check for Patent fee was a few days late in arriving) his British patent was invalidated, resulting in like action to his applications in France and Belgium. The Liege Small Arms Company soon after went into manufacture on the Dodge principle. Oddly enough, British manufacturers in Birmingham were marketing revolvers using his principle within six weeks of the time of the invalidation of his patents!

During this period multi-barrelled pistols such as the Lancaster were introduced in England and also on the Continent. They were usually hinged weapons with drop-down barrels and suffered from the defects of inaccuracy and great weight of the earlier pepper-boxes. English Adams and Tranter revolvers of this period and the Webley Royal Irish Constabulary revolvers were solid frame types with hand operated ejectors for ramming the cartridge cases individually from the chambers. Calibers ran as high as .577, the largest revolver caliber ever generally produced; and one which, except for the Pin-Fire equivalent, the 15mm., is no longer made.

In 1876, C. Pryse was granted a patent in England which covered a cylinder locking bolt jointed to the head of the trigger. The illustration in this patent had a rebound hammer. As a result Pryse has been given credit for the latter feature which he did not claim, but described the lockwork as being of "the ordinary kind." Pryse was also credited with a spring-loaded barrel latch and a turn-button cylinder release, which were used on the Webley-Pryse revolver, but current research indicates that these were not his designs. The rebound hammer can possibly be credited to J. Stanton who took out British patents on several types in 1867 and 1869. D. B. Wesson also received a patent for a rebounding hammer in 1877.

The rebound-and-steel wedge safety principle had appeared earlier in solid frame revolvers made in Austria and in Italy. It is the principle later made famous as the "Colt Positive Lock," variations of which are in general revolver use.

The English Thomas and the Belgian and French Galand types of extraction systems in which the barrel and cylinder slide ahead for extraction were passing developments. In this class the American Merwin & Hulbert, in which the barrel assembly could be unlocked to swing away from the standing breech; and then be slid ahead while the cartridge cases were held by extracting surfaces on the face of the standing breech, was a finely made weapon but one too complicated to achieve lasting success. The Enfield .476 designed and manufactured at the Government Enfield Small Arms Factory in England and adopted there as a service revolver in 1880, was a remarkable example of how not to develop a weapon. In this monstrosity, releasing the catch on the standing breech permits the barrel to be tipped down and the cylinder to slide *straight ahead* to eject. The design was impracticable and it was supplanted by revolvers of hinged-frame Webley manufacture in 1887. In 1894 a slightly modified version of this "Mark I" Webley, under the designation "Mark II" was officially adopted as the British Service Revolver. This used the Webley stirrup-type breech lock, which is mounted on the standing breech and locks over the barrel strap. This, the strongest hinged-frame locking system ever devised, was in use ever since by the British until the adoption of the Browning High Power in 1957.

In 1889 the U. S. Government adopted officially a Colt .38 revolver using a new locking system—the now familiar swing-out cylinder type in which the great strength of the solid frame design is combined with a cylinder mounted on a crane which permits it to be swung away from the frame for quick loading and unloading. This design was modified and adopted by the French in 1892. It was further modified in Europe by Pieper to permit use of a forward sliding chamfered cylinder to use the Russian gas-check cartridge (which up to this time had been used only in solid-frame hand ejector models). It was later adopted in principle, with modifications which included front as well as rear cylinder locking devices, by Smith & Wesson.

A multitude of types and makes which were little but variations of the Colt and Smith & Wesson systems—the swing-out cylinder and the hinged-frame with lock on barrel strap—have since flooded world markets. The Webley design, curiously, has never been imitated on a production basis. Smith and Wesson's "hammerless" (enclosed hammer) pocket revolvers have also been widely copied with only minor variations.

The Webley-Fosbery "Automatic Revolver" in which recoil serves to turn the cylinder and cock the hammer in the place of the customary spring action, first appeared in England in 1901. It had only one imitator, the Union Arms Company .32 and .38 made in Toledo, Ohio for a short period.

With the introduction of smokeless powder, more powerful cartridges have been developed but no real changes have been made in the basic revolver designs. Aside from developing improved metals, sights and grips, it would seem that little can be done to improve their efficiency. Automatic ejecting systems which throw the empty cases out as adjoining chambers are fired—either by gas operation as done experimentally in Spain or by mechanical leverage as introduced by Stieger of Thun—have more bad features than good.

PHASE VII—THE AUTOMATIC PISTOL

The *principle* of the automatic or self-loading pistol was grasped centuries before the necessary combination of fixed ammunition, solid drawn cartridge case, slow fouling smokeless powder, and metallurgical advances made it possible to *utilize* that principle.

In Birch's *History of the Royal Society* we find that on the 2d of March, 1664, Sir Robert Moray reported that a mechanic had approached Prince Rupert with the claim that he could "make a pistol shooting as fast as it could be presented and yet be stopped at pleasure; and wherein the motion of the fire and bullet within was made to charge the piece with powder and bullet, to prime it and to bend the cock."

When we see the difficulties the successful inventors of automatic pistols encountered in the late 19th century trying to interest governments and arms manufacturers, it is astonishing to find that the academic scientists of 1664 should even have gone so far as to record the idea of the nameless inventor who suffered from being more than 200 years ahead of his time.

While patent office records from 1863 on show numerous instances of attempts to develop various forms of gas or recoil operated arms, historically the first successful automatic pistol marketed was the Austrian Schonberger.

This weapon appeared in 1892 and was made by the Austrian Arms Works at Steyr. It is a retarded blowback pistol which was made for a very powerful cartridge for that day—the 8mm Schonberger. The trigger mechanism of this pistol, as many of the early automatics, is generally similar to that used on revolvers of that period. The weapon was loaded through the top, as with the Mauser pistol or the ordinary bolt-action rifle, with Mannlicher-type clips which fell out of the bottom of the magazine when the last round was chambered. It should be noted that this arm was made possible primarily because of ammunition developments. The strong rimless brass cartridge case which would stand the violent strain of automatic extraction, which permitted firm seating of the bullet, and which permitted cartridges to be easily stacked on top of each other in the magazine; the smokeless powder which burned rapidly and with a minimum of fouling; and the jacketed bullet which assured proper feeding—all these had evolved in the '80's. Together they were combined to make a type of successful automatic pistol cartridge which allowed new arms developments.

One of the great designers of automatic arms, the Austrian Andrea Schwarzlose, produced a model pistol operated by barrel recoil in 1893. This arm was never in production, but was the beginning of a long line of Schwarzlose designs.

The first *commercially successful* automatic pistol was an American design. Hugo Borchardt, a German immigrant, invented the clumsy pistol (also intended to be used with a stock as a carbine) which really started the era of military automatic pistols. Unable to finance his pistol in his own country, Borchardt took it to Germany. The great arms factory of Ludwig Loewe and Company undertook production and engaged Borchardt as an engineer. Borchardt's pistol was marketed in 1893. This was the first arm to use the detachable box magazine inserted in the handle which has come to be the most successful of all automatic pistol loading systems. It was the forerunner of the famous Luger, employing a locked breech in which the barrel recoiled a short distance locked to the breechblock; then was unlocked as the barrel travel was halted and a toggle was buckled to draw the breechblock away from the barrel to extract and eject the empty case. Quite as important as the pistol design was the cartridge design. The cartridge Borchardt developed was later made famous as the 7.63mm. Mauser, a cartridge so correct in conception that today, 75 years later, it is one of the world's outstanding pistol cartridges.

In 1893 Theodore Bergmann patented the first of his series of unique automatic pistols. During the succeeding 10 years he developed various pistols of both locked and unlocked types, all with exposed hammers and with readily accessible lockwork and with magazines placed in front of the trigger. In the period between 1894 and 1897 he made a series of pocket pistols, all unlocked blowback types, at Gaggenau in calibers 5mm. 6.5mm. and 8mm. German export and ammunition catalogs included ammunition for these arms as late as 1930, though the weapons themselves have not been manufactured since late in the last century. This is certainly a tribute to the original design and manufacture. A Bergmann cheaply manufactured in Belgium in 1897 and marketed under the name "Simplex" is of interest because the 8mm. cartridge it uses developed into the 7.65mm. Browning—or .32 Colt Automatic Pistol cartridge as we know it—the most widely distributed pocket automatic caliber in existence. In the same year another automatic was manufactured in Spain as the "Charola-Anitua."

In 1896 the great American inventor Hiram Maxim—who also had to go to England to have his new arms manufactured—patented an unusually simple automatic pistol of unlocked blowback design. Samples only were made; and it is a most interesting commentary that some were chambered for the *rimmed* .455 British Service cartridge. Except for a few experimental freaks and the American Reifgraber which used the rimmed .32 S&W cartridge, no later automatic pistol in production used rimmed cartridges until the Colt .22 Woodsman appeared. Recently automatic pistols to shoot the .38 S&W Special rimmed cartridges have been made by Colt and S&W. It has been assumed that proper feed could not be achieved in an automatic with rimmed ammunition—though an examination of an early Maxim would have shown the feasibility of it. Only recently, too, are modern designers and manufacturers re-discovering what Maxim demonstrated nearly 60-years ago—that heavy calibers can be safely made in cheap blowback design weapons.

The story of the truly successful automatic pistol in the light of modern experience begins in 1896 with the introduction of the 7.63mm. military Mauser which had been patented in 1895. This used the cartridge developed by Hugo Borchardt for his own pistol. The published history of the Deutsche Waffen und Munitionsfabriken (DWM), the greatest of the European ammunition manufacturers from the turn of the century to the end of World War II, credits Borchardt with much of the engineering work on the Mauser pistol.

The Mauser was so fundamentally right that it was later changed only in comparatively minor details. Winston Churchill in his history of the Sudan campaign of 1898 told in great detail how he purchased one of the first Mauser pistols to reach England; and credited it with saving his life because of its efficiency and magazine capacity when he shot his way out of a native trap, killing several Fuzzy Wuzzies.

Also in 1898 appeared a new pistol by Andrea Schwarzlose in Austria. Shooting the 7.63mm. Mauser cartridge from a detachable magazine in the handle, this pistol had a number of features which have since become standard on military pistols of the best type. In this weapon for the first time we find the device to hold the action open when the last cartridge has been fired; thereby warning that the arm is empty and also speeding up the reloading. In the unique locking system in this pistol, the barrel and bolt recoil a short distance locked together, then by cam action after the barrel is stopped the bolt is revolved out of locking recesses in the barrel extension. This principle has reappeared in recent years as the locking principle of the German Machine

27

Gun 34 and the American Johnson Light Machine Gun. This pistol was not very successful. Some were marketed in the U. S. by Bannerman of New York under the name "Standard."

John M. Browning, the greatest of all American small arms designers, patented the first Browning pistol produced by FN. The patent was applied for in 1897, and was granted on March 21, 1899, No. 621747. Mr. Browning had patented four different pistols prior to this one. Again the success of this entirely new form of blowback pocket automatic pistol rested partly on the cartridge which, as we have already seen, Browning and FN developed from the 8mm. Simplex. Over 1,000,000 of these pistols were sold. On April 19, 1900 the magazine *Shooting and Fishing*, which is the direct ancestor of *The American Rifleman*, the official magazine of the National Rifle Association carried the first public announcement of the first Colt Automatic pistol—the .38 Automatic invented by Browning. The editor of that day wrote that the Colt company had presented him with the Number One pistol for inspection and test. The report is of historical interest in many ways. It states that the *first* Browning pistol was *a hammerless full automatic*—a single pull on the trigger emptied the magazine. Browning found at once that a pistol so designed was both useless and dangerous: it was practically impossible to hit anything with it, and the rapid successions of recoil kicked the muzzle up so fast that spectators or the firer might be accidentally shot. The magazine would empty in 1 2/5 seconds. They found on testing the new pistol that the velocity, then given as 1,260 feet per second, actually registered as high as 1,350. This compared with the velocity of 750 feet per second then being obtained from the regular .38 Army revolver with its black powder load. They found further that the arm would not function at a lower velocity than 850 f.s. Penetration was 11 inches in pine.

In June of that year Browning wrote to the editor explaining that he had tried many varieties of safeties, some being released by gripping the handle and some being turned down by the thumb and held while firing. He also explained that in designing the .38 Automatic with a hammer (his earlier FN pistol was striker fired) he intended the firer to cock the hammer first, then pull back the slide; thereby lessening the amount of pull necessary for the first manual loading stroke. This arm was later improved by Browning and full data on the later models will be found in the section dealing with the Colt .38 automatic model which was widely used.

In 1901 the Austrian Mannlicher was introduced in Europe and in some sections of South America. It uses a special cartridge of considerable power whose case is straight sided in appearance, though on measuring it is found to be actually slightly conical to help easy extraction.

DWM brought out the Luger in 1898. This arm, which except for minor refinements is the same arm today, was developed by George Luger from the original Borchardt. Its cartridge, the 7.65mm. Parabellum remained in general use through the years. The German service caliber, 9mm. Parabellum was adopted in 1908. These are the only calibers in which this famous arm has ever been commercially manufactured. A few experimental models were made for the .45 Automatic Colt Pistol cartridge.

28

In 1903 the Colt Hammerless .32 Automatic Pistol, an enclosed hammer blowback designed by John Browning was introduced. This was developed from the "Grande Modele" Browning. It is one of the most widely imitated, copied and modified designs ever developed. Literally hundreds of variants of Belgian, German and Spanish manufacture exist.

A new Mannlicher locked breech pistol was introduced also in 1903, but it was never very successful. In this year also Bergmann produced the locked breech designs which were later manufactured in Belgium and met with considerable success under the name of Bergmann-Bayard and Bayard 1908 and 1910.

In England the first Webley Automatic Pistol, one of .455 caliber with the typical Webley V-recoil spring, was introduced in 1904. It was not a success and should not be confused with the official .455 Mark I adopted by the Royal Navy in 1913.

The 1905 Model Colt in .45 caliber and its later modification in 1908 were based on the general slide design of the earlier .38 Colt Automatics, and were designed by John Browning, of course.

Webley brought out their first blowback automatic, a .32 Pocket Model in 1906; while in the United States in the next year the Savage .45 was introduced at U. S. Government trials. This arm appeared in a modified form in .32 caliber in 1907. The last model of this make was introduced in 1917. Also, in 1906 the Italian Glisenti was first seen in 7.65mm. Parabellum and was introduced in 9mm. in 1910. Austro-Hungary officially adopted the Roth-Steyr 8mm. for cavalry use in 1907, marking the first large-scale production of an arm which had been patented eight or nine years earlier.

1908 marked the introduction of the .25 Colt Vest Pocket Model, a Browning striker-fired design which was also manufactured in 1906 by FN in Belgium under the name of the Baby Browning. Like its enclosed-hammer type big brother the .32 Colt Automatic, this arm has been copied, imitated and modified under a fantastic number of trade names.

Webley launched an automatic in 1910 to shoot the .38 Colt Automatic Pistol cartridge, using the breech lock of the type found in the more widely distributed .455 Mark I. This must not be confused with the blowback pistol of similar appearance called the 9mm. High Velocity, which appeared two years earlier and which shoots the weaker 9mm. Browning Long cartridge.

The Browning designed .45 Colt Government Model was introduced in 1911. This is one of the finest military pistols ever made; and still with a few modifications the official pistol of the U. S. forces. Also in this year another basic type, the powerful 9mm. Steyr-Hahn appeared in Austria. This was adopted by the Austrian Army in 1912 and converted to German Service caliber in 1940.

The Hungarian long-recoil .32 Frommer-Stop was marketed in 1912, an unusual locked type to shoot the low-powered .32 automatic cartridge. One year later S&W launched their .35 Automatic based on the Belgian Clement. As we have seen, the Webley & Scott .455 Mark I was produced in 1913; and except for the Italian Beretta of 1915 and a tremendous variety of pocket pistol types, nothing of consequence was developed until 1919 when the Remington .380 Automatic pistol with a hesitation-locked breech was made.

For the next ten years development was confined for the most part to Spain, where dozens of makes under hundreds of brand names were made for export trade. Practically every known variety was imitated or modified. The one real development of this area and this period was in the field of cheap blow-back pistols to shoot powerful cartridges which were generally believed to require an expensive locked-breech pistol. There is something to be learned from the Spanish development of blowbacks to shoot such cartridges as the 9mm. Bayard and the 9mm. Parabellum.

By 1922 the Czechs had developed arms plants which, rather curiously, seemed to show marked German trends in their designs. In that year Ceska Zbrojovka produced a Nicklee-type revolving barrel locked pistol of .380 caliber which possessed a lockwork of general Mauser design. This arm was later adopted as the official side-arm of the Czech army.

Later versions are the Model 24 and the Model 27. The Model 27 was redesigned by F. Myska as a simple blowback-operated weapon. The Model 27, manufacture of which was continued by the Germans during World War II, was chambered for the .32 A.C.P. cartridge.

In 1928 a Military Model of the Le Francais blowback was first sold in France, a weapon embodying several interesting features, including a simple double action firing mechanism and several novel safety features.

Chapter 2

An Analysis of Pistol and Revolver Types

I

PISTOLS

The term pistol, signifying the smallest general type of firearm—a type intended to be fired from one hand, wherein the cartridge or cartridges must be inserted directly into the chamber *which is an integral part of the barrel itself*—embraces the following types:

SINGLE-SHOT PISTOLS

Originally made with short barrels in calibers .22, .32, .38, and .41 Rim Fire as pocket pistols. Later manufactured in calibers as high as .50 as Army and Navy issue. Still later, as target pistols in calibers from .22 Rim Fire to .44 Russian Center Fire.

Modern *production model* single-shot pistols are almost entirely .22 Long Rifle. Special models, of course, may be any caliber or description. Practically all are intended for target use. Since single-shot target pistols represent the only class of true pistols (as distinguished from revolvers and automatic pistols) which have any present or predictable future value, an itemization of the characteristics of the outstanding types is given herewith, with particular reference to the tested systems of locking the breech. Successful pistol designs fall into the following classifications:

Breech-Locking Systems

1. *Hinge frame, standing breech.* In this type, the barrel is hinged to a forward extension of the receiver and is fastened with a spring-controlled latch to the upright section of the receiver forming the standing breech which supports the head of the cartridge case as the weapon is fired. When the latch is released, the muzzle of the barrel is tipped down to expose the cartridge chamber and to operate the extractor to lift the empty case up or to eject it completely from the pistol. This is the commonest form of successful single-shot pistol.

The outstanding examples are: The .22 Long Rifle Smith & Wesson tip-up pistols. In these, the latch is on the breech end of the barrel and snaps down over the standing breech to lock. The firing pin is attached to the hammer. Opening the pistol ejects the empty cartridge case from the pistol. The British

.22 Long Rifle Webley & Scott Single Shot. In this pistol, the breech latch is operated by pushing forward the front of the trigger guard. The firing pin is attached to the hammer. Opening the action ejects the cartridge case. The .22 Long Rifle Harrington & Richardson U.S.R.A. Model. This is similar to the S&W. The Stevens No. 10. The latch is on the left side of the receiver. A knob-type striker of the rifle type is used; there is no hammer. Opening the pistol extracts the case far enough to permit it to be withdrawn, but does not eject it from the pistol. The Stevens Conlin, Diamond, Gould, and Offhand Models. Calibers .22 and .22 Long Rifle. These models vary only in weights, trigger designs, sights, and grips. Mechanically they function alike. Latches in these pistols are push buttons mounted on the left side of the receiver. The U. S. Wurfflein and Hopkins & Allen .22 Long Rifle. Similar to the S&W but with different types of latches. The German Arminius operated by right- or left-side latches on the receiver, and the Stoeger Challenger operated by pushing forward the trigger guard tang.

2. *Crane frame, standing breech.* The barrel is assembled to a forward extension of the receiver on a swinging crane, and is fastened with a pull-type spring-controlled latch to the standing breech. When the latch on the left side of the receiver is pulled back, the barrel assembly can be swung out to the left on the crane, as in the case of a swing-out-cylinder revolver. Pressure on the base of the ejector rod ejects the empty case. This is a manual rod-ejector, as opposed to the automatic-lever type found in hinge-frame types. In exterior appearance this pistol closely resembles a regular Colt revolver.

The .22 Long Rifle Colt Camp Perry Model is the only modern pistol to use this system. The basic principle is derived from the old National and Colt Derringer .41 Rim fire pocket pistols. In those old pistols, however, it is necessary to half cock the pistol, then press a spring button to swing the barrel on its crane and push up the side ejector latch to eject. The Camp Perry has an ultra-fast single-action lockwork.

3. *Pivot frame, standing breech.* In this type, the barrel is fastened by a pivot to a forward extension of the receiver, permitting it to be swung away from the standing breech when the spring latch is released. The act of swinging the breech end of the barrel away (usually to the right) operates a lever arrangement to extract the empty case.

The .22 Long Rifle Smith & Wesson Straightline model uses this system. Instead of the regulation pivot-type hammer, this pistol has a striker which moves forward in a straight line to fire the cartridge. The basic principle is derived from the .22 Short pistol of Frank Wesson and from several early types of Derringer pocket pistols. In exterior appearance and in balance this type of pistol suggests an automatic pistol.

4. *Rigid frame, rolling breechblock.* In this type, the barrel is fastened securely to the receiver, and the cartridge in the chamber is supported by a breech piece containing a firing pin and extractor which is rolled forward on a heavy center pin after the cartridge has been inserted. The hammer is also the breech bolt and is mounted on the same center pin as the breech piece. A spring holds the breech piece against the cartridge head until the hammer falls. The fall of the hammer not only drives the firing pin ahead to discharge

the cartridge, but also rolls the hammer ahead to positively lock the breech. Recocking the hammer, then drawing back the breech piece extracts the cartridge case far enough to permit it to be withdrawn with the fingers.

The .22 Long Rifle Remington pistol on the Army model .50 caliber frame exemplifies this type. This pistol is extremely heavy for its type, weighing about 2¾ pounds. It is an extremely accurate pistol, not as subject to wear as is the hinge-frame type. It is no longer manufactured in this country.

5. *Rigid frame, falling breechblock.* In this type the barrel is screwed securely to the receiver, and the cartridge in the chamber is supported by a heavy Martini-type falling block. When a lever, often the trigger guard, is depressed it lowers a hinged block containing the firing pin. The bottom of the block strikes an arm of the extractor and ejects the empty cartridge case. Lowering the block may also automatically recock the pistol. A cartridge is inserted in the firing chamber. Returning the lever to its closed position raises the block and presses it securely against the head of the cartridge case.

Examples of this type are the German Udo Anschutz .22 Long Rifle Record match and similar pistols. The blocks in these pistols are usually actuated by pulling an extension of the back strap on the grip. Triggers are usually set on these models by a lever on the left side of the receiver. When the breechblock is down, the chamber is entirely exposed. Literally scores of pistols of this general type were made in Germany and Switzerland prior to 1945.

6. *Rigid frame, turning bolt.* In this type, the action is that of the familiar bolt-action rifle. Lifting the bolt handle and pulling it straight back ejects the empty cartridge case and cocks the striker. A cartridge is inserted, the bolt is pushed forward, and the handle is turned down to locked position exactly as in the case of the common door bolt.

Examples: German .22 Long Rifle Mauser target pistols and French M.A.S. Buffalo-Stand .22 Long Rifle target pistols.

DOUBLE-BARRELLED PISTOLS

These were originally made early in the metallic cartridge era as pocket pistols and Derringers. Barrels might (a) swing out on a pivot, as in the National Derringer; (b) hinge down, as in double-barrelled shotguns; (c) hinge up on the standing breech; (d) pivot to right or left away from the standing breech; (e) slide forward on the receiver extension over the trigger guard.

Modern *production models* of double-barrelled pistols are made only in Europe. Usually they are parallel-barrel types intended for shot cartridges or for heavy Continental cartridges which are obsolete in the United States or which were never manufactured here. It should be noted that while barrels in the early pocket types were usually mounted one on top of the other, or superposed, saddle pistols of the same era were generally of the parallel-barrel type. In England these were often made for the British .577 Boxer cartridge.

Double-barrelled pistols have outlived their usefulness, and have been replaced by more accurate revolvers. Early in the present century several European weapons of the .25 caliber BAR type were introduced having two superposed barrels. These do not class as straight pistols inasmuch as the cartridges were inserted in a swinging block; and the bullets have to jump a gap exactly as in the revolver before entering the barrel.

33

MULTIPLE-BARRELLED PISTOLS

These fall into two general classes, both of which are now obsolete because of great weight, unwieldiness, and bulk, as well as lack of accuracy. (a) Those in which several barrels are fastened together or bored from a solid cylinder like the old pepperbox pistols of the percussion cap era. These are freaks. (b) The obsolete Remington-Elliot .22 is a true revolving pistol. Barrels are bored the full length of the cylindrical block. Pressure on the trigger revolves a striker to fire them successively. Four- and six-barrelled pistols with parallel barrels superposed on lower barrels. These weapons are usually British and many will shoot current ammunition. They have a single trigger and are of hinge-frame construction. As some of these weapons were brought into use by the British after Dunkirk in World War II, and as they will handle the British Service .455 cartridges, these weapons may be classed as obsolescent only. In the Mitrailleuse pistol of Braendlin Armoury, each barrel has a separate striker and spring. The trigger is hooked to a vertical spindle on which are projecting studs which, when the trigger is pulled, pull back and release the strikers to fire the barrels in rotation. In the .455 Lancaster four-barrelled pistol, which resembles the Mitrailleuse closely in exterior appearance, the lockwork operates like that of the obsolete United States .22 Remington-Elliot pistol. The striker is in the form of a sleeve which has a projecting arm. Pressure on the trigger turns a ratchet to rotate the striker to permit its arm to hit the four firing pins in succession as the trigger is pulled four times.

Four-barrelled pistols with the barrels *mounted one on top of the other* were manufactured early in the century as transition arms in Europe. Some of these were exposed-hammer and some the enclosed hammer type. The four barrels formed a single unit which, when loaded, was inserted in guides in the standing breech section of the receiver or was hinged to the forward extension of the receiver. The American Marston was a popular arm of this type.

Examples: The Reform Pistol. This was made in Germany, Belgium, and Austria. It is usually chambered for the .25 Colt Auto Pistol cartridge. The barrel block is removed for loading. The block is inserted and the trigger pulled to fire the first shot. Pulling the trigger the second time lifts the barrel block to bring the second barrel in line with the firing pin and, as the second cartridge is fired, gas from it escapes through a breech hole into barrel number one to blow the empty case out of that barrel. The third pull fires number three and ejects from number two barrel. The fourth pull fires number four barrel and clears number three. The barrel block is then removed for reloading, and the fourth barrel must be cleared with a stick or cleaning rod. This ingenious pistol is widely distributed in Europe and South America, and, as it uses current cartridges, may be classed as obsolescent but not obsolete.

The Regnum Pistol. This European pistol also has four barrels bored one on top of the other from a solid block, but the barrel block is tipped down when the release catch on the left side of the receiver is depressed, to load and unload. The four barrels are loaded with .25 Colt Auto Pistol cartridges. Four pulls on the trigger will fire the four barrels in succession. The arm is then hinged open to unload. This is the enclosed-hammer type, which is flat and readily concealed. It is purely a close-quarters arm, of course, and is deficient in both accuracy and striking energy.

The only *production models* of multiple-parallel-barrelled pistols in the present century were freak four-barreled pistols like the United States Brownie made by Mossberg Arms as a cheap .22 caliber arm; and several European imitations of the U. S. Shattuck Unique, a short four-barrelled pistol intended to be concealed in the palm of the hand.

Repeating Pistols

These are weapons in which a number of cartridges (usually five) are inserted in the handle of the pistol, and in which the barrel is loaded and the cartridge fired and case ejected by mechanical spring action, usually brought about by squeezing levers in the grip against spring tension, then releasing the grip and repeating the motion to fire successive cartridges.

These are transition arms which were an attempt to provide the gas-seal feature of the pistol (where no gas can escape because the bullet does not have to jump a gap as in the revolver when going from the cylinder to the barrel) together with the mechanical sureness of action possessed by the revolver which, unlike the automatic pistol, is not dependent on the cartridge (which may be defective) for reloading.

The French Gaulois and Merveilleux are examples of this type. The Gaulois held its special 8mm. cartridges in the handle of the pistol. The Merveilleux closely resemble the Gaulois, but used a special 6mm. cartridge. With the magazine loaded, pressure of the hand around the grip squeezed in a section which forced a cartridge into the chamber of the single barrel, cocked and tripped the striker to fire the cartridge. Releasing the pressure permitted springs to force back the grip, open the breech, and eject the empty cartridge case. The magazine spring forced the next cartridge up into line.

These weapons were widely distributed in Europe, but no ammunition for them has ever been made in the United States. These are overly complicated and inaccurate.

Magazine Pistols

These differ from automatic pistols in that some manual operation by the *free* hand is necessary to prepare them for successive shots. They usually require the employment of both hands. They resemble automatics in that they carry extra cartridges—often in the handle—ready for mechanical feeding into the chamber of the single barrel.

Example: The .22 Long Rifle Fiala pistol. This weapon is no longer manufactured. While in exterior appearance it very closely resembles a regular .22 target automatic pistol and houses its cartridges in a removable magazine in a grip, it differs in that the sliding breechblock is mechanically locked whenever it is in forward position. When a .22 automatic pistol is fired, the slide is blown back to eject the empty cartridge case, cock the hammer, and compress the recoil spring, which then moves forward to reload the firing chamber from the magazine. In the magazine pistol of Fiala type, when the cartridge has been fired, it is necessary to press in and release the slide lock at the breech,

35

then pull the slide back by hand to eject the empty, recock the hammer, and clear the top of the magazine so the slide may go home to pick up a loaded cartridge.

Bittner, Schwarzlose, and similar repeating pistols were merely transition arms which do not merit attention here.

AUTOMATIC EJECTING PISTOLS

While this specific term is applied by Webley & Scott to their British made self-ejecting pistol, it is not properly applied. Actually this weapon resembles an automatic target pistol, but in reality is a single shot *automatic-ejecting-cocking* pistol. Each cartridge must be inserted in the firing chamber by hand. The breechblock slide must be pulled back by hand before the first cartridge can be loaded, then pushed forward by hand to close the breech.

As the cartridge fires, the pressure of gas in the cartridge case forces the head of the case back against the face of the breechblock. As the bullet leaves the barrel, backward pressure blows the slide back to cock the hammer while the residual pressure in the chamber blows the empty case out of the pistol—sometimes. A hand ejector is provided for use when ejection does not occur automatically. When a loaded cartridge is inserted, the slide must again be pushed forward manually.

II

AUTOMATIC PISTOLS

The term automatic pistol by accepted usage signifies a weapon intended to be fired normally with one hand in which pressing the trigger when the chamber and magazine are loaded (a) fires the cartridge in the chamber; (b) ejects the fired cartridge case; (c) cocks the firing mechanism ready for the next shot; and (d) loads a cartridge from the magazine into the chamber in position for firing. Strictly speaking, of course, automatic pistols should really be classed as "semi-automatic;" but popular usage makes it necessary to class them by the term under which they are generally known.

During the rearward movement of the breech mechanism which is normally accomplished by recoil, a disconnecting unit is automatically forced down to break the connection between the sear which holds the hammer or striker at full cock and the trigger bar. This principle (which may vary greatly in mechanical application in different arms and is considered in detail in discussing specific designs) prevents the firing of more than one shot for each pull of the trigger, since the trigger must be released to permit springs to force the connecting trigger bar into position to release the sear for the next shot.

Full automatic pistols in which a single pressure on the trigger will fire the full contents of the magazine are useless and generally dangerous. Such types are not made in the United States and they have no practical value for defense or target work.

Pistols of the Le Francais type (see under Caliber .32 ACP and Caliber 9mm. Browning Long) and of the Roth-Steyr type (see under Caliber 8mm. Roth-Steyr) are more correctly classed as "self-loading" pistols in that the rearward motion of the breechblock does not cock the firing mechanism but merely ejects and reloads the firing chamber. In these types pressure on the trigger cocks and releases the striker.

Commercially successful automatic pistols fall into the following classes:

SIMPLE BLOWBACKS

The vast majority of all .22, .25, .32 and .380 caliber automatic pistols operate on this system. A powerful spring holds the breechblock against the head of the cartridge in the firing chamber at the instant of discharge. Theoretically the expanding gases inside the cartridge case force the bullet down the barrel and simultaneously force the head of the case back against the face of the breechblock. In actual practice the light bullet is out of the barrel before the breech opens appreciably. This system works most efficiently when the weight of the bullet is 110 grains or less, the case is parallel sided and the chamber pressure is under 5000 pounds per square inch. However it must be noted that in Spain blowbacks are made with very heavy springs to shoot the most powerful pistol cartridges made; and the true mechanics of this system warrant much more scientific study by arms manufacturers.

Barrels. Since blowback pistols are operated by recoil (or projection of the fired case as it imparts momentum to the breechblock) the barrels are stationary, and may be easily removable as in the Colt .32 ACP or may be pinned into their mounting as in the case of the Walthers using the .32 ACP caliber cartridge.

Magazines are normally removable and positioned in the handle (see all pistols under Calibers .32 and .380 ACP) but in the Bergmann 6.5mm. are not removable and are positioned ahead of the trigger guard.

Breechblocks may be integral parts of the slide forging (Browning, Colt Sauer, Walther and Webley under calibers .25 ACP, .32 ACP and .380 ACP) or may be separate units of lesser weight requiring more powerful recoil springs (S&W and Steyr .32 ACP and .35 S&W Auto).

Firing mechanisms may be the striker-type in which trigger pressure releases the firing (striker) pin and permits its spring to drive it ahead to discharge the cartridge (Colt and Mauser Caliber .25 ACP); the concealed hammer (hammerless) type such as the Colt .32 ACP, Sauer Model 38 for the .32 ACP cartridge and the Browning 9mm. Long in which the slide completely encloses the hammer to provide a smooth exterior which will not catch on clothing when being drawn rapidly; and the exposed hammer type such as the Czech and Star automatic pistols for the .32 ACP cartridge.

In general, strikers in pistols require fewer parts than hammer mechanisms but are not as reliable. Concealed hammers (and strikers also) have the disadvantage commonly encountered (Colt type) that they are always fully cocked when the firing chamber is loaded, which weakens the mainspring by too long compression if the arm is carried constantly ready for action. In European types such as the Sauer Model 38 where an exterior lever permits the hammer to be safely lowered on a loaded chamber and a double action trigger permits bringing the arm into immediate action, this defect has been overcome. Exposed hammers have the advantage that they can be lowered to ease the mainspring, but have the disadvantage that they must then be thumb-cocked before the arm can be fired, unless they are of the double-action type as in the Walther PP and PPK.

Triggers may have trigger bars passing stirrup-fashion across the magazine well to transmit finger pressure and push the sear out of engagement with the hammer (.32 Colt Auto); connector bars to push the sear out of engagement with the striker (.25 Colt Auto.); a trigger nose to transmit pressure through an interceptor block to the sear to release it (Mauser Cal. 32 ACP); a pivoted trigger whose bar is pulled forward as the trigger is pressed and draws the sear out of engagement with the hammer (Walther PPK Cal. .380 ACP); and other operating differences which are covered under the descriptions of individual pistols where necessary.

Cocking systems of the double-action type have been highly developed in Europe. (Walther PPK, Sauer Model 38 and Little Tom, Caliber .32 ACP). In these pistols, as in all standard types, the slide must be drawn to the rear and released manually to load the firing chamber; this action also cocks the hammer. If the hammer is then lowered, the weapon may be carried in complete safety and without the mainspring being compressed. Instead of thumb-cocking the hammer or pulling the slide back as is normally required to fire an automatic pistol under these conditions, in the double action types it is necessary only to press the trigger to raise and drop the hammer. If the cartridge fires, the slide as it is blown back will recock the hammer. If the cartridge should misfire, a second pull on the trigger will again raise and drop the hammer, usually discharging the average defective cartridge.

Disconnectors are an essential design factor in all good automatic pistols since they prevent firing more than one shot for each pull of the trigger. The most common design is that developed by Browning and used in the Colt .32 Auto. In this type a bar mounted with the sear rises so that when the slide is fully home the top of the disconnector seats in a cut in the underside of the slide; and when it is so seated the sear is in contact with the trigger bar. Any opening movement of the slide causes it to ride over the projecting head of the disconnector, thrusting it down against its spring pressure and breaking the connection between trigger bar and sear. Thus when the slide returns to full forward position, it is necessary to momentarily release trigger pressure to permit the spring to force the disconnector up into its slide slot to complete the trigger connection. The various types of disconnectors are discussed where necessary under the individual automatic pistols described. All types require that the trigger must be deliberately released between shots, and that the slide or breechblock must be fully home before trigger pressure will release the hammer or striker.

Magazine disconnectors are spring controlled levers or bars projecting into the magazine well or so mounted in the grips that when the magazine is withdrawn their springs force them out or down to break connection between trigger and sear; when the magazine is in place the firing contact is maintained. These are designed as a safety measure to prevent discharge of a round in the chamber which is often overlooked when the magazine is extracted. The various types are discussed under the arms employing them (see Beretta, Colt, Mauser and Sauer under Caliber .32 ACP).

Safeties fall into two general classes, manual and automatic. Manual safeties are generally thumbpieces so mounted on the receiver or slide that pushing the exposed lever turns a cutaway pin to lock the hammer or striker and sometimes the sear also; though some types lock the trigger. Automatic grip safeties are movable pieces so mounted in the grip that in general they are held out by springs when at rest, and in that position they prevent connection between trigger and sear; but when the pistol is held firmly in the hand ready for shooting, the grip is squeezed in and completes the firing hook-up. The manual and grip safeties used in the Colt .25 and .32 Auto are the basis for most of the variations, but the important types are all considered under descriptions of specific weapons where necessary. One unusual type of automatic safety is that employed in double action Walther pistols, where the firing pin is securely locked by a floating cutaway pin at all times except when the sear, as it is pushed to full cock, lifts a hammer lever which raises the lock pin out of the path of the firing pin. (Under Caliber .32 ACP see Beretta, Browning, Colt, Mauser, Ortgies, Sauer, S&W, Star and Walther).

Mainsprings may be flat springs (Colt and Mauser .32 Auto) or coil springs (Beretta and Webley) mounted in the grip section of the receiver.

Recoil springs are generally coil springs. They may be mounted with guides below the barrel (all Colt Auto Pistols except the .22); above the barrel (Smith and Wesson .32 Auto); around the barrel (Walther PPK); in the front of the grip (Le Francais); or in the slide (Colt .22 Woodsman). The Webley .32 Auto uses a powerful V-spring mounted under the right hand grip.

BLOW FORWARD

This is essentially the same as the blowback except that the breech is solid and the barrel and other recoiling units slide forward to eject and reload the chamber on the return stroke. (See Schwarzlose under Caliber .32 ACP).

DELAYED BLOWBACK—HESITATION SYSTEM

This system mechanically delays the breech opening on the general principle of the common door-check. As in the standard blowback design, the breech opening starts simultaneously with the movement of the bullet, but in the case of the 7.65mm. Mannlicher a cam supported by the mainspring is held in contact with the breechblock providing additional resistance to rapid breech opening; while in the Remington for the .32 and .380 ACP cartridges the forward member of a two-piece movable breechblock supports the cartridge case head and transmits the momentum imparted to it to the rear member causing it to unlock the forward unit which has engaged with the receiver after short opening travel. In a recoil operated arm, when as in the case of the pistols just listed the barrel is rigid, it is obvious that the breechblock begins its opening action with the discharge of the cartridge, hence the action is not truly locked but is actually checked or delayed.

LOCKED-BREECH DESIGNS

When powerful loads or heavy bullets are used in an automatic pistol it is desirable to have the breech firmly locked until the bullet has left the barrel. Without exception all the successful automatic pistols ever put into production are recoil operated. (Primer and gas operated pistols have been made or produced experimentally but have never achieved commercial success and are only of interest to the collector). In locked-breech actions the barrel is secured to the breechblock by a variety of mechanical means at the instant of firing. The rearward thrust of the expanding powder gases push the head of the cartridge case back against the face of the breechblock exactly as in the common blowback design; but unlike the blowback the breech does not begin to open immediately. The breechblock, which is held forward by the recoil spring, starts back but is compelled to draw with it the barrel and lock. After the bullet has left the barrel, the motion of the barrel is halted and it is unlocked from the breechblock and at that point the momentum imparted to the face of the breechblock can continue to carry the breech mechanism still further to the rear to carry out the cycle of ejecting, cocking and compressing the recoil spring to provide the power for the forward loading stroke of the action.

1. Browning-Colt Locked-Breech System. This is the most widely imitated locking system ever designed for an automatic pistol. When the breechblock (which is part of the slide in this design) is fully forward the recoil spring holds it thrust forward against the face of the barrel, in which position the rear of the barrel is raised up on a swinging link so that ribs on its top surface lock securely into corresponding grooves in the ceiling of the slide. During recoil the slide and barrel travel locked together until the rear of the barrel swinging down on its link is disengaged from the slide and its travel halted, permitting the breechblock-slide to continue rearward travel to function the action. Under Caliber .45 ACP see U. S. Govt. Model 1911-1911A1 for complete description of this system. For modifications see Spanish Llama and Star under the same caliber. For the official French modification see MAS 1935 under caliber 7.65mm. French Auto Pistol. For the official Russian modification see Tokarev under caliber 7.62mm. Russian Automatic Pistol.

2. Browning Hi-Power Locked-Breech System. While this is essentially the system developed by John M. Browning for the Colt listed above, it uses a barrel nose forged as part of the barrel unit in place of the earlier swinging link to cam the barrel down and up to unlock and lock into the slide ceiling. The overall design is simpler than that of the earlier type. Under Caliber 9mm. Luger see Belgian (also Canadian) Browning Hi-Power 13-shot for a complete description of this system. For modifications see Caliber 9mm. Polish Radom.

3. Mauser Military Locked-Breech System. This is one of the oldest and most successful systems in use. Instead of the conventional slide this design utilizes a separate breechblock travelling in an extension of the barrel. A separate prop-up locking piece in the receiver is forced up engaging in recesses in the bottom of the breechblock when the action is closed. After short rearward travel locked together, the barrel is halted and the bolt lock forced down to free the breechblock (or bolt) to let it travel back to eject and cock. Under Caliber 7.63mm. Mauser see Mauser for complete description. Under the same caliber see Astra, Azul and Super Azul for Spanish modifications.

4. Steyr Hammer Military Locked-Breech System. This type uses a conventional breechblock slide which recoils locked to the barrel for a short distance. As the barrel moves it is revolved by cam action. Locking lugs on the barrel are rotated out of locking recesses in the slide freeing the slide to continue to the rear as the barrel travel is halted.

Under Caliber 9mm. Steyr see Steyr for complete descriptions of this system, which involves a barrel rotation of 60 degrees. Under Caliber .380 ACP see Czech CZ pistols for description of modification of this system involving barrel rotation of 30 degrees. Under Caliber .380 ACP see Savage for description of modification involving barrel rotation of about 30 degrees. (Savage pistols, since they employ revolving barrels, are a delayed blowback design; however the degree of rotation is so slight and the weight of the reciprocating parts is so light that they represent a comparatively inefficient lock. They open exactly as fast as an ordinary blowback and have heavy recoil for the cartridges employed. However, it is not strictly correct to class them as anything but delayed blowback types in view of their construction.) Under Caliber 8mm Roth-Steyr see Roth-Steyr for description of this system involving barrel rotation of 90 degrees.

5. Luger Parabellum Locked-Breech System. This design has never been imitated, probably due to the cost of manufacture. Instead of the familiar slide this pistol utilizes a breechblock unit mounted in arms extending back from the barrel. When the breechblock is fully forward it is securely locked to the face of the barrel by a toggle joint behind it which lies below the horizontal. After short locked recoil the barrel is halted and at that point the gripping surfaces on the toggle strike ramps on the receiver breaking the toggle joint, causing it to buckle and draw the breechblock straight back to eject and cock. (Under Caliber 9mm. Luger see Luger for complete description).

6. Glisenti Locked-Breech System. This is a design employing a vertical swinging block which locks in the underside of the breechblock. This is not a strong design. See under Caliber 9mm. Italian, Glisenti. This design has never been imitated.

7. Japanese Nambu and Pattern 14 Locked-Breech System. These pistols utilize the principle of a separate locking block swinging up from the receiver and locking securely in the underside of the breechblock. The breech lock is cammed down out of engagement after short locked travel. As rearward movement of the barrel is halted, the breechblock travels back to eject and cock. Under Caliber 8mm. Nambu see complete description of this excellent system.

8. Japanese Pattern 94 Locked-Breech System. Unlike the other Japanese service pistols, this weapon uses a slide which covers the barrel and comprises the breechblock. It is locked by a rising wedge cammed up from the receiver ahead of the trigger. Under Caliber 8mm. Nambu see Pattern 94 for complete description.

9. Webley & Scott Locked-Breech System. After short recoil during which the barrel and breechblock are securely locked together by a locking shoulder on top of the barrel engaging in a corresponding shoulder in the breechblock slide, the barrel moves down diagonal grooves in the slide and is halted while the freed slide continues on to the rear in its tracks in the receiver. Under Caliber .455 Automatic see Webley & Scott.

10. Bergmann-Bayard Locked-Breech System. This arm does not employ the slide principle but utilizes instead a falling block through which the separate breechblock can pass. Barrel and breechblock recoil locked together for a short distance until the block is forced down, the barrel is halted and the breechblock completes its rearward travel. Under Caliber 9mm. Bayard see Bayard Military (Bergmann-Bayard).

11. Walther P38 Locked-Breech System. This is the latest and one of the strongest designs. A locking block is hinged in a specially shaped lug which is an integral part of the barrel forging and is positioned below the chamber. The lock has projections on either side at the top which engage in recesses machined into the slide. The barrel and breechblock-slide recoil together about one-half inch. Then a plunger mounted in the barrel lug strikes against the receiver and is forced back to push the hinged locking block down out of engagement with the slide. The barrel is halted and the slide travels alone to the rear for ejection and cocking functions.

While this ingenious design is one of the strongest known it has the serious defect that when the arm is dismounted the locking block may be easily removed, and the pistol can be assembled without replacing the block. The pistol can be operated by hand in this condition without the defect being noted. If it is fired the slide will be jammed back and may ruin the pistol, as the cartridge used develops an extremely high breech pressure. Under Caliber 9mm. Luger see Walther P38 for complete description.

12. Frommer Locked-Breech System—Long Recoil. This arm differs radically not only in its method of locking the breech but also in its type of operation.

Under the short recoil system used in all other successful automatic pistols (the term is relative and indicates a barrel travel of one-eighth to one-half the length of the cartridge in different arms) the breechblock members continue rearward travel after the barrel has been halted. In the long recoil system the bolt and barrel travel back locked together for the full distance of the recoil stroke, which is necessarily longer than the length of the cartridge used. The bolt (or breechblock) is then mechanically caught and held while a barrel-return spring pushes the barrel ahead for extraction and ejection of the empty case; after which a second spring drives the bolt forward to chamber a new cartridge. The locking action consists of locking lugs on a revolving bolt head which engage in corresponding recesses in the barrel extension. When the action recoils and the bolt is held back by its catch, forward motion of the barrel pulls on the bolt head causing it to revolve out of locking engagement. (For a complete description of this operating and locking system see Frommer under Caliber .32 ACP).

13. Schwarzlose Locked-Breech System. In this unique short recoil system the continued rearward movement of the bolt (or breechblock) after the barrel travel is halted results in a cam action which revolves the bolt to turn its locking lugs out of recesses in the barrel extension. See Schwarzlose under Caliber 7.63mm. Mauser.

Other Characteristics of Locked-Breech Pistols

The mechanical features covered under blowback designs are utilized in locked-breech automatic pistols. In addition it should be noted that most military (and a few blowback type) pistols utilize a stop generally operated by the rising magazine platform (follower) to hold the action open when the last shot has been fired.

Slide Stops. For types which remain open when the magazine is withdrawn and are used to speed reloading see Colt under Caliber .45 ACP; Luger under Caliber 9mm.; Luger and Mauser under Caliber 7.63mm. Mauser. For types which close when the magazine is withdrawn, hence are intended only to warn that the pistol is empty, see Nambu under Caliber 8mm. Japanese.

Magazines. For description of removable-magazine-in-the-handle systems see Colt Auto under Caliber .45 ACP. For non-removable magazine in the handle see Steyr under Caliber 9mm. Steyr. For non-removable magazine ahead of the trigger see Mauser under Caliber 7.63mm. Mauser. For removable magazine ahead of trigger see Bayard under Caliber 9mm. Bergmann-Bayard.

III

REVOLVERS

The term revolver, signifying a weapon intended to be fired normally with one hand, and in which the cartridges are inserted in individual chambers in a cylinder so mounted behind the barrel that it can revolve to bring cartridge chambers successively in line with the firing pin at the rear and the barrel at its front end, and *in which the bullet must jump a gap from the chamber in the cylinder to the barrel,* embraces the following types:

Solid Frame, Swing-Out Cylinder, Hand-Ejector Revolvers

All modern revolvers intended to shoot powerful cartridges (with the sole exception of the British hinge-frame .455) are of this type. In this type of revolver, the frame is the structure to which the barrel is fastened and into which the revolving cylinder assembly is fitted, and which provides the standing breech, the grip, and the receiver for the lockwork. When this is a single-quality forging, it assures maximum strength. By mounting the cylinder on a crane assembled to the front of the frame, it is possible to swing the assembly out by releasing a latch, thus permitting speedy unloading and reloading without removing any part from the revolver, and without sacrificing the inherent strength of the solid-frame design. Pressure on the ejector rod, which passes down the center of the cylinder, forces the head of the ejector out the rear of the cylinder, bringing with it all the cartridge cases in the chambers, since their rims are resting partly on the ejector head. Releasing pressure permits the compressed ejector spring to force the ejector back into place in the cylinder ready for reloading.

While experimental models have been made (notably in Belgium and Germany) of solid-frame, swing-out-cylinder revolvers in which the act of swinging out the cylinder affected a series of levers which automatically work the ejector, these models were too cumbrous or too complicated to stand the test of time.

United States Examples. All recent Colt and Smith & Wesson revolvers, including pocket, police, army, and target models. These are the finest in the world from the standpoint of manufacture, accuracy, and dependability. (For detailed descriptions and working drawings of these basic types, see .45 Caliber Colt and .38 Caliber Smith & Wesson). All these weapons swing their cylinders out to the left. All are exposed-hammer, selective-double-action types: that is to say, either the hammer may be cocked by the thumb so that the only function of the trigger when pressed is the single one of releasing the hammer to fire the cartridge, or the hammer may be cocked and dropped by simple continuous pull on the trigger itself, which thus performs the double action of cocking and releasing. All of these revolvers have built-in mechanical devices to prevent the weapon from being fired except by deliberate pull on the trigger. None are provided with manually operated safeties, as they are not deemed necessary.

French Example. The former French Army revolver, Model 1892, is in principle the same as the U. S. types. However, its cylinder swings out to the *right,* and its latch operates on a pivot. It is provided with a hinged side plate which may be swung open to afford access to the lockwork. This differs from U. S. types in which the side plates are fastened by screws. While this is a good revolver in its class, it is not to be compared to the Colt and Smith & Wesson. It is, however, well made of good materials. (For detailed description and working drawings of this as a basic type, see 8mm. Lebel, the name by which its cartridge is known throughout Europe).

Belgian Examples. Literally scores of types of solid-frame, swing-out-cylinder, rod-ejector revolvers have been manufactured in Belgium. The quality of any of these has never been better than fair by U. S., British, and German standards. Those made by Pieper are the most reliable. These revolvers in general are imitations of the Colt and are usually classed in Europe as "Colt ejector" types. The most common calibers are 5.5mm. Velodog (a cartridge manufactured in this country before the war to a limited extent), the 7.62mm. Russian Nagant, and the 8mm. French Lebel cartridges. Neither of the latter cartridges is generally known here.

Belgian revolvers of this type are made with cylinders swinging to the right, with cylinders swinging to the left, with exposed hammers, with enclosed hammers (the so-called "hammerless" type), with and without trigger guards, with and without manually operated safety catches such as are common to automatic pistols in this country, and in an endless variety of barrel lengths and shapes, cylinder flutings, and grip designs. Complete coverage of this group of freaks would require hundreds of pages of discussion which would be of little value since ammunition is not generally available for them in the United States and since they are all of inferior workmanship or design. Normally they bear proof marks, but no manufacturer's name.

Spanish Examples. All Spanish revolvers of this type are imitations or modifications of Colt or Smith & Wesson designs. The best of them are good; the worst are positively dangerous. In those which are made of fair-quality forgings, the fitting and tolerances are poor. Some were made from castings which frequently blow up when used with standard U. S. ammunition. While there are some Spanish automatic pistols of reasonably reliable quality, at the time of this writing there are few Spanish revolvers worthy of American ownership.

South American Examples. Some time ago there appeared numerous swing-out-cylinder weapons made in Argentina which are letter-perfect copies of Colt revolvers in exterior appearance. Usually these arms do not bear any identifying marks to show their point of origin, and are intended to be sold in

South America as genuine Colts. All specimens of such weapons so far examined have been of good quality forgings, very well finished on the outside and fairly well finished inside. Most of them, curiously, have the S&W type of rifling. However, any weapons whose origin cannot be determined at a glance should not be listed as reliable, since only the products of an established organization can be depended upon to maintain quality. Good quality revolvers are now made in Argentina and Brazil.

Other Nations. No nations other than those listed manufacture revolvers of this type on a production basis.

SOLID FRAME, SWING-OUT-CYLINDER, HAND-EJECTOR, "GAS-CHECK" REVOLVERS

This type of revolver corresponds generally to those already described, but differs in the mechanical arrangement by which the cylinder is revolved. It has the added feature of a block which *thrusts the cylinder forward* as the hammer is cocked, so that the cut-back (or chamfered) chamber is pushed over the tapered mouth of the barrel. A specially designed Russian cartridge is used with this type of action, and the escape of gas between cartridge chamber and barrel is minimized.

While United States manufacturing tolerances are so close that comparatively little gas escapes between the chamber in the cylinder and the barrel, this design is capable of considerable development.

The Belgian Pieper, as made for the Russians, exemplifies this type. It shoots the 7.62mm. Russian Nagant gas-check cartridge, and has been widely sold commercially throughout Europe. The cylinder swings to the left.

SOLID FRAME, FIXED CYLINDER, ROD EJECTOR REVOLVERS

The good types on this system fall into two classes: Single action and Double action.

Single Action. In the Colt Single Action Army Frontier Model the frame is solid as in the swing-out-cylinder types, but the cylinder is mounted on a bushing and retained in place by a cylinder pin inserted through a hole in the frame below the barrel, which passes through the bushing and locks its head in the standing-breech section of the frame. A hinged "loading gate" covers the head of the cylinder on the right side of the revolver. When the hammer is half cocked to permit the cylinder to be turned by hand, the loading gate is swung out and a cartridge chamber lined up with the loading slot. A cartridge is inserted and the cylinder turned by hand the distance of the next chamber. The hammer must be drawn back manually. Pressure on the trigger has no function except to drop the hammer to fire the cartridge.

Since the cylinder is fixed, the weapon is normally unloaded by half cocking the hammer, opening the loading gate, lining up a chamber with the loading slot, then pushing back the rod ejector mounted in a tube below the barrel. The tip of the rod will enter the chamber and eject the cartridge. When pressure is released, a spring around the rod will move it back to its original position. Turning the cylinder the distance of a chamber and pushing the rod will eject the next case. As an alternative method, the fixing pin may be removed and the cylinder withdrawn to the left to permit the cartridge cases to be forced out of their chambers in the cylinder. However, this is not standard procedure.

While this is one of the oldets and most widely known systems, and is noted for its grip, balance, and strength of frame, in actual practice it is not as dependable as the Colt and S&W swing-out-cylinder types. For detailed description and working drawing of this system, see .45 Colt S.A. Army.

Double Action. In the .455 British Royal Irish Constabulary revolver the frame is solid and the cylinder is free to revolve on a fixed pin; but the ejector rod normally must be pulled forward out of its seating in the front of the frame, then turned on a pivot or collar before it can be thrust up into the cartridge chamber. The cylinder, of course, must be revolved by hand to bring the chambers in line for ejection. This type normally is not provided with an ejector return spring; hence the ejector must be pulled out of the chamber manually and must be returned manually to its seat in the frame.

Italian Types. Numerous varieties of this type were developed in Italy from 1870 on, and were in use with practically no design changes as official Army weapons in World War II. They have the Chamelot Delvigne lockwork. If made by Glisenti of Brescia, they are of good material and fair workmanship.

The extraction is generally of the RIC revolver type. They are most often encountered in Italian 10.35mm. caliber. Barrel lengths and styles, as well as finishes and trigger styles, vary greatly. It must be noted that these revolvers *when designed* were ahead of their time. They employed rebounding hammers, counter-bored chambers, positive mechanical locks, and loose hammer noses years before such developments were thought of in the United States. Usually they have quick-detachable side plates which permit cleaning the lockwork without removing any parts.

Austrian Types. Like the Italians, the Austrians in the 1870's developed double action and other mechanical features far ahead of their general acceptance. Austrian Gasser revolvers in particular are made of good materials and are of good design, of their type. Gasser 8mm. revolvers used by the Italians and by some Balkan countries in World War II had been in service since 1880! Extraction is generally of the RIC type.

European Imitations. Imitations of the Colt S.A. Army have been made in Spain with a double-action lockwork, but otherwise resembling the Colt in exterior appearance. All such revolvers are uniformly inferior and are often dangerous.

Belgian and German imitations, particularly of the Webley design, are numerous. If German-made by Pickert, they are good cheap revolvers. Belgian makes are fair or poor. None are as good as the United States low-priced Harrington & Richardson or Iver Johnson arms.

Like the swing-out-cylinder imitations made in Europe, this design appears with exposed and enclosed hammers, with and without trigger guards, with and without manual safeties, with folding triggers, and in a tremendous range of lengths, weights, grip styles, etc.

The range of calibers, too, is tremendous. It includes the following:

Pin Fire: 5mm., 7mm., 9mm., 12mm. and 15mm.

Rim Fire: .22 Short, Long, Long Rifle, and Longue Portee: .297 (7.5mm.), .30 (7.8mm.), .320 Extra Short, .320 Short and .320 Long (8.05mm.), .340

(8.75mm.), .380 Short and Long (9.6mm.), .410 (10.2mm.), .442 (11.3mm.), .440 (11.1mm.), and .44 (11.2mm.).

Center Fire: .230 (5.7mm.), .320 Short and Long, .340, .380 Short and Long, .442 (11.3mm.), .450 (12.05mm.), several types of 11.5mm. and 11.55mm., the entire line of United States and British cartridges, the 7.5mm. Swedish, Velodog, 7.5mm Swiss, 8mm Austrian Gasser, 8mm French Lebel, 9.4mm Dutch, .430 Short and Long (11.35mm), 11.75mm Long Montenegrin Gasser, 12mm French, .500 (13.15mm.), and .577 (15mm.) Eley.

To add to the confusion, these revolvers are also made to take *rimless and semi-rim automatic pistol cartridges,* including the .25 and .32 Colt Automatic Pistol cartridges!

SOLID FRAME, FIXED CYLINDER, NON-EJECTOR

This is the cheapest form of revolver ever manufactured. In recent years it has been manufactured in the United States only by Harrington & Richardson and Iver Johnson. The frames are uniformly solid, and the cylinders are securely mounted on a fixing pin inserted through the frame below the barrel and passing back through the axis hole in the cylinder to the standing breech face of the frame. Revolvers of this type may or may not have a hinged loading gate on the right side of the frame to cover the loading slot when the weapon is ready for firing. They are uniformly double action with exposed hammers, though the type and shape of hammer may differ in various models. While the regular spur hammer is the standard one, and is intended to permit thumbcocking, special models intended for quick drawing have a cut down hammer without spur.

The line of baby revolvers of this type made by Sedgley in .22 caliber differ from all others in being hammerless—that is, having the hammer inside the frame and concealed by side plates. This type also has a folding trigger to make the weapon more compact.

Since the turn of the century, revolvers of this type have been produced in quantity for the American market in short- and long-barreled, pocket and target types only, in calibers .22 Short, .22 Long Rifle, .32 Smith & Wesson, .32 Smith & Wesson Long, and .38 Smith & Wesson. Some for European use have been made, notably by Harrington & Richardson, in caliber .455 British.

The characteristic difference of this basic type is that *no provision is made for mechanical extraction.* The cartridge cases must be pried or punched individually out of their chambers through the loading slot if the cylinder is in place, or from the cylinder if it is removed from the frame.

Examples of this type are .22 Iver Johnson Solid Frame and .32 Harrington & Richardson Solid Frame.

Obsolescent American Types. Revolvers of this type were manufactured in the late 90's and early 1900's under dozens of brand names for mail-order houses. Some were well made of forged steel but many were made with cast frames. Hopkins and Allen revolvers were the best of these, and thousands are still in use. Early Colt and Webley's, of course, were outstanding.

European Types. All the data under solid frame, fixed cylinder, rod ejector as to makes, styles and calibers apply to this classification also.

Hinged Frame, Tip-Down Barrel, Barrel Latch

This is the American type of hinged-frame revolver originally introduced by Smith & Wesson. The barrel is forged with a mounting for the cylinder and extractor assembly, and with an extension or strap which passes over the top of the cylinder and is provided with a latch which can be snapped down over the standing breech to lock the arm in firing position. The form of latch varies with the manufacturer and also with the date of manufacture; but in every case it is attached to the barrel strap.

The barrel is fastened to an extension of the frame or receiver ahead of the trigger guard at its locking point forward of the cylinder. Raising (or pressing) the latch permits the barrel and cylinder assemblies to be tipped down. This action automatically forces the extractor up from its seat in the center of the cylinder to extract and eject the cartridge cases in all the chambers, and to compress the extractor spring which snaps the extractor back into its seating in the cylinder at the end of the tip-down motion.

Except when manufactured by Smith & Wesson, this type was never produced as a quality revolver. As manufactured by Harrington & Richardson, Hopkins & Allen, and Iver Johnson, it was a substantial pocket revolver worth its selling price but not to be rated wth Colt, S&W, or Webley. Recent target models of this type in .22 caliber by H&R and Iver Johnson are good revolvers in their class.

United States Examples. Smith & Wesson hinged-frame .32 and .38 S&W; Harrington & Richardson and Iver Johnson .22, .32, and .38 hinged-frame. Hopkins & Allen (no longer manufactured but still widely distributed) are also a representative type. For detailed drawings and descriptions of the basic locking system, extracting system, and varieties of lockwork see .32 S&W Hammerless Hinged-Frame and Iver Johnson .38 S&W caliber Hinged-Frame.

Lockwork Variations. This type of revolver as made in the U. S. varies in lockwork with manufacturer and also with date of manufacture. The following, however, are the principal successful types:

1. Smith & Wesson: Double action, exposed hammer. Can be thumbcocked for accurate firing.

2. Smith & Wesson: Double action only, enclosed hammer. Can be fired only by continuous trigger pull. This is the so-called "hammerless" type, and is fitted with automatic grip safety.

3. Harrington & Richardson: Double action, exposed spur or cutdown hammer.

4. Harrington & Richardson: Enclosed hammer (called hammerless). Rebounding hammer safety but no grip safety.

5. Iver Johnson: Double action, exposed hammer. Unique automatic safety and special coil mainspring.

6. Iver Johnson: Enclosed hammer. Otherwise like hammer model. In IJ safety system, hammer never touches firing pin or cartridge, but when brought to full cock it can strike an intermediate lifter which in turn strikes the firing pin.

7. Hopkins & Allen: Manufacture discontinued, but was made in hammer and hammerless models with a special safety which worked on an eccentric

to bring the hammer in line with the firing pin *only* at the full cock position and when the trigger was pulled.

Calibers. While early Smith & Wesson revolvers on this system were made in large calibers, in the present century this type has been confined to low calibers (.22 Short, .22 Long Rifle, .22 Winchester; .32 S&W Short; .32 S&W Long and .38 S&W) because of the comparative weakness of the system of frame locking.

Obsolescent American Types. Dozens of makes of this type were turned out by factories no longer in business for the mail-order trade. Some were sold under as many as 50 different trade names. None should be used with today's ammunition.

European Imitations and Variations. In general, all that has been said about European solid-frame revolvers applies here also, with the further warning that because of the hinge (instead of a solid frame), this variety is potentially much more dangerous to the user.

German weapons of this class are the best; Belgian when proof-marked (as they customarily are) rate next; while Spanish types foot the list. All these countries made nearly exact copies of Smith & Wesson revolvers at one time or another. Many of these copies were made to shoot very powerful cartridges which no American manufacturer would countenance using in a barrel-latched hinged-frame design. When chambered for the .38-40, .44-40, .45 Colt, and similar cartridges, these European makes are very nearly without exception dangerous. Only those made in Germany by Ludwig Loewe are reasonably safe. These European makes may be chambered for any American, British, or European cartridge already listed. They may be hammer or hammerless. They may have grip safeties, thumb safeties, folding triggers, barrel lengths from 1½ to 12 inches or more, all types of finishes or engraving. A thousand variations could easily be identified. The one thing they have in common by United States standards is unreliability.

Japanese Variation. The Japanese, in 1893, adopted and used through World War II a variant of the Smith & Wesson hinged frame. The latch is the same, being on the barrel strap. The lockwork is quite different, however, employing a hinged side plate adapted from Italian and Austrian designs which can be swung out on a hinge to give quick access to all the working parts for immediate cleaning and easy replacement. The hammer is of peculiar design and cannot be thumbcocked. (For description and photos of this as an important variant, see 9mm. Japanese Revolver).

HINGED FRAME, TIP-DOWN BARREL, BARREL LATCH, AND THUMB LATCH

This is identical with the hinged frame S&W in the previous section *with the addition* of a thumb latch of the type used in solid-frame swing-out-cylinder revolvers. Not only must the barrel latch be lifted, but the thumb latch on the left side must be simultaneously pushed to unlock the barrel for tip-down. While this is an improved form and gives a much stronger lock, it has been discarded for the solid frame type in American manufacture.

European Imitations. As in all other categories, poor European imitations of this system are known. None can be recommended.

HINGED FRAME, TIP-DOWN BARREL, STIRRUP BREECH LATCH

This is the British type of hinged-frame revolver originally introduced by Webley & Scott. Its principal difference from the American variety lies in the ultra-strong breech fastening, consisting of a stirrup-shaped lock *pivoted to the standing breech* under spring tension. When the lower thumbpiece end of the lock on the left side of the frame is pushed forward, the upper locking stirrup is drawn back from over the top of the barrel strap (or extension), permitting the barrel and cylinder assemblies to be tipped down for automatic ejection and for loading. For detailed description and drawings of this as a basic type, see .455 Webley Revolver and .38 Enfield Revolver.

British Types. This system has never been used in U. S. manufacture, but has stood up under the most rigid service conditions wherever British troops have fought. While not as strong theoretically as the American swing-out-cylinder design, in field practice is has proven strong enough for any loads used in it, and for general sturdiness is usually rated ahead of the solid-frame varieties. It was the official British service revolver in the original .455 caliber and in the more recent official .380 caliber. The two differ in lockwork as relates to firing gear and cylinder indexing, but are identical in frame locking.

Such Webley Pocket Revolvers as do not require such a positive stirrup lock, use a modification of it in the form of a thumb latch mounted on the standing breech and locking over the barrel strap.

European Types. European imitations of this design are uniformly poor, with the notable exception of some Belgian types originally made for Montenegro.

Montenegrin Stirrup. This is a variant of the Webley stirrup based on an early Webley once made for the Chinese Navy in caliber .476. It consists of two separate thumbpieces pivoted on either side of the standing breech. When the lower ends are pressed, the upper locking ends are drawn to right and left away from the barrel strap in some types, while in others, where the strap fits down into a cut in the standing breech, they are drawn out of locking holes in the barrel strap. As made to shoot the tremendous .45 Montenegrin (a cartridge unknown in the United States, but much longer than the .45 Colt) this is a formidable arm of excessive weight for a revolver. Much of the strength of its locking device derives from the weight of the parts rather than the efficiency of the system.

"AUTOMATIC" REVOLVERS

Actually these are *a self-cocking variant* of the Webley Hinged-frame, Tip-down-barrel, Stirrup-breech-latch type. The barrel lock is identical. In this type the barrel and cylinder assemblies are free to ride backwards and forwards a short distance in the receiver or frame, being driven back by the force of recoil, then thrust forward by the compressed return spring. During this travel the hammer is automatically cocked and the cylinder revolved one chamber. Loading and unloading require the same manual pressure on the stirrup end and tipping down of the barrel as in the regular type. For complete description and photos of this as an important variant, see .455 Webley-Fosbery Automatic Revolver.

Imitations. The only imitation of this design put into limited manufacture was by the American Union Arms Co., of Toledo. This design might be capable of further development.

MISCELLANEOUS REVOLVER TYPES

Among the frame types which did not stand the test of time may be listed the strong but complicated pivot frame of the Merwin Hulbert, an American revolver in which the barrel and its strap turn out of engagement with the standing breech on a pivot in the frame ahead of the cylinder. Many of these finely constructed revolvers are still in use. The design however, is inferior to the current types. The design was imitated in England by Kynoch.

Very early Smith & Wesson revolvers and their imitators had frames in which the barrel strap was hinged to the standing breech and the release catch was on the frame ahead of the cylinder. In these, the barrel hinged and was tipped up to remove the cylinder for loading and unloading. This design was imitated in Europe. In some European types, the barrel and barrel strap could be moved straight ahead when the catch was released.

AUTOMATIC REVOLVER EJECTING SYSTEMS

Attempts to provide for automatic ejection of empty cartridge cases from revolvers take two forms: use of gas, and mechanical action in connection with the fall of the hammer.

In the first class, numerous experimental revolvers have been designed in which gas escaped through a small hole in the barrel as the bullet passed over it, to drive back a short piston much in the manner of the Winchester Carbine M1. This piston had an arm extending to the right ahead of the cylinder, with an attached short ejecting rod. The unit with a return spring was mounted in a tube below the barrel. As a shot was fired and the piston was driven back, the ejector rod was driven up into the chamber *to the right* of the one just fired, hurling the contents of that chamber out of the weapon, whether said contents was a loaded cartridge or an empty case. As this missile came straight back at the shooter, a deflecting shield was sometimes employed.

In the second class, which was widely developed and to some degree produced in Germany and Switzerland, the mainspring was made unusually powerful. When the trigger was pressed, as the hammer fell it hit a pivoted lever in the standing breech to the right of the firing pin hole at the same time that the hammer nose struck the cartridge in the chamber ahead of it. The tip of this pivoted lever was engaged under the rim of the cartridge to the right of the one being fired; which it hurled out the loading slot on the right side. This system was even a worse failure than the gas system because of over-complication.

In passing it should be noted that much experimental work along this line was also done in Italy, and that the Italian Ricci gas-operated revolver—now unknown—was at the turn of the century given some attention by U. S. Navy authorities.

QUICK LOADING SYSTEMS FOR REVOLVERS

Some European revolvers have been issued with quickly removable cylinders and with extra loaded cylinders intended to be inserted in the manner of extra magazines in automatic pistols. These all suffer from the fact that the cylinders are bulky; and that the cartridges will fall out of the spare unless they are protected by a cover which must be removed.

Special metal clips and disks perforated to receive cartridges and to drop over the head and ratchet of the ejector rod have been used, notably in the Webley Fosbery Automatic Revolver in Caliber .38 A.C.P. Besides being bulky and easily deformed, these are impractical because the cartridges take too long to line up with the chambers. Linked chargers suffer from this failing, also.

The only practical quick loader yet produced is that intended to permit the use of rimless cartridges in a revolver intended to be used with rimmed ammunition. (Described under .45 ACP Smith & Wesson).

POST WAR NOTE ON LOCKING SYSTEMS

The Swiss "Neuhausen 47/8" and "47/16" pistols, as well as earlier models by the same company, are actually of pre-World War II design. They are based on the "Petter" System. In appearance and breech lock construction they are modified Brownings. They differ slightly from their prototype, the French M 1935 A.

The breech locking system and front slide construction is a variant of the Belgian Browning 13-Shot Pistol. However, the locking nose on the barrel is pierced instead of solid, the lock pin on the slide stop passing through it. The sear and hammer units are housed in a removable sub-assembly as in the Russian Tokarev Pistol.

The Swedish P 40 and Finnish Lahti represent the nearest approach to new design, though the resulting pistol performance is not superior to other designs except for some possible sub-zero use.

These are short recoil pistols with modified Bergmann-Bayard locks. The pistols resemble the Luger externally. Magazine is in butt, with butt release catch. Barrel is screwed into a sub-receiver which is pierced on the right for an ejection opening. A pivoting accelerator is positioned at the front underside of this sub-receiver. As in the Browning machine gun, its function is to impart added drive to the breechblock on rearward motion. In ultra-cold climates, this added motion is credited with increasing reliability of functioning.

Sub-receiver and barrel assembly travel back only far enough for unlocking. A breechblock, square in section, positions inside the sub-receiver. Wings at its rear project to permit pulling breechblock back to cock. Firing pin and spring are in breechblock. Recoil spring and guide secured to rear of receiver nest in a tunnel in the breechblock. A three-sided locking bolt rides up and down by cam action in the rear of the sub-receiver. When locked, the top cross bar of the block rests in a cut in the top of the breechblock. During rearward breechblock movement, appropriate cam surfaces work against opposing surfaces on the lock causing it to rise out, of locking engagement. The pistol has an internal rotating hammer, and a single trigger bar with disconnector. Thumb safety is a positive sear and hammer lock.

Chapter 3

Caliber 3mm to .22

KOLIBRI
Auto and Single Shot

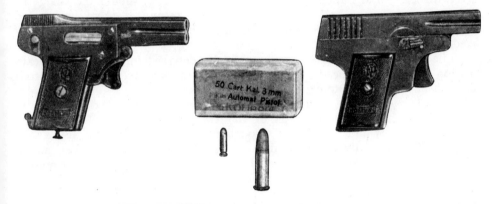

The smallest center-fire cartridge ever manufactured is the Austrian 2.7mm Kolibri. It is the smallest cartridge ever designed to operate an automatic pistol.

This cartridge is usually erroneously referred to as 3mm. There are actually two different cartridges, the 2.7mm and 3mm Kolibri. The pistol covered here is the 3mm.

These cartridges are in every way true miniatures—the cartridge case is of brass, a center fire primer is used, and the bullet is a lead core surrounded by a metal jacket. The bullet weighs about 5.3 grains, the powder charge about 1½ grains.

This cartridge was developed for the Kolibri Automatic Pistol—a miniature blowback pistol functioning on the same basic principle as the regular pocket automatics of standard caliber. It may also be used in the Kolibri Single Shot Pistol, a hinged-frame tip down barrel arm.

While these arms are in no sense *practical* weapons, it must be noted since there are rather large numbers of them in existence that at close quarters they will penetrate as much as 1½ inches of pine; and when it is remembered that a penetration of ½ inch in pine is equivalent to a dangerous flesh wound, it is at once apparent that they must be handled with due care.

4mm.

While cartridges of this caliber have never been manufactured in the United States, they have long been popular in Europe and large numbers of automatic pistol adapters to shoot them are now in this country. Whereas in Europe the cost of such ammunition was extremely low, when imported here it has always cost more than regular .22 caliber ammunition.

The 4mm. caliber has been manufactured in many styles—none of them interchangeable. It appears in central fire with rim and without rim, the rear part of the cartridge case being larger than the front, thereby lending a bottle-neck appearance to the cartridge. This type with rim is also made in rim fire. It is also made with a standard straight sided (cylindrical) case in short and long center fire calibers; and the capped cartridge cases are also sold with the round bullets separate. In the latter case, should the charge be too weak to drive the bullet out of the barrel, a second case may be inserted in the chamber for firing instead of punching the bullet out as is necessary if fixed cartridges are used.

While cartridges of this type were originally designed for shooting in heavy "parlor" rifles in Europe, in recent years adapters have been made to permit using them in pistols, automatic pistols and even in swing-out cylinder revolvers.

The center fire types resemble a copper shotgun primer necked down in front to hold a round lead pellet of about 7 grains weight. Geco adapters made in Germany and distributed throughout the world permitted using such cartridges in practically all standard European automatic pistols. These adapters are generally of two types. (1) The single shot type which is merely a smooth tube inserted and locked in the barrel of the automatic pistol (as in the Luger adapter) or a 4mm. barrel which will replace the barrel (in the Pocket Mauser); and (2) a unit consisting of a barrel which can be inserted and locked in the barrel of a Walther PPK or Sauer .32 automatic pistol, together with dummy cartridges of steel which are hollowed out to hold the 4mm. cartridges, and which can be worked through the magazine. In the latter type, the charge is not sufficient to operate the slide, which must be drawn back after each shot to eject and reload. The empty cases must then be punched out of the steel cartridge dummies to permit reloading.

Single shot pistols specially designed for 4mm. cartridges have been made in small quantity. They will seldom be encountered.

These cartridges are not loaded with powder—the priming mixture is also the propellant. They are practically noiseless, but have a penetration of about $\frac{1}{2}$ inch at close range, and are remarkably accurate.

4.25mm. Lilliput

This center fire cartridge, while potentially dangerous because of its ability to penetrate $1\frac{1}{2}$ inches or more of pine at short range, is not to be rated as either a target or a defense cartridge. It has a brass cartridge case, a jacketed bullet weighing about 12 grains and a powder charge of slightly over 1 grain of special mixed powder. It is strictly in the novelty class.

Originally designed for the Austrian Erika pistol which is little known in the United States, the 4.25mm. cartridge was used in 1920 in the original Lilliput automatic pistol introduced by August Menz of Suhl, Germany. (Note: This is not to be confused with the later and much more practical 6.35mm. (.25 A.C.P.) Lilliput of the same design but slightly heavier weight widely distributed by Menz).

The Lilliput is a striker-fired blowback automatic pistol of simple design fitted with a thumb safety and a standard removable box magazine with a capacity of 6 cartridges. The pistol measures only 3.54 inches overall and is one of the most compact arms ever designed.

MENZ   **4.25mm.**
Lilliput

Ammunition for this weapon is not manufactured in the United States but the pistol was sold in this country and is a desirable collector's oddity.

CARTRIDGE   .22 BB (Bulleted Breech)
Data

This cartridge may be used for indoor or short range target work in any revolver or single shot pistol chambered for .22 Short, .22 Long or .22 Long Rifle ammunition. It will not, of course, operate the action of an automatic pistol but may be inserted directly into the chamber for single shot use, though this is not recommended.

The B.B. was originally developed in the 1850's in France for use in Flobert gallery rifles and the priming mixture also acted as propellant. As loaded today it is usually copper cased with a small quantity of powder and a nearly round nosed bullet weighing about 19 grains, which may be straight lead, cadmium plated or copper covered. This cartridge measures about .43 inch

55

overall and develops a muzzle velocity of about 750 feet per second when fired through a 6 inch barrel.

These cartridges should be considered gallery ammunition only.

.22 C. B. (Conical Bullet or Ball) Cap

CARTRIDGE
Data

This rim fire gallery cartridge uses the same case as the B.B. Cap with a light powder load, but uses the regular 29-grain bullet of the .22 Short Cartridge. It may be used in weapons outlined for the B.B. Cap above. It develops 30 feet per second more velocity than the B.B. with more flash, noise and penetration.

In general the C.B. is not as satisfactory for gallery work as the B.B.

5.5mm. (.22 Center Fire) Velo Dog

CARTRIDGE
Data

This cartridge differs radically from the American types of this caliber. It is center fire, has a brass case, and is generally loaded with a metal jacketed bullet to give maximum penetration.

The loaded cartridge measures about 1.35 inches overall. The case is about 1.12 inches long with inside diameter of .253 at rear tapering to .248 at case mouth. Rim diameter is about .308 inch. Usual bullet weight is about 45 grains. Bullet length is about .48 inch.

As loaded in the United States by Remington, this cartridge develops a muzzle velocity of about 750 feet per second and a muzzle striking energy of 55 pounds when fired from a revolver with 2-inch barrel.

Revolvers Using this Cartridge. While this .22 center-fire cartridge has for years been an outstanding caliber in European pocket arms, no weapon has ever been commercially manufactured for it in the United States or Great Britain. Since the ammunition was manufactured in some quantity by Remington and Winchester before World War II for home consumption, European revolvers of this caliber must be more widely distributed here than is generally known.

Most of the revolvers made for this cartridge came from the Liege factories or from the German Pickert plant, and very few bear any identification marks to indicate manufacturer or caliber. Belgian makes are proof marked.

Pickerts may be recognized by their trade mark, the head of the German warrior Arminius, on the stocks. They are the best of the cheaper European revolvers and may be found in literally hundreds of designs, types, weights, finishes, and barrel lengths.

Their most common form is the "Bulldog"—the short solid-frame, double-action, nonejector, hammer revolver with trigger guard. However, this non-ejector type is also made with enclosed hammer and with and without manual thumb safeties on the frame. In the hinged-frame types also they appear with full exposed hammers, with spurless hammers, hammerless with and without thumb safeties, regular triggers and folding triggers and with cylinders of varying capacities and a broad range of types of breech locks. The swing-out cylinder types appear in as many modified forms as the hinged-frames and their cylinders swing out to the left in some models and to the right in others.

See under caliber .32 ACP for a picture of a common type of Pickert revolver.

CARTRIDGE
Data

.22 Short

.22 Short S-X

29 Gr. Lub. Plated

Muzzle Velocity in f.s.:	1035
Vel. at 50 Feet:	996
Vel. at 150 Feet:	931

Calculated Energy

Muzzle Energy in ft.-lbs.:	69
Energy at 50 Feet:	64
Energy at 150 Feet:	56

Calculated Drop

At 50 Feet:	.46
At 150 Feet:	4.50
At 300 Feet:	19.90

Penetration at 15 Feet

7/8" soft pine boards:	3

Length of Barrel in Which Tested

inches:	6

Shell Case

Weight:	7.45 grains
Max. Length:	.425
Outside Body Dia. Max.:	.2258
Inside Mouth Dia. Max.:	.2095
Volumetric Capacity to Base of Bullet in cubic inches:	.011

Bullet

Weight:	29 grains
Approx. length:	.340
Diameter Max.:	.2235
Area, Cross-Sectional:	.0391
Shape:	Round

Powder

Amount and type varies with different lots manufactured.

Cartridge

Approx. length, loaded:	.693
Approx. total weight, loaded:	38.0 grains

.22 Short Expert

29 Gr. Lead

Muzzle velocity in f.s.:	925
Vel. at 50 feet:	896
Vel. at 150 feet:	845

Calculated Energy

Muzzle energy in ft.-lbs.	55
Energy at 50 feet:	51
Energy at 150 feet:	46

Calculated Drop

At 50 Feet:	.64
At 150 Feet:	5.56
At 300 Feet:	24.30

Penetration at 15 Feet

7/8" soft pine boards:	2

Length of Barrel in Which Tested

inches:	6

Shell Case

Weight:	7.45 grains
Max. length:	.425
Outside body Dia. Max.:	.2258
Inside Mouth Dia. Max.:	.2095
Volumetric capacity to base of bullet in cubic inches:	.011

Bullet

Weight:	29 grains
Approx. Length:	.340
Diameter Max:	.2227
Area, Cross Sectional:	.0387 square inch
Shape:	Round

Powder

Amount and type varies with different lots Manufactured.

Cartridge

Approx. Length, Loaded:	.693
Approx. Total Weight, Loaded:	37.5 grains

57

While the .22 Short cartridge should preferably be used only in weapons chambered specifically for it, it will chamber and function in all revolvers and single-shot pistols designed for the .22 Long and the .22 Long Rifle. However, since the sight adjustments differ and since the rate of twist is more rapid in arms designed for the .22 Long Rifle cartridge, maximum accuracy cannot be expected.

Use of the Short cartridge in arms chambered for the longer cartridges will not seriously affect the accuracy of the weapon; but since powder gases can roughen the chamber further back than would occur with the longer cartridge case, continued use will make it difficult to extract the longer cartridges.

The .22 Short cartridge will not work well through the magazine of an automatic pistol designed for the .22 Long Rifle cartridge; and normally it will not provide enough recoil energy to blow back the slide to operate the action. While the .22 Short may be inserted directly into the chamber of a .22 Long Rifle automatic for single-shot fire, the practice is not recommended.

BB and CB caps may be used in arms chambered for the .22 Short, though except for some forms of indoor practice their value is negligible.

.22 Short   HI-STANDARD
                                                                    Model C

HI-STANDARD MODEL C. Pistol shown has a 4½-inch barrel. This model is usually found with 6¾-inch barrel. Weight as shown is about 32 ounces.

Construction: This is an elementary blowback type of target pistol very closely resembling the Colt Woodsman. The principal parts are: (1) the receiver which forms the grip and the mounting to receive the barrel. It is machined to receive the lockwork, and is fitted with suitable guides to receive and direct the travel of the sliding breechblock. A 10-shot magazine, can be inserted in the handle from below. (2) The barrel, fitted into a mounting which forms a forward protuberance on the receiver. It is pinned. (3) The breechblock slide which extends rearward from the breech and in which the firing pin, extractor and recoil spring assemblies are mounted in appropriately machined places. (4) The lockwork consisting of a pivoted trigger with a side bar connecting it with the sear, together with appropriate springs and plungers, and a hammer concealed within the slide and attached to a main-spring and plunger. (5) A standard sheet-metal box magazine which is interchangeable with the Colt Woodsman. Within the hollow box is a follower on which the first cartridge rests and which is provided with a button protruding through a slot in the right side of the mazagine wall to make it easy to load the magazine; a spring extending from the follower to the bottom of the magazine; and a base plate on which the spring rests and which provides a compression point as cartridges are forced down into the magazine.

Operation and Functioning: (1) Pushing the catch on the bottom of the butt to the rear permits the magazine to be withdrawn. (2) One to ten cartridges may be inserted in the magazine. (3) The magazine is inserted in the handle and pushed in until it locks. (4) The pistol is held firmly in one hand and the slide pulled fully back with the other hand. This action forces the hammer back and down causing it to compress the mainspring. The sear catches and holds the hammer at full cock. The magazine spring forces the cartridges up and the top one is held by the folded lips of the magazine in line with the breechblock. The rearward movement of the slide compresses the recoil spring around its guide. (5) Releasing the slide permits the recoil spring to assert itself and drive the slide forward. The breechblock face of the slide is machined to permit it to strip the cartridge from the top of the magazine and drive it into the firing chamber. The extractor in the right face of the breechblock snaps over the rim of the cartridge case. When the breech is fully closed, the sear bar running from the trigger to the sear on the left side of the receiver is brought in contact with the sear.

When the trigger is pressed it pivots to act on the sear bar to free the sear from the hammer. The mainspring drives the hammer ahead to hit the firing pin to cause it to pass through its hole in the breechblock to fire the cartridge, meanwhile compressing the firing pin spring. This spring reacts to pull the pin back into the breechblock. As the bullet goes down the barrel the rearward thrust of the gases within the cartridge case force the head of the case back against the spring-held breechblock slide starting it to the rear. A surface on the inner side of the slide strikes the hammer sharply rotating it on its axis pin and thereby cocking it and compressing the mainspring; while the sear catches and holds it back. The slide is so machined that as it moves back in its tracks in the receiver it depresses the sear bar, thereby breaking connection between trigger and hammer so that a second shot cannot be fired until the breech is again closed and pressure on the trigger has been released to remake the connection. The breechblock carries the cartridge case back gripped by the extractor claw until the case strikes against the arm rising from the receiver which acts as the ejector. This pivots the case out of the grip of the extractor and hurls it out of the weapon. The recoil spring is automatically compressed. The magazine spring forces the next cartridge up in line. The breechblock is carried forward by the recoil spring to chamber the next cartridge. This action is repeated each time the trigger is pressed until the weapon is empty.

This arm is provided with the thumb-latch safety on the left side of the receiver. (On "C" and other early models there are two thumb latches. The forward one is the safety.) When the arm is cocked, pushing up this latch locks the sear and also engages in a cut in the slide to prevent the slide from being opened.

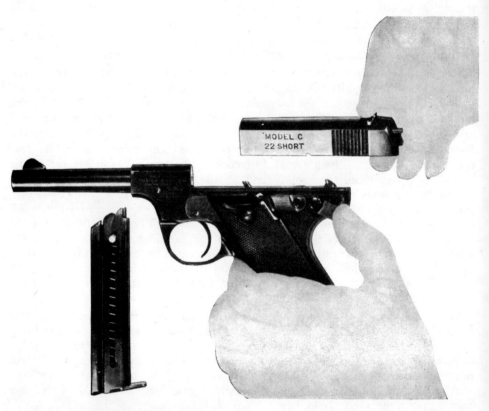

Dismounting: (1) Withdraw magazine. (2) Pull back slide and look in chamber to be sure pistol is empty. (3) While holding slide fully to the rear, press down the plunger rising from the top of the slide. This will thrust down a flat spring in the ceiling of the slide and cause it to lock the recoil spring and its guide in compressed position. (4) Push down the takedown latch (in this model it is the rear latch on the left side of the receiver) and while holding it down draw the slide directly to the rear off the receiver. Further dismounting of this pistol is not recommended. The plunger should be held down while the slide is being withdrawn.

Reassembling: (1) While pushing the cocked hammer still further to the rear to permit the slide to clear it, start the slide on its tracks. (2) Push the hammer back again and hold it while moving the slide far enough ahead to clear the hammer completely; then push slide fully forward. This will release the recoil spring. (3) Pull the slide back and let it drive forward to test it. If the recoil spring and guide slip out of control of the flat lock spring while the slide is off, use a nail or other pointed instrument to push the recoil spring units ahead into their hole in the breechblock and push the top plunger in to lock them. The pistol cannot be assembled if the recoil spring is not under compression.

Manufacturer: High Standard Mfg. Corp., New Haven, Conn.

STEVENS   **.22 Short**
Single Shot

See Stevens under .22 LR.

WALTHER   **.22 Short**
Olympia Rapid Fire

For photographs, drawing and description see Caliber .22 Long Rifle Walther Olympia Self-Loading Sport Model.

The Rapid Fire Model is a .22 Short version. It differs from the Sport Model as follows: It weighs only 27½ ounces, has a magazine capacity of only six cartridges, and is supplied with a single detachable balance weight which cannot be adjusted. It has a special light-weight alloy slide; in some models the receiver also may be made of this same alloy.

This weapon was designed specifically for rapid-fire target work and has practically no observable recoil. No finer target arm exists.

Manufacturer: Carl Walther, Germany.

Other Arms Using This Cartridge   **.22 Short**

Any revolver or pistol (not automatic) listed under calibers .22 Long and .22 Long Rifle.

.22 Long

.22 Long S-X

29 Gr. Lub. Plated

Muzzle Velocity in f.s.:	1125
Vel. at 50 feet:	1070
Vel. at 150 feet:	988

Calculated Energy

Muzzle Energy in ft.-lbs.:	81
Energy at 50 feet:	74
Energy at 150 feet:	63

Calculated Drop

At 50 feet:	.40
At 150 feet:	3.92
At 300 feet:	17.64

Penetration at 15 Feet

7/8" soft pine boards:	4

Length of Barrel in Which Tested

inches:	6

Shell Case

Weight:	9.8 grains
Max. Length:	.613
Outside Body Dia. Max.:	.2258
Inside Mouth Dia. Max.:	.2095
Volumetric Capacity to Base of Bullet in Cubic inches:	.0174

Bullet

Weight:	29 grains
Approx. Length:	.340
Diameter Max.:	.2235
Area, Cross Sectional:	.0391 square inch
Shape:	Round

Powder

Amount and type varies with different lots manufactured.

Cartridge

Approx. length, loaded:	.881
Approx. total weight, loaded:	40.5 grains

.22 Long Expert

29 Gr. Lead

Muzzle Velocity in f.s.:	930
Vel. at 50 feet:	901
Vel. at 150 feet:	848

Calculated Energy

Muzzle Energy in ft.-lbs.:	56
Energy at 50 feet:	52
Energy at 150 feet:	46

Calculated Drop

At 50 feet:	.58
At 150 feet:	5.50
At 300 feet:	23.90

Penetration at 15 Feet

7/8" soft pine boards:	3

Length of Barrel in Which Tested

inches:	6

Shell Case

Weight:	9.8
Max. Length:	.613
Outside Body Dia. Max.:	.2258
Inside Mouth Dia. Max.:	.2095
Volumetric Capacity to Base of Bullet in cubic inches:	.0174

Bullet

Weight:	29 grains
Approx. Length:	.340
Diameter Max.:	.2227
Area, Cross Sectional:	.0387 square inch
Shape:	Round

Powder

Amount and type varies with different lots manufactured.

Cartridge

Approx. length, loaded:	.881
Approx. total weight, loaded:	40.0 grains

SEDGLEY
Baby Hammerless

.22 Long

This is a cheap solid frame, manual-extraction revolver with an enclosed hammer and a folding trigger to make it a compact arm. It was advertised originally as a "garter pistol." Loading and extracting may be done individually through a loading gate on the right side of the frame or by removing the cylinder from the frame by withdrawing the cylinder axis pin.

It weighs six ounces, measures four inches overall and has a six-shot cylinder. The arm was designed for the .22 Long cartridge, low velocity. A hinged-frame version of this arm was also manufactured and is pictured above.

An improved model is provided with a novel ejector rod and cylinder assembly which may be removed from the frame as a unit for quick extraction. Sedgley introduced this feature about 1925 and it appeared in modified form in Spain ten years later. The principle, however, was not strictly original with Sedgley, having been used in Swiss experimental arms before 1890, and in the Pettingell percussion revolver during our Civil War.

This weapon and others of its type should not be used with high-velocity cartridges.

Manufacturer: R. F. Sedgley, Inc., Philadelphia, Pa.

STEVENS
Single Shot

.22 Long

See Stevens under caliber .22 LR.

.22 Long

WEBLEY AND SCOTT
Semi Auto

This arm is unique in that while resembling an automatic pistol it is actually a single-shot pistol.

This weapon is manufactured in two barrel lengths, four and one-half and nine inches. The front sight is mounted on the barrel and is adjustable. The rear sight is mounted at the end of the slide. Over-all length with nine-inch barrel is ten and three-quarters inches; weight is twenty-four ounces.

While the barrel is stamped "Cal. .22 Rim Fire Long," both Short and Long Rifle cartridges may also be used. High-velocity ammunition is not recommended.

The exterior appearance of the weapon, as well as its trigger and hammer mechanism, are the same as those described for the Webley & Scott Pocket Hammer Pistol (See under Caliber .32 Colt Auto Pistol).

Construction and Functioning: This weapon consists of a receiver which acts as a handle, a barrel mounted solidly in the receiver, and a slide under spring tension which is free to move backward under the force of recoil of the cartridge to extract and eject the empty cartridge case.

There is no recoil spring in this weapon to drive the slide forward after the empty case has been ejected.

When the breechblock is drawn back as far as it will go, it rides over the hammer and pushes it to full cock, where it is caught and held by the sear. A cartridge is inserted and the breechblock is pushed forward by hand until it chambers the cartridge and is flush against the breech of the barrel.

When the trigger is pulled, the trigger bar in contact with the sear releases it from the hammer notch, permitting the hammer to go forward on its axis under pressure from the coil spring mounted in front of it in the receiver to strike the firing pin and fire the cartridge. The slide is blown back with the empty cartridge case held in the extractor which is mounted in the face of the breech lock part of the slide, until the case strikes the ejector and is hurled out the top of the pistol. The slide then stays open ready for insertion of a new cartridge by hand and for the slide to be pushed forward by hand.

A special feature of this weapon is a thumb-operated extractor mounted on top of the barrel directly ahead of the forward end of the slide. In case of failure to eject in the normal manner, pushing back the auxiliary thumb extractor will force the empty case back to permit it to be jacked out of the pistol. The extractor must then be pulled forward to its resting place.

A detachable shoulder stock is provided for this weapon to convert it to a short rifle.

Dismounting: Hold the handle of the pistol firmly in the left hand. Put the first finger of the right hand through the trigger guard and press the thumb of the right hand up below the barrel just in front of the trigger guard.

The trigger guard acts as a spring. Pulling it slightly down and forward toward the muzzle will free its lower end from its recess in the receiver directly below the trigger. This frees the breechblock and barrel which may then be pulled directly forward on the receiver guides out of the receiver. The barrel may now be pulled down out of the slide.

Reassembling: First make sure that the hammer is fully cocked. Insert the barrel in the slide (breechblock) from below so that its chamber is flush with the breechblock section of the slide.

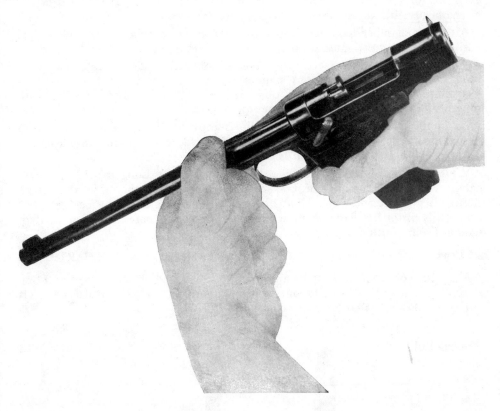

Slide the assembled units back in the guides in the receiver as far as they will go, when the rear end of the slide lines up with the rear top edge of the receiver. Exerting pressure on the lower end of the trigger guard, push the trigger guard up until it snaps into its recess in the receiver.

Should further dismounting be necessary, removing the stock screws and taking off the stocks will give access to the trigger and hammer mechanisms. Driving out the appropriate pins there and in the breechblock will remove all the components.

Manufacturer: Webley & Scott, Ltd., England.

.22 Long
WEBLEY AND SCOTT
Single Shot Target

This is a standard hinged-frame, drop-down barrel pistol. With the regular ten-and-one-quarter-inch barrel it weighs about thirty-seven ounces, and measures fifteen inches overall.

Description and Functioning: This differs from the American pistol of its type in the system of barrel opening. When the rear end of the trigger guard is pulled down it swings the breech of the barrel up away from the standing breech section of the frame. The barrel, of course, is hinged to a forward extension of the frame which permits its muzzle to be lowered. This action mechanically lifts the extractor in customary fashion.

After the chamber has been loaded and the barrel snapped back into locked position, the hammer must be thumb cocked before the pistol can be fired.

This is one of the most accurate target pistols ever made. While it appears heavy and clumsy by American standards, and the trigger pull and type of lock employed are heavier than ours, the hang and balance combine with superb rifling to make this an outstanding arm.

As in the W&S Semiautomatic, a hole is provided in the butt to receive a special wooden stock to permit it to be used as rifle with considerable accuracy up to one hundred and fifty yards.

While this pistol was originally designed for the .22 Long cartridge, it will handle both the Short and the Long Rifle cartridges. Furthermore, the breech closure is so tight and strong that high-velocity ammunition may be used. As issued this pistol has fixed sights which must be compensated for if other than standard ammunition is used.

.22 Long
OTHER ARMS USING THIS CARTRIDGE

Any pistol or revolver (but no automatic pistol) listed under caliber .22 Long Rifle. Note that high-velocity ammunition should not be used in early models unless specifically stated herein.

.22 Long Rifle
CARTRIDGE
Data

.22 L. R. S-X

40 Gr. Lub. Plated

Muzzle Velocity in f.s.:	1160
Vel. at 50 feet:	1114
Vel. at 150 feet:	1043

Calculated Energy

Muzzle Energy in ft.-lbs.:	120
Energy at 50 feet:	110
Energy at 150 feet:	97

Calculated Drop

At 50 feet:	.39
At 150 feet:	3.55
At 300 feet:	15.70

Penetration at 15 Feet

7/8″ soft pine boards:	6
Length of Barrel in Which Tested inches:	6

Shell Case

Weight:	9.8 grains
Max. Length:	.613
Outside Body Dia. Max.:	.2258
Inside Mouth Dia. Max.:	.2095
Volumetric Capacity to Base of Bullet in cubic inches:	.0178

Bullet

Weight:	40 grains
Approx. Length:	.460
Diameter Max.:	.2235
Area, Cross Sectional:	.0391 square inch
Shape:	Round

Powder

Amount and type varies with different lots manufactured.

Cartridge

Approx. length, loaded:	.990
Approx. total weight, loaded:	52.0 grains

.22 Long Rifle Xpert

40 Gr. Lead

Muzzle Velocity in f.s.:	980
Vel. at 50 feet:	956
Vel. at 150 feet:	913

Calculated Energy

Muzzle Energy in ft.-lbs.:	85
Energy at 50 feet:	81
Energy at 150 feet:	74

Calculated Drop

At 50 feet:	.52
At 150 feet:	4.73
At 300 feet:	20.78

Penetration at 15 Feet

7/8″ soft pine boards:	4
Length of Barrel in Which Tested inches:	6

Shell Case

Weight:	9.8 grains
Max. Length:	.613
Outside Body Dia. Max.:	.2258
Inside Mouth Dia. Max.:	.2095
Volumetric Capacity to Base of Bullet in cubic inches:	.0178

Bullet

Weight:	40
Approx. Length:	.465
Diameter Max.:	.2227
Area, Cross Sectional:	.0387 square inch
Shape:	Round

Powder

Amount and type varies with different lots manufactured.

Cartridge

Approx. length, loaded:	.990
Approx. total weight, loaded:	51.5 grains

.22 Long Rifle Super Match MII

40 Gr. Lead

Muzzle Velocity in f.s.:	975
Vel. at 50 feet:	951
Vel. at 150 feet:	908

Calculated Energy

Muzzle Energy in ft.-lbs.:	84
Energy at 50 feet:	80
Energy at 150 feet:	73

Calculated Drop

At 50 feet:	.54
At 150 feet:	4.9
At 300 feet:	20.9

Penetration at 15 Feet

7/8″ soft pine boards:	4
Length of Barrel in Which Tested inches:	6

Shell Case

Weight:	9.8 grains
Max. Length:	.613
Outside Body Dia. Max.:	.2258
Inside Mouth Dia. Max.:	.2095
Volumetric Capacity to Base of Bullet in cubic inches:	.0178

Bullet

Weight:	40 grains

Approx. Length:	.465	*Powder*
Diameter Max.:	.2227	Amount and type varies with different
Area, Cross Sectional:	.0387 square inch	lots manufactured.
Shape:	Round	*Cartridge*

Approx. length, loaded: 1.000
Approx. total weight, loaded: 51.5 grains

Note On Use of High-Velocity Cartridges

While many standard pistols and revolvers are structurally strong enough to handle modern .22 Long Rifle high-velocity ammunition, because of the danger of case heads blowing out and possibly injuring the weapon, it is recommended that the high velocity loads be used only in those of comparatively recent manufacture in which the chambers are counterbored to embed the entire case head in the cylinder; and in automatic pistols of recent design.

.22 Long Rifle   **COLT**
                                                                     Camp Perry

General Description: Factory Model W. A single-shot target pistol using the frame of the Colt .38 caliber Officers model. The cylinder is replaced by a steel block through which the barrel passes and which swings out to the left on a crane with the barrel for loading. Rod ejection.

Ammunition: .22 L. R.
Manufacturing Dates: December 6, 1926 to February 2, 1939.
Serial Numbers: From Number 1.
Finish: Blue.
Barrel Length: 10″ (Old Model). 8″ (New Model).
Stocks: Checked walnut with medallion.
Bore Diameter: .215″—.001.
Groove Diameter: .222″—.001.
Rifling: (Left twist): 6 grooves. 1 turn in 14″.
Number of Shots: 1.
Action: Single.
Approximate Weight: 34 ounces.
Over-all Length: 12″ with 8″ barrel.

Sights: Target type. Front: adjustable for elevation. Rear: adjustable for windage.

Note: A special, exceptionally fast lock was designed for this pistol which provides unusually quick hammer fall.

This is one of the finest single-shot target pistols ever manufactured in the United States. It received its first public test at the Camp Perry Matches in 1920, and was next taken to Europe for the Olympic Shoots. However, it was not marketed until 1927.

As originally issued, it had a barrel length of 10" and a sight radius of 9½".

While it was essentially a .22 caliber single-shot pistol built on the general exterior specifications of the .38 caliber Officer's Model Target, it was the first target pistol for use in the United States which really fulfilled the need for a heavy weapon with a large grip suitable for use as a companion gun for target shooters using the .38 Special.

Early in 1934 an improved version of this pistol was marketed by Colt.

While the barrel in the original model resembled that of the 7½" barrel Officer's Model very closely since the breechpiece is an extension of the barrel, it actually measured 10" instead of the 7½" which is standard in the Officer's Model of similar appearance.

In the new model, the over-all length of the barrel (including the breechpiece section) is 8". The barrel has been made thicker in diameter to maintain the approximate weight of the original model.

This new model has an embedded head chamber (to permit the use of improved high-power .22 caliber loads without danger of the head being split and causing injury to the weapon or shooter); a more slender and somewhat straighter, backlashless trigger which, when the weapon is cocked is in the same position as the trigger in the .38 Officer's Model at full cock, and a faster firing lock utilizing a shorter hammer fall.

This new model measures 12" overall.

While it will handle any type of .22 caliber ammunition (BB or CB cap, Short, Long, and Long Rifles, regular and high-speed, dry and greased) it does its best work with the .22 Long Rifle ammunition.

The front sight is adjustable for elevation. The rear sight is adjustable for windage.

This weapon has all the advantages of the heavy Colt revolver, together with most of the advantages of a high-class single-shot target pistol from the standpoints of weight, balance, distance between sights, short and quick hammer fall.

It is surpassed only by special German and Swiss pistols of the "free" types in which hammers are set lower in the hand, giving shorter hammer fall and quicker and faster ignition.

In theory, the fact that the front sight is mounted on the barrel (which swings out), and the rear sight is mounted on the frame (which is rigid), may result in poor target work. In actual practice, however, this weapon is capable of far more accurate fire than any individual can possibly attain.

Instead of the customary cylinder, the barrel and single-shot breech are a single unit. The section between the top and bottom of the frame in which the cylinder normally rests, is occupied by a flat breechpiece which is fluted. The appearance is much the same as though the cylinder had been ground down until it was flush with the frame.

The pistol is fitted with the customary pull cylinder latch on the left-hand side. When this latch is drawn back, the barrel, crane and breech section swing over to the left away from the frame.

Operation. To eject a cartridge in the breech, push back the ejector rod mounted below the barrel exactly as in a swing-out cylinder revolver. The coil spring mounted around the extractor rod will return it to forward position when the pressure is withdrawn.

Removing the left-hand stock and the side plate exposes a firing lock mechanism entirely different from any normal revolver. It is one of the simplest and fastest firing locks ever developed in this country. The firing pin is mounted in the hammer. A stirrup attached to the hammer compresses a coil spring when the hammer is drawn to full cock. This spiral mainspring extends downward the full length of the grip. The trigger is returned by a spiral spring also. The only other units in this lock are a half-round pin which runs through the frame just in front of the hammer below the firing pin hole; and an arm extending from the trigger through a toggle joint to this heavy pin.

When the hammer is cocked as the trigger is drawn back the arm attached to the trigger rotates this heavy pin on its axis. In the full cocked position, this rebound pin lies flush with the frame out of the way. Its flat face is toward the hammer.

When the trigger is pressed releasing the hammer to be driven forward by the mainspring, the spiral trigger spring forces the trigger forward. The trigger draws the toggle arm which again rotates the rebound pin so that its round surface forces the hammer back about 1/16″ until the tip of the firing pin is drawn back into the recoil plate behind the fired cartridge case.

There is a lug on this toggle arm which prevents the latch from being pulled to the rear if the gun is at full cock. This lug also prevents the weapon from being fired in this position. If the latch is not properly fastened, the position of this lug prevents the hammer from being cocked.

.22 Long Rifle   **COLT**
                                                                          Note

Note On Colt Revolvers

All modern Colt double-action revolvers are of solid-frame, swing-out cylinder construction. Pulling back the cylinder latch on the left side of the frame permits the cylinder to be swung out on a crane which is attached to the forward end of the frame. Pushing back the ejector rod which passes down the center of the cylinder ejects all cartridges simultaneously.

While modifications in lockwork have been made through the years, the description of the construction and operation of the New Service Model (described under Caliber .45 ACP) essentially covers all modern double action Colt's.

With the exception of the Pocket Positive Model in caliber .32 CPP, all Colt revolver models are made in from two to nine or more calibers. The various models differ in lengths of barrel, weight, sights, shapes of butt, types of stocks and similar minor details; but in general the appearance is distinctively Colt and each model resembles the others very closely. A study of the photographs and the detail drawings under New Service Model Cal. .45 ACP will give a clear idea of the mechanism of all modern Colt revolvers.

COLT   .22 Long Rifle
Officers Model Target (E Frame)

General Description: Factory Model I. A target revolver on a .41 caliber frame designed to give maximum accuracy. Has hand-finished action, checked trigger and back strap with bore and chamber dimensions held to minimum tolerances.

Ammunition: .22 L. R.   .32 Police Positive   .38 Special

Manufacturing Dates: Center-fire frame .32 caliber August 23, 1932 to present. Center-fire frame .38 caliber 1908 to present. Rim-fire .22 caliber L. R. from February 11, 1930 to present.

Serial Numbers: .32 and .38 Special concurrent with Model E (Army Special and Official Police). .22 Models E & I concurrent from Number 1 from 11 February 1930 to present.

Finish: Blue (standard).

Stocks: Checked walnut with medallion.

	.22 L.R.	*.32 Police Positive*	*.38 Special*
Bore Diameter:	.215"−.001	.305"−.001	.347"−.001
Groove Diameter:	.222"−.001	.312"−.001	.354"−.001
Barrel Length:	6"	6"	4", 4½", 5", 6", 7½"

Rifling: (Left twist) 6 grooves. .22 caliber, 1 turn in 14". Center fire, 1 turn in 16".

Number of Shots: 6.

Action: Double.

Approximate Weight: .38 Special: 6" regular barrel, 34 oz. With heavy 6" barrel, 36 oz.

Over-all Length: 11¼" with 6" barrel.

Sights: Target. Front: adjustable for elevation. Rear; for windage.

.22 Long Rifle   COLT
Officers Target (E Frame)

Note: As a "shooters" gun many variations from the standard arm have been produced, by the factory, by individuals, and gunsmiths. The variations include special stocks, special sights, and alterations to the action or limb work.

Comments: One special arm provided by the factory complies with the conditions of "the Pocket Revolver Match." Included in the specifications are: weight under 32 ounces with a 4" barrel, and a fixed front sight made by using an insert blade of special shape, pinned in place. The "Kelly"-type Patridge front sight was developed originally for this model (This is a straight sighting surface relieved at the sides to eliminate light reflection).

.22 Long Rifle   COLT
Police Positive Target (.38 Frame)

General Description: Factory Model C, replaced Models H and G. A revolver of sufficient size and weight to be used in competition yet not unsuited for trap line and general use.

Ammunition: .22 L.R. .22 W.R.F. .32 Police Positive.

Manufacturing Dates: October 7, 1925 to 1943.

Serial Numbers: From Number 25,000.

Finish: Blue.

Barrel Length: 6", all models.

Stocks: Checked walnut with medallion.

Bore Diameter: .22 L.R., .215"−.001. .22 W.R.F., 215"−.001. .32 Pol. Pos., .305"−001.

Groove Diameter: .22 L.R., .222"−.001. .22 W.R.F., .222"−.001. .32 Pol. Pos., .312"−.001.

Rifling: (Left twist): 6 grooves. .22 caliber, 1 turn in 14". .32 caliber, 1 turn in 16".

Number of Shots: 6.

Action: Double.

Approximate Weight: .22 caliber 26 oz.; .32 caliber 23 oz.

Over-all Length: 10½".

Sights: Target. Front: adjustable for elevation. Rear: for windage.

Note: This model was put on a heavier .38 caliber frame with the increased interest in target shooting (both formal and informal) that started in the 1920's. Originally with a narrow butt, a wider heavier butt was adopted after production of many thousands. Later a check trigger and recessed-head cylinder were added, with a dull top strap to eliminate glare.

.22 Long Rifle   COLT
Police Positive (.32 Frame)

General Description: Factory Model B. A light-frame, square-butt revolver designed for general service. Enjoyed wide acceptance in police circles until changing conditions demanded heavier calibers and frames.

Ammunition: .32 Long Colt. .32 Police Positive. .22 L.R.

Manufacturing Dates: 1908 to August 11, 1941. (last shipment).

Serial Numbers: Continuation of the New Police series starting with approximately Number 13,000.

Finish: Blue and nickel.

Barrel Length: .32 Long Colt: 2½", 4", 5", 6"; .32 Pol. Pos. 2", 2½" 4", 5", 6"; .22 L.R., 4", 6".

Stocks: Rubber, checked walnut with medallion.

Bore Diameter: .305"—.001 (.32 Long Colt and Pol. Pos.) .215"—.001. (.22 L.R.)

Groove Diameter: .12"—.001 (.32 Long Colt and Pol. Pos.) .222"—.001. (.22 L.R.)

Rifling: (Left twist). 6 grooves. 1 turn in 16".

Number of Shots: 6.

Action: Double.

Approximate Weight: With 4" barrel: 18 ounces.

Over-all Length: 10½" with 6" barrel.

Sights: Fixed Front: integral with barrel. Rear: groove and notch in top strap.

Note: The .32 Long and Short Colt (now obsolete) called for the same barrel dimensions as the .32 Police Positive but were not interchangeable because of differences in case and bullet dimensions. The .32 Colt cartridge depended on the expansion of a hollow-base bullet for proper functioning through the barrel.

This arm is called *El Pequeño* (the little one) in some Spanish-speaking countries. This model in .22 caliber was largely sold in Cuba although many were sold and distributed in the United States. In the transition from the New Police, the positive lock (safety device) was added as well as the loose firing pin.

COLT .22 Long Rifle
Police Positive Target (Light .32 Frame)

General Description: This arm was significant in that it began the present line of Colt target revolvers in this caliber.

Ammunition: .22 L.R. .22 Short and .22 Long until after 1912. .22 W.R.F.

Manufacturing Dates: .22 Short, Long and L.R.. March 5, 1910. .22 W.R.F., September 14, 1925.

Serial Numbers: From Number 1.

Finish: Blue (standard).

Barrel Length: 6", All models.

Stock: Rubber, checked walnut.

Bore Diameter: .215"—.001, all models.

Groove Diameter: .222"—.001, all models.

Number of Shots: 6.

Action: Double.

Approximate Weight: 22 ounces.

Over-all Length: 10½".

Sights: Front: insert blade (adjustable type incorporated later). Rear: drive in (with binding screw added later).

Note: Models G (rim fire) and H (center fire) actually began as far back as 1905 as a development from the New Police. Many were produced without a positive lock before the changes which were made in 1910. Models G and H may be considered, in general, as the same arm.

.22 Long Rifle **COLT**
Police Positive (.38 Frame)

See Colt Police Positive under caliber .38 Police Positive, which describes this model and also its modification the Banker's Special.

.22 Long Rifle **COLT**
Official Police

See Colt Official Police Model under Caliber .38 Special.

.22 Long Rifle **COLT**
Single Action Army

While this model was manufactured for a time in Cal. .22 Long Rifle, the quantity produced was very small. For description, drawing and photograph see Colt Single Action Army under Caliber .45 Colt.

.22 Long Rifle **COLT**
Woodsmen Series

There are four varieties of this .22 Long Rifle automatic pistol. The description of functioning and operation covers all models, and the drawing shows the lockwork common to all. The Sport model and the Target model are identical in appearance except that the former has a shorter barrel. The Match Target model while radically different in exterior appearance is essentially the same in interior work.

Note that the early form of this pistol (making the fourth variety) was originally issued under the name "Colt .22 Automatic Pistol, Target Model." This was designed for low velocity ammunition. Any pistol of this class whose serial number is lower than 83790 should not be used with high velocity cartridges unless the mainspring housing has been replaced. This housing forms the back of the grip and its upper end has to take most of the shock of the breechblock slide as it is blown back by the explosion of the cartridge. Remember that this slide is mounted on the receiver from the rear end, and that bending the stop on the housing can be very dangerous. If the housing is the original one, the curved section above where the hand closes around it will be checked with a fine diagonal pattern. If the housing is the heat treated type, which is safe to use with modern ammunition, the checking at this point is carried straight across the arch in the housing.

.22 Long Rifle **COLT**
Woodsman Target

General Description: Originally Automatic Pistol, Target Model. (Factory Model S.) A holster arm designed to give the sportsman an automatic pistol of target accuracy with the necessary simplicity of operation, using inexpensive and easily available ammunition.

Ammunition: .22 L. R.
Manufacturing Dates: From March 29, 1915 to date.
Serial Numbers: From Number 1.
Approximate Weight: 29 ounces.
Over-all Length: 10½".
Note: Present barrel is of a heavy straight tapered design—the two earlier

74

barrels were of smaller outside diameter with a fillet in front of the shoulder. The original magazine used a cast brass follower with a zigzag spring, current design has pressed metal follower and coil spring. Changes were made with Number 83790 to permit the use of high-velocity .22 L.R. ammunition.

All other data same as for Woodsman Sport Model.

COLT   .22 Long Rifle
Woodsman Sport

General Description: Factory Model S. An adaptation of the original Colt .22 Automatic Pistol, Target Model, with a shorter barrel for more convenient use by sportsmen.

Ammunition: .22 L. R.
Manufacturing Dates: 1933 to the present.
Serial Numbers: Concurrent with the present Woodsman Target Model.
Finish: Blue.
Barrel Length: 4½", straight tapered.
Stocks: Checked walnut.
Bore Diameter: .215"—.001.
Groove Diameter: .222"—.001.
Rifling: (Left twist): 6 grooves, 1 turn in 14".
Number of Shots: 10.
Action: Semiautomatic blowback.
Approximate Weight: 27 ounces.
Over-all Length: 8½".
Sights: Rear: Adjustable for windage. Front of two types, one of the fixed ramp with a serrated face, the other of the target type, adjustable for elevation.

Note: This model has the special mainspring housing found in the late model Woodsman which permits using .22 L. R. high-velocity cartridges.

.22 Long Rifle

COLT
Woodsman Match Target

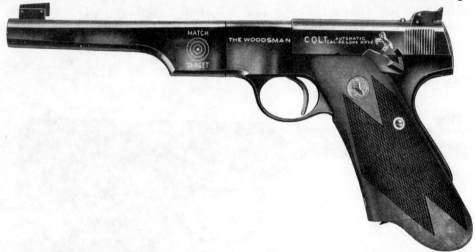

General Description: Factory Model S-MT. A target arm designed for Slow, Timed and Rapid Fire competition. Developed from the Woodsman Target.

Ammunition: .22 L. R.

Manufacturing Dates: From June 2, 1938 to 1942.

Serial Numbers: From Number MT1.

Finish: Blue.

Barrel Length: 6½".

Stocks: One-piece target style of checked walnut. Many supplied to our armed forces are fitted with two-piece plastic stocks.

Bore Diameter: .215"—.001.

Groove Diameter: .222"—.001.

Rifling: (Left twist). 6 grooves. 1 turn in 14.".

Number of Shots: 10.

Action: Semiautomatic blowback.

Approximate Weight: 36 ounces

Over-all Length: 11".

Sights: Target. Front: insert blade. Rear: adjustable for elevation and windage.

Note: The barrel of this model is of special design milled from flat stock rather than turned. To accommodate the heavier barrel the front end of the receiver is deeper in section. The action is hand finished. Has a grooved, antibacklash trigger.

The principal parts of this weapon are the receiver, barrel, breechblock and slide, and mainspring housing.

The barrel is securely fitted in a long seat at the front end of the receiver. It is screwed in, a screw thread being machined into part of the receiver seat.

The handle section of the receiver is hollow to permit the insertion of a steel box magazine from below. The magazine is secured in place by a catch at the bottom of the grip section of the receiver. Pushing the catch releases the magazine and permits it to be withdrawn.

Inside the trigger guard in the receiver is the finger piece of the trigger. The upper part of the trigger extends into a recess in the receiver where the trigger spring and trigger pivot are also enclosed. The trigger bar, which is pivoted at its front end to the top of the trigger and its rear end engaged to the sear, is housed in a long slot in the side of the receiver stretching rearward from the trigger and above it.

This trigger mechanism is covered and held in place by a side plate attached to the receiver by a screw on the left-hand side.

As in the case of the Luger automatic pistol, a thumb button is attached to the magazine follower and protrudes through a slot on the right-hand side of the magazine. Pulling down this button draws the magazine follower down and compresses the spring so that each cartridge may be inserted without having to exert any pressure on the cartridge itself.

The combination breechblock and slide is solid at its front face, forming the breechblock. Its rear is recessed to permit the concealed hammer to swing up inside it. The rear of the slide is closed to prevent gas leaks.

A shell extractor, extractor plunger, and spring are placed in the right side of the breechblock near its forward end. The firing pin and its coil spring are seated inside the breechblock, and retained by a firing pin stop screw.

The rear portion of the slide (which is recessed to enclose the upper part of the hammer) also receives the upper section of the mainspring housing, as well as the recoil spring and its guide. The rear end of this guide and the spring are supported by the face of the mainspring housing, while the forward part of the recoil spring is seated in the breechblock to the left of the firing pin. The tension of this spring holds the breechblock forward.

A flat spring mounted above the recoil spring and guide holds the assembly lock plunger in its seat in the slide. This lock plunger protrudes through the slide. Pressure on it will depress the spring, permitting the weapon to be dismounted when desired.

The pistol is equipped with an automatic safety to prevent it being fired until the breechblock is in fully forward (closed) position. It operates as follows: The sear in this weapon is a lever pivoted in the receiver behind the magazine seat, its upper end supporting the hammer at full or at half cock. The flat sear spring acting on the lower arm of the sear normally presses *the upper end* towards the hammer. An arm extends upward on the left side of the sear, its upper rear face being the part to which trigger motion is transmitted by the trigger bar. Just below this face, the sear has a recess which is open at the rear.

The forward end of the long trigger bar is pivoted to the trigger. There is a flat space on the trigger bar ahead of the pivot, and one end of the trigger spring bears against it. This spring is coiled around the trigger pivot. Its other end rests against the receiver.

This trigger spring both raises the rear end of the trigger bar and holds the finger piece of the trigger in forward position. The lower end of the trigger bar has two projections. An upward projection rises into the path of the breechblock slide, while the lower left-hand edge of the slide bears down upon this projection to force the rear end of the trigger bar down whenever the slide moves rearwards in an opening movement.

There is a recess cut into the lower edge of the slide on the left-hand side at a point just above the projection of the trigger bar when the slide is closed. This permits the projection to rise when the slide is fully forward; but, as the slide moves back from the face of the barrel, the inclined forward end of this slide recess forces the trigger bar down to break the sear connection.

The trigger bar and sear are connected by a projection on the end of the bar. This extends through an opening in the wall of the receiver (when the slide is closed) just behind the upper rear face of the sear.

When the trigger is pressed, it rotates on its pin and pulls the trigger bar forward. The inward projection on this bar engages the sear arm and forces the sear to release its hold on the hammer. The hammer spring forces the hammer to rotate forward on its axis.

If the trigger is pressed while the slide is not in fully forward position, the rear end of the trigger bar will not engage the upper rear face of this sear arm, as its rear end, being depressed by the rearward motion of the slide, enters the recess below and cannot move the sear. The sear holds onto the hammer which cannot move forward.

This effective disconnector positively prevents the weapon from firing except when the breechblock slide is fully forward, and also requires the trigger to be released slightly after each shot so that an individual pull is necessary to fire each cartridge.

Loading: The catch in the bottom of the handle is pushed back to permit the magazine to be withdrawn. The magazine follower button is drawn down to permit insertion of cartridges until the magazine is filled. The magazine is then inserted in the handle until it locks. While the pistol is held firmly in one hand with finger outside the trigger guard, grasp the slide firmly by the other hand at its milled surfaces and draw it as far back as possible to cock the hammer and permit a cartridge to rise in the magazine in line with the breechblock. This action compresses the recoil spring. When the slide is released it goes forward to chamber a cartridge, slip the extractor over the head of the cartridge, and close the breechblock against the face of the barrel. The weapon is now ready for firing.

Operation: When the trigger is pressed, it rotates on its pivot pin and draws the trigger bar forward to permit the sear to release the hammer. The compressed hammer spring in the mainspring housing forces up its cap and, through the strut connecting it to the hammer, forces the hammer upward and forward to strike the flying firing pin to fire the cartridge in the chamber.

As this is a straight blowback pistol, the breechblock slide is held forward only by its own weight and the inertia of the moving parts, and by the recoil spring. It starts back as soon as a shot has been fired, the gases in the barrel in rearward motion forcing the case back against the breechblock. As the action opens, the empty cartridge case, its head firmly gripped by the extractor, goes back until it strikes the ejector and is hurled out of the ejection port.

The recoil spring is compressed around its guide behind the breechblock.

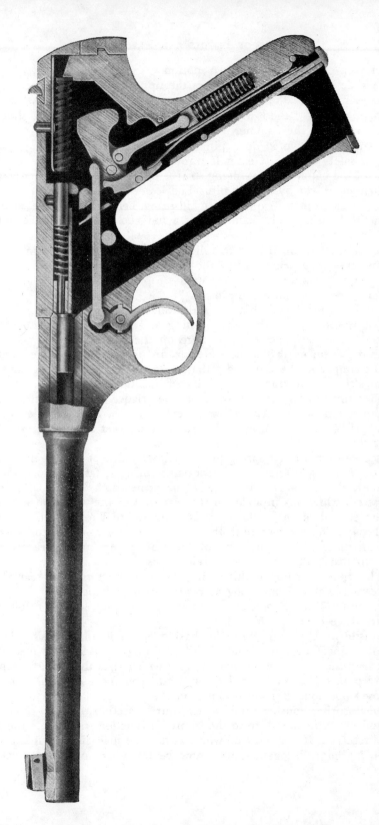

COLT WOODSMAN AUTOMATIC PISTOL. Side view with magazine withdrawn to show details of the lockwork. The hammer is at full cock with its strut compressing the mainspring in the handle. Mechanically all the Woodsman practically are identical.

This stores up energy for the return motion.

As the slide begins to open, it forces the upper projection of the trigger bar down below its face in the receiver. This effectively disconnects the arm.

A beveled section of the lower rear of the breechblock end of the slide pushes back and rolls over the hammer, bringing it to full cock.

This hammer is pivoted on a pin in the receiver. This pin is also part of the thumb safety catch. It extends through the receiver and is supported on each side of the hammer. A swinging strut is fastened to the hammer at the rear of the hammer pivot by a strut pin. The lower end of this strut rests in the head of the mainspring cap. The mainspring below this cap is seated in a niche in the housing. The hammer has a half-cock or safety notch below the full-cock notch.

As the hammer is rolled back to full cock, its strut pressing down on the cap compresses the mainspring within the mainspring housing.

The ejector is mounted in a slot in the top of the receiver near its center. It is held there by a transverse pin.

It must be remembered that the slide moves back so rapidly and is driven forward again so rapidly that the opening and closing actions are completed before the finger can release its pressure on the trigger.

As the recoil spring drives the slide forward to strip a cartridge from magazine and chamber it, the sear under the action of its spring, having engaged the hammer as soon as it reached the full-cock position, cannot connect with the trigger bar until the finger pressure on the trigger is released to permit the upper projection on the trigger bar to enter its slot on the underside of the slide and bring it into line with the sear at the lower side to permit firing of the next shot.

The sear spring is a flat spring placed below, and kept under tension by, the mainspring housing. The lower end of this spring is fastened to, and held in position by, the magazine catch. The magazine catch is held in place by a transverse rib which fits in a slot in the rear wall of the magazine seat.

The lower end of the mainspring housing is fitted to rest on a pin which passes through the receiver near the bottom. The tension of the sear spring keeps it in place. The upper end of the mainspring housing rises above the receiver up inside the breechblock slide. It is kept vertically in place by the slide. The upper portion of this mainspring housing forms the rear abutment which keeps the slide from flying rearward out of the receiver.

Dismounting: Remove magazine. Draw back slide and look in firing chamber to be sure there is no cartridge there.

Hold pistol in left hand. Pull slide back as far as it will go, using the thumb and middle finger of right hand. While holding it back, with first finger of right hand push down the locking plunger which rises through the top of the slide. Keep this plunger pressed down while you move the slide to full forward closed position. Release pressure on the plunger. Pull the trigger.

Press mainspring housing firmly at its knurled section with the thumb of the right hand. Push it in and up to the front. This action will release the housing from the receiver. It may now be withdrawn. The magazine catch and the sear spring, being pinned together, may now be taken out of the receiver.

The breechblock slide can now be pulled back in its guide off the receiver. Unscrew the firing pin stop screw in the bottom of the slide and tilt the slide with the front end up. The firing pin will drop out. Spring may be withdrawn.

Insert a small awl or drift through the extractor aperture and press back the extractor plunger as far as it will go. This will block the plunger, and the extractor may now be lifted out.

Unscrew the stock screws and the stock may be removed. Unscrew the side plate screw and the side plate may be lifted off. The safety lock, which also acts as the hammer axis pin, may be pulled out.

The hammer and strut may now be lifted out; and the strut can be removed by driving out the strut pin.

Push out the sear pin and the sear will drop out.

Press against the right side of the trigger and the trigger, trigger pivot spring, and trigger bar will come out. Drive out the ejector pin and the ejector.

Hold slide in left hand and, with a small screw driver, exert pressure forward against the recoil spring guide. This will disengage the assembly lock spring. Ease up the pressure on the guide until its end rests against the rear of the pocket in the slide. Now lift it out.

Lift the front end of the assembly lock spring above its locking lug and, with a small punch placed against the rear of the pocket in the slide, drive forward. When the lugs on the spring enter the recess on each side of the pocket, turn the slide right side up and the assembly lock and its spring will fall out.

The thumb safety on this weapon has a projection from the outside. When it is pushed up, this projection enters a recess cut for it in the slide. This effectively locks the slide. The stud on the inner face of the safety extends through an opening in the receiver. This positively locks the sear and hammer in the full-cocked position. The forward end of this safety lock is a projection which is covered by the side plate. This side plate acts on it as a spring to keep the safety from jarring out of position while the weapon is being fired.

Assembly: Replace ejector and fasten it with its pin.

Assemble the sear with its lug on the top left side of receiver and drive in its pin.

Assemble trigger (with the head of its pivot pin on the left side) and the trigger bar; and insert the spring on the right side of the trigger with the pivot pin passing through the coils of the spring. One end of the spring should engage flat against the trigger bar while the other rests in the notch in the trigger. *This is important.* Replace the trigger mechanism in position on the left side of the receiver with the end of the spring resting against the front of the trigger clearance-cut and with the trigger bar lying in its longitudinal slot in the receiver.

Fasten the hammer strut to the hammer with its pin. Place the assembly in position in the receiver and push the pin section to the left side of the receiver, on through the hammer, then through the right side of the receiver as far as possible. Replace the side plate and stocks.

Place the spring on the extractor plunger and insert it in the slide with its flat on the underside of the plunger. Compress the spring and hold the plunger back with a punch while inserting the extractor. Allow the plunger to move forward and test the extractor to be sure that it is working properly.

Mount the firing pin spring over the pin and insert the two in the slide. Press it forward and screw in the firing pin stop pin to retain the assembly.

Insert the lock plunger in the counterbored hole, *making sure that the plunger matches the shape of the top of the slide.* Insert spring, press it down, and force backwards until plunger engages the small hole in the spring.

Mount the recoil spring on its guide pin and insert them in the slide. Push the spring back until the guide pin can be forced down into position. Then press the guide pin forward until the assembly lock spring can be pressed down by the plunger. The point of the plunger will engage the groove in the end of the pin and hold it ready to assemble the slide to the receiver.

Place the slide on the receiver from the rear and push it forward to fully closed position.

Insert the magazine catch and the sear spring in position. Make sure that the lug on the magazine catch fits into its slot in the handle. The sear spring must rest on the sear and under the hammer strut. When this is done, make sure that the hammer is in full forward position with its strut resting on the sear spring, and press the trigger to be sure that the hammer is fully forward.

Place the top of the mainspring housing under the end of the receiver and rest it on the sear spring.

Press in the lower end of the mainspring housing and it will snap forward into place.

Right-side view of the Ace with slide open and magazine withdrawn. Except for differences in magazine and stamping on slide, this picture shows appearance of right side of the Service Ace, .38 Super and .45 Government models.

COLT .22 Long Rifle

Ace Target

General Description: Factory Model 0.22. Built on the same frame as the Colt .45 caliber Automatic this arm was designed for training users of that arm as well as for general service. Because of its weight, there is but little recoil, and the size of the parts and the hand-finished action provide exceptional smoothness of operation.

Ammunition: .22 L. R.

Manufacturing Dates: From April 20, 1931 to 1941.

Serial Numbers: From Number 1.

Finish: Blue.

Barrel Length: 4¾".

Stocks: Checked walnut; no medallion.

Bore Diameter: .215"—.001".

Groove Diameter: .222"—.001".

Rifling: (Left twist) 6 grooves; one turn in 14".

Number of Shots: 10.

Action: Semiautomatic, blowback (barrel is fixed without link).

Approximate Weight: 38 ounces.

Over-all Length: 8¼ inches.

Sights: Front: fixed-ramp type. Rear: adjustable elevation and windage.

Note: This weapon is equipped with all the mechanical features of the Government Model .45 except the breech locking system. Safety grip, thumb safety, slide hold-open device, magazine release, and disconnector function the same as in the Government Model.

The three main parts of this pistol are the receiver, barrel, and slide.

As in other Colt automatic pistols of this general design, the receiver has guides to receive the slide from the front and a hollow handle to permit the insertion of the magazine.

The magazine in this arm is fitted with a checkered stud attached to the follower and protruding through a slot in the right-hand side of the magazine. Pulling this down compresses the spring below the follower and permits insertion of cartridges without exerting pressure on the cartridges themselves.

The magazine is retained in the handle of the receiver by a magazine catch operated by a push-through button in the receiver directly behind the trigger on the left-hand side. It engages in a cut in the front wall of the magazine.

The trigger is mounted in the trigger guard portion of the receiver where its front end projects, and is of the stirrup type with an arm passing across the receiver on each side of the magazine well.

The hammer, sear, automatic disconnector, grip safety, and the safety lock, as well as the mainspring, its housing, and the sear spring are also mounted in the rear of the receiver behind the magazine well. The mainspring itself is housed in a steel housing inserted in guides in the receiver from below and contains the mainspring, mainspring cap, and housing pin retainer.

The cocking strut attached to the hammer in rear of its pivot has its lower end resting in the mainspring cap where it can force down the cap and compress the mainspring as the hammer is brought to full cock.

The sear spring is a three-armed flat spring with a rib which fits into a slot in the rear wall of the receiver to prevent the spring from moving vertically. The mainspring housing when inserted presses against the rear of this sear spring and locks it in position as well as giving it the required tension.

The slide stop and safety lock plunger are mounted in a tube on the receiver directly above the handle. Their ends protrude from each end of this tube. A spiral spring plunger is mounted between the two and holds them in position but permits them to be compressed.

The front forward end of the receiver ahead of the trigger guard is a semi-tubular extension which provides a seat for the rear portion of the recoil spring.

This is a blowback pistol. The barrel is not locked to the slide at any time. No lock is necessary with this cartridge in a well-designed arm.

The barrel is provided with a solid lug at its rear end in which is a single transverse cut through which the pin of the slide stop passes to lock the barrel firmly to the receiver. This pin is initially inserted in a slot in the receiver, then through the transverse barrel slot, then through the right side of the receiver where it projects.

The ejector is fastened to the rear of the barrel.

As in all Colt pistols of this type, the slide is mounted on the receiver from the front end and its rearward travel is stopped by the tubular abutment on the receiver which positively prevents it from being thrust too far back by a recoil of the action.

The forward end of the recoil spring and the recoil spring plug are seated in the abutment at the forward end of the slide below the line of the muzzle. The rear end of this spring and guide are supported by the shoulder at the front of the receiver.

The barrel bushing is secured by being revolved into slots machined into the front end of the slide, and serves to support the muzzle end of the barrel as well as retain the recoil spring plug.

When the weapon is assembled, the slide is positively fastened by the slide stop. The slide, with the barrel mounted inside it, is inserted in the grooves in the receiver and the pin section of the slide stop securely fastens the barrel and receiver together, but permits recoil of the slide.

A checkered thumbpiece on the outside of the slide stop on the left side of the receiver permits releasing it from the open position.

The grip safety is pivoted in the upper part of the receiver and it automatically locks and releases the firing mechanism as the weapon is gripped. The thumb safety is so arranged that when it is pushed up into its locking slot in the slide, the stud on its inner face locks the sear and hammer in the full-cock position. *Note that it can only be applied when the weapon is cocked.*

The standard Colt automatic disconnector riding up out of the receiver into its niche in the underside of the left-hand side of the slide when the weapon is fully closed, and only then permitting the trigger to engage the sear, provides assurance that only one shot will be fired on each pull of the trigger and also that the weapon will not fire until it is fully closed.

Note that while there is a half-cock notch provided on this hammer, it is not recommended that the weapon be so carried when the chamber is loaded.

The slide starts to the rear when the cartridge is exploded, because of energy imparted to the face of the breechblock portion of the slide by powder gases pressing back against the inside of the empty cartridge case.

While this weapon resembles the locked type of Colt .38 and .45 automatic pistols, *in external appearance,* and uses the famous Colt firing and disconnector mechanism, its interior construction is adapted to use the .22 Long Rifle cartridge. Low- or high-velocity cartridges may be used.

Note that the barrel is pinned directly to the receiver and is not swinging on a link as in the case of the locked Colt models.

As this is a rim-fire weapon, the firing pin and spring are also modified, as is the extractor, to handle this cartridge.

Except that the magazine is fitted with a button to depress the follower, the weapon is loaded and fired and generally handled exactly as in the case of the Government Model .45.

Dismounting: Press magazine catch on left side of the receiver behind trigger and remove magazine. Check to see that the firing chamber is empty.

Push in the recoil spring plug below the muzzle of the barrel and turn the horseshoe-shaped bushing around it to the right until the plug can be eased forward out of the weapon. Let the tension of the recoil spring out easily.

Pull the slide back until the rear edge of the smaller of the two recesses at the center of the lower edge of the slide on the left-hand side lines up with the rear end of the slide stop. Push the end of the slide stop pin (which projects from the right-hand side of the receiver above the trigger guard). If the stop is properly lined up, it may now be drawn out the left side of the receiver.

The barrel and slide are now free to be drawn forward off the receiver. The barrel bushing, recoil spring, and the recoil spring guide will come with this assembly.

The recoil spring and guide may now be lifted up off the barrel.

Turn the barrel bushing to the left as far as it will go. This will disengage it from its slots in the slide and it may be pulled out to the front.

The barrel may now be drawn forward and out of the slide.

Further Dismounting: Complete dismounting of this weapon follows the same outline as that for the .45 Government Model Automatic Pistol.

COLT .22 Long Rifle
Ace Service

General Description: Factory Model O-SM. Primarily a training arm for users of the Colt .45 caliber Automatic and built on that frame. A "floating chamber" makes the recoil intentionally heavier than a conventionally designed arm of like weight and caliber.

Ammunition: .22 L. R.

Manufacturing Dates: From 1937-38 to 1947.

Serial Numbers: From Number 1.

Finish: Blue.

Barrel Length: 5".

Stocks: Checked walnut; no medallion.

Bore Diameter: .215"−.001".

Groove Diameter: .222″—.001″.
Rifling: (Left twist) 6 grooves—1 turn in 14″.
Number of Shots: 10.
Action: Semiautomatic of the blowback type (there is no locking of slide and barrel).
Approximate Weight: 42 ounces.
Over-all Length: 8½ inches.
Sights: Front: fixed-ramp type. Rear: adjustable for both elevation and windage.

Right side view of Government Model .22-45 conversion with slide closed, hammer up and magazine withdrawn (Note that magazine differs from that of the Target Ace). In general this picture shows the appearance of the Target Ace, .38 Super and .45 Government models.

The description and details given for the Colt Ace automatic pistol will generally cover this pistol, except for one unusual feature:

A floating or movable recoil chamber is inserted in the breech end of the barrel to form a floating breech. This is provided to increase the recoil sufficiently to operate a heavy slide and also to approximate the recoil of the .45 Automatic. (This permits .45 caliber training with low-cost .22 ammunition).

This floating chamber gives approximately four times the amount of recoil action as that in the regular Colt .22 Ace automatic pistol.

Because of this extra power, the weight of the slide, recoil spring, and mainspring are the same as those used in the service automatic pistol. In the standard .22 Ace, all these units are of lighter weight.

The cartridge chamber, which is inserted in the head of the barrel, is a separate piece which fits into a cylindrical recess in the barrel. It can move back for a short distance in the barrel until it strikes a stop machined out of the locking lug at the bottom of the barrel through which the slide stop pin normally passes.

Operation: This weapon is loaded and fired as the other Colt automatic pistols which it resembles closely in exterior appearance.

It differs from the .38 and .45 in that the breech is not locked and the barrel does not move.

It differs from the Colt .22 Ace in that while the barrel is fastened in the same manner, the movable floating chamber inserted in the head of the barrel does move back as the weapon is fired.

In the Ace, as in other straight blowback pistols, recoil energy is transmitted through the head of the fired case to the face of the breechblock to drive the slide of which it is a part backwards and function the action.

In this floating chamber Service Model Ace, on the other hand, this gas pressure acts *not only on the inside of the cartridge case* but also escapes into the open space between the barrel and the front end of the movable chamber.

Left: Slide and receiver cut away to show cartridge in chamber and weapon ready to fire. Note that the floating chamber is fully forward against the breech faces of the barrel and stop. Right: Slide has started back and bullet has just left barrel. Action is opening as the floating chamber is driven back against the breech face of the slide. The back travel of the floating chamber has been halted by striking its abutment. From here on the slide travels back alone to extract and eject the empty case.

The rearward thrust is therefore *imparted to a very much greater area than* in the case of a straight blowback pistol, where it is confined strictly to the head of the cartridge case.

The momentum imparted to the slide *is approximately four times greater* than that in the blowback pistol because *the entire chamber* (as well as the cartridge case) strikes back sharply against the breechblock face of the slide to start the rearward movement.

Dismounting: Dismounting and assembling this weapon is the same as for the Ace, with the one exception that the floating chamber may be lifted out of the barrel. This chamber should be cleaned after using to prevent corrosion.

87

SERVICE ACE cut away to show details of lockwork, recoil spring function and floating chamber. Hammer has been manually lowered on loaded chamber. All springs except the magazine spring are at rest. Barrel is cut away to show details of the floating chamber. Except for this chamber, this drawing generally applies to the Target Ace.

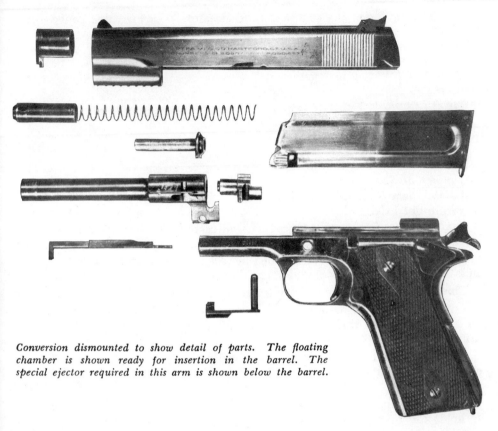

Conversion dismounted to show detail of parts. The floating chamber is shown ready for insertion in the barrel. The special ejector required in this arm is shown below the barrel.

COLL .22 Long Rifle
COLT
.45-.22 Conversion

General Description: A complete slide assembly with magazine permitting users of the Colt Service Model Ace (.22 caliber) to convert that arm to the .45 A.C.P. and to use either caliber at will.

Ammunition: .45 A.C.P.

Manufacturing Dates: From September 28, 1938 to date.

Serial Numbers: From Number 1.

Finish: Blue.

Barrel Length: 5".

Bore Diameter: .44"—.001.

Groove Diameter: .451"—.001.

Rifling: (Left twist). 6 grooves. 1 turn in 16".

Number of Shots: 7.

Action: Semiautomatic blowback type.

Sights: Front: ramp type, fixed. Rear: adjustable for elevation and windage.

Note: The unit consists of a slide assembly with adjustable target sights, .45 caliber barrel with link and pin, barrel bushing, magazine, slide stop with a recoil spring for the .45 A.C.P. cartridge, recoil spring guide, and plug.

General Description: A complete slide assembly with magazine converts the the Colt .45 caliber automatic to use .22 caliber ammunition.

Ammunition: .22 L.R.

Manufacturing Dates: From June 22, 1938 to date.

Serial Numbers: From Number 1.

Finish: Blue.

Barrel Length: 5″.

Stocks: Walnut.

Bore Diameter: .215″−.001.

Groove Diameter: .222″−.001.

Rifling: (Left twist) 6 grooves—1 turn in 14″.

Number of Shots: 10.

Action: Semiautomatic blowback type using floating chamber; slide and barrel do not lock.

Sights: Front: fixed, ramp type. Rear: adjustable for elevation and windage.

Note: The assembly consists of a slide assembly complete with adjustable target sights, .22 caliber barrel with floating chamber and ejector, barrel bushing, slide stop, 10-shot magazine, and a recoil spring, guide, and plug.

This unit consists of the following items:

1. A complete slide assembly. This comprises the slide itself, a fixed front sight, an adjustable rear sight, an extractor, firing pin, firing pin spring, and firing pin stop.

2. A .22 caliber barrel. This is specially designed to receive a floating chamber. It is also machined to receive the special ejector required in this weapon.

3. The floating chamber is inserted in the breech end of the barrel. It holds the cartridge. When the weapon is fired, it recoils with the empty cartridge case until a lug on its lower end strikes a projection on the barrel locking lug which comes up in its rear and stops its backward motion.

4. An ejector of special design which is fitted into a slot prepared for it in the left side of the barrel.

5. A special barrel bushing to fit over the barrel and lock in the slide to support the barrel and retain the recoil spring plug.

6. A special recoil spring with its guide and its plug.

7. A special magazine with a serrated button attached to the magazine fol lower and protruding through a slot in the right side wall of the magazine. Pressing this down compresses the follower against the magazine spring and permits insertion of cartridges without pressure on the cartridges themselves.

8. A special slide stop of somewhat different design is provided, as the one used in the standard .45 caliber will not function with this slide and barrel assembly.

To Install This Unit In the Government Model Automatic Pistol. 1. Remove the magazine by pressing the magazine catch. Check the firing chamber to be sure no cartridge remains in it.

2. Push in the recoil spring plug below the muzzle. Then revolve the bush-

ing to the right until the plug can be eased out under tension of the recoil spring.

3. Pull the slide back until the rear edge of the smaller recess in the lower edge of the slide on the left side lines up with the rear end of the slide stop.

4. Push the pin end of the slide stop which protrudes from the right-hand side of the receiver and draw the stop out to the left.

5. The barrel and slide assemblies may now be drawn forward off the receiver.

No further dismounting is necessary to assemble this .22 unit to the .45 caliber receiver.

Installing the .22 caliber conversion: 1. Insert the floating chamber in the breech of the barrel. Make sure the lug on its bottom engages in the slot in the barrel lug below and behind it.

2. Fit the special ejector into the groove on the left side of the barrel, making sure that the upper vertical arm is properly positioned.

3. Holding slide upside down, carefully insert the barrel unit into the slide through the front opening.

4. Make sure the ejector slides freely into the groove above the firing pin in the slide.

5. Mount the recoil spring on the recoil spring guide and push through the opening in the front end of the slide. Be sure the guide is resting on the barrel. Push the receiver into the slide from the rear making sure the grooves engage properly.

6. When the hole in the barrel lug is lined up with the hole in the receiver provided for the slide stop, insert the slide stop pin from the left-hand side. Note that the barrel may be moved slightly front or back to line the lug up with the opening in the receiver.

7. Push the slide into proper position to permit the slide stop to be forced all the way in. The correct position is when the small cut in the slide is directly above the square opening in the receiver.

8. Now pull the slide all the way forward.

9. Place the recoil spring plug on the end of the recoil spring and turn it to the right to engage the spring.

10. Push the plug firmly down inside the abutment in the slide below the barrel until it is below the line of the barrel bushing.

11. Now turn the barrel bushing down and permit it to snap into place to retain the plug.

12. Insert a loaded magazine into the handle until it locks. Pulling the slide back for the opening loading movement now leaves the weapon ready for firing.

This unit is particularly valuable to those who regularly use a .45 Colt Government Model automatic, as it permits cheap target practice with .22 caliber ammunition at the same time providing the identical trigger pull and about the same balance and recoil as the .45 itself.

.22 Long Rifle

CRIOLLA
Automatic

This is an imitation of the Colt Target Ace .22 automatic pistol. It is made in Argentina of good materials and fair workmanship. Photos and description of the Colt cover it completely.

.22 Long Rifle

ERMA
Target

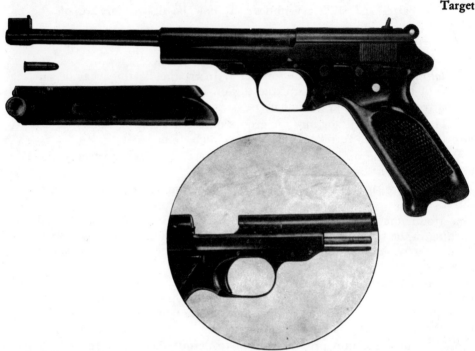

This German pistol is furnished with three interchangeable barrels. As shown it is fitted with barrel about 8.2 inches long, measures 12½ inches overall and weighs 2 lbs. 3 oz. The supplementary barrels measure 3.9 and 11.7 inches respectively. Insert shows breech open and recoil spring guide protruding through the slide crossbar.

Construction and Operation: This is a target automatic pistol of elementary blowback design. It differs from the Colt type principally in the location of the recoil spring and in having an exposed hammer. The recoil spring is mounted around a guide rod below the barrel-mount section of the receiver. The breechblock slide is machined with arms which extend forward on either side from the breech, and are connected by a crossbar which has a hole to permit the emergence of the guide rod as the slide goes back and compresses the recoil spring to store up energy for the forward slide movement.

The functioning, lockwork and disconnection are standard for arms of this type. However, this pistol has a number of unusual manufacturing and design features. Most important is a barrel removal system which permits changing barrels to convert the arm for use as a sport, a target or a free pistol; and which locks the barrel securely enough that accuracy is not affected. The barrel-mount section of the receiver is split. Between its two sections is a loose ring with screw threads which will take the barrel threads. Turning it to the left permits the barrel to be unscrewed. (On early models the barrel is held by two retaining pins.)

The magazine is a solid machined box of the finest and sturdiest type, provided with the standard follower guide button to facilitate loading. The follower and the magazine lips are of heavy construction and the left lip is spring held so that the slide moving forward can spring the lip open to facilitate feeding.

Erma with slide fully open as magazine follower rises to hold slide back when last cartridge has been fired. Slide goes forward when magazine is withdrawn and must be pulled back over loaded magazine to load the chamber.

Stocks are plastic. The grip is pitched much like the Luger and the hang and balance are excellent. This arm is fitted with adjustable target sights. A magazine release button is provided on the right side of the receiver as is also a positive safety which is pushed down to make the arm safe. Turning down the lock lever above the trigger-guard on the left side permits the slide to be pulled back and lifted up, then eased forward off over the barrel for dismantling. The pitch of the grip is such that unless a strong mainspring is used the arm may misfire with standard American ammunition, which in the caliber employed is not as sensitively primed as the German.

Manufacturer: ERMA Machine Works, Erfurt, Germany. Export models are stamped "ERMA Waffenfabrik Erfurt—Made in Germany D.R.G.M." on left side of slide.

EUROPEAN .22 Long Rifle
Single Shots

As several thousand variants might readily be listed, it is not practical to deal with this field. Before the War it was standard practice for firms in France,

One type of German Single Shot pistol. This is a hinged-frame design with special adjustable trigger. The thumb lever seen below the hammer unlocks the breech for loading or automatic ejection.

Belgium, Germany and Switzerland to provide various types of lockworks to gunsmiths who fitted barrels and stocks of individual design.

Outstanding, however, were pistols made in Germany by Udo Anschutz (notably his Record Match pistols with a falling block Martini-type action); the Tell and Luna falling block pistols of Ernst Friedr. Buchel; the hinged-frame Pickert Arminius; August Lunebrug's Alk-Pistole, which resembles the Webley & Scott semiautomatic, but is fitted with a slide stop and a recoil spring so that pressing the stop closes the action when a cartridge is inserted in the chamber and the bolt-action Mauser pistols. The Swiss Widmer made on the Tell system, Hartmann and the Weber are also excellent arms of this type, and are practically custom built in different detail for various customers. The French bolt-action Buffalo-Stand made by M.A.S. is also a fine weapon.

Arms of this sort with freak grips, actions, locks and sights have never achieved real popularity in the United States.

.22 Long Rifle

FIALA
Magazine

In exterior appearance this arm closely resembles the Colt Woodsman. With 7½-inch barrel it measures 11¼ inches overall and weighs about 31 ounces. It has a Woodsman-type magazine in the handle which holds ten cartridges.

However it is *not* an automatic pistol. It is a magazine pistol. When a loaded magazine is inserted in the handle a bolt lock on the receiver must be pushed in to release the breechblock slide. The slide is then drawn to the rear to clear the top of the magazine and permit a cartridge to rise in line. As the arm does not have a recoil spring, the slide must be pushed forward to chamber the cartridge. Each time the pistol is fired the slide must be unlocked and drawn back to extract and recock, then thrust forward to chamber and lock

the breech. A disconnector prevents the arm from being fired unless the breech is fully closed.

This arm was originally offered with three barrels—three inches, seven and one-half inches and twenty inches long respectively. A thumbscrew on the right side secures the barrel to the breech, permitting easy removal. A stock used with the twenty-inch barrel converted the arm to a rifle.

A combination of good balance, Patridge sights and four-grooved rifling as developed for the .22 Springfield rifle makes this an accurate target arm.

Fiala Arms Co., New Haven, Conn. No longer made.

HARRINGTON AND RICHARDSON .22 Long Rifle
U. S. R. A. Single Shot

Designed by the noted pistol expert, Mr. Walter Roper, this is a fine accurate target pistol. Seven different shaped stocks were obtainable to provide for a wide selection for various types of hands. Manufactured with a standard barrel length of 10 inches, special lengths of 7 or 8 inches were also provided. With the 10-inch barrel the weight is 31 ounces. Numerous changes were made during the issuance of this pistol, which is no longer manufactured. Therefore, only a general outline of its salient points is feasible.

A special speed lock was developed for this arm. The hammer throw is very short, making for rapid discharge. The breech closure is exceptionally tight, preventing danger from blownout cartridge heads. The lockwork is unusual in that the trigger is provided with a shoulder on which the hammer rests when in rebound position; thus providing a secure safety. The sear with this system has no function except to release the hammer from full cocked position on pressure of the trigger. The trigger pull on the later models was adjustable. An adjusting screw in the forward end of the trigger guard can be turned to exert pressure on the trigger to alter adjustment. Like the Iver Johnson revolvers, this arm is fitted with a coiled-type mainspring. Standard issue front sight was a one-tenth inch under-cut Patridge type with a detachable guard. The rear sight was adjustable by screw for elevation or windage. With the 10-inch barrel, the sighting radius is 9.2 inches. This is a conventional hinged frame, dropped-down barrel breech lock in which the catch is mounted on the barrel and snaps down over the standing breech of the frame. When the weapon is opened and the barrel tipped down, the cartridge in the chamber is automatically ejected.

.22 Long Rifle   HARRINGTON AND RICHARDSON
                                             Revolver Note

These low- and medium-priced revolvers fall into two classes, hinged-frame automatic ejectors and solid-frame nonejectors. The hinged-frame varieties may be single or double action, hammer or hammerless (enclosed hammer). Barrel lengths, exterior barrel shapes, weights and styles of stocks and grips vary widely. All, however, follow the standard American practice of having the barrel lock hinged to the barrel extension so that it locks over the standing breech when the arm is ready for firing. Opening the catch and bending the barrel down on its hinge function the extractor and throws the contents of all the chambers simultaneously out of the cylinder.

In the solid-frame varieties chambers are loaded through a slot on the right side of the frame, or the cylinder is removed from the frame by releasing the spring catch below the cylinder axis pin and pulling out the pin from below the barrel.

These arms should never be used with high velocity ammunition unless they come equipped with the H&R Safety Cylinder which completely encloses the heads of the cartridge cases.

For representative photographs of H&R revolvers, see Harrington & Richardson under Caliber .38 Smith & Wesson and the Identification Section.

Following is a detailed description of current H&R revolvers.

.22 Long Rifle   HARRINGTON AND RICHARDSON
                                                   No. 944

This is a standard hinged-frame breech-lock type. The barrel length is 6 inches, and the overall length is 11 inches. The pistol weighs 23 ounces. A notched rear and a gold front sight are standard equipment. The cylinder has 9 chambers. This is a medium-priced weapon which is designed to use low- or high-speed ammunition. It does not, however, have counter-sunk chambers to protect the heads of high-speed cartridges. As an alternative, the cylinder has an elevated section outside the line of the cartridge head, the inner section of the cylinder face being recessed. This serves essentially the purpose of the counter-sunk chambers.

When the barrel is hinged down, all cartridges in the cylinder are automatically ejected. An assortment of eleven styles of stocks are available for use on this arm.

.22 Long Rifle   HARRINGTON AND RICHARDSON
                                                   No. 199

Standard barrel length of this arm is 6 inches, overall length is 11 inches. The weight is 30 ounces. The cylinder is bored with 9 chambers. Six styles of stocks are available.

This arm is patterned after the U.S.R.A. model single-shot pistol. The Patridge front sight may be adjusted for elevation by use of the screw in the front end of the barrel. The rear sight is adjustable for windage, two screws being provided, one on the right and one on the left.

The lockwork resembles that of the U.S.R.A. pistol, being fitted with a special rebound arrangement providing one point on which the trigger rests when the weapon is at safety and another one when it is in contact with the sear for firing. This device permits the use of a very low trigger pull without the danger of accidental discharge if the hammer is struck a sharp blow while in the position of rest.

Dismounting. When the barrel catch is raised and the barrel bent down on its hinge, if the catch is held up the cylinder may be unscrewed and lifted together with the extractor off its mounting below the bore.

HARRINGTON AND RICHARDSON .22 Long Rifle
Sportsman No. 999

Except that it is fitted with a double-action trigger lockwork permitting the arm to be fired either by drawing back the hammer with the thumb and then pressing the trigger, or by direct pull through on the trigger, this arm is identical with number 199 described above.

HARRINGTON AND RICHARDSON .22 Long Rifle
Note on Hinged Frames

Under the name of H&R Premier, a standard-type hinged-frame pocket-type revolver was produced for some time. It was supplied in barrel lengths of 2, 3, 4, 5 and 6 inches. The cylinder in this weapon had 7 chambers. The arm weighed about 13 ounces.

The H&R Sportsman No. 999 (double action) was also issued with a 2-inch barrel, under the trade name of The New Defender. A 3-inch barrel model was also available.

HARRINGTON AND RICHARDSON .22 Long Rifle
No. 922

This is a low-priced solid-frame revolver in which the cartridges must be extracted individually. The standard barrel length is 6 inches and the over-all length 10½ inches. This arm weighs 21¾ ounces. Notched rear and gold front sights are provided. The cylinder is bored with 9 chambers. The cylinder is the recessed type already described in H&R Revolvers. It permits the use of high-speed .22 ammunition.

This is a double-action arm. Pressing in the release catch in the forward end of the frame permits the withdrawal of the cylinder axis pin from the front, which allows the cylinder to be removed from the right side of the arm.

HARRINGTON AND RICHARDSON .22 Long Rifle
Note on Solid Frames

Under the designation No. 722, and popularly called the Trapper Model, a 7-shot revolver of solid frame design was issued. The barrel length is 6 inches and the weight 12¾ ounces. This is a low-priced arm.

The No. 70 or Young American Model was issued with 2- 4¼- and 6-inch barrels. The No. 96, also 7 shot, was also issued with 2½- 4½ and 6-inch barrels. Arms of this type are not recommended.

Manufacturer: Harrington & Richardson, Inc., Worcester, Mass.

.22 Long Rifle

HI-STANDARD
Note

HI-STANDARD MODEL H-D. Left side view with magazine and hammer down. This is typical pistol of this make differing from the hammerless variety only in that the slide does not enclose the hammer, and differing from other models in weight of barrel. Button at top of stock is the slide stop operated by the magazine follower when the magazine is empty. The latch on the receiver is the takedown device in connection with the plunger rising from the top of the slide directly in line with the magazine release.

All Hi-Standard automatic taget pistols commercially marketed to the end of World War II employ the general mechanical principles already covered under Model C, Caliber .22 Short.

Following is a list of models with different characteristics.

Models B and H.-B. Same as Model C except for caliber. Issued with four and one-half- and six and three-quarters-inch barrels. Weight with the long barrel is thirty-three ounces. Takedown latch may be on right side of receiver. H-B indicates an exposed hammer.

Models A and H-A. These models have longer grips and walnut stocks, adjustable rear sights and a slide lock. When the last shot has been fired the lock on the right side of the receiver is forced up to intercept the breechblock slide and hold it open. In A the hammer is enclosed within the slide. With six and three-quarters inch barrel it weighs thirty-six ounces. The H-A has an exposed hammer, and no safety latch.

Models D and H-D. These models are the same as the A and H-A except that they are furnished with heavier barrels which bring the weights up to forty ounces. D has an enclosed hammer and H-D an exposed hammer. Wide blade Patridge front and adjustable rear sights are provided. The hammer model does not have the thumb safety provided on the hammerless.

Models E and H-E. These are the same as the A and H-A except for a still heavier target barrel than in the D, and a thumb rest in the stock. These models weigh about forty-two ounces.

Note on Hi-Standard. Hi-Standard developed a line of newly designed pistols of superior type permitting quick change of barrels in 1947. Essentially these weapons employ the barrel-locking system of the Webley & Scott type in which the barrel and slide are mounted on the receiver from the front and are locked firmly by a spring controlled block rising from below and wedging into a suitable cut of the underside of the heavy barrel near the breech end. The recoil spring is mounted in the slide as in the earlier models.

HOPKINS AND ALLEN .22 Long Rifle
Note

While these revolvers are no longer manufactured, there are hundreds of thousands in existence. The general descriptions of Harrington and Richardson and Iver Johnson early models apply generally to these also.

They are also standard American hinged-frame, automatic ejecting revolvers of hammer and hammerless (enclosed hammer) types; or are solid-frame American-type nonejectors. High velocity ammunition should never be used in H&A revolvers.

Photographs of Hopkins & Allen under Caliber .38 Smith & Wesson and in the Identification Section give a representative idea of the appearance of the many models and modifications.

IVER JOHNSON .22 Long Rifle
Note

Iver Johnson revolvers also fall into the two general patterns of American type hinged-frame, automatic ejecting hammer and hammerless (enclosed hammer); and solid frame nonejectors.

However, the Iver Johnson system of using coil springs throughout and the incorporation of a positive "hammer-the-hammer" safety in most of their hinged-frame types raise these revolvers rather above the average for their class in the medium-price field. (For representative photographs, drawings and explanations of these features see Iver Johnson under Caliber .38 Smith & Wesson). Late models in both types use embedded-head cylinders permitting the use of high velocity ammunition.

Following is a list of the current Iver Johnson revolvers.

IVER JOHNSON .22 Long Rifle
Supershot Sealed Eight Series

This is the finest target revolver in the medium-priced Iver Johnson line. It is a standard American-type hinged-frame revolver of target pattern.

This arm is equipped with a special 8-shot cylinder in which the chambers and the head of the extractor are counterbored so that the heads of the cartridge cases are imbedded in the cylinder. In the event of a case head blowing out, as may happen with high-speed ammunition, this counter-sinking assures protection to the shooter. The famous Iver Johnson "hammer-the-hammer"-type

This is a typical Iver Johnson double-action hammer revolver with barrel locked to frame and hammer at rest. The model illustrated is the 833 in the Supershot Series.

safety is incorporated in the lockwork of this weapon. As in all Iver Johnson hinged-frame revolvers, coil springs are used throughout instead of flat springs. An independent cylinder stop which locks the cylinder firmly in line as the hammer is brought to full cock is another feature of this arm. When the weapon is closed, the cylinder is held rigidly preventing accidental rotation.

Sights are of the Patridge type. The rear sight is adjustable for both elevation and windage. An adjustable finger rest on the grip may be set to conform to the best gripping method of the individual shooter.

This arm with the standard 6-inch barrel measures 10¾ inches overall. It weighs 24 ounces. Both low- and high-velocity cartridges may be used in it. This is a double-action revolver.

Model 833 is identical with the model 834 described above except that it does not have a finger rest.

Model 88 is identical with model 834 except that it does not have the finger rest and is equipped with fixed sights.

.22 Long Rifle   IVER JOHNSON
                                                Protector Sealed Eight

This is a pocket model of the .22 Supershot Sealed Eight. It has the counterbored chambers and extractor, has fixed sights and no finger rest—though these extras may be provided if desired. This arm, known as the Model 84, has a 2½-inch barrel and an over-all length of 7¼ inches. It weighs 20 ounces.

.22 Long Rifle   IVER JOHNSON
                                               Supershot Nine Shot

This revolver while it has the general appearance of the model 834 and incorporates the Iver Johnson safety feature, uses the regular type of cylinder without the countersunk chambers. This cylinder has the capacity of 9 cartridges. It is not intended for use with high-velocity ammunition. No finger rest is provided in this weapon.

IVER JOHNSON
Champion Target

.22 Long Rifle

IVER JOHNSON CHAMPION TARGET SINGLE ACTION. Note adjustable finger rest on grip to accommodate hands of different sizes. Extra barrel shows details of cylinder axis pin and breech lock on barrel extension.

This arm, known as the Model 822, is also a standard hinged-frame type in which raising the barrel catch on the barrel extension frees the barrel to be bent down on its hinge to provide automatic extraction and ejection of all cartridges in the cylinder.

The frame and lockwork differ from earlier models. It is equipped with a finger rest. This weapon is equipped with the counterbored cylinder with 8 chambers. Adjustable Patridge target sights are provided.

Note that this weapon has a standard rebounding hammer which is pulled back inside the frame when pressure on the trigger is released. It is not equipped with the positive Iver Johnson "hammer-the-hammer" safety lock.

IVER JOHNSON
Trigger Cocking Single Action

.22 Long Rifle

This is a hinged-frame target arm with finger rest and adjustable target sights. The barrel length is 6 inches and the over-all length 10¾ inches. It weighs 24 ounces. It has a counterbored cylinder holding 8 cartridges.

Note that this arm has a standard rebounding hammer and is not equipped with the usual Iver Johnson positive safety. This arm is unusual in that the hammer may be cocked by pressing on the trigger. A second pressure on the trigger will release the hammer to fire the cartridge. This differs from the usual double action in that a single pull-through will only revolve the cylinder and raise the hammer. This feature permits more rapid precision shooting on targets since it is possible to aim accurately and fire from a cocked hammer, a feature which is impossible in the standard type where there is no halt between the rising of the hammer to the full-cocked position and its release.

101

.22 Long Rifle

IVER JOHNSON
Hinged Frame Pocket

Iver Johnson's hinged-frame pocket revolvers are of two types, hammer and hammerless. Both use the famous Iver Johnson safety. Accidental discharge is impossible. These revolvers are made with 3-inch barrels and 7-shot standard cylinders. High-speed ammunition should not be used in them. They weigh approximately 14 ounces. In the hammer model, the hammer may be thumb cocked to permit taking accurate aim for firing each shot. In the hammerless type, the hammer is enclosed within the frame and weapon can be fired only by pulling directly through on the trigger. Arms with built-in hammers of this sort, popularly called hammerless, have the advantage that they can be fired through a pocket without danger of the hammer catching; but because of a difficult trigger pull which must revolve the cylinder as well as raise and drop the hammer, accurate shooting as a general rule is not possible. They are arms for close-quarter use. Both types may be encountered in early models with 3- 4- or 5-inch barrel lengths weighing from 15 to 17½ ounces. A wide variety of round- and square-butt types may also be found.

.22 Long Rifle

IVER JOHNSON
Target Sealed Eight

COUNTERBORED CHAMBERS

IVER JOHNSON TARGET SEALED EIGHT. This is a typical Iver Johnson solid-frame revolver. Insert shows extra cylinder with detail of counterbored or sealed chambers which completely embed the cartridge case heads in the steel cylinder as a protection against blown heads. High-speed ammunition should be used only with cylinders so protected. All American nonejector solid frame revolvers are of this general design.

This is a low-priced weapon of solid-frame construction in which the cylinder must be removed from the frame for individual ejection of cartridge cases. As an alternative, the cylinder may be revolved and the cartridges punched or pried out singly through the ejection port on the right side of the arm.

This model is equipped with the safe counterbored cylinder holding 8 cartridges. High-speed ammunition may safely be used in this model. However, it is fitted with the ordinary type of rebounding hammer and not the positive Iver Johnson safety hammer.

102

This arm, known as the model 68, is issued with 6-inch barrel and an over-all length of 10¾ inches. It weighs 24 ounces.

Model 78. This is the same as the model 68 except that the barrel is 10 inches, giving an over-all length of 14¾ inches and a weight of 27 ounces.

Model 69. Iver Johnson .22 target 9 shot. The construction in general of this weapon is the same as the model 68 but it is equipped with a standard type cylinder in which the cartridge case heads rest on the cylinder face and hence their rims are exposed. Weapons with cylinders of this design should not be used with high-speed ammunition. This model has a 6-inch barrel. When equipped with a 10-inch barrel, it is known as the model 79.

Model 1900 Double Action. This is a very low-priced weapon with a 2½-inch barrel. 4½- and 6-inch barrels are also provided on order.

This is the standard type of solid-frame nonejector revolver. The cylinder holds 7 cartridges. High-speed ammunition should not be used in this weapon. Note that this model is not equipped with the famous Iver Johnsosn safety and that some flat springs are used in its manufacture.

Note: From 1871 to 1900 over one million five hundred thousand Iver Johnson revolvers were sold. Among these early types were the solid-frame revolvers known as the American and the Bull Dog, which were replaced by the 1900 Model, a simpler arm with fewer parts.

LUGER-ERMA
Conversion
.22 Long Rifle

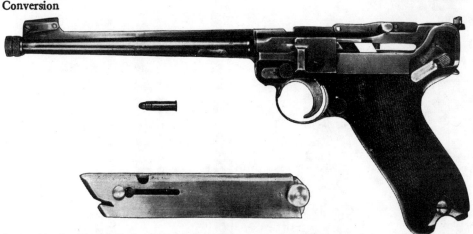

Luger pistol with 6-inch barrel and Erma .22 conversion unit inserted. Magazine extracted to show detail of loading button which operates the hold-open device when the last shot has been fired. Insert barrel is tightened by the adjusting nut at the muzzle.

Luger pistols have never been commercially manufactured in .22 Long Rifle caliber.* However, the Erma conversion unit permits the use of these cartridges in Luger pistols of both 7.65mm. and 9mm. calibers, fitted with 3⅝-, 4½-, 6- and 8-inch barrels.

* In 1964 Erma began production of a .22 caliber blowback pistol which has the appearance of a Luger.

LUGER-ERMA CONVERSION UNIT shown with 4-inch barreled Luger. Note that an adjusting sleeve over the .22 barrel is inserted inside the Luger barrel to aid rigidity. The regular Luger recoil spring assembly remains in the grip of the pistol. Detail view shows top of .22 breechblock which buckles like the Luger to unlock. Note that recoil springs are contained in the breechblock. The barrel is machined at the breech end to lock securely in the Luger chamber, being secured at the muzzle end by the lock nuts after the adjusting sleeve has been placed.

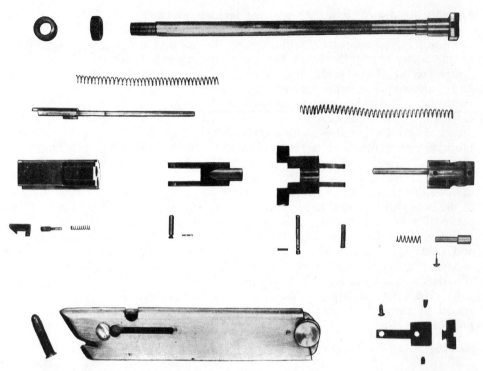

Luger-Erma conversion unit dismounted. Top line shows barrel and lock nuts. Below are recoil springs and guide, breechblock, extractor and firing pin assemblies. Bottom line shows magazine and dismounted rear sight.

The unit consists of a special magazine, ejector, breechblock unit, insert barrel, adjusting sleeve and lock nuts.

Assembling the Unit. First remove the magazine, barrel assembly, breechblock assembly and ejector from the Luger (See dismounting instruction under Luger, Caliber 9mm. Parabellum). Next insert the .22 barrel in the Luger barrel from the breech end. There is a notch at the breech end of the .22 barrel which must be kept on top so it can receive the extractor which is mounted in the top face of the breechblock.

If the Luger barrel is short enough that the .22 barrel protrudes too far for the lock nuts to fasten it, a sleeve which is part of the unit is slid over the muzzle end of the .22 barrel and down into the muzzle of the Luger barrel. The lock nuts are then screwed on the threaded muzzle end of the .22 barrel until they securely lock the sleeve and barrel unit. The .22 breechblock is slid into the guides on the arms extending back from the barrel exactly as in the case of the Luger breechblock. When is is flush with the breech of the barrel, the block may be buckled to permit insertion of the regular Luger connecting pin to lock it to the two receiver arms in standard fashion.

The special six-shot magazine is loaded and inserted in the handle.

Operation. When the protruding arms at the center of the breechblock assembly are drawn back they pull the face of the block away from the breech in its guides in the receiver. Continued rearward and upward pull compresses the recoil spring mounted in the rear of the .22 breechblock, and when faces on the underside of the block hit the ramps machined into the receiver, the center section of the breechblock rises in toggle fashion as in the case of the Luger, drawing the front breechblock face back until it clears the top of the magazine. The magazine spring pushing up against the follower forces the cartridges up and the first one is held by the magazine lips in line with the breechblock. During the buckling movement the cocking finger in the breech-block assembly functions as in the Luger to draw the striker pin back and compress its spring. The cocked striker is caught and held by the sear.

When the breechblock is released the recoil spring forces it ahead and down to lock the action in Luger fashion, after stripping a cartridge from the top of the magazine, chambering it and snapping the extractor over its rim. When the striker is at full cock a signal pin is forced back and protrudes from the rear of the breechblock to warn the shooter. The standard Luger trigger and safety mechanisms function with this conversion unit without alteration.

After the first manual loading operation, pressure on the trigger will release the striker to fire the cartridge; and the pressure inside the cartridge case head will provide the power to thrust back the breechblock and cock, eject and reload in regular automatic pistol fashion. Only one shot is fired for each pull of the trigger.

.22 Long Rifle   REISING
                                                                   Automatic

REISING AUTOMATIC with magazine withdrawn and right side showing to illustrate detail of perforated side wall. Button above trigger is takedown lever. This arm has no manual safety.

The principal parts of this pistol are the barrel, slide, and receiver.

This being a blowback weapon intended to use a low-powered cartridge, no locking device is incorporated. The breech is held closed at the moment of firing by the weight of the slide and the weight and inertia of the recoil spring and other moving parts.

The grip section of the receiver is hollow to permit the insertion of a tubular box magazine containing the cartridges, in normal automatic-pistol fashion. Perforations in the wall of the right side of the magazine permit counting the number of cartridges.

The receiver extends forward of the trigger guide and a hole is drilled near the extreme front end. The receiver is machined to permit the barrel to be inserted from above and hinged to the front end of the receiver. The barrel can be tipped up to facilitate cleaning. When it is snapped down into firing position, a lug on its lower face below the firing chamber seats snugly in the receiver and is held in place by a turning dismounting bolt.

The recoil spring (or operating spring) is mounted in the receiver well above and ahead of the trigger guard below the line of the barrel. The forward end of the slide, suitably machined to travel in guides in the receiver, mounts below the barrel on top of the receiver at its front end. A connecting crossbar at the front of the slide, resting against the head of the operating spring, serves to compress it during rearward motion of the action.

Note that this spring compression system is derived from the early Mannlicher pistol.

The rear half of the slide forms the breechblock and has the extractor, firing pin, and spring mounted within it. The exposed spur hammer is mounted at the rear of the receiver. The hammer spring or mainspring is in the handle behind the magazine well, where it is compressed by a strut attached to the hammer as the hammer is driven back by the slide. The adjustable front sight is mounted on the barrel while the rear sight is mounted in the slide. This weapon is fitted with an automatic disconnector which rises into a niche in the underside of the slide, as in the case of the Colt disconnector. This prevents the weapon from firing more than one shot for each pull of the trigger. It also prevents contact between the trigger and sear mechanism except when the breechblock is fully forward against the face of the barrel.

A magazine disconnector is also built into this weapon. When the magazine is inserted, it pushes one end of the sear spring aside to permit contact of the sear bar with the hammer release mechanism.

Operation: The magazine catch at the bottom of the receiver in the rear of the handle is pushed back and the magazine is extracted. When a loaded magazine is inserted in the handle, it is pushed up past the line of the trigger and strikes a leaf of the sear spring, bringing the disconnector and sear into proper alignment with the sear bar. The slide must now be drawn fully to the rear to compress the coil spring in the receiver below the line of the barrel, and to permit the magazine spring to force a cartridge up in line with the breechblock.

When the slide is released to go forward, it strips the top cartridge from the

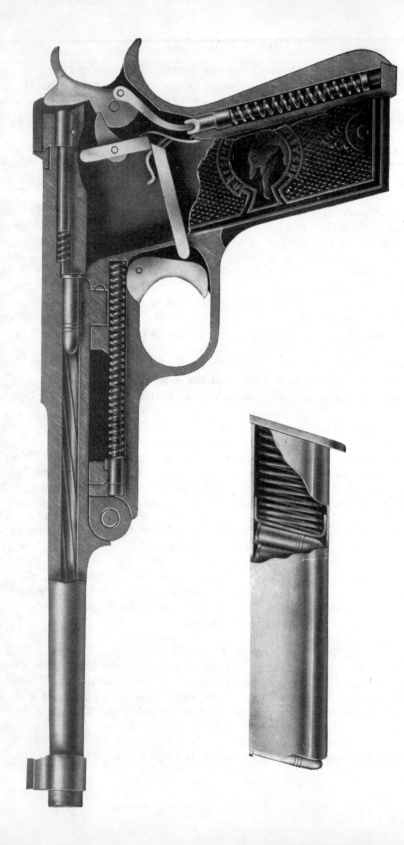

REISING AUTOMATIC. Magazine cutaway to show detail of spring under compression and of magazine follower. Barrel, slide and receiver are cut to show all mechanical details. Note that position of recoil spring follows the European system for such pistols. Hammer has been manually lowered on loaded chamber. Sear is ready to engage hammer cocking notch when hammer is cocked. Note detail of disconnector and trigger bars magazine and chambers it, while the extractor slips over the head of the cartridge case.

Pressure on the trigger is transmitted through a sear bar which is attached to the lower left end of the trigger and passes under the left-hand stock across the magazine well to the disconnector and sear units. The sear is thereby freed from its notch in the hammer and the compressed spring in the grip, thrusting upward against the stirrup of the hammer, revolves the hammer on its axis pin to drive it forward to strike the flying firing pin. The firing pin fires the cartridge in the chamber at the same time that the firing pin spring is compressed. The spring instantly withdraws the firing pin back into the breechblock.

As the bullet passes down the barrel, the rearward pressure of the gases exerted through the head of the empty cartridge case starts the breechblock back. An arm across the front end of the slide portion mounted below the barrel in the receiver presses back against a plunger mounted within the forward section of the recoil spring. As the slide goes back in a straight line, this spring is compressed in its seat in the receiver above the trigger. This provides the energy for the return motion of the moving parts. The rear of the slide transmits the force applied to its face to the hammer, which is rocked back on its pivot to compel the stirrup attached to the hammer to force down the mainspring and compress it. The slide passing over the disconnector, which rises up into it, forces it down to disengage the trigger from the sear. When the hammer comes to full cock, the sear spring forces the sear to engage in the full-cock notch. However, the sear is disconnected from the sear bar until pressure is released on the trigger to permit the spring to force the trigger back to firing position.

On forward motion, the breechblock face of the slide strips the top cartridge from the magazine into the firing chamber. Spring action from below forces the disconnector up into its notch in the slide and the weapon is now hooked up ready for the next pressure on the trigger to fire the next shot.

Dismounting: 1. With the hammer at half cock, remove the magazine.

2. Holding the pistol in the right hand, force the slide back about one-eighth of an inch against the hammer and retain it there with the right thumb.

3. While holding the slide back, with the left hand push the thumb button just above the trigger on the left side as far to the rear as it will go. This turns the bolt out of its locking engagement in the cut in the lug attached to the barrel below the chamber.

4. Still holding the slide slightly to the rear, tip the muzzle of the barrel down as far as it will go. The slide may now be released.

5. Raise the front end of the slide as you draw it forward. It will disengage from the projecting ends of the hammer stop pin at the rear of the receiver, and may be lifted off.

Further dismounting: To complete dismounting, for purposes of repair, first insert the magazine into the handle.

1. Holding the thumb over the hammer so you can ease it down, pull back on the trigger and let the hammer go forward against its stop pin. Snapping

109

REISING AUTOMATIC field stripped for cleaning. Showing 10-shot magazine removed from handle, hammer cocked, takedown button turned up to free barrel, barrel turned down on its hinge and slide after being lifted off.

it may injure it.   (Remember that this pistol has a magazine disconnector and, unless the magazine is in the handle, the trigger cannot be pulled.)

2. Remove the magazine.

3. Withdraw the stock screws and lift off the stocks. The sear bar may now be lifted out of its seat across the receiver. (It is seated in a diagonal slot extending from the lower end of the trigger guard up above the openings in the left-hand side of the receiver.)

4. The round end of the sear bar may be used to push out the hammer pin. The hammer and its strut may then be removed.

5. The point of the strut may now be used to force out the sear pin. This will release the sear, sear spring, and disconnector, which may be removed.

110

6. Unscrew the barrel screw, withdraw it, and the barrel may be lifted out of the receiver.

7. Remove the recoil-spring stop screw. This will permit the recoil spring and its guides to be pushed out to the front.

8. Driving out the trigger pin at the upper part of the trigger will permit it to be removed.

9. Turn the barrel lock button to the rear as far as it will go and it may be pulled out of the receiver.

10. Punch out the magazine catch pin at the bottom of the handle, and the magazine catch and spring may be removed.

11. Punch out the mainspring plunger stop pin seated near the bottom of the handle, and withdraw the mainspring and its plunger. (They may be forced out from above with the hammer strut if they do not shake out easily.)

12. Punch out the firing pin stop pin and withdraw the pin and spring.

ROMERWERK
Automatic

.22 Long Rifle

ROMERWERK AUTOMATIC. Magazine extracted to show detail of magazine when empty. Extra target barrel is lined up to show over-all length of pistol when long barrel is in place. Note that slide and barrel extension join solidly on exterior.

This German pistol while of customary blowback design has a number of unusual features which lift it out of the class of the average pistol.

It is fitted with a quick-change barrel system and is regularly issued with two barrels, a two-and-one-half inch barrel for use as a pocket arm; and a six-and-one-half-inch barrel for use as a target pistol. These are over-all lengths and include a gas seal projection extending back one-half inch from the face

111

of the cartridge chamber. With the long barrel the arm measures nine and one-quarter inches overall.

Construction and Operation: The receiver forms the grip and receives the magazine inserted from below in standard fashion. The magazine itself is unusual in that both walls are slit and follower buttons are provided on both left and right to furnish dual finger grips for ease of loading. It holds only seven cartridges. The grip suffers from being too short. A thumb safety on the left of the receiver may be swung on its axis pin until the knurled section points directly to the rear to set the safety.

The slide is machined on the outside to mate with the barrel extension which is part of the barrel forging. It houses the recoil spring and firing pin assemblies, of course. The breechblock face of the slide is machined to project about half an inch forward from the wider outer surface; and when the slide is fully home and its outer face is in contact with the barrel extension, its inner breechblock section is actually housed within the barrel extension with its face against the firing chamber.

The barrel fits rigidly into appropriate guides in the receiver and is securely locked in position by a steel wedge rising from the receiver above the triggerguard. This wedge is under spring tension and serves to take up play automatically. It is released by forward pressure on a thumbpiece at the front of the triggerguard. The barrel may be slid forward out of the receiver. The pocket barrel is equipped with a fixed sight and the target barrel with an adjustable target sight.

Since the breechblock is completely enclosed within the barrel extension for a half-inch of travel, this design in theory at least affords a maximum of safety from blown cartridge cases in a light weight blowback arm.

Manufacturer: Romerwerk, A. G., Suhl, Germany.

.22 Long Rifle   SMITH AND WESSON
                                                        Single Shot 1891

Official Model Names: Model Single Shot—First Model—Model of 1891.
Model Single Shot—Second Model.
Ammunition: First Model—.22 Long Rifle, .32 S & W, or .38 S & W.
Second Model—.22 Long Rifle only.

Manufacturing Dates: First Model—May 1893-1905.

Second Model—1905-1909.

Serial Numbers: First Model—Numbered in same series with the .38 Single-action Third Model Revolver.

Serial Numbers: Second Model—Numbered in same series with the Third Model or "Perfected" single-shot pistol. (Second Model numbered from 1 to about 4600).

Finish: Blue is standard, though some guns were nickel-plated to order. order.

Special Characteristics: The First Model was made up as a combination revolver and single-shot pistol with 6″, 8″, or 10″ single-shot barrel in .22, .32, or .38 caliber and an interchangeable revolver barrel/cylinder assembly in .38 caliber only but with a choice of lengths of 3½″, 4″, or 5″.

The Second Model was made up as a single-shot pistol only, and was standard with a 10″ .22 caliber barrel. However, the First Model single-shot barrels could also be installed on this gun in all three lengths and calibers. On the Second Model the frame ears and the hand and cylinder-stop slots were omitted, since they were not needed in a single-shot pistol.

These guns and the "Perfected" which succeeded them were used by the American Olympic teams from 1900 until 1910, in which year Smith & Wesson put through a special run of tight-chambered "Perfected" single-shot pistols for the team. Though these special guns are, strictly speaking, the "Olympic" single-shots, that name has become popularly associated with all three models.

	.22 Caliber	*.32 Caliber*	*.38 Caliber*
Land Diameter:	.217-.218	.303-.304	.350-.351
Groove Diameter:	.2225-.2235	.312-.313	.360-.361
Number of Lands:	....	5	5
Twist: One turn in	....	18.75″	18.75″
Direction of Twist:	Right	Right	Right
Length of Chamber:	.796	....	.724
Diameter of Chamber:	.226	.3395-.3405	.388-.389

Note: When loading the tight-chambered pistols it is necessary to force the cartridge home firmly with the thumb, as the bullet seats directly in the rifling. Unless this is done, this particular model cannot be closed for firing because the cartridge case will project from the chamber.

This system of tight chambering originally appeared in early pistols manufactured by Frank Wesson.

SMITH AND WESSON   .22 Long Rifle
Single Shot Perfected

Official Model Name: Model Single Shot Third Model .22 "Perfected."

Ammunition: .22 Long Rifle.

Manufacturing Dates: 1909-1923.

Number Manufactured: 6,949.

Serial Numbers: Numbered in same series as Second Model Single Shot Pistol starting at about 4618.

Finish: Standard blue—nickel on special order.

SMITH & WESSON MODEL SINGLE SHOT (THIRD MODEL) .22 PERFECTED. **Barrel** *hinged open far enough to show details of automatic extractor and barrel breech lock.*

Barrel Length: Normally 10″ only in .22 caliber. However, First Model barrels in 6″, 8″, and 10″ length and .22, .32, .38 caliber could be installed.

Land Diameter:	.217-.218	*Direction of Twist:*	Right
Groove Diameter:	.2225-.2235	*Length of Chamber:*	.796
Number of Lands:	6	*Diameter of Chamber:*	.226
Lead:	15″		

.22 Long Rifle

SMITH AND WESSON
Straight Line

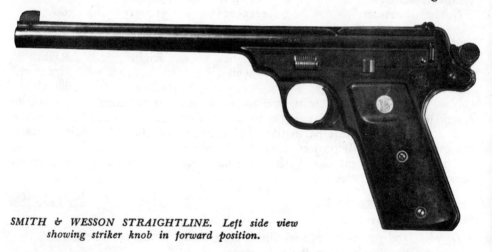

SMITH & WESSON STRAIGHTLINE. Left side view showing striker knob in forward position.

Official Model Names: Model Straight Line Single Shot Pistol (First Model).
Model Straight Line Single Shot Pistol (Second Model).

Ammunition: .22 Long Rifle.

Manufacturing Dates: April 30, 1925-1936.

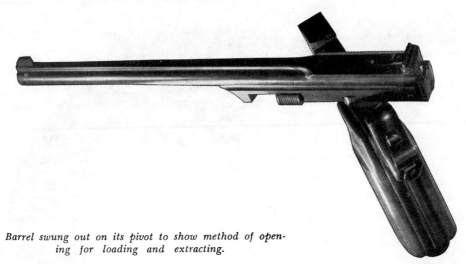

Barrel swung out on its pivot to show method of opening for loading and extracting.

Finish: Blue.
Barrel Length: 10".
The First Model and Second Model differed in that on the later gun the frame was heat-treated and a rebounding hammer was installed.

Land Diameter:	.217-.218	*Direction of Twist:*	Right
Groove Diameter:	.2225-.2235	*Length of Chamber:*	.796
Number of Lands:	6	*Diameter of Chamber:*	.226
Twist: One turn in	15"		

Notes: This was the first modern handgun made with a recessed-head chamber to protect against the danger of blown cartridge rims. Smith & Wesson also applied this principle to a modern rim fire revolver in the K-22 Outdoorsman in 1932, and to a center-fire revolver in the .357 S & W Magnum in 1935.

Note: While this weapon is the first of the *modern* types to use the recessed-head chamber, the principle was used earlier in the Remington-Rider pepperbox cartridge revolver, as well as in several types of Italian revolvers made at Brescia, Italy, by Glisenti and other manufacturers from 1875 on.

SMITH AND WESSON   .22 Long Rifle
Model M Hand Ejector

Official Model Names: Model (M) .22 Caliber Hand Ejector (First Model
         Model (M) .22 Caliber Hand Ejector (Second Model)
         Model (M) .22 Calber Hand Ejector (Third Model)
Ammunition: Chamber will take .22 Long Rifle. The gun, however, was designed for what is known today as the .22 Long. Originally this cartridge was known as the .22 S & W and for many years was catalogued by the ammunition manufacturers as the .22 S & W Long Rim Fire Cartridge.
Manufacturing Dates: First Model—Feb. 1902-Aug. 1906.
        Second Model—Aug. 1906-May 1911.
        Third Model—May 1911-Mar. 1921

115

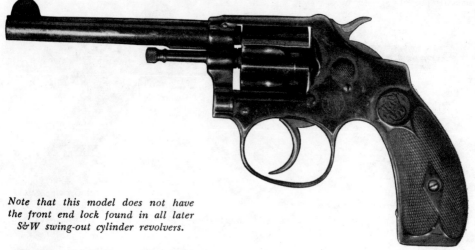

Note that this model does not have the front end lock found in all later S&W swing-out cylinder revolvers.

Number Manufactured: First Model—4,500
                       Second Model—9,375
                       Third Model—12,204

Serial Numbers: All three models numbered in same series.

Finish: Blue and nickel.

Barrel Lengths: First Model 2¼", 3", 3½".
                  Second Model 3", 3½".
                  Third Model 3", 3½".

Land Diameter:	.218-.219	*Direction of Twist:*	Right
Groove Diameter:	.225-.226	*Diameter of Chamber:*	.227-.228
Number of Lands:	6	*Number of Chambers:*	7

Notes: This gun was primarily designed for women to carry in their handbags while bicycling in lonely country, which was a favorite sport in early days. From this it has become popularly known as the "Ladysmith" or "Bicycle Gun."

Design Changes: The First Model was locked and unlocked by the action of a bolt operated by a thumbpiece on the left side of the frame. It did not have a locking bolt or lug on the underside of the barrel.

The Second Model differed in that the thumbpiece and bolt were eliminated and the cylinder locked by a locking bolt in a lug under the barrel. A knob at the front of this lug was pulled forward to unlock the cylinder.

The Third Model differed from the Second Model principally in that it was a square-butt gun instead of a round-butt model. Also minor lockwork changes were incorporated.

Note: This revolver was widely carried by the dance hall girls so familiar to everyone who has ever seen a Western movie.

Its manufacture was finally stopped, so legend goes, when it was called to the attention of D. B. Wesson that the weapon he had designed for the protection of housewives was actually seeing more service in the hands of early dance hall girls.

SMITH AND WESSON
.22/32 Target—Bekeart

.22 Long Rifle

Official Model Name: .22/32 Target—Also known as the Bekeart Model due to the fact that it was designed at the request of Phil B. Bekeart, for many years Smith & Wesson's West Coast representative.

Ammunition: .22 Long Rifle.

Manufacturing Date: June 1911; 1953.

Serial Numbers: Numbered in the .32 Hand Ejector series from about 135,000.

Finish: Blue finish standard—nickel finish on special order only.

Barrel Length: 6".

Land Diameter:	.217-.218	*Number of Chambers:*	6
Groove Diameter:	.2225-.2235	*Sights:* 1/10- or 1/8-inch Patridge	
Number of Lands:	6	front. Square-notch rear	
Lead: Originally 10"—Later 15".		sight adjustable for both	
Direction of Twist:	Right	windage and elevation.	
Diameter of Chamber:	.227-.228		

Stocks: Usually fitted with oversize square-butt target stocks; however, can be fitted with round-butt stocks or with small square-butt Regulation Police stocks.

Design Changes: Essentially, this gun was designed from the Model .32 Caliber Hand Ejector (Model of 1903-Fifth Change) chambered for the .22 Long Rifle ammunition and using a firing-pin mechanism instead of the hammer-nose principle of center-fire guns.

Cylinders heat-treated from about 1920—serial numbers from about 321,000.

Recessed-head cylinders installed beginning April 1935. Serial numbers from about 525,600.

Note: Any .22 Short, Long, or Long Rifle rim-fire ammunition may be used in this revolver. Naturally, the sights must be adjusted to suit the particular ammunition used, if best accuracy is to be obtained.

When this weapon was originally introduced it was classed as a heavy-frame .22. It weighs 23 ounces. By today's standards it is actually a medium-frame .22. When it was first introduced, it was the heaviest .22 revolver made.

117

.22 Long Rifle

SMITH AND WESSON
.22/32 Kit Gun

This is a typical S&W round butt design, swing-out cylinder revolver.

Official Model Name:—.22/32 Kit Gun.

Ammunition:—.22 Long Rifle.

Manufacturing Dates: April 1935; 1953.

Serial Numbers: Numbered in same series with .22/32 Target and .32 H. E., starting at about 525,0co.

Finish: Blue and nickel.

Barrel Length: 4".

Land Diameter:	.217-.218	*Direction of Twist:*	Right
Groove Diameter:	.2225-.2235	*Diameter of Chamber:*	.227-.228
Number of Lands:	6	*Number of Chambers:*	6
Twist: One turn in	15"		

Stocks: Normally fitted with round-butt stocks, or small square-butt regulation police stocks; however, can be fitted with oversize target stocks.

All guns of this model equipped with recessed-head cylinder, heat-treated.

Note: As its name implies, this weapon was especially designed to be carried in a camping kit. The four-inch barrel and rounded handle make it reasonably compact, giving an overall length of only eight inches. It weighs 21 ounces. This revolver will handle any .22 RF ammunition from BB and CB caps through .22 Long Rifle Hi-speed cartridges. Sights may be either USRA Pocket Revolver or 1/10-inch Patridge front: rear sight is adjustable for elevation and windage.

.22 Long Rifle

SMITH AND WESSON
K-22 Outdoorsman

Official Model Name: Model K-22 Hand Ejector (First Model)—K-22 Outdoorsman.

Ammunition: .22 Long Rifle.

Manufacturing Dates: January 2, 1931—December 1940.

Serial Numbers: Between 632,118 and 682,419 in the .38 Military & Police Series.

Finish: Blue standard—Nickel on special order only.

Barrel Length: 6″ only.

Notes: About 1912, a small number of .22 caliber target revolvers were built on the .38 Military & Police round-butt frame on special order. They were later destroyed due to a tendency to throw flyers and because the .22/32 Target Revolver was considered heavy enough and was at the height of its popularity. The cause of this trouble was finally traced to the 10″ twist that was used, but since the .22/32 continued to be the popular weight for target shooting, nothing was done until 1931 when the K-22 Outdoorsman was designed and introduced with a 15″ twist as used in modern Smith & Wesson .22 caliber revolvers.

Land Diameter:	.2135-.2145	*Direction of Twist:*	Right
Groove Diameter:	.2225-.2235	*Diameter of Chamber:*	.2275-.2285
Number of Lands:	6	*Number of Chambers:*	6
Twist: One turn in	15″		

Sights: Target sights normally fitted, but a few guns were made with fixed service sights.

This was the first *modern* revolver incorporating a recessed-head cylinder. This revolver was developed to combine the best in target accuracy with the heaviest striking energy possible in its special caliber cartridge. The best accuracy with high-speed .22 Long Rifle cartridges can be obtained only by using them in an arm of this type, in which the weight, barrel length, distance between sights, and over-all hang and balance are engineered for this purpose.

This weapon, originally designed as a companion revolver to the S & W .38 Military and Police Model, was provided with a special cylinder in which the recesses for the cartridge heads are countersunk to protect and support the cartridge rims completely. This feature makes possible the use in revolvers of the high-speed .22 Long Rifle cartridge.

119

.22 Long Rifle

SMITH AND WESSON
K-22 Masterpiece

For representative photograph of this arm see under Caliber .38 S & W Special The picture of the .38 M & P.

Official Model Names: Model K-22 Hand Ejector (Second Model)—K-22 Masterpiece.

Ammunition: .22 Long Rifle.

Manufacturing Dates: From January 25, 1942.

Serial Numbers: From 682,420 in the .38 Military & Police numbering series.

Finish: Blue standard—nickel on special order only.

Barrel Length: 6″.

Note: This was the first commercial target revolver incorporating micrometer click-adjustable sight, short cocking action, antibacklash trigger.

Land Diameter:	.2135-.2145	*Direction of Twist:*	Right
Groove Diameter:	.2225-.2235	*Diameter of Chamber:*	.2275-.2285
Number of Lands:	6	*Number of Chambers:*	6
Twist: One turn in	15″	*Weight:*	35 ounces.

Sights: 1/10- or 1/8-inch Patridge front. S & W Micrometer rear. Other types of target sights also available.

The S & W Micrometer rear (Patent 2187096) has two-point click adjustments for both elevation and windage. One click moves the point of impact ½ inch at 25 yards, or 1 inch at 50 yards. The adjusting screws are large and strong, and will not shoot loose once they have been adjusted and fastened.

Note: This model incorporates for the first time an antibacklash trigger. No adjustment is necessary, as the entire system is mechanical. As the hammer starts its fall, the trigger is automatically prevented from further rearward movement.

The new speed lock makes cocking easier, hammer fall shorter and quicker. This new lock design renders the earlier "humpback" hammer unnecessary.

.22 Long Rifle

SMITH AND WESSON
Revolver Note

While high velocity ammunition may be used in any S&W single shot pistols, since the breech closure is strong and tight, it should not be used in revolvers unless the cylinders have countersunk chambers.

While minor differences in cylinders, locks, and in lockwork occur as indicated under the different models, in general the description of the construction and operation of all Smith & Wesson hand ejector (swing-out cylinder) revolvers is similar to that of the .38 S&W Special as illustrated and described under caliber .38 S&W Special.

.22 Long Rifle

STAR
Target

This target automatic pistol is made at Eibar, Spain by B. Echeverria; with 7″ barrel it is called the Model F Target; with 5.9″ barrel it is the Model F Sport. It is of good materials and workmanship but falls far short of American standards.

STEVENS
Offhand

.22 Long Rifle

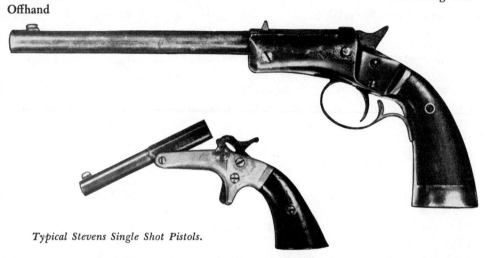

Typical Stevens Single Shot Pistols.

While these pistols are no longer manufactured, very many are still in use. All the early types, though they vary in weights, lengths, barrels, grips, sights and triggers, employed the same unique lockwork. The barrels were always finely made and most accurately rifled. They were hinged-frame single-action pistols. A locking stud resembling a common screwhead protruded from the left side of the frame. Pressing it in freed the barrel and permitted it to be turned down on its hinge for loading and extraction. These catches are uniformly weak and the barrels tend to work loose. Only the heavy models should be used with high-velocity ammunition, and then only if the breech closure is really tight.

STEVENS
No. 10

.22 Long Rifle

STEVENS NUMBER 10. Left side view with striker drawn back to full cock to show cocking knob protruding from rear of receiver. Insert shows pistol open to demonstrate details of extraction.

Barrel: 8-in.
Length Overall: 11½-in.
Weight: 2¼ lbs.
Caliber: .22 Long Rifle.
Sights: Open front and rear with adjustments for elevation and windage.

This Stevens pistol is of unusual design, resembling an automatic pistol in exterior appearance. It was introduced after the World War I.

Like all previous Stevens pistols, this weapon is of the tip-up variety with the barrel hinged to the frame ahead of the trigger guard. It differs markedly from other Stevens types, however, in that the grip is shaped like that of an automatic pistol, and it has a new lock and firing mechanism. Its shape, weight distribution, and barrel rifling make it a weapon capable of exceptional accuracy.

The barrel lock is mounted directly behind the breech of the barrel on a section of the frame above the grip. Pushed back it frees the barrel from the frame. This lock is cam-shaped and automatically takes up any play, thus preventing looseness which very often develops in tip-up pistols.

Instead of the conventional thumb hammer, a rod with a knob at its end projects through the rear of the frame parallel to the line of the bore. The pistol is cocked automatically as the barrel is tipped up and the projecting knob at the rear tells instantly that the weapon is cocked.

Sight adjustment on this weapon is somewhat unusual. A screw on the left side of the rear sight binds it in its slot and also binds the elevation leaf. To adjust for elevation it is necessary to loosen the left-hand screw, and then the leaf may be raised or lowered by means of the right-hand screw. The left-hand screw should then be tightened after the adjustment has been made.

When loading this pistol, the barrel must be opened as far as it will go to permit the extractor to snap back into its seat so the cartridge may be inserted in the chamber and the barrel closed without striking against the frame.

.22 Long Rifle **STOCK**
Sport Auto

This is a medium-priced automatic target pistol of elementary blowback design popular on the Continent. With seven-and-one-half inch barrel it measures ten and one-eighth inches overall and weighs about twenty-six ounces. The grip is too short for really effective target use, as the receiver was designed from a pocket pistol type. Magazine capacity is ten cartridges.

The sights are the only unusual feature in this arm; their mounting affords a maximum sight radius. The pistol uses the customary type of thumb safety found on hammerless automatic pistols, and the standard bottom magazine release catch. The design of the breechblock slide somewhat resembles that of the Walther.

The name "Franz Stock, Berlin" will be found stamped on the left side of the slide.

The Stock Pocket Model is the same as the .32 Stock except for caliber and magazine capacity. The magazine holds nine cartridges. See Stock under Caliber .32 ACP.

STOCK SPORT AUTOMATIC PISTOL. Left side view with magazine extracted. Magazine is not equipped with follower button as a loading help, hence is awkward to load. It holds ten cartridges and may be used with regular or high-speed ammunition.

WALTHER
PP and PPK

.22 Long Rifle

*WALTHER MODEL PP. The model illustrated was prewar standard except for the engraving. **The barrel is 3⅞ inches long, over-all length is 6⅓ inches and weight is about 23 ounces. Magazine capacity is 8 cartridges. The PPK Model is similar in every way to the PP except as follows: Barrel length 3¼ inches, over-all length about 5⅞ inches and weight is 19 ounces.***

Except that they do not have the signal pin which tells if the chamber is loaded, these pistols in .22 Long Rifle are the same as those in .32 and .380 ACP calibers. These were the first truly modern double action blowback safety pistols; until the past 15 years or so they were more advanced than any made in this country.

For other photographs, drawing and complete description of type see Walther PP and PPK under caliber .32 Automatic Colt Pistol (7.65mm. Browning). The two models differ in length, weight, and magazine capacity but are otherwise the same. Note that these models are pocket pistols, not target weapons. They function best with high-speed ammunition. Some types have slides and even receivers made of duraluminum.

.22 Long Rifle   **WALTHER**
                                                         Hammerless

Right side view showing magazine detail. Note that slide lock lever protrudes from front of trigger guard.

This pistol was originally designed for use in the 1932 Olympic shoots. With a 9-inch barrel and an over-all length of 12.9 inches it has a sighting radius of 11.2 inches and weighs about 35 ounces.

It is a regular blowback action but the cartridge is discharged by a striker instead of the conventional hammer.

Construction and Operation: The receiver forms the handle and is designed to permit the use of shaped one-piece stocks of the original Pocket Mauser type. The magazine is inserted in the handle from below and is held by the conventional bottom lock. As no follower button is provided on the magazine, it is difficult to load with the ten cartridges it will hold.

The general receiver design and takedown system pattern after that of the early Mannlichers. A barrel mounting forms part of the receiver forging, while an arm extends below it forward from the trigger guard. The recoil spring and its guide are mounted in the space between the barrel and the receiver arm. The sear bar is mounted on the right side of the receiver. The slide is forged with parallel arms extending on either side ahead of the breech-block section. These arms are connected by a crossbar at their forward ends which acts to compress the recoil spring as the slide goes back.

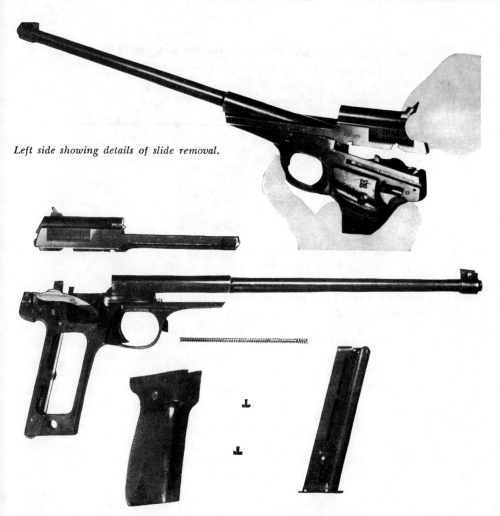

Left side showing details of slide removal.

Dismounted to show details of slide construction, barrel mounting, grip, stock, and magazine design. Recoil spring and guide nest in receiver below barrel mounting. Stock unit is one piece and may be wood or plastic.

Dismounting: First remove the magazine. Then while maintaining pressure on the spring-held slide release catch which projects from the front of the triggerguard, pull the slide back in its guides with a lifting motion. When the slide has cleared the receiver guide cuts it may be lifted up at its rear end and then slid forward over the barrel. The recoil spring and its guide will unseat forward out of the receiver below the barrel mounting. Removing the stock screws and working off the stock unit will give access to the lockwork.

While this is an excellent pistol in many respects, it does not compare with the Walther Olympia which succeeded it.

125

*WALTHER OLYMPIA. The model shown is the prize-winning
Funfkampf with adjustable balance weights. Weights of metal
and wood are both used.*

This is one of the world's outstanding automatic target arms. It won the
first five places in the 1936 Olympic shoots in which it was entered. With
barrel length of 7.44 inches, over-all length of 10.7 inches and a sight radius
of 9.25 inches, this model weighs about 31 ounces without the detachable
weights provided to hold it down during rapid fire shooting. While the external
appearance resembles that of the earlier Walther Target, and the slide and recoil spring assemblies are much the same, the lockwork is radically different.

Instead of a striker this arm uses a flying firing pin and a quick-falling
hammer concealed within the slide. The safety instead of being on the receiver
and engaging in the slide is on the left side of the receiver just behind the
trigger. Pushing it down blocks the action to prevent accidental discharge.

The takedown follows the pattern of the Walther PP models in that the
lower end of the trigger guard is hinged to the receiver while its upper end
projects through a cut in the receiver into the path of the slide crossbar.
When the front of the trigger guard is pulled down the projection is removed
from the path of the slide; meanwhile the lower end of the guard compresses a spring in the receiver. While the trigger guard is held down out of
engagement, pulling back and up on the slide will free it from its guides in
the receiver and permit it to be eased forward over the barrel. The recoil
spring and guide may then be removed. Taking off the stock unit gives
access to the lockwork.

This arm was made in four models for the .22 Long Rifle cartridge.

1. Standard Model as already described except that no provision is made
for use of detachable weights.

2. Model 184N already described. This is provided with a detachable balance weight.

3. Model 184J. Same as the Standard except that the barrel length is only
4 inches.

4. 184F—the Funfkampf. This model shown in drawing, has a 9.6-inch barrel

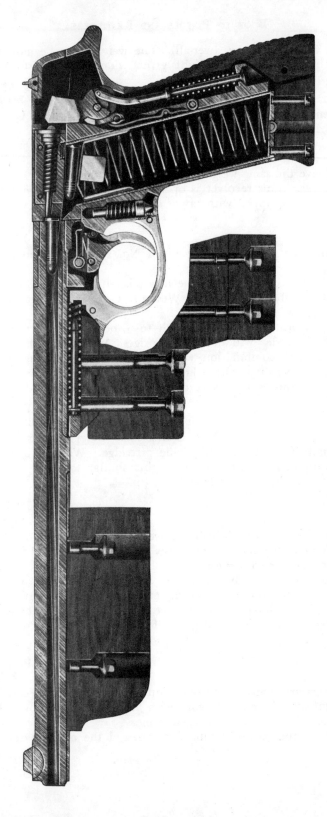

The pistol is completely sectioned to show all operating detail. Magazine is provided with a wooden extension on the butt which gives the appearance of being a continuation of the grip and functions in that capacity. Magazine release is a button on the left side of the receiver.

and measures about 13 inches over-all. The weights can be moved on a rail and are quickly adjusted. Four weights give a wide range of pistol balance.

.22 Long Rifle   WEBLEY AND SCOTT
                                                           Mark VI Target

For representative photograph see W & S Mark VI under Caliber .455.

This is a British hinged-frame revolver intended as a trainer for those armed with the official British Mark VI Caliber .455 revolver. The barrel length is 6 inches, the weight about 40 ounces. When both are loaded, this revolver and the .455 have the same weight and about the same balance. The cylinder holds 6 cartridges. This revolver is operated in the same manner as the companion .455. It is equipped with target sights.

.22 Long Rifle   WEBLEY AND SCOTT
                                                           Mark IV Target

For representative photograph see Pistol No. 2, Mark I under Caliber .38 S & W.

This is a companion revolver to the new official British .380-in. Pistol No. 2 described under caliber .38 Smith & Wesson. General appearance, hang and balance are practically identical.

Barrel length is 6 inches, overall length 10½ inches and the weight is about 33 ounces. The cylinder will hold 6 cartridges. A blade front, an adjustable square rear sight in combination with the fine Webley firing and cylinder aligning lockwork permit accurate firing. The trigger pull is designed for fine target work and requires a pressure of only 3½ or 4 pounds.

.22 Long Rifle   WEBLEY AND SCOTT
                                                           Single Shot Target

Late models of this pistol, which is described under Caliber .22 Long, are designed specially for the .22 Long Rifle cartridge. While a fixed rear sight is standard equipment, adjustable rear sights similar to those used by Smith & Wesson are available for this model.

.22 Long Rifle   PARKER-HALE
                                                           .22/45 Converted

This arm is the standard British Service .455 as converted by Parker-Hale, Great Britain's premier gunsmithing house. The original barrel is permanently converted to .22 caliber with the accurate "Parkerifled" liner or internal barrel. A special 6-shot cylinder is bored off center to permit the use of the regular firing pin. A special adjustable rear sight is mounted on the stirrup fastener. The barrel is 6 inches long and the converted revolver weighs about 42 ounces. It is guaranteed by the makers to group 6 shots in a three-quarter-inch circle at 20 yards.

.22 Long Rifle   PARKER-HALE
                                                           .22/38 Adapters

These adapters are English conversion units for changing the British Service revolvers to .22 caliber for target work with low-cost ammunition. Adaptation is possible because the arms are hinged-frame.

In the .22/455, the barrel is hinged down and the cylinder removed from the .455. A special .22 barrel is inserted in the regular barrel and a sleeve is screwed on at each end to lock this subcaliber barrel securely. These special barrels are furnished in 4,- 6- and 7½-inch lengths to fit all the late model .455 Webley's. A special arm carrying the rearsight is secured to the insert barrel at the breech end. The sight therefore is mounted above the barrel extension (or strap) *ahead of* the cylinder. This allows for the difference in jump of the .22 and the .455 when the arm is fired. A special cylinder, chambered just the length of the .22 Long Rifle cartridge is mounted. Since the .22 is rim fire and the .455 is center fire, the chambers are bored off center to permit the regular center fire firing pin to be used.

In the .22/38, the .22 barrel is threaded only at the muzzle end and the arm on which the rear sight is mounted is fixed to the breech end of the barrel. Otherwise the unit is substantially the same as the .455 except for dimensions, except that it uses the .22 Long cartridge, not the .22 Long Rifle.

WEBLEY AND SCOTT .22 Long Rifle
.22 Conversions

In England Webley-Scott manufacture an "aiming tube" for the .455 revolver. The revolver cylinder is removed and a .22 insert barrel placed in the regular barrel. The breech end of this barrel or tube fits into a steel block which fills the space normally filled by the upper half of the cylinder, extending from the breech of the .455 barrel back to the face of the standing breech section of the frame. This block carries the cartridge chamber above and a special extractor and spring unit below. A special adjustable rear sight is also fastened to an arm rising from the block. When the adaptor is placed in the breech end of the .455 barrel and slid forward, the mounting carrying the rear sight unit passes over the barrel extension and positions ahead of the regular sight. The extractor unit works off the regular .455 assembly. The barrel, of course, is bored off center so it can be used with the regular firing pin.

SINGLE SHOT .22 Long Rifle
Automatic Conversions

The best-known commercial types are the Sedgley and the Stoeger. In the former an insert barrel is provided for the Colt .45 Government Model Automatic which is specially bored off center not only to permit the use of the regular firing pin but also the regular sights. The regular extractor in theory will pull the .22 case out as the slide is drawn back by hand after firing. In practice this does not work very well. Both loading and extraction may give trouble.

The Stoeger attachment, supplied for the .45 Government and .38 Super Colt Automatics, is much more practical. With it only the receiver and its assemblies are used. A special unit is mounted on the receiver guides, and fastened with the regular slide stop pin. This unit resembles the Colt slide in appearance. It mounts its own sights and is equipped with a barrel hinged at the front to permit the breech end to be lifted up to operate the extractor and to load. This makes a very accurate single-shot pistol.

129

.22 Winchester Rim Fire

CARTRIDGE
Data

.22 W. R. F. S-X
45 Gr. Lub. Plated

Muzzle Velocity:	1170
Vel. at 50 feet:	1139
Vel. at 150 feet:	1060

Calculated Energy

Muzzle Energy at ft.-lbs.:	137
Energy at 50 feet:	130
Energy at 150 feet:	112

Calculated Drop

At 50 feet:	.59
At 150 feet:	3.5
At 300 feet:	15.3

Penetration at 15 Feet

7/8" soft pine boards:	5

Length of Barrel in Which Tested

inches:	6

Shell Case

Weight:	17.0 grains
Max. Length:	.965
Outside Body Dia. Max.:	.243
Inside Mouth Dia. Max.:	.2270
Volumetric Capacity to Base of Bullet in cubic inches:	.0265

Bullet

Weight:	45 grains
Approx. Length:	.490
Diameter Max.:	.2282
Area, Cross Sectional:	.0408 square inch
Shape:	Flat

Powder

Amount and type varies with different lots manufactured.

Cartridge

Approx. length, loaded:	1.170
Approx. total weight, loaded:	65.0

Pistols and Revolvers for this Cartridge. All single-shot pistols and revolvers described under Caliber .22 Long Rifle *when the barrel is stamped ".22 WRF."* As this cartridge is too long to chamber in the ordinary .22 Long Rifle, it can be inserted only when the chamber is specially designed for it. Even when the weapon is designed for the .22 WRF cartridge, however, the use of High Velocity ammunition is not recommended except in late models of the Colt Police Target revolver.

All American revolver manufacturers have at one time or another produced revolvers in this caliber, and most single-shot pistols have also been chambered for it. In Europe it is seldom produced except in custom-made single-shot pistols.

Chapter 4

Caliber .25 to .26

John M. Browning invented the first .25 caliber automatic pistol in 1905, using the 6.35mm Browning cartridge, known in this country as the .25 ACP or simply the .25 Automatic. The pistol was patented in Belgium in 1905 and production was started the same year by Fabrique Nationale des Armes de Guerre (FN), Liege, Belgium, who controlled his patents in Europe. FN made approximately 100,000 within 5 years, and over 1,000,000 in all.

Colt's started production of the same gun in the U.S. under a Browning license late in 1908, when Mr. Browning applied for a U. S. patent that was granted January 25, 1910.

The arm was designed as a "vest pocket" weapon which would be easily concealed on the person. The German Mauser factory promptly imitated the general design and soon the market was flooded with a host of imitations and modifications.

Because of the very low power of the cartridge employed, it is not necessary to use a costly locking system to secure the breech at the instant of firing. The walls of the cartridge case are momentarily expanded against the firing chamber by the same gases which drive the bullet down the barrel and thrust the head of the case back against the breechblock. Further resistances to breech opening are afforded by the inertia of the breechblock and other sliding members as well as by the springs which are thrusting the sliding members and the hammer or striker ahead. These resistances are co-ordinated so that the breech opens very little until the bullet is out of the barrel and the pressure drops to safe limits.

Because of the simplicity of this system and the cheapness of manufacture, several hundred types of .25 ACP caliber automatic pistols have been marketed

.25 ACP (6.35mm.)

50 Gr. MC
Muzzle Velocity in f.s.:	820
Vel. at 50 Feet:	801
Vel. at 150 Feet:	765

Calculated Energy
Muzzle Energy in ft.-lbs.:	75
Energy at 50 Feet:	71
Energy at 150 Feet:	65

Calculated Drop
At 50 Feet:	.72 inch
At 150 Feet:	7.0 inch
At 300 Feet:	30.2 inch

Penetration at 15 Feet
7/8" soft pine boards:	3

Length of Barrel in Which Tested
inches:	2

Shell Case
Weight:	26 grains
Max. Length:	.615 inch
Outside Body Dia. at Head, Max.:	
	.278 inch
Outside Body Dia. at Neck, Max.:	
	.278 inch
Inside Mouth Dia. Max.:	.2495 inch
Volumetric Capacity to Base of Bullet	
in cubic inches:	.013

in Europe. Since with only one exception their operating principle is the same, this section deals specifically only with unusual variants and outstanding modifications. In the Identification Section will be found photographs and mechanical details of over 150 additional variants. It should be noted that in Spain, and to a lesser degree in Belgium, many of these pistols have been marketed under a wide variety of trade names. Thus the same pistol may appear in catalogs throughout the world with fifty or more different names stamped on the slide or receiver.

The one commercially marketed exception is the Hungarian Frommer Baby, which is a locked-breech weapon whose design is fully discussed.

BAYARD   .25 ACP
Automatic

For photograph and details of this excellent Belgian variation of the Browning see the Identification Section. The 1923 Model has a 6-shot magazine. The 1930 Model has a 6-shot magazine. This model is about the same length as the Baby Browning but is considerably heavier. The Bayard 1908 is of original design. In this arm the barrel forms part of the receiver forging. It is an exceptionally sturdy weapon of its class.

BROWNING   .25 ACP
Automatic

Except that the slide bears the name of the Belgian manufacturer on the slide and the monogram "FN" on the stocks, this arm is the same as the Colt Vest Pocket. It is not, however, as well made as the Colt. For photograph see the Identification Section. For detailed description see Colt Pocket Model. The 1947 FN catalogs state that over 1,000,000 of this model have been sold.

BROWNING   .25 ACP
Baby

This arm was introduced to meet European competition and demand for a vest pocket arm even smaller than the Browning 6.35mm. (.25 ACP).

It weighs only 10 ounces with the 6-shot magazine loaded. (The regular Browning weighs 13½ ounces similarly loaded). It is 4 inches overall and has a 2⅛-inch barrel. The regular model is one-half inch longer with the same barrel length.

The word *Baby* was on the bottom of each stock of many older pistols but is not on recent production pistols. The safety lever is on the left side to the rear of the trigger and a cocking indicator is provided.

For photograph and further details see the Identification Section.

CLEMENT   .25 ACP
Automatic

These are pistols of good workmanship made at Liege, Belgium by the firm of Charles P. Clement. The American Smith & Wesson .35 Automatic was based on the Clement patent and in general the description of the S&W covers the Clement, except that the latter has no grip safety. For photograph and

133

mechanical data see the Identification Section. Some models were made with the characteristic Clement separate breechblock but without the hinge-down barrel.

.25 ACP

COLT
Auto Pocket

General Description: Factory Model N. A small, light automatic pistol designed for personal protection. This weapon has a striker mechanism in place of a hammer; automatic grip safety, automatic disconnector and manual thumb safety. It was discontinued in 1941.

Ammunition: .25 A.C.P. (6.35mm).
Manufacturing Dates: October 30, 1908 to 1941.
Serial Numbers: From Number 1.
Finish: Blue or nickel.
Barrel Length: 2″.
Stocks: Rubber or checked walnut with medallion.
Bore Diameter: .244″–.001.
Groove Diameter: .251″–.001.
Rifling: (Left twist). 6 grooves, 1 turn in 16″.
Number of Shots: 6.
Action: Semiautomatic blowback.
Approximate Weight: 13 ounces.

Over-all Length: 4½".

Sights: Fixed: integral with the slide.

Note: At number 141,000 a safety disconnector was incorporated to prevent discharge of a cartridge in the barrel with the magazine withdrawn. This is the only Colt pistol fired by a striker; all others have hammers—either external or concealed by the slide.

The main parts of this pistol are the receiver, slide, barrel, and firing pin assembly.

It should be noted that this model differs from all other Colt automatic pistols in that it is not fitted with a hammer but is discharged by a striker mechanism as in the case of the Luger automatic pistol and the Springfield rifle. It is perhaps the most widely imitated pistol ever made.

The receiver has a hollow handle into which is inserted the box cartridge magazine from below. The magazine is held by a catch in the lower rear end of the receiver. This weapon does not have the conventional stirrup-type trigger of the other Colt automatic pistols (embodied in all except the Woodsman model).

The receiver has guides for the slide. At the end above the line of the trigger the receiver is fitted with recesses to receive transverse locking ribs on the bottom of the barrel.

The magazine is the standard tubular type with cartridges placed one on top of the other upon a follower, below which is a zigzag spring resting on the magazine bottom. Holes in the side walls of the magazine permit counting the cartridges therein. The rear end of the slide forms the breechblock and houses the extractor and the striker firing mechanism. The forward part of this slide is semi-tubular and extends forward over the barrel. As the slide on this weapon is placed on the receiver *from the front,* it cannot be blown off the receiver. The breechblock end of the slide is bored to receive the firing pin, the mainspring, and the guide.

Safeties: When the weapon is cocked, the thumb slide-lock safety on the rear left-hand side of the receiver may be pushed up into its cut in the slide. A projection on the underside of the slide-lock safety will lock the sear and prevent movement of the firing mechanism.

A grip safety mounted in the rear of the receiver in standard fashion normally prevents movement of the sear. This prevents the firing mechanism from being released until the weapon is held securely in the hand and this grip safety depressed.

A positive Browning-type disconnector is mounted in this weapon which prevents the trigger from acting on the sear unless the weapon is fully closed; at which point *the top* of the disconnector is in its seat in the underside of the slide above the receiver line, and its *lower end* permits the engagement of the trigger mechanism.

In all pistols numbered above 141,000 there is also a magazine safety. This magazine safety breaks the connection between the trigger and the sear when the magazine is withdrawn. Unless the magazine is in its place in the handle to force the safety disconnector into firing alignment with sear and trigger, the firing mechanism cannot be released.

When a loaded magazine is inserted in the handle of this pistol, drawing the slide back to its fullest extent will compress the recoil spring mounted around its guide in the receiver directly below the barrel. At the first movement of the slide to the rear, the disconnector is forced down inside the receiver to positively disconnect the firing mechanism from the trigger.

The mainspring in this pistol is housed in a recess in the rear of the slide *behind the breechblock face.* Its forward end is inserted in a tube at the end of the firing or striker pin. This spring is compressed as the slide is brought back and a projection on the striker pin is caught and held by the sear.

The magazine spring forces a cartridge up in line with the breechblock, and when the slide is released it moves forward to load the firing chamber.

As the slide goes to its fully forward position, the trigger and connector unit hook up with the sear.

Operation: When the trigger is pressed it transmits energy through the connector to the sear pulling it out of engagement with the striker projection. The mainspring drives the striker home to fire the cartridge in the chamber.

The slide starts back at the instant of firing, as this is a straight blowback pistol. However, the weight and inertia of the moving parts and of the spring hold it closed during the moment of high breech pressure. After the bullet has left the barrel, the extractor snapped into the extracting groove in the cartridge case guides the case back and it is ejected through the port in the right-hand side of the slide.

The recoil spring guide protrudes through a slot in the abutment in the slide below the line of the barrel. The slide compresses the recoil spring mounted around the guide; and this furnishes the energy to close the pistol after it has recoiled to its full extent.

Dismounting: First make sure that there is no cartridge in the chamber. Then pull the trigger. *This weapon should not be cocked when it is dismounted.*

Remove the magazine.

Holding the weapon in the left hand with the thumb over the breechblock end of the slide, with the right hand push the slide back about a sixteenth of an inch and tighten the left hand to hold the slide firmly in that position.

With the right hand twist the barrel one-quarter turn to the right.

Twisting the barrel turns the locking lugs on its underside out of their engaging recesses in the receiver, permitting barrel and slide removal.

.25 ACP **CZ**
Céska Zbrojovka

This unusual little pistol introduced in 1936 is a fine example of Czech small-arms design. The general design of receiver, barrel and barrel mounting, slide and recoil spring position all follow the Browning design very closely. However, the weapon employs an enclosed hammer firing system which fully shields the hammer when the arm is carried uncocked, yet provides the safety factor of an exposed hammer. Moreover, an extremely simple and efficient double-action system is incorporated, as is also a magazine safety. When the magazine is in the pistol it forces up a bar which is in contact with the sear bar, thereby bringing the latter in position to operate the sear and hammer mechanism. The trigger is mounted on a pivot pin and is linked to the sear bar which passes across the left side of the magazine well in the grip. A hook on its rear end is in engagement with a pivoted member connected with the hammer. When the hammer is down, pressure on the trigger pulls the sear bar forward causing it to work through its linkage to cock the hammer. The hammer depresses its strut and the mainspring in standard fashion. As it comes to full cock, the hammer is freed to pivot on its axis pin to strike the firing pin and discharge the cartridge in the chamber. This pistol measures about 4 4/5 inches overall and weighs about 13¾ ounces and has a magazine capacity of 8 cartridges. Note that cocking is by trigger action, not by slide.

Manufacturer: Ceska Zbrojovka, Prague.

FMG .25 ACP
Automatic

This weapon, manufactured in Chile by the Fabrica de Material de Guerra, is an interesting development in the field of arms manufacture, representing the entrance of Chile into the quality armament field. It is made of excellent materials and of good workmanship, though it is not to be classed with the genuine Colt.

Except for a few externals such as the stamping on the hard rubber grips and a slight change in the form of the slide notches, this arm is a direct imitation of the Colt. The detailed description of the Colt applies to this pistol also.

FROMMER .25 ACP
Baby

This is the only locked-breech automatic pistol ever commercially manufactured in this caliber. The locking system is unnecessary. For photograph and data see the Identification Section. For detailed description of construction and operation of the long recoil locking system and for explanatory drawings see Frommer under Caliber .32 ACP.

HAENAL .25 ACP
Automatic

These German arms were made under patents of Hugo Schmeisser who designed the famous German submachine (or "burp") guns of World War II. They are of uniformly good materials and workmanship but are not particularly unusual except for signal pins which serve as cocking indicators.

HARRINGTON AND RICHARDSON .25 ACP
Automatic

This low-priced American arm is no longer manufactured. It is based on the British Webley & Scott patents. For specific photograph and data on this caliber see the Identification Section. For photographs and detailed descriptions of arms of this type, see H&R and W&S under Caliber .32 ACP. This design is noteworthy for its barrel removal system.

137

.25 ACP ITALIAN
Beretta or IAG

The pistols bearing the Beretta name or the I.A.G. initials are good weapons made of good materials. These are the best Italian arms. Several are illustrated in the Identification Section. The general construction and operation of these types will be found under Calibers .32 ACP and .380 ACP.

.25 ACP KOBRA
Automatic

For photograph and details of this arm see the Identification Section. It is unusual in grip design and is equipped with an outside hammer.

.25 ACP LE FRANCAIS
Automatic

This is the premier arm of this caliber made in France. It was widely used as a Staff Officer's Pistol there and the commercial pistol when issued in the Army is so classed. In view of the general ineffectiveness of the caliber its adoption as a military weapon is difficult to understand.

It is made of excellent materials and of good workmanship by French standards. It differs from most automatic pistols in that the back travel of the slide does not cock the weapon. In this unique design, the force of the explosion merely blows the slide back to permit the gases to eject the empty case (the arm has no extractor) and to compress the recoil spring. The recoil spring drives the breechblock slide ahead to strip the top cartridge from the magazine and chamber it.

Pressure on the trigger pushes the striker back to full cock and also releases it to fire the cartridge. This double-action system is intended as a safety feature, since the arm is never cocked except when under direct trigger finger pressure. Other unusual features include a magazine safety which prevents the arm from being fired when the magazine is withdrawn and a hinged barrel which may be tipped down on its hinge to load or unload the chamber, or to clean the barrel.

For specific photograph and data on this caliber see the Identification Section. For drawing and detailed description of the type see Le Francais under Caliber 9mm. Browning Long.

LIGNOSE   **.25 ACP**
Einhand

LIGNOSE EINHAND. Slide forward. This weapon is designed to have the slide pulled back with a finger of the firing hand. Note that the front part of trigger guard forms part of the unit below the muzzle and is free to be pulled back against recoil spring tension and to carry the slide with it. It can pull the slide back, but its upper surface fits into the slide to prevent movement except when deliberately drawn back by manual pressure.

This German pistol, though standard in most respects for its type, is noteworthy for its unusual slide retraction feature. In the typical automatic pistol, after the loaded magazine has been inserted in the handle it is necessary to hold the weapon in one hand and draw the slide back with the other to cock

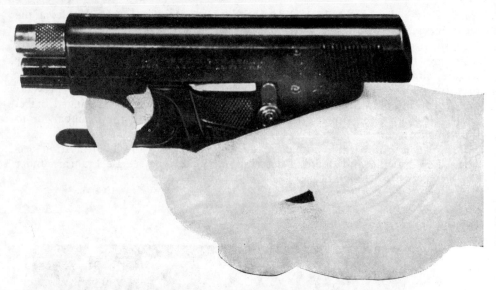

LIGNOSE slide being drawn back to load and cock the arm by finger pressure on sliding trigger guard member.

the arm and load the chamber. If the cartridge misfires, the second hand must be employed to pull the slide back to eject the cartridge, cock and reload the arm.

In the Lignose One Hand model the trigger guard is two separate pieces. The forward section of the guard is movably mounted in the bottom of the receiver. So long as the slide functions properly it abuts the sliding trigger guard section but does not affect it. However, if a finger of the firing hand is placed around the front of the trigger guard, the moving section may be drawn back so that its upper end which abuts the underside of the slide will function to push the slide back to open the breech and cock the arm. A similar system is used on the Chylewski pistol. The idea of one-hand chamber loading and cocking was used in the experimental White-Merril pistol submitted for U. S. Government trial in 1907. It is not practical, of course, on a large-caliber arm where heavy springs must be compressed.

For data on the Lignose see the Identification Section.

.25 ACP   **LILLIPUT**
                                                            Automatic

This .25 caliber pistol is slightly heavier than the Baby Browning but is actually shorter overall. A later version is longer and heavier and much sturdier. This latter type is marketed under the name of the original manufacturer of the Lilliput, August Menz. See the Identification Section for photographs and details of various models. A small version of the original Lilliput was made in caliber 4.25mm.

MAUSER
WTP (Vest Pocket)

.25 ACP

MAUSER W. T. P. 1. (Westentaschen Pistole) Note indicator pin at rear of receiver to show that chamber is loaded.

This is the original design of the vest pocket pistol made by Mauser at Oberndorf, Germany. It measures 4.08 inches overall, weighs 9½ ounces and has a 6-shot magazine. The magazine release catch is in the bottom of the butt and the thumb safety is on the receiver directly behind the trigger on the left side of the weapon. This is a striker-fired weapon. While this is an excellent arm of its type, it is inferior to the Colt in design and safety.

This model introduced in 1923, was replaced by the W.T.P. 2 in 1938 and replaced the earlier Mauser type originally produced to compete with the Baby Browning.

MAUSER
Pocket 1910

.25 ACP

This pistol is one of the best made and finished pistols ever produced. Because of its design and longer barrel it is accurate and effective within the limits of its cartridge at much greater ranges than any other pistol of this caliber. It is a pocket pistol, however, and must not be confused with the hundreds of Colt imitations which are of the Vest Pocket type. Many Czech CZ pistols are based on this design.

For specific photograph and data on this caliber see the Identification Section. For explanatory drawing and details of construction and operation of this type see Mauser 1910 under Caliber .32 ACP.

141

MAUSER POCKET MODEL 1910. Thumb lever to rear of trigger is pushed down to set the safety when the striker is cocked. It is released by pushing the button directly below it.

.25 ACP   MELIOR, MENTA, MENZ

For photographs of these German types which are widely distributed in Europe and to some extent in the United States, see the Identification Section.

.25 ACP   ORTGIES
                                                                               Automatic

This is a striker-fired pistol of good quality made in Germany and widely distributed in the United States and South America. While it is of elementary blowback design, it has a number of unusual features. For specific photograph and data see the Identification Section. For photographs and detailed description of the type see Ortgies under Cal. .32 ACP.

.25 ACP   OWA
                                                                               Automatic

This Austrian pistol is a hammer fired blowback of unusual design. It is one of the cheapest and simplest automatic pistols ever manufactured. The magazine catch is the conventional butt type. The thumb safety is a sliding member on the receiver directly above the left hand stock and is pushed forward to set on safe.

Austrian OWA. The sliding thumbpiece above the grip is the safety. Swinging the thumb catch on the barrel extension releases the barrel so it can be hinged down. Note that a light independent breechblock slides in the barrel extension to load, cock and eject.

The barrel is hinged to the receiver directly above the front end of the trigger guard; and latches by its extension to a center post rising from the rear of the receiver. Pushing the catch on top of the barrel extension at the rear releases it and permits the barrel and breechblock assembly to be hinged away from the rear of the receiver.

If the breechblock is pulled back it can be freed from a stud on the underside of the barrel extension. This unhooks it from the recoil spring which is mounted in the upper tube above the barrel. Sliding the left hand stock and its attached plate down out of the receiver handle exposes the simple lockwork.

While the pistol as made is of fair workmanship, the design has much to recommend it from the standpoint of simplicity, ease of manufacture and accessibility for cleaning and repairs. For other data see the Identification Section.

PIEPER .25 ACP
1909

This pistol, made by the Belgian firm of N. Pieper is a well-constructed arm which incorporates an unusual takedown feature. Pushing down the barrel and slide lock on the left side of the receiver above the trigger guard permits the barrel and slide assemblies to be lifted up out of engagement and removed without effort. For photo and data see the Identification Section.

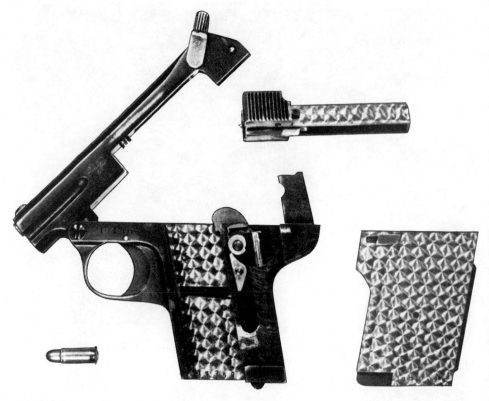

OWA dismounted. Recoil spring and guide are in the ceiling of the barrel extension. Breech-block arms fit over receiver post preventing breechblock from being blown off the receiver. Hammer is down with tension off the mainspring which is housed in the tube in the grip.

.25 ACP   CZECH
                                                                          Duo

Arms bearing the stamp F. DUSEK, OPOČNO are fairly reliable weapons of good materials, fair workmanship and standard design.

.25 ACP   SAUER
                                                                    Automatics

The products of Sauer und Sohn of Suhl, Germany, are among the finest **arms** made. The two common Vest Pocket (W.T.) types are of generally standard design and appearance but of excellent workmanship. They are equipped with thumb safeties. The two common pocket types in this caliber are distinctive pistols with cylindrical slides enclosing the barrel and recoil springs mounted around the barrels. All are hammerless types.

Some of the arms will be encountered with slides and receivers of duralumin. While extremely light in weight, these weapons are thoroughly reliable and

144

safe for use with standard cartridges. See the Identification Section for photographs and details.

SCHMEISSER AND SIMSON .25 ACP
Automatics

For photographs and general data on the four Schmeisser types and on the German Simson, see the Identification Section. These are all well-made arms. They have no outstanding features, however.

SPANISH .25 ACP
Automatics

Several hundred brand names and trademarks have been issued by Spanish manufacturers in this caliber. Those bearing the *Star* brand name of B. Echeverria of Eiber, pistols made by Berestain y Cia. and Eulogio Arrostegui of the same city and Unceta y Cia of Guernica are among the best of the Spanish makes. The new Astra 200 is excellent. Several are illustrated in the Identification Section.

STEYR .25 ACP
Baby

This is the outstanding Austrian pistol of this caliber. It is of unusual design in that it employs no extractor (the residual gas in the chamber blows the empty case out after pushing the breechblock back) and in having a tip-down barrel which may be hinged down by pressing the release catch on the left side of the receiver above the trigger. The breechblock is also unusual in that it is a separate unit and slides in the receiver back from the breech face of the barrel. The recoil spring is mounted above the barrel; and if the barrel is hinged down for loading the chamber, the breechblock can be drawn back to cock the hammer with a minimum of effort, since it does not have to compress the recoil spring. For photograph and data of this specific caliber see the Identification Section. For photographs and additional description of construction and functioning see Steyr under Caliber .32 ACP.

STOCK .25 ACP
Automatic

This arm closely resembles the Stock .22 Long Rifle Target Pistol, but differs in that the slide is cylindrical to cover the barrel almost to the muzzle. The breechblock has a rising extractor which acts as an indicator to show when the chamber is loaded. See the Identification Section for photograph and details. See also Stock under Caliber .32 ACP.

WALTHER .25 ACP
Note

Model 1 of the Walther .25 caliber vest pocket automatics was introduced in 1908. In general it resembles the Stock pistol, having the slide cut away in the section back of the front sight to the breechblock face. It is hammerless. Model 2 introduced in the following year is heavier and has a slide which fully encloses the barrel. The next model in this caliber is the Model 5, a modified type introduced in 1913. Model 7 is a regular pocket-size pistol

STEYR .25 AUTOMATIC (also manufactured by Pieper)

Pistol cross sectioned to show all details. Note that the barrel and recoil spring housing are a single forging with the spring and guide positioned above the barrel. The barrel is hinged forward of the trigger guard. Turning the barrel catch on the left side of the receiver frees the light breechblock unit from contact with the recoil spring assembly and the barrel and permits the barrel to be hinged down on its joint. This feature makes cleaning simple and also permits easy loading, since the breechblock may be drawn back to cock the hammer with a minimum of effort.

The trigger bar operates across the magazine well to release the sear from engagement with the hammer. The hammer is shown at full cock pushing the plunger down and compressing the mainspring.

When the breech is closed the recoil spring guide is fastened to the face of the breechblock. As the light block is blown to the rear by the action of the discharge, it draws the guide back and compresses the recoil spring to provide energy for the forward movement.

This arm does not have an extractor. Residual pressure in the chamber blows the empty case clear of the pistol.

with greater length, weight and magazine capacity which was marketed in 1917. All these, while good arms, are not as well designed as those that followed them.

With the introduction of the modern Models 8 and 9 the Walther really reached the stage of first-grade weapons, and from then on until the close of World War II Walthers were foremost in design and experimentation.

All these arms will be found pictured and described in the Identification Section. However, Models 8 and 9 are of sufficient importance and are so generally distributed throughout the world that some special notice must be given to them.

WALTHER .25 ACP
No. 8

This arm was widely carried as an auxiliary arm by German ranking officers in World War II. It is a compact weapon in which the recoil spring is mounted around the barrel under the slide. The slide forms the breechblock and encloses the barrel completely. It measures 5⅛ inches overall, weighs about 12½ ounces and has a magazine capacity of 8 cartridges. It has a thumb safety but no grip safety. Like all Walther arms it is of fine materials and workmanship and excellent design. Pushing in a release catch on the right side of the receiver at the forward end of the trigger guard permits the slide to be drawn back until it can be lifted up out of the receiver travel guide, then pushed forward off over the barrel. For photo and other data see the Identification Section.

WALTHER .25 ACP
No. 9

This is a vest pocket design. A signal pin protrudes from the rear of the receiver when the chamber is loaded. The arm measures about 4 inches over-all, weighs 9 ounces and has a magazine capacity of 6 cartridges.

In this model the breechblock section of the slide is of conventional design, but the slide forward from breech to muzzle does not enclose the top of the barrel. An arm extending forward on each side encloses the recoil spring and guide which are housed below the barrel. Safety and takedown are similar to the Model 8.

WEBLEY AND SCOTT .25 ACP
Hammer Model

This British arm is one of the few pistols of its type manufactured in this caliber with an external hammer which can be lowered on a loaded chamber for safety when carrying. It weighs 11¾ ounces with magazine empty and has an over-all length of 4¾ inches. Magazine capacity is 6 cartridges. Thumb safety on the left side of the receiver is pulled down to set the pistol on safe.

For photograph and data see the Identification Section. For description of type, see Webley & Scott under Caliber .32 ACP.

.25 ACP
WEBLEY AND SCOTT
Hammerless

The construction of this model differs radically from the hammer model described above. This is one of the lightest and most compact of all the arms of this caliber, weighing only 10¾ ounces with empty magazine and measuring only 4¼ inches overall. Magazine holds 6 cartridges.

Like all the products of this famous British firm, this pistol is well made of the finest materials. However, its appearance is typically Webley and unlike the Colt it has few direct modern imitators.

It is a standard blowback type, of course. The shape and position of the trigger bar or auxiliary differs from that on other models. Instead of the typical V-type recoil spring mounted under the right hand stock as in the .32 W&S, this arm employs dual coil springs housed in the breechblock section of the slide. The safety is the same as in the hammer model. Instead of the ejection port in the right side of the slide, in this model the slide is cut away from the breech forward almost to the muzzle to expose the top section of the barrel and to provide maximum ejection opening surface. It is a uniquely simple weapon but is awkward to handle.

For photographs and data see the Identification Section.

.25 ACP
ZEHNA
Automatic

This is a German arm of good quality and workmanship but of undistinguished design. See the Identification Section for photograph and details.

.25 ACP
MISCELLANEOUS
BAR and Regnum

BAR Pistol. Has two super-posed barrels and 4-shot surging block.

Reform Pistol, with 4-super-posed barrels.

This semirimless cartridge, while designed specifically for automatic pistols, was adapted by German and Belgian manufacturers to all the varieties of cheap revolvers already discussed under Caliber .22 Velo-Dog.

In addition a special revolver, the Mueller, was designed to use it. This revolver resembles an automatic pistol with a revolver cylinder mounted above the trigger guard. It employs a unique action whereby a long plunger operated by the trigger rotates the cylinder, cocks and drops the concealed hammer with much less disturbance than in the regular double action revolver.

Freak pistols of the type of the double barrelled, swinging block BAR and the parallel barrelled 4 shot double action Regnum and Merveilleux also use this cartridge, as does the widely distributed Reform Pistol.

Bullet weights and design as well as powder charges differ considerably with the manufacturer. Bullets may be lead, cupro-nickel jacketed, or steel jacketed, and their weights range from about 65 to 80 grains. Muzzle velocities vary from 710 to 777 feet per second with powder charges ranging from 2½ to 3 grains of fast burning smokeless.

BERGMAN
Automatic

.26 (6.5mm.)

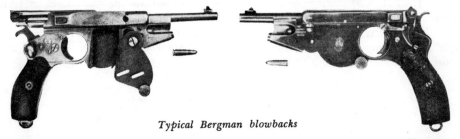

Typical Bergman blowbacks

Cartridges for this pistol may be rimless and without an extracting groove or with an extracting groove in the case. The latter type was manufactured on the Continent until nearly the beginning of World War I. Bergman cartridges were never manufactured commercially in the United States; 6.5 Bergman No. 3 Auto Pistol Cartridges were imported by Stoeger Arms, New York City. A specimen D.W.M. 413A (a grooved case) had a head diameter of .370" and case length was .865." The 65 grain bullet was .2655" in diameter. Dimensions apply to a single sample and may not be maximum or "standard."

However, large numbers of pistols of this type were in use in Europe and South America though in our own country they are little more than collector's items.

Probably the first pocket type automatic pistol was one of these Bergmann's (they were made in a wide variety of sizes, weights, styles and calibers, but all the blowback designs were essentially the same in design and appearance).

Early models were made without extractors, the gas pressure in the chamber being depended upon for extraction and ejection. Later an extractor was added and the cartridge case redesigned. These were the earliest blowback pistols.

Construction and Operation: Barrels in most models are screwed to the receiver and can be unscrewed after the locking screw has been removed. Recoil spring is housed within the sliding bolt and is compressed on the rearward movement of the bolt. The magazine is mounted ahead of the trigger guard and is provided with a hinged cover plate on the right side. Pushing the plate down exposes the magazine well for loading. The arm was intended to be loaded from a special clip holding 5 cartridges, inserted so the magazine follower arm within the magazine would push up against the bottom cartridge. Cartridges can be inserted singly by holding the pistol on its side. If a clip is used, after the magazine plate is swung back into place the clip is pulled out from below by its loop.

Pulling back the breechblock permits the follower spring to force the follower and the cartridges up into line. The breechblock is cut away for part of its length to permit a retaining pin to pass through and lock it to the receiver. This pin serves also as a compression point for the recoil spring which is mounted ahead of it, and acts as a stop to prevent the breechblock from being blown out to the rear. A gas escape hole is provided on the right side at the chamber to drop the breech pressure rapidly. When the hammer is cocked a thumb safety on the left side of the receiver may be set.

The lockwork is extremely simple, closely resembling that of a single action revolver. The mainspring is a flat spring mounted in the grip and so positioned that it catches in the hammer tumbler when the hammer is cocked to provide the driving force for forward movement of the hammer against the head of the long firing pin. The firing pin is not provided with a spring, but floats easily in its housing. Literally dozens of modifications of this pistol exist in special calibers 5 mm, 6.5 mm, 7.65 mm, 8 mm.

Chapter 5

Caliber .30 to 7.65mm

CARTRIDGE   7.62mm. Nagant
Data

As used by the Russians in World War II this cartridge has a metal packeted bullet weighing 108 grains, a powder load of 12.3 grains of smokeless powder and measures 1.53 inches overall. The actual bullet diameter is .350 inch. This is a special gas seal cartridge in which the bullet is seated entirely inside the brass cartridge case. The body of the case measures .356 inch near the head, .350 inch over the seated bullet, then tapers to .289 inch at the mouth.

Although there are standard revolvers chambered for this cartridge, it was specifically designed for revolvers in which the act of cocking the hammer also thrust the cylinder forward so the breech end of the barrel was enclosed by the end of the cartridge chamber to be fired, to minimize gas leakage at the joint.

In the standard Russian revolver with 4.3-inch barrel it develops a muzzle velocity of about 890 feet per second.

This cartridge is sometimes referred to as 7.5mm. caliber, but the official designation is 7.62mm. (.30).

NAGANT   7.62mm. Nagant
Gas Check

NAGANT 1895, showing details of special cartridge. Inset shows later Soviet weapon which is identical.

BASIC MODEL DATA

REVOLVER: *Russian Gas Check Nagant.*
LENGTH: *9.06 inches.*
BARREL: *4½ inches.*
WEIGHT: *1.65 pounds.*
TWIST: *Right Hand, 1 in 9.45 inches.*
CYLINDER: *7 Chambers.*
ACTION: *Single (a double is also made).*
EJECTION: *Rod.*
FRAME: *Solid.*
CALIBER: *7.62mm. Russian Gas Check.*

Left side cutaway showing details of mainspring, hand and resistance block. Loading gate whose upper end locks in edge of cylinder to prevent left rotation of cylinder when cocked is open and shown protruding below the hand.

NAGANT REVOLVER COCKED

Cylinder cutaway to show nature of cartridge and method of introducing its mouth into barrel as cylinder is thrust forward when hammer is cocked.

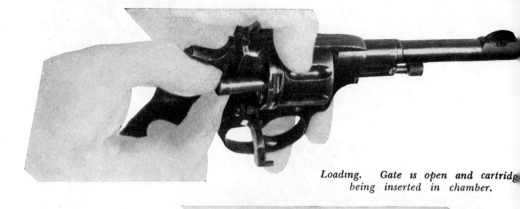

Loading. Gate is open and cartridge being inserted in chamber.

Unloading. Gate open. Extractor rod swung out on its collar being thrust up into chamber.

This unusual revolver was invented by a Belgian, Nagant, and was first adopted by the Russians in 1895. It has since been widely manufactured both in Belgium and Tula Arsenal in Russia, recent specimens bearing the Soviet Star and dates of 1938 and 1940 indicating its recent popularity among the Russian military.

Two models are made, a single action originally issued to enlisted men and a double-action originally an officer's revolver.

The Nagant weighs about 1.65 pounds and is fitted with a standard 4.33-inch barrel. The twist is right hand, one turn in 9.45 inches. It is of solid frame, rod ejector type. Opening the loading gate on the right side of the frame permits inserting cartridges in the chambers as the cylinder is revolved to receive them. The ejector rod below the barrel is not provided with a return spring as in the Colt Single Action Army. The cylinder must be revolved until each chamber is successively in line with the ejection slot. As a chamber is lined up, the ejector rod is pulled forward until it clears its seating in the frame. The rod is mounted on a movable arm attached to the barrel which permits it to be swung to the right into line with the chamber to be unloaded. When the rod is pushed back to unload the chamber, it must then be pulled forward to clear the cylinder before the next chamber can be brought into line for unloading. Capacity of the cylinder is 7 cartridges.

Functioning: The hammer is cocked in the standard single-action fashion by pulling back with the thumb on the comb of the hammer. The hammer nose, which is the hooked member at the lower end of the hammer below its axis pin, lifts the arm of the trigger thus causing the trigger to rotate on its axis pin. This forces the pawl (or hand) attached to the rear of the trigger to engage the ratchet at the end of the cylinder and by pushing it up to rotate the cylinder until the trigger stop directly below the rear of the cylinder snaps into the recess in the cylinder and halts the rotation.

The continued motion of the pawl as the hammer goes back, and the trigger action thus caused, transmits action to the pawl, exerting forward pawl thrust against the cylinder. The chamber in line with the barrel is thus forced over the end of the barrel which is beveled off to receive it.

The Nagant cartridge case extends *beyond the nose of the bullet* and therefore enters the rear end of the barrel. This bridges the junction between barrel and cylinder to minimize the escape of gas there.

Also as the hammer is being cocked, a trigger arm raises a resistance plate in the frame in line with the cartridge lined up to be fired, moving it in vertical grooves in the frame.

The top part of this resistance plate, striking against an angle of the breech piece which forms the top end of a lever pivoted at its bottom end, is thus pressed forward against the head of the cartridge to support it firmly.

The resistance plate continues to rise and makes a support for the rear face of the breech piece as the cartridge is fired.

Pressing the trigger pivots it on its pin to disengage it from the hammer and permits the hammer spring (which was compressed during cocking) to rotate the hammer forward on its pin. This fires the cartridge.

When the pressure of the trigger finger is released, the lower arm of the spring forces the trigger back to its normal position. The cylinder is pulled back off the barrel by the action of the spiral spring wound around its axis pin passing through the center of the cylinder. The trigger arm withdraws the resistance plate. As the trigger goes forward, it carries the pawl down with it ready to engage the next tooth on the ratchet to revolve the cylinder one chamber when the hammer is again cocked and also disengages from the locking recess in the cylinder.

Double-Action Nagant Gas Check Revolver

Except that a double-action cocking system is employed which permits the weapon to be fired either by pulling the hammer back by hand and then pressing the trigger or by direct pull through on the trigger itself, the action is the same as in the single-action Nagant Gas Check. A mechanical safety is built into these revolvers in the form of the resistance piece which, when the hammer has rebounded, prevents it from rotating. Rebounding of the hammer away from the face of the cartridge after firing is caused by an extension of the long arm of mainspring pressing against the shoulder of the hammer.

EFFECTIVENESS OF THE GAS SEAL

Shortly after the Nagant was introduced tests were made with 5½ and 11.8 inch barrels. With the shorter barrel the velocity was 1082 feet per second average, while with the 11.8-inch barrel velocity climbed to the then phenomenal figure of 1394 feet per second.

The same cartridges used in the standard type of revolver made by Pieper in Belgium gave a velocity of about 725 feet per second with the short barrel, while using the 11.8-inch barrel raised the velocity only about 30 feet per second.

American revolvers have always been made to far closer tolerances than any European revolvers, and the practical value of the gas seal in a Colt or Smith and Wesson is very questionable.

7.62mm. Nagant   **PIEPER**
                                                                                Gas Seal

A special gas seal revolver to shoot the Russian cartridge was designed in Belgium to overcome the slow loading feature of the Nagant. This Pieper revolver used a cylinder which swung out to the left on a crane in the fashion of American types.

It was necessary to administer the cylinder thrust in different fashion, of course. In this type as the hammer is cocked and exerts its pull on the trigger, an arm on the upper face of the trigger forces the cylinder ahead. A swinging brace operated by linkage from the hammer locks the cylinder in forward position.

This design was used in Russia but did not prove satisfactory. It was never manufactured in quantity.

7.62mm. Nagant   **PIEPER**
                                                                                Standard

BELGIAN PIEPER FOR RUSSIAN NAGANT CARTRIDGE
Note that this arm is standard solid frame and the cylinder revolves but is not thrust forward.
Barrel is stamped 7.62mm. Russe.

This revolver resembles the Nagant in exterior appearance, weight and dimensions. However, it is a standard solid frame rod ejector design double action revolver in which the cylinder is merely revolved on its axis pin without any forward movement.

MISCELLANEOUS   7.62 Nagant
Revolvers

This cartridge is quite popular in Europe, and Belgian, German and Spanish manufacturers all have manufactured revolvers for it. None are outstanding. As the cartridge is not manufactured in the United States and has little to recommend it, these European types should not be considered standard revolvers. Most of the European revolvers for this cartridge bear no manufacturer's name, hence it is impracticable to discuss them at length. The caliber may be encountered in rod-ejector, swing-out cylinder or hinge-frame design. In all these designs it occurs in both hammer and hammerless types, in both single and double action, and with all styles and lengths of barrels. Cylinder capacities vary from 5 to 9 cartridges.

7.62 Russian **CARTRIDGE**
Data

This cartridge must not be confused with the 7.62mm. Russian Revolver cartridge which it in no way resembles. This is a cartridge adopted for use in submachine guns and automatic pistols in 1930.

While officially the Tokarev is designed for the Russians 7.62 mm., it also uses the standard Mauser 7.63 mm. pistol cartridge.

All captured German handbooks instruct that this cartridge may be used in the Russian pistol. Actual tests of Mauser ammunition in it show that except for somewhat stiffer recoil it shoots equally as well as the cartridge issued by the Russians. Some prewar U. S. ammunition may not chamber.

The 7.63 mm. Mauser cartridge as used and manufactured in the United States prior to the war developed 1420 feet per second in a five and one-half-inch barrel. The bullet weighed 85 grains, and developed about 400 ft.-lbs. energy, with a penetration of eleven inches in pine.

DWM and other European cartridges, as well as some American, are also issued with soft-point bullets weighing from 85 to 90 grains. Velocities range from 1330 to 1600 feet per second with some of these cartridges; velocity varying with barrel length and powder lot.

7.62 Russian **TOKAREV**
Automatic

This weapon originally introduced in 1930, is a Russian modification of the original Colt-Browning automatic pistol design. It is called the Tokarev—after its designer. A modified design was introduced in 1933.

It was designed for mass manufacture and is cheaper, simpler, and easier to, make than the comparable United States and Belgian types of Brownings and Colts.

While the over-all design of the Colt has been quite closely copied, modifications have been made to simplify the working mechanism and to make the original strong design even stronger where advisable.

Construction: The principal parts of this weapon are the receiver, barrel, slide, receiver subassembly, and magazine.

The slide is the Colt (Browning) type machined at the front end to permit the barrel to emerge; also machined to receive and lock a barrel bushing which surrounds the barrel on top and serves to keep the recoil spring and plug in place at the front end below the barrel.

The rear end of this slide is machined to form the breech and to hold the extractor and firing pin units.

Suitable guides are machined on the receiver to permit it to take the slide which travels back and forth in it; and also to receive *the receiver subassembly.* The rearward travel of the slide is stopped as in the case of the Colt when the lower part of the slide abuts against the receiver stop extending forward above the line of the trigger guard.

A steel subassembly fits into the receiver proper. It is provided with two arms of unequal length, that on the right being longer. The *outsides* of these arms line up with the regular receiver guides to direct the travel of the slide backward and forward.

158

The *inside surfaces* of these arms are grooved to serve as cartridge guides to facilitate feeding into the chamber as each cartridge is successively stripped from between the very flat lips of the magazine.

This is a very important development. Machining the feed guides, in a firm steel surface, instead of depending on the folded-over lips of an inherently weak box magazine as is done in most automatic pistols, *assures elimination of jams caused by improper feeding.*

When it is remembered that most automatic pistol jams are occasioned by feed trouble, and that most feed trouble stems from bulged or injured magazine lips, follower or split magazine case, the desirability of this Russian system of feeding will be at once apparent.

The subassembly comprises a single block machined and drilled to accommodate the hammer mechanism.

This hammer mechanism includes the hammer proper, which has a hole drilled in it *from below* to permit a coil mainspring or hammer spring to be inserted in it, a hole for the hammer axis pin and a half-cock and full-cock notch.

The sear and Colt-type disconnector are attached with the one pin as in the case of the Colt. A small flat sear spring is mounted in the notch in the sear.

This subassembly block is drilled through with three holes. (1) The large center hole through which the hammer axis pin is inserted; (2) a smaller hole just below through which passes the pin on which the sear and disconnector is mounted; and (3) a hole housing a special pin on which the bottom of the coil spring inside the hammer rests and above which the circular cut at the lower end of the hammer slides during the rotary cocking motion. (This third pin provides the lower compression point for the mainspring.)

During the rearward rotary motion of the hammer, the spring inside the hammer is compressed between its chamber at the top of the hammer and this pin at the bottom.

The sear spring is a small flat spring attached directly to the sear itself. It may be removed. Normally, however, it locks firmly in a notch in the sear.

A hole is drilled on the right-hand side of this subassembly block to permit inspection and oiling of the sear and the hammer notch without dismounting the subassembly.

The disconnector resembles the Colt quite closely. In action it is rather simpler, however.

The bottom end of the disconnector normally rides on top of the trigger stirrup when the pistol is ready to fire. This forces its upper end into a slot machined on the underside of the firing pin housing section of the breechblock.

When the bottom of the disconnector rests on the top of the trigger stirrup and the upper end protrudes into its notch in the bottom of the breechblock, the sear attached by the same pin as the disconnector is lifted into contact with the rear of the trigger stirrup. Thus as the trigger is squeezed, it can force directly back against the sear. As the upper end of the sear is engaged with the notch in the hammer holding it back, action of the trigger thus frees the end of the sear from engagement and permits the hammer spring (or main-

159

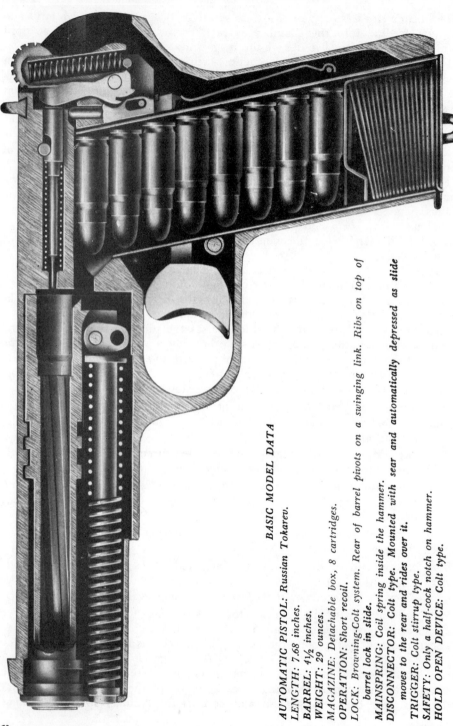

BASIC MODEL DATA

AUTOMATIC PISTOL: Russian Tokarev.
LENGTH: 7.68 inches.
BARREL: 4½ inches.
WEIGHT: 29 ounces.
MAGAZINE: Detachable box, 8 cartridges.
OPERATION: Short recoil.
LOCK: Browning-Colt system. Rear of barrel pivots on a swinging link. Ribs on top of barrel lock in slide.
MAINSPRING: Coil spring inside the hammer.
DISCONNECTOR: Colt type. Mounted with sear and automatically depressed as slide moves to the rear and rides over it.
TRIGGER: Colt stirrup type.
SAFETY: Only a half-cock notch on hammer.
HOLD OPEN DEVICE: Colt type.

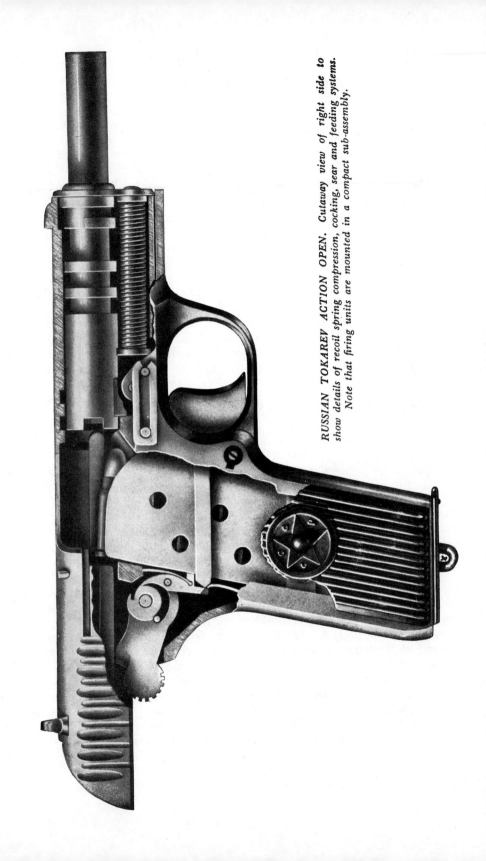

RUSSIAN TOKAREV ACTION OPEN. Cutaway view of right side to show details of recoil spring compression, cocking, sear and feeding systems. Note that firing units are mounted in a compact sub-assembly.

spring) to rotate the hammer on its axis pin and drive forward to strike the flying firing pin housed in the breechblock end of the slide.

Operation: As the cartridge is fired, the slide and barrel start back firmly locked together exactly as in the case of the Colt Government Model, by the locking sections of the barrel ribs engaging at the top in corresponding recesses on the inside of the slide. The barrel is positioned by the barrel bushing at the front end and is attached to the receiver at the rear by a swinging link attached to the lug on the barrel below the breech. Thus barrel and slide travel to the rear fully locked during the moment of high breech pressure.

The bottom of the link on the barrel is fastened to the slide stop pin which passes through it and through the receiver. This causes the rear end of the barrel to be pulled down out of engagement with the slide after short locked travel. Barrel movement stops when it strikes against the barrel stop machined into the receiver.

The recoil spring below the barrel is compressed over its guide as the slide goes back. The extractor set in the face of the breechblock section of the slide draws the empty cartridge case out of the barrel and carries it back until the rearward motion is about complete, when it strikes it against the ejector mounted in the receiver which causes the empty shell to be hurled out the right-hand side of the pistol through the ejection port which is now fully open.

At the first motion to the rear of the slide, a sloped base on the lower breechblock section of the slide above the disconnector forces the head of the disconnector down into the receiver below the line of the slide.

As the sear is mounted on the same pin as the disconnector, this downward movement of the disconnector carries the sear down with it.

The initial rearward thrust of the slide drives the hammer back to roll on its axis pin and compress the spring contained within it. The slide as it goes back to full-open position rides over the head of the hammer. The tip of the sear is now in position to catch in the full-cock notch in the hammer and hold it securely as the slide goes forward to closed position.

Since the lower end of the disconnector has been forced down below the level of the top of the stirrup, *it is impossible for another shot to be fired until pressure on the trigger is released.*

The recoil spring draws the slide fully home (stripping a cartridge from between the feed arms of the receiver subassembly where it has risen above the magazine below), chambers it and snaps the extractor into the extracting groove of the case; the breechblock section thrusts the barrel forward so that it swings up on its link and the upper surfaces of the locking lugs on it lock securely in their recesses in the underside of the slide. The niche in the underside of the breechblock is then directly above the line of the head of the disconnector, which rises into it under spring tension.

While the disconnector and the sear are fastened together by the same center pin, the hole in the sear is just large enough to receive the pin; while the hole in the disconnector is an elongated one which permits the disconnector to be forced up or down on the pin so that it can protrude above the line of the receiver into the niche on the underside of the breechblock and can also be forced down by rearward action of the slide on the opening movement.

The trigger spring is a flat spring mounted in the rear of the grip, anchored in a slot near the bottom, its rear end resting against the bar which connects the two arms of the trigger stirrup.

Thus when the trigger is released, this flat spring which is under tension, reasserts itself and pushes the trigger forward to firing position. This action permits the disconnector to come into its proper place on top of the stirrup, at which point the stirrup can effect contact with the sear and a pull on the trigger will again fire the weapon.

The extractor is a typical Colt type but is mounted and fixed by a pin in the breechblock.

The firing pin is of the flying type with a coil spring surrounding it. It is very simply fixed in its well in the slide by a split pin. A hole is drilled through the slide laterally and a section of the top of the firing pin is notched out. When the pin is held in its hole under tension, driving this split pin through the slide hole forces it through this notch on the firing pin. This secures the firing pin in place and also limits the length of its forward and rearward travel as it is first driven forward by the hammer blow and then pulled back into the breech-block by the spring which has been coiled by the action of the hammer blow driving the firing pin itself ahead.

The magazine in this weapon is of very interesting design. While in general it follows the standard tubular form of the Colt-Browning magazine, it is of simple and efficient design in that it can be speedily dismounted for cleaning or repairs.

The magazine follower (the platform on which the first cartridge rests) is split as in the case of the Colt Government Model. The lower arm pushes up the slide stop when the last cartridge has been fired as in the case of the Colt, to force the slide stop into a niche in the slide and hold the slide back ready for reloading.

The magazine differs from the Colt type in that its bottom has grooves in it to receive the magazine base plate which can be slid in from the front. While the magazine spring presses against the follower above it, it does not, as is usual in magazines, rest on the magazine base plate. There is a false bottom on which it rests, which has a nib which protrudes through a hole in the magazine base plate itself.

Pushing in this nib against spring tension above it raises the false base plate enough and unlocks it from the base plate to permit the magazine bottom to be pushed forward in its grooves out of the magazine case. The false base plate, magazine spring, and magazine follower may then be removed.

Another interesting design feature in this weapon is to be found in the barrel slots, which instead of being machined only on the top of the barrel as in the case of the Colt, are simply turned around the entire circumference of the barrel. While only the upper sections engage in the recesses in the slide exactly as in the case of the Colt, the machining of the barrel is greatly simplified by this manufacturing system.

Instead of the customary horseshoe-shaped bushing used in the Colt, the Tokarev uses a heavily forged bushing with a large hole at top through which the barrel protrudes and a smaller one below through which a steel disc which is fastened at the end of the recoil spring seats firmly.

The magazine release catch, which locks the magazine in place much as in the case of the Colt Government Model, passes through the receiver to the rear of the trigger guard from the left-hand side. It is to be noted that *it is a split pin device* with a small coil retracting spring mounted about it. At the right side of the receiver it passes through a housing and expands to hold it firmly in place. It also serves to retain the trigger which may be lifted out when this release catch is punched out of the weapon from the right-hand side of the receiver.

Additional machining on the receiver has been saved in this weapon by the system of locking the slide stop pin which passes through the receiver and through the link attached to the lug at the bottom of the barrel. A pin is mounted on the right side of the receiver above the line of the trigger and a simple spring clip with two locking jaws is slid over this pin. As the slide stop pin emerges being pushed through from the left-hand side, locking ends on this spring clip snap over and catch into niches in the end of the protruding pin when the clip is pushed forward.

The hammer is of the "burr" type. While this is not at all satisfactory from the American standpoint because of the difficulty in gripping it for cocking, it is much favored in some areas of Europe.

Note that this weapon has no thumb safety and no grip safety. It has a half-cock notch in the hammer, however.

The front sight is machined onto the top of the slide while the rear sight is slid into a niche in the slide and may be adjusted laterally.

Dismounting: Dismounting this weapon is very simple.

First, press the magazine release catch and withdraw the magazine. Then draw the slide back and check to be sure there is no cartridge in the firing chamber.

With the nose of a cartridge or the tip of the magazine bottom, push the recoil spring button where it protrudes through the small hole below the muzzle of the barrel and compress it until it is below the line of the barrel bushing. Then swing the barrel bushing up until its locking lugs disengage from their slots in the slide.

Ease out the recoil spring and turn the bushing up until it can be pulled out of the slide.

Now pull back the spring clip on the right side of the receiver to release the slide stop pin.

Pull the slide stop pin out from the left-hand side of the receiver.

The barrel, slide and recoil spring may now be pushed forward out of their guides in the receiver.

The recoil spring and its guide may be withdrawn.

Push the link forward as far as it will go and the barrel may be pushed out the front of the weapon.

164

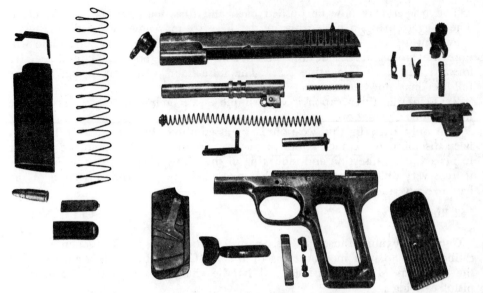

RUSSIAN TOKAREV 7.62mm. COMPLETELY STRIPPED. Note that while it closely resembles the Colt in many ways, it is simpler and has fewer parts.

Punch out the firing-pin retaining pin, from the right-hand side of the slide. (Hold a hand over the end of the slide when this is done to prevent the firing pin and spring from flying out the rear.) The extractor may now be punched out.

The receiver subassembly may be lifted directly up out of the receiver. This should not be dismounted unless required. While it can be done without tools, the spring tension is quite strong and difficulty may be encountered in reassembling the mainspring.

If the pin at the lower left side of the assembly is driven out, the disconnector and sear and sear spring attached to it will drop out. Driving out the hammer axis pin will permit the hammer to be withdrawn and the mainspring to be lifted out of the hammer. It is not necessary to remove the third pin on which the mainspring rests.

The grips are unusual in that they are fastened with turn-button latches operated from the inside.

If a pencil, piece of wood, or a screw driver is inserted into the handle from below, the latch on the left-hand stock may be turned. This will revolve the spring steel locking arm which is pivoted on a pin riveted through the grip. This will disengage the two spring arms from the sides of the receiver and permit the stock to be lifted off.

The turn-button latch on the right-hand stock may now be turned and that one lifted off also.

Punching the split-pin magazine release catch through from the right-hand side of the receiver will bring it out with its return spring and permit removal of the bushing in which it is housed.

165

The trigger may now be pushed back and drawn up through the receiver. The trigger spring, a flat spring inside the grip, may now be lifted out.

Pressing up on the protruding nib in the bottom of the magazine plate will raise the false plate inside and permit the magazine bottom plate to be slid forward out of the magazine case. The false floor plate, the spring, and the follower may now come out.

Reassembling this weapon is very simple and merely calls for reversal of the instructions given above.

The only trick in this weapon is in assembling the subassembly if it has been dismounted. Unless a tool of the proper size is used to hold the hammer in place during insertion and mounting of the mainspring against the pin below it, it is very difficult to center the hammer properly to permit insertion of the hammer axis and retaining pin.

7.62 Russian

MISCELLANEOUS
Weapons

Genuine 7.63mm Mauser pistols, Spanish imitations of the Mauser in 7.63mm. caliber, and Spanish modifications of the .45 Colt Auto when chambered for the 7.63 mm Mauser cartridge will handle the 7.62 mm Russian automatic pistol cartridge.

Some American-made ammunition of 7.63mm Mauser caliber made prior to the organization of the Sporting Arms and Ammunition Manufacturers Institute, and occasionally available in gun stores, had case body dimensions tight for many Mausers and for most Tokarevs. Such ammunition may also be difficult to chamber in Spanish pistols. If this difficulty is encountered, try a competing brand of ammunition.

CARTRIDGE
Data

.30 Mauser

.30 Mauser

86 Gr. M.C.

Muzzle Velocity in f.s.:   1420
Vel. at 50 Feet: 1350
Vel. at 150 Feet: 1232
Calculated Energy
Muzzle Energy in ft.-lbs.:   385
Energy at 50 Feet: 349
Energy at 150 Feet: 290
Calculated Drop
At 50 Feet: .27 inch
At 150 Feet: 2.5 inches
At 300 Feet: 11.3 inches
Penetration at 15 Feet
7/8" soft pine boards: 11
Length of Barrel in Which Tested
inches: 5.5
Shell Case
Weight: 68.5 grains

Max. Length: .990 inch
Outside Body Dia. at Head, Max.: .388 inch
Outside Body Dia. at Neck, Max.: .333 inch
Inside Mouth Dia. Max.:   .3075 inch
Volumetric Capacity to Base of Bullet
   in cubic inches: .058
Bullet
Weight: 86 grains
Approx. Length: .580 inch
Diameter Max.:   .309 inch
Area, Cross Sectional: .0749 square inch
Shape: M.C. Round Nose
Powder
Amount and type varies with different
lots manufactured.
Cartridge
Approx. Length, Loaded: 1.360 inches
Approx. Total Weight, Loaded: 165 grains

167

7.63mm. Mauser

MAUSER
Military

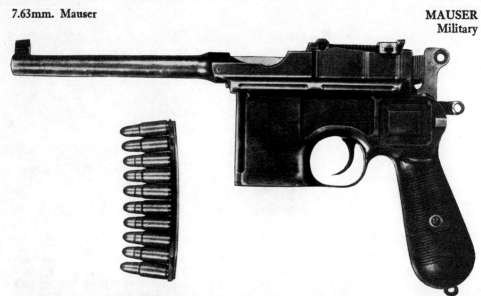

TYPICAL 7.63mm. MAUSER MILITARY. The cartridges are stripped into the magazine through the top when the bolt is drawn to the rear as in the Springfield rifle. Pulling the clip out lets the bolt go forward to chamber a cartridge ready for firing.

Construction and Operation: The barrel and barrel extension in this weapon are one piece. The bolt, in which is housed the firing pin and its spring travels inside the barrel extension. The extractor is a short spring claw mounted in the top of the bolt.

At the instant of discharge, the bolt lock positioned in the receiver has its two upper locking teeth securely in the underside of bolt. The barrel, barrel extension, and bolt are thus securely locked.

As the bullet starts down the barrel, the rearward action of the gas pressure forces the locked barrel, barrel extension, bolt and lock straight to the rear about two-tenths of an inch. Grooves in the barrel extension permit it to travel a short distance in its mount in the receiver. The energy transmitted through the head of the bolt to the hammer throws the hammer back on its axis until it is caught in the full-cock notch and held by the sear.

After this short travel, the lower rear projection (or tongue) of the locking block enters a rear recess machined out of the receiver, and under pressure from the coiled mainspring below (which is compressed by the cocking motion), the claw of the coupling directly above the trigger in the receiver *pulls the locking block down* out of its two niches in the underside of the bolt.

At this point the barrel is stopped in its rearward action when the block comes in contact with the receiver.

The bolt continues its rearward travel in its guide in the barrel extension. The spring extractor in the bolt head pulls the empty case out of the chamber and carries it back until it strikes against a projection on the receiver which extends up into the bolt way. This ejects the empty case up through the top of the weapon.

MAUSER
Military

As the bolt moves back it compresses the recoil spring which is situated between the closed head of the bolt and the abutment which locks into the barrel extension. This stores up energy to return the bolt to closed position on the forward movement of the action.

As the empty case is ejected, the spring inside the magazine pushing against the follower forces the next cartridge up into line with the bolt.

Also during this rearward motion, the disconnector mounted directly above and behind the trigger in the receiver is forced back; and it in turn forces the sear lever around the trigger to prevent full automatic fire.

As the short powerful recoil spring drives the bolt forward, the bolt picks up the cartridge in line and chambers it. The extractor slips over the extracting groove in the cartridge case.

When the head of the bolt reaches the face of the chamber, pressure from the coil mainspring is transmitted through the plunger at its forward end to force the claw of the coupling to turn *forward* and force the barrel assembly forward to complete firing position.

While this is happening, the tongue of the locking block is forced up the ramp on top of the receiver and swings the locking block upwards until its teeth engage with their recesses in the underside of the bolt to complete the locking.

The trigger cannot engage the disconnector until this locking motion is completed. The point of the firing pin is withdrawn behind the face of the bolt by a coil spring around its length.

When the trigger is pressed, it engages the disconnector above and behind it which lifts the sear from its notch in the hammer. This permits the compressed mainspring to rotate the hammer on its axis and send it forward to drive the flying firing pin forward against the primer of the cartridge locked in the firing chamber.

When the last cartridge in the weapon has been fired, a projection on the magazine follower (the platform on which the cartridge rests) is forced up by the magazine spring in line with the bolt, holding the bolt open.

Loading and Firing: This weapon is loaded from a clip which contains ten cartridges. Load as follows:

Cock the hammer.

Grip the bolt wings on either side of the bolt and pull the bolt back as far as it will go. It will stay open.

Insert either end of the loaded clip into the feed grooves on the barrel extension.

Place a thumb over the top cartridge case and push the ten cartridges straight down into the box magazine below. They will feed in a double staggered row.

When the clip is pulled out, the bolt will go forward automatically and load the firing chamber.

To unload: Keeping the firing finger well outside the trigger guard, grip the bolt wings securely and pull the bolt to the rear sharply. This will eject the cartridge in the firing chamber. Repeat this motion until the bolt is held open by the empty magazine follower.

169

BASIC MODEL DATA

AUTOMATIC PISTOL: German Mauser Military.

LENGTH: About 12 inches.

BARREL: 5.5 standard.

WEIGHT: 43 ounces.

MAGAZINE: Fixed box, 10 cartridges loaded through top of action from clip.

OPERATION: Short recoil.

LOCK: Bolt lock from below has teeth which engage in recesses in bolt. Bolt travels in extension which is part of barrel forging and lock is cammed down out of engagement as barrel travel halts.

MAINSPRING: Coil operating through plunger.

DISCONNECTOR: Positive type prevents firing more than one shot per trigger pull.

TRIGGER: Pivot type, engaging with sear.

SAFETY: Thumb piece on left side of receiver.

HOLD OPEN DEVICE: Bolt held back by rising magazine follower when last shot is fired.

CALIBER: 7.63 mm. Mauser (also made in Mauser 9 mm. Special and 9 mm. Luger).

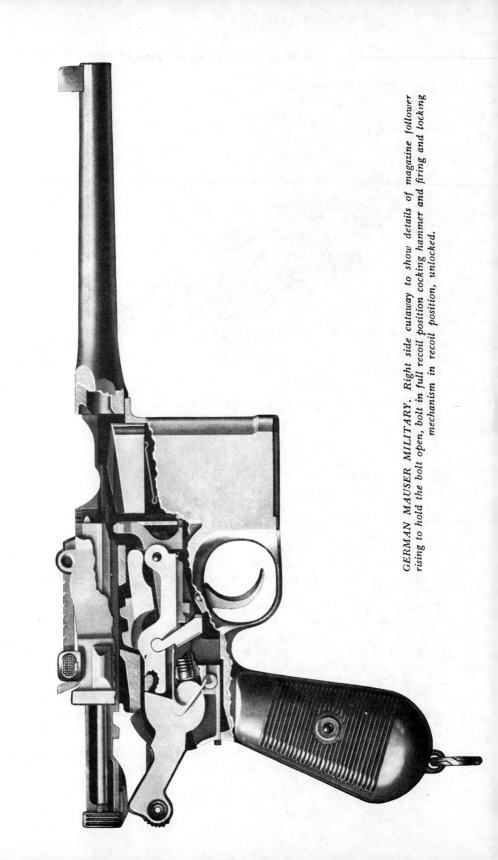

GERMAN MAUSER MILITARY. Right side cutaway to show details of magazine follower rising to hold the bolt open, bolt in full recoil position cocking hammer and firing and locking mechanism in recoil position, unlocked.

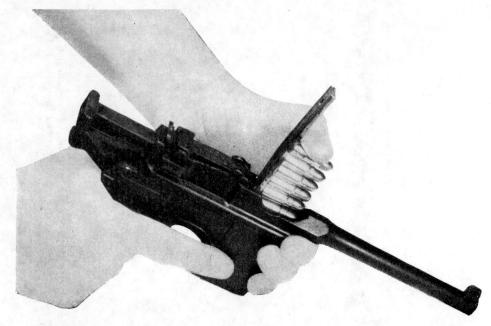

LOADING THE MAUSER MILITARY. Cartridges being stripped into magazine.

To close the action when the pistol is empty, grip the bolt firmly with thumb and finger of one hand and with a finger of the other hand depress the magazine follower. While holding the magazine follower down, ease the bolt forward over the follower and then let it slide forward.

Setting the Safety: All models of this Mauser military pistol are equipped with a manual thumb safety at the left rear of the receiver. This safety may be applied whether the hammer is up or down.

On models of this weapon issued prior to 1930, the safety is set by pressing the hammer down with the thumb of the pistol hand and raising the safety lever with the thumb of the other hand.

On model 1930 and later, (factory numbers over 800,000) these pistols have an improved universal safety lock. This may be operated by the thumb of the pistol hand alone. The lever must be pushed until it clicks into the correct notch. When it is at safe (which is the vertical position of the lever) the letter "S" can be seen on the lever. When the lever is down and the weapon is ready to fire, the letter "F" may be seen on the lever.

The universal safety on these new models is a definite advance in that the hammer is completely locked by a lug from striking the firing pin, thus permitting the hammer to be lowered in absolute safety under all conditions.

Dismounting: 1. A plunger protrudes below the magazine just ahead of the trigger guard. Push this in with the point of a cartridge or screw driver and

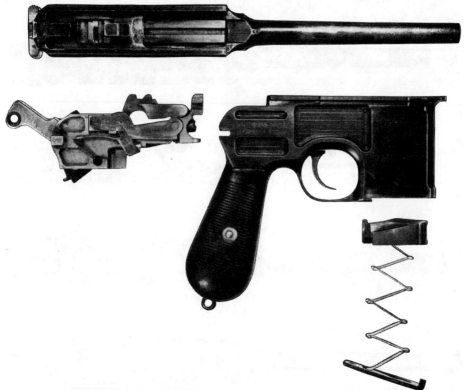

MAUSER MILITARY FIELD STRIPPED. Note that barrel and barrel extension are a single forging which mounts on the receiver. Lockwork does not use pins, or screws. All parts interlock. This assembly slides into the receiver from the rear. Magazine parts are easily removed.

the magazine floor plate may be slid off towards the muzzle. The magazine spring and the magazine follower may then be withdrawn from the pistol.

2. With the hammer cocked, hold the pistol in the left hand with the muzzle resting on a table or some other support and with a screw driver or a cartridge clip lift up the latch which protrudes above the grip and directly below the hammer. Push down on the receiver with the left hand and the barrel, barrel extension, and lockwork may be slid off the receiver.

3. To dismount the lock assembly, hold the barrel extension in the left hand with the lockwork upwards and with the right hand pull the lock assembly up and off the barrel group. The locking block can then be lifted out. The units of the lockwork can now be separated.

4. To dismount the barrel assembly, insert the blade of a small screw driver or some similar instrument into the slot of the firing pin. Push the pin forward and twist one-quarter turn to the right. This will release the recoil spring which will protrude from the block and can be removed. Push the recoil spring abutment towards the muzzle and draw it out to the right from its seating. The bolt and recoil spring can then be withdrawn.

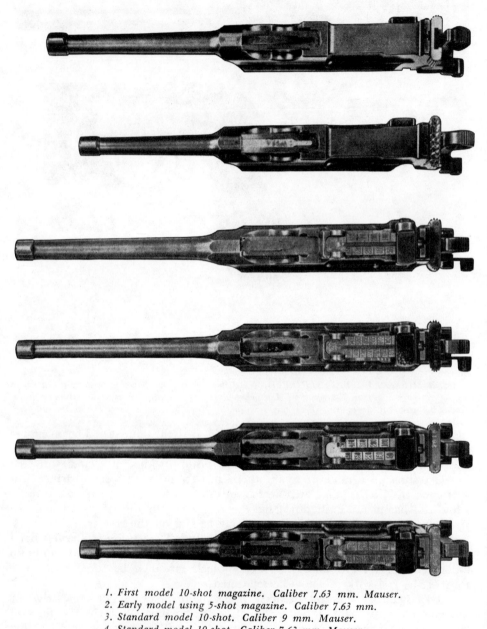

1. *First model 10-shot magazine. Caliber 7.63 mm. Mauser.*
2. *Early model using 5-shot magazine. Caliber 7.63 mm.*
3. *Standard model 10-shot. Caliber 9 mm. Mauser.*
4. *Standard model 10-shot. Caliber 7.63 mm. Mauser.*
5. *War model 10-shot. Caliber 9 mm. Luger.*
6. *Postwar I model 10-shot Bolo type. Caliber 7.63 mm.*

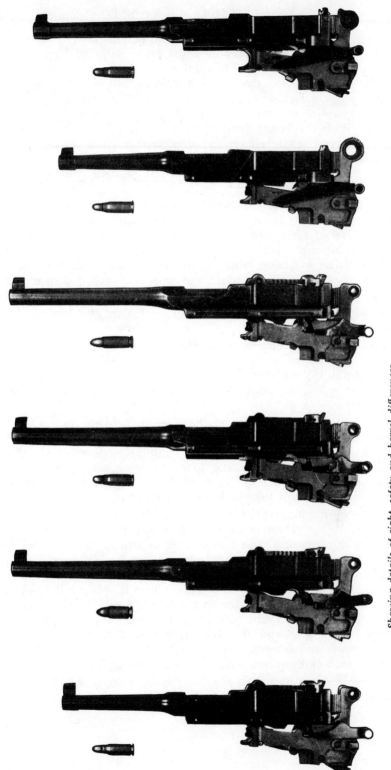

Showing details of sight, safety and barrel differences.
Barrels, bolts and lockwork removed to show comparison of slight changes made throughout
50 years of manufacture.

5. To strip the lock assembly on this weapon, put the safety lever midway between safe and fire, where it may be lifted out. Ease the hammer down by pressing on the disconnector. Then raise and lift out the retaining latch. Holding the lockwork on a table or other solid surface, with the hammer downward, place screw driver or cleaning rod crosswise on the plunger and press firmly. The coupling can now be stripped out. Remove the mainspring with its plunger. Push the longer limb of the hammer pin spring toward the sear with screw driver. This relieves the disconnector from the pressure of the spring permitting it to be removed. Turn the sear upward and lift it out. The hammer pin may be pressed out from left to right with the safety lever and the hammer removed.

Assembling: To assemble the barrel group, replace the recoil spring in the bolt and insert the bolt in the barrel extension with the extractor uppermost. Compress the recoil spring with screw driver or cleaning rod so that the abutment can be inserted with its sleeve to the front from the right into its place in the barrel extension where it will lock. Insert the firing pin and its spring, press in with the screw driver and twist one-quarter turn to the left.

2. To replace the locking block, pull the block with its claw toward the muzzle and its locking piece toward the bolt and hook over the lug on the barrel extension.

3. To reassemble the coupling and barrel assemblies, place the lock assembly on the locking block so the claw of the block is forward of the coupling and the tongue lies in the unlocking recess of the lock spring. Press the lock frame and the barrel extension firmly together with both thumbs and they will snap into engagement.

4. To replace the moving parts in the receiver, hold the receiver in the left hand, press the barrel and locked groups lightly together with the right hand and slide them into the receiver until the retaining latch snaps into place. To reassemble the magazine, insert the follower, being sure that the hold-open stud is to the rear. Insert the spring, press the locking pin inward and slide the floor plate backward until the pin locks it in its place.

To reassemble the lockwork, first replace the hammer and insert the hammer pin from the right. Then replace the mainspring with its plunger on each end. Holding the lock firm with the hammer downward against a solid surface while a screw driver is held across the plunger, press the plunger in firmly and with the other hand insert the coupling hook downward, *concave side outward* and press lightly on the trunnions to seat it into its place. Replace the sear. Insert the disconnector. Place the lockwork on a table with the hammer to the right and pointing toward you, press the *longer limb* of the hammer pin spring toward the sear and the disconnector may be slipped into its seat Cock the hammer and insert the safety lever until its lower limb is about midway between each end position. Replace the retaining latch.

This pistol is very unusual in that no screws are used anywhere in it. All parts are coupled or are seated by bayonet-joint assembling or by mutual interlocking.

MAUSER
7.63mm. Mauser

Military Imitations

About 1920 several Spanish factories and assembly plants began issuing quantities of imitations of the Military Mauser to supply Chinese and South American markets. It must be emphasized that none of these is an *exact copy* of the Mauser, though all resemble it so closely in exterior appearance that it is possible to confuse them with the original. The manufacture of these weapons centered very largely around the two Spanish cities of Eibar and Guernica. The closest Spanish approach to the Mauser is the Azul pistol. This is manufactured at Eibar by Eulogio Arrosteguie. Where the barrel and barrel extension of the Mauser form one piece, the barrel on the Azul is a separate unit shrunk into the barrel extension. The magazine is a 10-shot box which is released for withdrawal from the bottom of the magazine housing by a retaining catch on the right side. (This spring catch feature is employed in the Mauser machine pistol.) Where the bolt lock in the genuine Mauser is fitted in, in the Azul it is retained by a pin to the barrel extension; its locking and unlocking operation follow those of the Mauser, however. The lockwork and disconnector are of somewhat different design from that of the Mauser and are *not* interchangeable with Mauser parts.

The Astra "Model 900" was marketed in 1928, shortly after the appearance of the improved Model 1926 Mauser pistol. At a quick glance it looks exactly like the Mauser. However, if it is observed closely it will be noted that there is a removable side plate on the left side, provided to oil and repair the action. Just below the rear of the barrel extension in the Astra is a polished pin which when the lower edge of the safety lever is turned until it is opposite the cuts on the side plate can be pulled out to the left. The side plate may now be slid out to the rear from the receiver. The lockwork is entirely different from the Mauser. A separate barrel return spring is used in the Astra. The barrel is fitted into the extension and is not a part of it as in the case of the Mauser. As in the case of the Azul, the bolt lock is pinned to the barrel extension.

The barrel return spring is housed in a shallow depression below the barrel, the main part resting in a tunnel in front of the magazine. It is a coil spring. Much of the operating mechanism of this pistol is fastened with pins and the side plate serves to keep them in place. The mainspring in the Astra is mounted in the rear part of the receiver under the grip. Where the coil mainspring in the Mauser also serves as a part of the functioning of the breechwork, that in the Astra does not. This is a weapon of good design and manufacture.

Another Spanish imitation is marketed under the name of "Royal." This weapon follows very closely the general construction of the Astra. However, where the Astra appears only in a 5½" barrel length, this weapon is made in barrel lengths of 5¼, 6¼ and 7⅛". Beside the 10-shot removable box magazine provided with the Astra, the Royal also comes equipped with a 20-shot box magazine projecting far below the bottom of the magazine casing.

Some pistols resembling the standard Model 1926 Military Mauser are equipped with a switch on the *left* side plate for full automatic fire. As made by Mauser these were called "Schnell-Feuer-Pistole" and were extensively used by SS troops. The Spanish Astra equivalent of this pistol is the Model 902 Astra Machine Pistol, which has the change lever mounted on the *right* side of the receiver. The Spanish "Super Azul" imitation has a lever on the *left* side of the receiver.

7.63mm. Mauser   **SCHWARZLOSE**
                                                                                      1898

Barrel length: 6 inches (exclusive   *Weight:*   23½ ounces
   of ½-inch locking space at   *Caliber:* 7.63 mm. *(not safe to use*
   breech.)   *with modern 7.63 mm. Mauser*
Over-all Length: .. .. 10¾ inches   *ammunition)*

Andrea Schwarzlose was an Austrian, and one of the world's outstanding developers and inventors of basic weapons. His was one of the original forms of the successful locked breech, short-recoil-operated pistols. It is a long and rather awkward weapon, but has built into it all the essentials of a fine self-operating weapon.

We are particularly concerned here with the locking system which Schwarzlose designed for this pistol.

The barrel is machined to permit it to slide forward and backward in the receiver for the distance of the unlocking motion, which in this weapon is about .47 inch.

The front sight is machined on the muzzle end of the barrel.

The construction of the rear end of the barrel is particularly noteworthy in that it serves some of the purposes of a receiver since it has a space of about one-half inch behind the chamber in which are locking recesses into which lugs on the bolt lock when the weapon is fully closed.

The breechblock is in the form of a cylinder with a cocking piece projecting through the rear. This weapon has a striker, as in the case of a rifle of the Springfield type, instead of the conventional hammer. The striker spring is a coil spring inside the bolt which is compressed around the striker in the bolt.

The front end of the breechblock has four lugs, two on top being set at right angles and the other two at 60 degree angles to the top lugs. The breechblock cylinder is the same diameter as the exterior of the firing chamber. The striker and striker spring (which is also the recoil spring in this pistol) are quite thick and require a hole of large diameter in the breechblock.

The rear of the breechblock is closed by a guide ring pinned to the receiver. In this there is a rectangular slot to receive the striker. A slot is machined on the underside of the breechblock. This slot runs straight back for about half the bolt length and from there on twists to the left in a helical groove. As the guide ring moves in this slot, when the breechblock goes back it travels first in a straight line and then twists sharply from left to right.

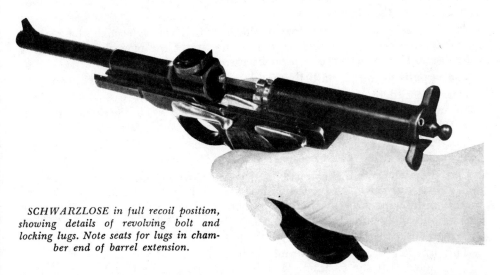

SCHWARZLOSE in full recoil position, showing details of revolving bolt and locking lugs. Note seats for lugs in chamber end of barrel extension.

Operation: The knob on the striker protruding through the rear of the breechblock is drawn straight back to its full extent. This piece will revolve as the outer breechblock surface moves straight back in its guide in the receiver. Cartridges are then stripped down into the magazine in the handle from a clip as in the case of the Mauser pistol; or the magazine may be inserted from below and pushed up into the handle. The magazine catch is pushed forward to release the magazine.

This pistol is the first one commercially made which provides an arrangement whereby the magazine follower pushes up a catch to hold the weapon open when the last shot has been fired.

As the breechblock is released to go forward and drive a cartridge from the top of the magazine into the firing chamber, the guide ring traveling in the curved slot twists the bolt so that the head of it is rotated until the four locking

179

lugs lock firmly in their recesses in the barrel directly behind the chamber. The barrel return spring is mounted directly below the chamber section of the barrel and also acts as the trigger spring.

When the trigger is pressed, the rear arm of the trigger is forced upward to release the sear from its resting place in a projection on the barrel locking pin.

The compressed spring inside the breechblock drives the striker forward to fire the cartridge.

As the bullet goes down the barrel, the locked barrel and breechblock start to the rear firmly locked together. The breechblock as it slides on the guide ring travels straight back during the moment of high breech pressure in the straight cuts in the underside of the breechblock. As the guide ring strikes against the curved section of this slot, the *breechblock is rotated* so that the locking lugs disengage from their seat in the barrel behind the chamber. At this point the rearward action of the barrel is halted and it is driven forward by a recoil spring above and ahead of the trigger guard which has been compressed during this rearward motion.

As the breechblock is now free of the barrel, it travels straight back in its guides in the receiver, moving back over the top of the magazine to permit a cartridge to rise to be picked up on its forward travel.

It also pulls to the rear a bell crank lever which is both sear and extractor.

Near the end of the rearward travel of the bolt, as the spring within it is compressed, a lug on the lower bolt surface pulls the ejector back causing it to rise up and strike the empty cartridge case sharply enough to eject it.

The rear sight is mounted on the rear of the barrel over the locking recesses. It is graduated from 100 to 500 meters and is of unusual design.

Like the early Mannlicher pistol, this weapon, will chamber the current 7.63 mm. Mauser cartridge. The recoil will be very violent, however, and as the parts in this pistol are finely machined but not of very great thickness, good functioning will not result from use of this cartridge. While it may not necessarily be dangerous to shoot, it certainly will be unpleasant.

This weapon was formerly quite popular in Russia. In this connection it will be noted that the 7.63mm. Mauser pistol was also very widely distributed in Russia.

Schwarzlose Model 98 pistols were widely sold in this country by Bannerman in the early 1900's. These weapons will very seldom be found with any name or identification marks on them other than proof marks. The pistol illustrated is numbered 134.

7.63mm. (7.65mm.) Mannlicher   CARTRIDGE

Data

This is a special cartridge which can be used only in Models 1900 and 1901 Mannlicher delayed blowback pistols and their Spanish imitations. It is a straight sided case and must not be confused with the bottle-necked case used in the 1903 Mannlicher. There is a slight but almost imperceptible taper to the case as an aid to extraction. The bullet is the same size and shape as that of the 7.63mm. Mauser—85 grains average, full jacketed or soft point. Velocity is about 1025 feet per second.

This cartridge as manufactured in England for South American export is called the 7.63mm. Mannlicher. In Germany, however, this caliber designation was applied only to the Mauser cartridge; and this cartridge was there called the 7.65mm. Mannlicher.

MANNLICHER   7.63mm. (7.65mm.) Mannlicher
1900 and 1901

These pistols were made by Steyr Waffenfabrik. The 1900 weighs 29 ounces, has a 5½-inch barrel, measures 8¾ inches overall and holds eight cartridges. The 1901 weighs 32 ounces, has a 6 5/16-inch barrel, measures 9⅝ inches overall and also holds eight cartridges.

The frame is the same size in both models. The grip is the same shape but the 1900 is ⅝″ shorter than the 1901. On the 1900 model the barrel is milled back to within 1¼″ of the breech end. In the 1901 the round shape of the barrel extends only as far as the frame, a distance of 2⅜″. Both models have a barrel rib.

In the 1900 model the rear sight is at the end of the barrel, integral with the metal forming the chamber. This gives a sighting radius of 5″ as against 7¾″ in the later model. The front sight is integral with the barrel. In the 1901 the sight is adjustable laterally in a dovetail slot. Workmanship is excellent in both pistols.

The 1901 was officially rejected as a service weapon by the Austrian government in 1905, but was widely sold as a commercial arm.

This is an unusually simple and well-constructed design. It has no locking system. However, its blowback is augmented by a decelerating device. The slide in this pistol consists of the breechblock and two attached arms extending forward below the barrel with the recoil spring mounted between them, together with its guide.

The mainspring is a heavy "V" spring mounted in the right side of the receiver. While the short arm of this spring presses against the cam in engagement with a notch in the underside of the breechblock when the weapon is closed, the long lower arm of the spring ends in a hook engaged in the right-hand fork of the hammer.

Thus the mainspring operates the hammer and supports the cam against the slide. Pressure on the trigger, which is pivoted to a long arm, transmits the rearward pressure when the weapon is to be fired. As this long attached arm rests against the tail of the sear, and the sear is under the tension of a "V" spring which is both trigger and sear spring, the nose of the sear is pushed out of engagement with its bent in the left fork of the hammer.

Side plates cover the firing mechanism on the left side of the pistol and the mainspring and resistance cam on the right. These two plates join in front to form a cover for the recoil spring. This unit is slid on the weapon from the front below the barrel and is held in place by a spring catch just forward of the trigger guard.

7.63mm. (7.65mm.) Mannlicher

*MANNLICHER 1900.
7.63mm. Straight case. Eight
shot.*

*MANNLICHER 1901. 7.63mm. Straight case
delayed blowback. Eight shot.*

*MANNLICHER 1903. 7.63mm. Bottleneck case, locked
breech. Six shot.*

The front end of the recoil spring rests against the bridge connecting the forward arms of the slide extension. Its rear is mounted in the receiver wall.

Operation: As the cartridge is discharged, and the bullet travels down the barrel, the slide starts to the rear.

Unlike the standard blowback pistol in which only the recoil spring compression and the weight of the recoiling parts offers a resistance to the rearward motion, in this pistol the resistance of the decelerating cam which is engaged under spring pressure in the bottom of the breechblock must be overcome. As the slide goes back to ride over the hammer and to compress the mainspring, the upper arm of which bears against the decelerating cam, added pressure is exerted to hold it forward. This helps to slow the rearward travel of the breechblock.

When the breechblock has gone back as far as it can, the decelerating cam slips into a second notch in the slide. This notch holds the action open for cleaning when the weapon is opened manually.

However, when the action is being operated by the recoil, the hammer is forced back past its full-cock position and the hook on the lower leaf of the mainspring pushes against the tail of the decelerating cam; this forces it up out of engagement with the second slide notch. On forward motion of the breechblock, as the recoil spring pulls it to the front, the decelerating cam slides over the rear notch because of the shape of the cam nose.

The barrel in this weapon (as in the Luger) is screwed into the chamber end of the receiver. However, the chamber itself is an integral part of the receiver forging.

The magazine is in the handle but is of the nondetachable type. Guides are provided at the forward end of the breechblock section of the slide into which a charger holding eight cartridges may be inserted.

A stud on the right side of the grip below the side plate may be pushed to pull the locking lip away from the top cartridge when the magazine is full. This permits the magazine spring to eject all the cartridges through the top of the weapon without pulling the slide back and forth. The ejector is a bar at the rear of the magazine. It runs in a groove on the lower side of the breechblock. The extractor is mounted on top of the breechblock. This pistol is fitted with an external hammer. An inertia firing pin is mounted in the breechblock.

At the rear of the breechblock is a safety catch in the form of a bar with a milled thumbpiece. Turning this down turns the bar into position between the hammer and the firing pin to positively prevent discharge.

This is one of the simplest and most efficient manual safeties ever devised, and has been widely copied in Europe.

The magazine chargers may be speedily loaded. Once on the charger, however, it is difficult to remove cartridges except by inserting the charger in the guide and stripping the cartridges down into the magazine.

7.63mm. (7.65mm.) Mannlicher

MANNLICHER
1901

While genuine Steyr pistols of this type are of fine workmanship and materials, a wide variety of imitations have been manufactured in Spain. These are usually of very inferior metal and workmanship.

This weapon must be considered as one of the earliest successful automatic pistols. It was very popular throughout South America. Many of its features have been widely copied.

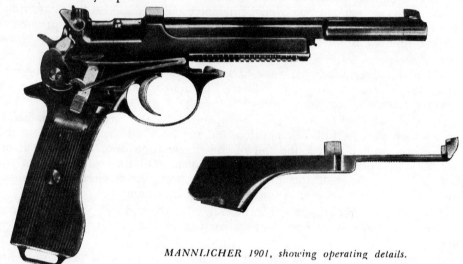

MANNLICHER 1901, showing operating details.

The illustration shows the right-hand side of the Model 1901 with side plate removed.

Note the positive thumb safety at the upper end of the breechblock slide. Turning this down revolves a metal bar into the path of the hammer to prevent it from reaching the firing pin.

The hammer is down in this picture. Note that the long arm of this spring is engaged with the hammer which compresses it as the hammer is brought to full cock.

The upper arm is forcing up the hesitation cam which is engaged in a slot in the underside of the slide to delay and slow down the rearward travel of the breechblock as the weapon recoils.

The thumb catch directly below the hooked end of the mainspring is the release catch for the magazine follower. Pulling it down moves its upper end away from the top cartridge in the magazine and permits the magazine spring in the handle to force the cartridges out through the top of the pistol.

Note the position of the recoil spring below the barrel. It is ready to be compressed by the bridge piece extending across and joining the two forward arms of the slide as the slide moves to the rear.

The small lever at the forward end of the trigger guard is the spring-held locking catch which is pressed to remove the dual side plates (seen directly below the pistol).

184

The lower picture shows this same pistol (Mannlicher 1901) in left side view with hammer at full cock.

The trigger is pivoted to the long bar extending back to the sear. The "V" spring above the trigger bar holds the trigger bar in engagement, returns the trigger to forward position, and also acts as sear spring.

The sear is mounted on a pivot pin directly behind the trigger bar and "V" spring; and its notch is in engagement with the bent in the hammer, holding it back.

Thus it will be seen that when the trigger is pressed it forces the trigger bar back to push the tail of the sear far enough to release the nose of the sear from its bent in the hammer. This permits the mainspring on the right side of the pistol to rock the hammer forward on its axis pin to strike the firing pin which is mounted within the breechblock, and fire the cartridge.

The breechblock may be pulled back a short distance, then lifted up and slid forward over the barrel to permit its removal, and to permit the removal of the recoil spring.

MANNLICHER 1901, showing operating details.

MANNLICHER
1903

7.63mm. (7.65mm.) Mannlicher

The standard model of this type weighs 36 ounces, has a 4½-inch barrel, measures 11 inches overall and has a magazine capacity of six cartridges. While the box magazine is detachable, it is normally loaded with a clip through the top of the open action.

This pistol will chamber the standard 7.63mm. Mauser cartridge, but it is

185

unwise to use this cartridge. Ammunition originally issued in Germany for this weapon was called 7.65mm. Mannlicher 1903; and though it has not been manufactured in recent years and samples of the original are difficult to locate, it is evident from the results found when firing Mauser cartridges that the powder load must have been such as to give much lower pressures. Tests with the 7.63mm. Mauser cartridge by H. P. White Co. of Cleveland and other ordnance experts have resulted in bulged backplates and jammed breechblocks.

While the weapon is of a locked-breech type in which a prop-up locking unit pinned to the barrel extension serves to keep the breech locked at the moment of discharge, the bolt (or breechblock) is so short and light that when used with modern cartridges it unlocks so rapidly and is driven back with such force that it will usually bulge out the rear of the receiver above the line of the hammer. The receiver itself is a very lightly machined piece.

The triangular-shaped piece projecting above the line of the grip from the rear of the receiver is a thumb safety.

A curved lever projecting from the receiver directly above the line of the trigger on the right side is the cocking piece. Pushing this down will cock the hammer concealed within the receiver. The knob projecting from the top of the weapon at the front end of the ejection slot is the bolt-retracting handle. This is drawn back to permit loading. Pressing the catch in the forward end of the trigger guard permits removal of the 5-shot magazine. This weapon may be loaded by inserting a magazine from below or by stripping in cartridges through the top.

It is of general interest only as a weapon issued at the turn of the century when the Mauser had already become very popular. It is a much more complicated design than the Mauser, and was never any serious competition to that fine weapon.

This Mannlicher was also issued with a detachable stock; still another model with a long barrel was issued as a carbine. This has a standard pistol-grip shoulder stock and a wooden fore-end extending from the receiver forward to the front sight band.

CARTRIDGE
Data

7.65mm. Luger

.30 Luger

Bullet
93 Gr. M.C.

Muzzle Velocity in f.s.:	1250
Vel. at 50 Feet:	1202
Vel. at 150 Feet:	1122

Calculated Energy

Muzzle Energy in ft. lbs.:	323
Energy at 50 Feet:	298
Energy at 150 Feet:	260

Calculated Drop

At 50 Feet:	.24 inch
At 150 Feet:	3.1 inches
At 300 Feet:	13.5 inches

Penetration at 15 Feet

⅞″ soft pine boards:	11

Length of Barrel in Which Tested

Inches	4.5

Shell Case

Weight:	63 grains
Max. Length:	.850 inch
Outside Body Dia. at Head, Max.:	.391 inch
Outside Body Dia. at Neck, Max.:	.332 inch
Inside Mouth, Dia. Max.:	.3070 inch
Volumetric Capacity to Base of Bullet in cubic inches:	.037

Bullet

Weight:	93 grains
Approx. Length:	.575 inch
Diameter Max.:	.3095 inch
Area, Cross Sectional:	.119 square inch
Shape:	M.C. Round Nose

Powder

Amount and type varies with different lots manufactured.

Cartridge

Approx. Length, Loaded:	1.155 inches
Approx. Total Weight, Loaded:	165 grains

187

7.65mm. Luger

LUGER
Various Models

7.65 MM. LUGER original type with grip safety and toggle lock.

Note: For complete data on construction and operation of Luger pistols, drawings and additional photographs, see Luger under Caliber .354 (9mm.) Luger.

General Note on Luger Pistols

Model 1900: Caliber 7.65 mm. (.30). This weapon has a grip safety, and the safety lock on left side. The barrel length is 4¾ inches.

Model 1902: This is the 9mm caliber with 4-inch barrel, grip safety, and safety lock on left side. Also made with 4¾-inch barrel.

Model 1904: 9mm caliber, 6-inch barrel, grip safety, and safety lock on left side. This model has the adjustable rear sight. It was issued with a leather holster attached to a wooden stock and two spare magazines.

The Models 1900-06, 1902-06, and 1904-06 are all the same as the Models 1900, 1902, and 1904 with the following exceptions:

The flat recoil spring has been replaced by a coil type. These weapons have grip safeties. The marking of the extractor with "geladen" (loaded) apparently started with the Model 1904 German Naval.

Model 1908: 9mm caliber, 4-inch barrel, coil recoil spring, and no grip safety. There are at least 35 variations of the Luger pistol in existence.

The Swiss adopted the Model 1900 and published handbooks and bulletins on it in 1901 and 1902. It was the official Swiss pistol.

Pistols of this manufacture will normally be found to carry the Swiss cross on the receiver directly ahead of the breechblock. They are 7.65mm Luger caliber.

The Germans adopted the Models of 1904 and 1908 for general service. The long Model 1908 with 8-inch barrel (adjustable sight on the barrel) also was accepted for special service. These were produced in German government arsenals, and by DWM, Krieghoff, Simson and Mauser.

The Bulgarians, Portuguese, and Hollanders used the standard 1902 manufactured by DWM.

Commercially manufactured Lugers were never dated on the breech. Pistols with dates stamped on the receiver just ahead of the breechblock are *German Army issues.* Prior to World War I, these pistols were never offered commercially for sale.

In the early 1920's, Lugers of all qualities from good to terrible were made up from wartime receivers and were widely sold throughout the world. These usually have the date of receiver manufacture stamped on the breech.

It is interesting to observe that in the 1920's the British armament firm of Vickers-Armstrong manufactured 9,000 Lugers in 9mm caliber for the Dutch. As the manufacture of these pistols required German machinery and technical knowledge, this is an interesting commentary.

After 1918, the Germans were prohibited by the Treaty of Versailles from manufacturing pistols for the Army in 9mm. except in one plant.

Simson and Co. of Suhl was chosen by the German Staff to be the producers of the 9mm Luger for the Army. DWM resumed production in the 1920's for commercial and export military sales. Mauser procured the tooling from DWM in the early thirties. Mauser markings started appearing on the pistols about 1934. The 7.65mm and 9mm were advertised for sale until the time of World War II although production of the weapon in 7.65mm by Mauser reportedly stopped around 1935. The Krieghoff firm, which initially assembled many Lugers from World War I components, produced about 5,000 9mm Po8 Lugers in 1939 for the Luftwaffe.

DEUTSCHE WAFFEN UND MUNITIONSFABRIKEN

The D.W.M. organization was formed by a combination of the arms factory of Ludwig Loewe and Sons of Berlin with the cartridge manufacturing plant of the Deutsche Metallpatronenfabrik, Karlsruhe. They continued manufacturing weapons in Berlin and ammunition at the Karlsruhe plant. When the D.W.M. organization was later dissolved and a new organization formed called the Berlin-Karlsruhe Industrie Werke, Mauser purchased all the Luger machinery and moved it to their plant at Oberndorf. Lugers made by D.W.M. or by Mauser are uniformly fine, reliable pistols.

The Luger automatic carbine, Model 1902, appeared also in 7.65mm and 9mm calibers and some later models will be found in 9mm.

It has an eleven-and-three-quarters-inch barrel with a checkered wooden fore-end and a detachable wood stock with checkered grip. Otherwise the carbine is, in general detail, similar to the standard Luger automatic pistol with grip safety. The rear sight, adjustable to 300 meters, is mounted on top of the barrel. These carbines are fitted with an auxiliary recoil spring in the fore-end.

7.65mm. Luger

LUGER
Carbine

7.65 MM. LUGER CARBINE with stock attached and detached. Note that this arm has a wooden fore-end and a special long range sight. Because of the heavy recoil springs used, standard Luger cartridge will not operate the action properly.

The cartridges (not manufactured in recent years) were identified by having black cases. They carried a powder charge approximately one-seventh greater than that of the standard pistol cartridge, and developed nearly 1515 feet per second muzzle velocity.

7.65mm. Luger

MISCELLANEOUS
Weapons

No first class pistol but the Luger has ever been commercially manufactured for this cartridge. Several experimental types such as the Knoble were chambered for this cartridge but none ever went into production. In recent years European inferior modifications of the Colt Government Model such as the Spanish Llama have been chambered for this cartridge.

7.65mm. Borchardt

CARTRIDGE
Data

The cartridge originally developed by the American Hugo Borchardt for the first Borchardt pistol manufactured and introduced in Germany in 1893 differed but slightly from the current 7.63 mm. Mauser cartridge. The bullet type, weight and diameter and the case specifications were later introduced with a somewhat heavier powder charge and the bullet more deeply seated as the 7.63 mm. Mauser. While original 7.65 mm. Borchardt ammunition is no longer available, the 7.63mm Mauser cartridges will fit in Borchardt pistols, but are too powerful for the action.

BORCHARDT
Automatic

7.65mm. Borchardt

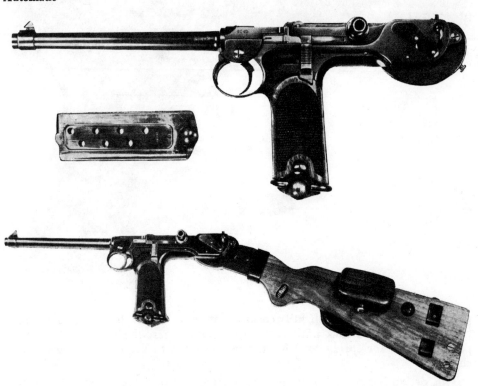

This pistol is the forerunner of the Luger. This was the first pistol to use the toggle joint locking system and the first to feature a magazine housed in the grip. The shoulder stock and carrying case were part of the original equipment sold with the Borchardt. With the stock a remarkable degree of accuracy is obtainable with this weapon. (It must be remembered, however, that in the United States the use of a stock of this type brings the pistol under Federal laws; and it is illegal to own one unless it is registered).

This special 7.65mm. pistol will not take the standard 7.65mm. or .32 Colt automatic pistol cartridge. Its actual caliber is .301. It measures 6⅝ inches, weighs 23 ounces and has a magazine capacity of seven cartridges. The velocity of this special cartridge is about 1,070 feet per second. This pistol has much in common with the Roth-Steyr Military Model. Like that weapon, the trigger is not connected to the recoil mechanism; so that the weapon is never completely cocked except at the instant of final trigger squeeze as the gun is fired. The recoil ejects the empty cartridge case and reloads a fresh cartridge. Only

191

pressure on the trigger itself fully cocks the striker. When the trigger is pressed, the striker is moved back until it reaches a point where the sear can slip it and permit the striker spring to drive the pin forward to fire the cartridge in the chamber.

This design has the advantage of permitting two or three quick pulls on the trigger in the event of misfire; but it has been outmoded by the recent development in double-action automatic pistols.

To load this weapon, the bolt is drawn back by hand to open the action. A special type of clip loaded with cartridges is inserted in the clip guides. This clip is fitted with a thumbpiece to make it easier to push the cartridges into the magazine. It must be removed after the cartridges have been stripped in. When the action is held open, pressure on a release stud on the left slide plate permits the magazine spring to eject all the cartridges from the magazine in the handle. Note that this magazine is integral with the handle and is not detachable. Used as a single-shot weapon, the action stays open after each shot has been fired, permitting insertion of a single cartridge.

This is a long-recoil weapon having a locking lug which is turned out automatically after the action has recoiled far enough for the bullet to leave the barrel. The barrel and bolt (or breechblock) recoil together as the cartridge in the chamber is discharged. A bolt lug locked in a recess above the barrel chamber holds the members securely together at the instant of discharge, and the bolt head is rotated about 20 degrees out of locking engagement to permit the action to eject and reload.

FROMMER   .301 (7.65mm) Frommer
1906

This pistol uses the Frommer 7.65mm which, although similar to the 7.65mm Roth cartridge, is a more heavily loaded cartridge. It is a long-recoil locked-breech pistol weighing about 22½ ounces, measuring about 7¼ inches overall and having a magazine capacity of nine cartridges.

This arm, sometimes called the Roth-Frommer, has an external hammer, a grip safety and a detachable magazine which is removed by pressing a release stud on the bottom rear of the grip.

Like the later Frommer Stop 1912 (see under Caliber .32 A.C.P.), this pistol operates on the long-recoil system in which the recoiling barrel and breech-block travel locked the entire distance of the recoil stroke. The bolt is a two-piece affair. The head carries two locking lugs and the extractor. It has a projecting tail with two helical grooves which projects into the bolt body where it engages with corresponding feathers. Only the head can rotate. The body is provided with ribs which travel in grooves in the slide and can move only back and forth. The head cannot move away from the face of the barrel until the feathers in the bolt body, working in the helical grooves during travel, act on the projecting tail causing it to rotate and thereby remove the two lugs from their seats. In general the operation follows that of the Frommer Stop.

Ammunition for this pistol is not obtainable commercially in the United States and it is not adaptable to other cartridges.

7.65mm French, Long   CARTRIDGE
                                                                Data

This is a special cartridge which cannot be used in any pistol except the French MAS designed for it. (It is, however, also used in a submachine gun made by MAS). While the caliber is nominally .32, the cartridge case is longer than the .32 Colt Auto and is straight cased. It shoots a jacketed bullet of about 88 grains average weight at a muzzle velocity of about 1000 feet per second. This cartidge, of course, is not manufactured in the United States.

7.65 French, Long   MAS
                                                            1935-A

This is one of several French Service pistols used in World War II. It is enameled finish, and has a barrel about 4 1/3 inches long, an overall length of about 7⅜ inches, weighs about twenty-six ounces and has a magazine capacity of 8 cartridges. (See Identification Section for illustration.)

Manufacture D'Armes St. Etienne (MAS) S.A.C.M., MAC and SAGEM made these pistols under Petter patents. Modifications are being made at Neuhausen, Switzerland.

There is no barrel bushing in the front end of the slide to retain the recoil spring as in the case of the earlier Colt. Instead this weapon employs a slide which is solid at the front end below the barrel opening to provide a resting place for the forward end of the recoil spring, except for guide emergence hole.

The locking system is based on the system developed by Browning and used in the Colt Government Model automatic pistol. It too is modified. It is provided with a link to disengage the two barrel-locking lugs from the slide as the slide moves to the rear after the gun has been fired. As in the case of the Colt, the link is secured by the slide stop pin which passes through the receiver, through the link, and out through the far side of the receiver. The 1935S has a single locking lug.

This MAS pistol has its hammer and mainspring mounted in a subassembly in the receiver. The ejector is a forward part of this subassembly, which forms a housing.

This pistol is fitted with a highly desirable safety device in the form of a magazine disconnector which prevents the cartridge in the chamber from being fired if the magazine is removed from the handle. A pin projects from the top of the slide when the chamber is loaded. The hammer has a half-cock notch. The manual safety is mounted on the slide; it is of pivot design to block the hammer from reaching the firing pin when safety is applied and does not lock slide, trigger or hammer mechanism. The magazine release catch and slide stop follow the general Colt pattern.

The locking and unlocking action of this weapon is essentially that of the Colt-Browning automatic pistol, as is also the disconnection system which provides a safety factor by preventing the firing of more than one shot for each pull of the trigger.

Chapter 6

Caliber 8mm

CARTRIDGE   **8mm. Gasser**
Data

  This is a special cartridge originally of Austrian design which was popular in Europe but has never been manufactured in the United States. The caliber is nominally .32. The case is straight sided and is considerably shorter than our .32-20. Muzzle velocity is in the neighborhood of 750 feet per second and striking energy is about 125 foot pounds at muzzle. While essentially a military cartridge used in Austria and Italy, this cartridge is usually encountered loaded with a lead bullet.

RAST-GASSER AND ROTH-GASSER   **8mm. Gasser**
Revolvers   **M1898**

  These revolvers were originally patented by L. Gasser in Vienna early in the 1870's.

  The earliest model of this revolver was chambered for an 11.2mm black powder cartridge and introduced in 1870. In the 1880's, a 9mm version, also black powder, was introduced. It is almost identical in appearance with the Model 1898 shown here.

The 1898 Rast-Gasser has the following specifications: Barrel length 4½ inches, overall length 9 inches, weight thirty-three ounces, cylinder capacity 8 cartridges.

The Gasser system is one of the oldest and best solid-frame designs ever conceived, though it suffers from being a rod-ejector type which is necessarily slow to load and unload.

Construction and Operation. These are solid-frame revolvers with hinged loading gate on right side. When the gate is opened cartridges may be inserted in chambers through loading slot, the cylinder being revolved by hand to bring each chamber successively in line. The ejector rod mounted below the barrel is locked at its front end to a projection on the barrel forging by a clasp which may be turned to unlock it. This frees the rod permitting it to be drawn ahead and swung out to the right on a special mounting. Pushing it back drives the cartridge case in the chamber lined up with it out the loading slot. This rod, unlike the Colt type, is not spring supported and must be drawn out of the chamber by forward pull before the cylinder may be revolved to line up the next chamber for ejection.

The firing pin is a separate unit which with its spring is mounted in the standing breech in line with the chamber behind the barrel. The hammer rebounds after firing upon release of the trigger, hence never rests on the firing pin except when the trigger is deliberately pulled.

The front sight is adjustable for windage. The rear sight is a notch machined into the top of the frame.

The really remarkable feature of the design, however, is the simplicity of takedown and the lockwork. The trigger guard is hinged at the rear and its forward end is sprung up to lock the left side plate securely to the receiver or frame proper. When the front end of the trigger guard is pulled down, the left side plate may be swung out on its hinge behind the hammer. The stocks being locked by the plate and not by screws may now be removed. When the plate is back every detail of the firing mechanism is exposed for cleaning or for needed repair. The lockwork itself is double action. Removing the ejector rod and bushing permits the withdrawal of the cylinder.

These revolvers were used in World War I by the Austrians and large numbers were seized by the Italians at the end of the war. As a result, many of these revolvers saw service in World War II in the hands of Italian troops.

8mm. Gasser

MISCELLANEOUS
Revolvers

Dozens of solid-frame rod-ejector and also swing-out cylinder revolvers were manufactured in Belgium and Germany for the Gasser cartridge. These weapons seldom bear a maker's name. Those stamped Alfa are among the best and may be encountered with right or left hand swinging cylinders, exposed or concealed hammers, and in a wide range of weights, lengths and cylinder capacities. These are purely collectors items in this country, as no available ammunition will fit them.

CARTRIDGE   8mm. Modele d'Ordonnance (Lebel)
Data

This was the standard French revolver cartridge. While it is widely distributed in Europe it is not manufactured in this country and is seldom encountered. The cartridge very closely resembles our .32-20 in exterior appearance but the bullet is normally copper jacketed. The bullet weight is about 120 grains, the case measures about 1.07 inches overall while the length of the complete cartridge is about 1.45 inches. The normal load is black powder. Muzzle velocity is approximately 715 feet per second and muzzle striking energy about 104 foot-pounds.

MODELLE D'ORDONNANCE (LEBEL)   8mm. Modele d'Ordonnance (Lebel)
1892

This was the official French Army Revolver popularly known as the Lebel. It has a 4-inch barrel, measures about 9¼ inches overall and weighs approximately 30 ounces. The cylinder contains 6 cartridge chambers.

Construction and Operation. This revolver is a solid-frame design in which the cylinder swings out in the manner of the Colt on a crane, but swings to the right instead of to the left. The cylinder release catch is on the right-hand side of the frame and must be rocked back before the cylinder can be pushed out on its crane for loading or ejection. The lockwork is of standard double-action construction utilizing a firing pin loosely pinned to the hammer, which is rebounding.

The one unusual characteristic of this design is in the hinged side plate which permits simple cleaning and dismounting. A large screw protrudes from the right side of the grip directly behind the hammer. When this is turned with a screw driver it forces the left hand side plate away from the

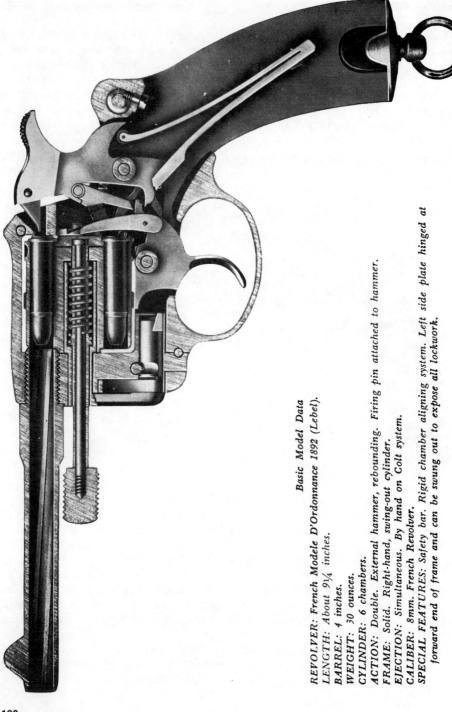

Basic Model Data

REVOLVER: French Modele D'Ordonnance 1892 (Lebel).
LENGTH: About 9¼ inches.
BARREL: 4 inches.
WEIGHT: 30 ounces.
CYLINDER: 6 chambers.
ACTION: Double. External hammer, rebounding. Firing pin attached to hammer.
FRAME: Solid. Right-hand, swing-out cylinder.
EJECTION: Simultaneous. By hand on Colt system.
CALIBER: 8mm. French Revolver.
SPECIAL FEATURES: Safety bar. Rigid chamber aligning system. Left side plate hinged at forward end of frame and can be swung out to expose all lockwork.

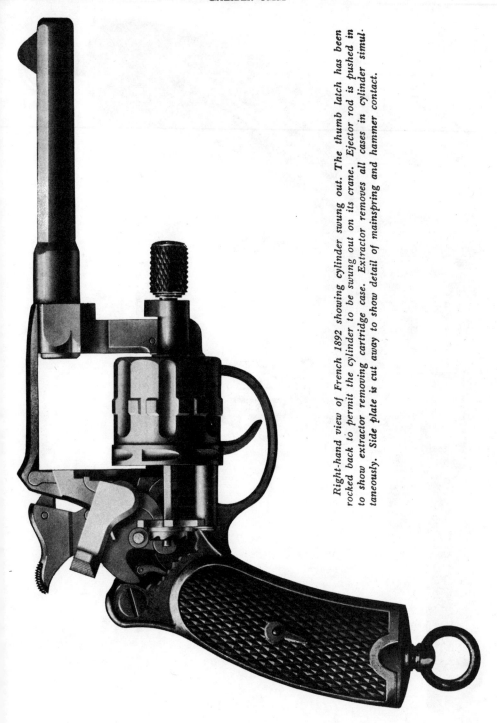

Right-hand view of French 1892 showing cylinder swung out. The thumb latch has been rocked back to permit the cylinder to be swung out on its crane. Ejector rod is pushed in to show extractor removing cartridge case. Extractor removes all cases in cylinder simultaneously. Side plate is cut away to show detail of mainspring and hammer contact.

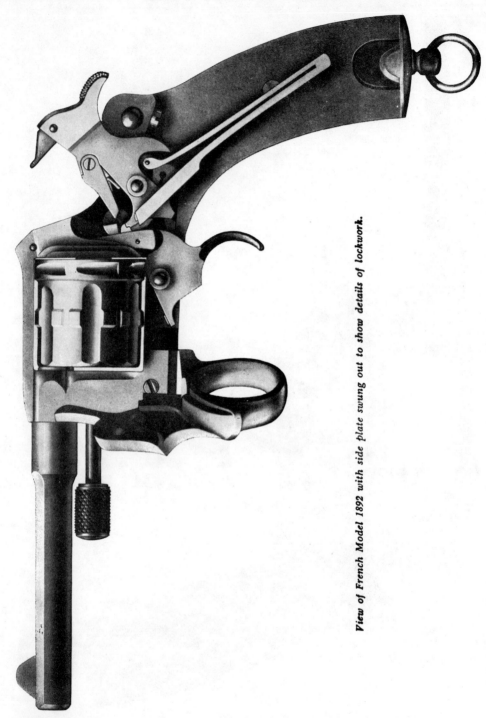

View of French Model 1892 with side plate swung out to show details of lockwork.

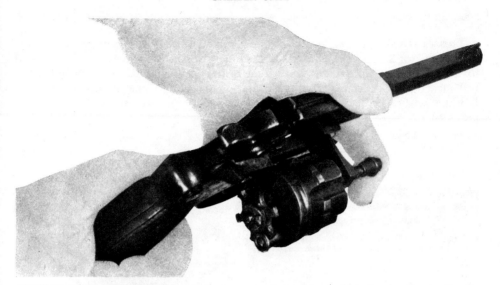

FRENCH 1892 REVOLVER with cylinder swung out showing method of extraction by pressing up on ejector rod.

frame, causing it to pivot on its hinge at the forward end of the frame. This exposes not only the lockwork but also the receiver or frame section below the line of the cylinder. The cylinder itself may be dismounted if necessary in a manner similar to the Colt. Operation is the same as for the Colt Revolvers except for the difference in cylinder release catch and direction of swing.

MISCELLANEOUS   8mm. Modele d'Ordonnance
Weapons

Bayard, Pieper and other Belgian makers as well as some German firms manufactured solid-frame and swing-out cylinder revolvers for this cartridge. None of these weapons have unusual characteristics and are not suitable for use in the United States because of difficulty in obtaining ammunition. While .32 Caliber Smith & Wesson cartridges will chamber in these revolvers, they should not be used because the difference in case diameters results in bulged cases and possibly dangerous resultant pressures.

8mm. Roth-Steyr

This cartridge was originally designed at the turn of the century in Austria for use in the 8mm. Roth-Steyr self-loading pistol. It has never been adapted to any other production weapon. The bullet weighs about 115 grains and is full jacketed. The case is rimless. Cartridges usually come on special chargers holding ten cartridges. Muzzle velocity is in the neighborhood of 1045 feet per second.

8mm. Roth-Steyr

ROTH-STEYR
Automatic

8MM. AUSTRIAN ROTH-STEYR with Charger.

This pistol was officially adopted by the Austro-Hungarian cavalry in 1907. It is widely distributed throughout the Balkans and appeared in considerable quantity in those areas during World War II. It has a 5⅛-inch barrel, the overall length is about 9⅛ inches and the weight about 36 ounces. The magazine capacity is 10 cartridges. This is one of the earliest forms of successful locked-breech pistols. It employs a turning barrel lock, the barrel being revolved through 90 degrees rotation by camming action of stud as the slide recoils. It is unusual also in that the recoil does not cock the mechanism for firing as in typical autoloading pistols. The striker is drawn back to full cock by the recoil but must be pulled further back by trigger action before it will slip off the sear to fire.

Construction and Operation. The design of this arm is unusual. It is

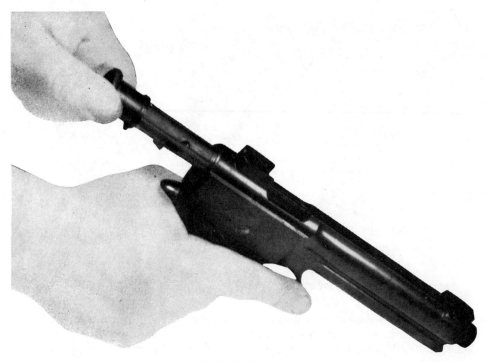

AUSTRIAN ROTH-STEYR open for loading.

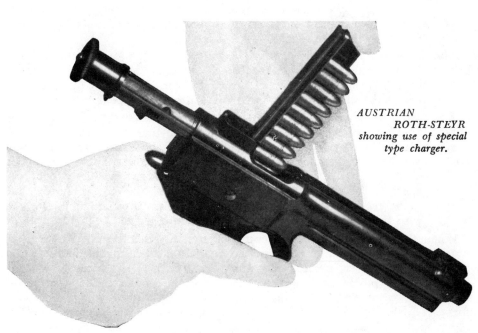

*AUSTRIAN
ROTH-STEYR
showing use of special
type charger.*

8MM. AUSTRIAN ROTH-STEYR with left side exposed to show lockwork detail.

complicated and expensive and hence has never been duplicated or imitated. The receiver forms the grip in standard fashion but the magazine is built in. When the bolt is drawn to the rear by pulling on its round projecting head piece, the magazine follower rises to hold it open. The sleeve covering the barrel is not a slide as commonly encountered. However, it does have guide slots into which the special 8mm. charger is placed. This charger has a special thumbpiece which can be pushed down to provide leverage to strip the cartridges easily into the magazine.

The sleeve, which is tubular, covers the pistol from the muzzle to the cocking piece. The forward end encloses the barrel and has a heavy lug which holds the recoil spring. The extractor, striker, and breechblock are covered by the rear section of the sleeve which is fitted with an ejection opening.

The barrel mounted to the receiver inside the sleeve has two pairs of opposed lugs, one at the muzzle and the other about half way back. The front lugs, which are cam type, engage in a helical cut in the muzzle cap and while holding the barrel firmly in position, permit it to recoil a distance of about ½ inch during which it is revolved through 90 degrees rotation. The rear lugs engage in a helical slot in the front section of the sleeve. The forward section of the receiver itself is also tubular and extends to the muzzle of the weapon with the recoil spring housed in it below the barrel.

When the weapon is loaded, pressure on the trigger draws the striker back until it slips off the sear to fire the cartridge. Unlike late model double-action pistols, however, it is necessary to draw the bolt back by hand before the trigger can be pulled again. The striker must be cocked by hand or recoil before the trigger can act. Thus, this system, which was intended primarily for use by horsemen where there was danger from a light trigger pull is really a safety feature. It is not designed to permit striking the primer a second blow as in other double-action semi-automatic pistols.

As the bullet goes down the barrel, the recoil starts the locked barrel and breechblock to the rear. During a travel of about ½ inch, the rear barrel lugs sliding in their helical slot on the inside of the block rotate the barrel out of locking engagement. The barrel strikes its stop and is halted while the breechblock or bolt continues to the rear to extract and eject in standard fashion. The breechblock drawn forward by the compressed recoil spring chambers a new cartridge.

This pistol is of interest today principally for the design features involved which have been widely developed in some sections of Europe.

8mm. Nambu

CARTRIDGE
Data

This is a special cartridge adapted only to pistols of Japanese manufacture. It is a bottle-necked cartridge somewhat resembling the 7.65mm. Luger in appearance but developes much less energy. The case is semirim and the bullet is a round-nose full jacket weighing 102 grains. This ammunition has often been reported with lead bullets but none have appeared during the course of recent years. The muzzle velocity is about 1065 feet per second.

8mm. Nambu

NAMBU
1904

This pistol, apparently, was never a standard arm in the Japanese Army, but was used extensively by Japanese troops. The barrel length is about 4¾ inches, overall length 9 inches and weight is about 30 ounces. The magazine capacity is 8 cartridges. Many samples of this pistol will be found very well finished, since it was manufactured in peacetime. It is of excellent design, though the caliber is inadequate for a military weapon. There are fewer parts in the firing mechanism than in our own type of pistol.

Construction and Operation. The principal parts of this pistol are the receiver, barrel assembly, bolt, magazine, and lockwork. (1) The receiver forms the grip and is hollowed out to receive the detachable magazine in standard fashion from below. It is machined to permit the trigger guard and automatic safety lever assembly to be slid up into place in grooves from below. It is tunneled out on top to receive the barrel extension and breechblock mechanism and is provided with a separate tunnel on the left to house the single recoil

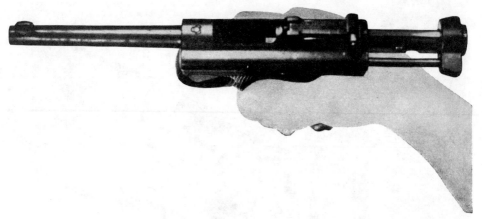

NAMBU in full recoil position. Rod to left of breechblock is recoil spring guide and compressor.

spring and its guide. The rear sight is mounted on top of the receiver. In some models this is a sight intended for use with a detachable stock and can be elevated. The receiver is also machined to receive the lockwork.

(2) The barrel and barrel extension which is hollow form a separate forging as in the Mauser Military. The extension is cut away on top to provide an ejection port and on the bottom to permit a dismountable locking block to be cammed up and down to lock in the underside of the breechblock. The extension is grooved to travel in the receiver.

(3) The bolt or breechblock is machined to carry the extractor and to receive a striker assembly. This striker assembly consists of a striker with a cocking bent, a coil spring inserted in the barrel of the striker and a guide pin with a knurled locking head which serves to lock the units when the arm is assembled. The locking block is a separate steel unit mounted in the receiver so it can be cammed up through the cut in the barrel extension to engage in the recess provided for it in the bottom of the breechblock. Its lower face rides on a shelf in the receiver when the arm is locked and drops into a cut at the edge of the shelf during recoil as the barrel action is halted to permit the breechblock assembly to travel back inside the barrel extension to perform the functions of cocking and ejection.

(4) A cocking piece projecting from the rear of the barrel extension is fastened over the projecting head of the breechblock and has an arm extending to the left in line with the recoil spring tunnel in the receiver. The recoil spring plunger passes through a hole in this breechblock cocking piece and passes into the tunnel. During recoil, the breechblock drives the cocking piece back at the same time that it compresses the mainspring within the striker. During this recoil, the cocking piece must also draw the recoil spring plunger with it. As the forward end of the spring is resting on a flange at the forward end of the plunger, this rearward travel compresses the spring to provide energy for the forward motion of loading.

(5) The magazine is of very heavy construction but. of standard type. It is fitted with a guide button on the right side to draw the follower down and

Basic Model Data

AUTOMATIC PISTOL: Japanese Nambu Caliber 8mm.
LENGTH: 9 inches.
BARREL: 4¾ inches.
WEIGHT: 30 ounces.
MAGAZINE: Detachable box 8 cartridges. Release button left side of grip.
OPERATION: Short recoil, locked breech.
LOCK: Special prop-up system. A swinging block pivoted to the underside of the barrel
    extension rests on a receiver shelf with its end passing up into a cut in the breechblock.
    During recoil this block is cammed down out of engagement into a receiver cut.
MAINSPRING: Coil spring within striker.
DISCONNECTOR: Trigger bar can reach sear only when action is closed.
TRIGGER: Pivoted draws trigger bar ahead.
SAFETY: Trigger block automatic squeezer below trigger guard. Also manual safety on right
    side of receiver tunnel. Has also magazine removal safety.
RECOIL SPRING: With guide in receiver tunnel left side.
HOLD OPEN DEVICE: None. Bolt is held back by magazine follower on last shot, but goes
    forward when magazine is withdrawn.
SPECIAL FEATURE: Some models have adjustable sights and groove in rear of grip for
    shoulder stock to permit use as a carbine.

Top line shows barrel and barrel extension forging with locking nut. Detachable locking block is shown directly below its mounting. Next line shows breechblock with hollow striker, spring and guide pin ready to be inserted. Recoil spring and guide are directly below. Receiver is shown with trigger guard assembly pushed down to permit general dismounting. Right stock and magazine are also shown.

permit easy loading. However, the follower, while it can rise and hold the breechblock open when empty, does not act on a slide stop. As a result, it is difficult to withdraw the magazine when empty, and the breechblock runs forward on the empty chamber when the magazine is withdrawn.

An automatic grip safety is mounted below the trigger guard. It serves as an effective trigger block by interposing a steel bar behind the trigger when at rest. When the arm is gripped for firing, the safety is squeezed in pivoting the bar down out of the line of the trigger. As this device does not lock the sear or the striker, it is not completely satisfactory. There is a manual safety on the receiver above the left grip.

The action is quite simple. When the trigger is pressed, it pivots and draws the trigger bar to release sear engagement. The compressed striker spring pushes the striker ahead to fire the cartridge. At this moment, the locking block is resting on its shelf in the receiver with its upper arm engaged through the barrel extension cut into the breechblock. The barrel and breechblock

209

start recoil and as the pressure drops the barrel strikes its stop in the receiver and is halted. At this point the bottom of the locking block is on the edge of the shelf and continued rearward movement of the breechblock cams it down out of engagement. The breechblock continues to the rear. On forward motion the recoil spring pulls the breechblock ahead to strip the top cartridge from between the lips of the magazine and chamber it. The locking block is carried forward as the barrel extension moves and as it rises up the cam face to its shelf its upper end is forced into the breechblock cut. The striker bent is caught and held but the trigger bar cannot complete the firing hook up until pressure on the trigger is released permitting the trigger spring to move the trigger and bar into proper position.

On some models a magazine safety is incorporated. A pivoted block passes over a lug on the trigger to prevent movement until a magazine is again inserted.

Dismounting. Remove the magazine. Force the muzzle against a solid object and while the barrel is back about a quarter of an inch depress magazine catch at the same time that you pull the trigger guard down. This assembly may then be moved. Again pushing the barrel back and holding it, give cocking piece plug a quarter turn and remove it. The striker and spring will then come out. Barrel and breechblock assembly may then be slid forward out of the receiver. The breechblock and recoil spring may then be withdrawn.

8mm. Nambu

JAP PATTERN
14 (1925)

This pistol is a modification of the Japanese Nambu. It may be encountered with the standard, round trigger guard of the Nambu or with an oversized trigger guide intended for use with gloves in cold climate.

This pistol almost entirely replaced the Nambu in Japanese service in World War II. This model has a 4¾-inch barrel and an overall length of about 9 inches. The weight is about 32 ounces and the magazine capacity is 8 cartridges. The principal points of difference are those determined by manufacturing requirements for mass production. The receiver is modified. The grip safety is dispensed with. A manual thumb safety is provided on the left side of the receiver above the line of the trigger. The tunnel for the recoil spring is eliminated. In its place, the right and left side of the breechblock itself are tunneled out to receive individual recoil springs which are compressed against their seats in the breechblock as it travels to the rear during recoil. The locking nut over the projecting end of the breechblock is simplified since it does not have to accommodate a recoil spring plunger.

Dismounting. Push in the head of the firing pin extension which protrudes through the center of the bolt nut and turn the bolt nut. As the nut is removed the spring will force the extension out of its seat in the bolt. The pin and its spring may now be shaken out. With magazine removed, press muzzle on solid surface to thrust the barrel back at the same time that the magazine catch is pushed in. The left-hand stock should be removed to facilitate sliding the trigger guard assembly out. The barrel assembly may now be slid forward

JAPANESE PATTERN 14 (1925). Left side view cut away to show all operating detail. Magazine is fully loaded. Striker is in full forward position. Locking block is on receiver shelf with upper end engaged in cut in underside of bolt which it reaches by passing through a cut in the underside of the barrel extension. In this type, magazine is retained by spring button of Colt type and also by bottom spring in front of grip, requiring very stiff pull to withdraw magazine.

JAPANESE PATTERN 14 (1925). Left side view showing parts in full recoil. Magazine follower has raised cartridges to bring top in line for feeding. Striker spring has been compressed as have dual recoil springs. Locking block has been forced down into its cut in the receiver. Breechblock is cut away beyond receiver to show striker tube housed within bolt. Breechblock locking cut is to rear of cutaway section.

on its grooves out of the receiver. The locking block may be taken off its pivot on the barrel extension. (Warning: This block must be replaced before firing the weapon. While the pistol can be assembled without it, lack of the block makes this a blowback pistol and the cartridge is powerful enough to damage an unlocked action.) The breechblock and the recoil spring may now be removed from the barrel extension.

JAP PATTERN
94 (1934)

8mm. Nambu

Caliber: 8mm. Japanese Service cartridge.

Length of Barrel: 3.8″

Over-all Length: 7.2″

Weight: 1 lb. 11 ounces

Magazine Capacity: 6 shots

Operation: Recoil

Rifling: Uniform right

Number of Lands: 6

Construction: The principal parts of this pistol are the receiver, barrel, slide, and lock. Note that in this weapon the locking block is a separate entity.

As the cartridge is fired the slide and barrel recoil firmly locked together for about ⅛″.

At this point the lock drops at a forty-five degree angle to the bottom step of a recess milled across the receiver to receive it. (The open space left by this milling operation is covered up by two thin steel plates dovetailed and staked into place, one on each side of the receiver.)

The barrel now strikes against the barrel stop in front of the magazine well in the receiver and its rearward motion is halted.

The slide is now free of the locking block and it continues its rearward motion carrying with it the empty cartridge case fastened by the extractor in its breechblock face. This case strikes against the ejector which is mounted directly behind the magazine below the firing pin and is hurled out of the pistol.

The recoil spring is compressed during this movement.

The magazine functions in the standard manner, to push the follower and the cartridges in the magazine above it up into line as the breechblock face of the slide passes over the top of the magazine. When the recoil energy is exhausted, the compressed recoil spring pulls the slide forward to strip the top cartridge from the magazine, chamber it, and snap the extractor in the face of the breechblock end of the slide into place in the extracting groove of the cartridge case.

The locking action starts when the slide is about three-sixteenths of an inch from the forward position. The breechblock strikes the chamber end of the barrel, driving it forward. At the same time, the barrel cams the lock up the 45-degree incline into the top step of the recess milled across the receiver.

In this position the barrel and the slide are locked together and can separate only after a one-eighth of an inch movement to the rear.

The barrel has a total movement of seven-thirty-seconds of an inch to complete unlocking. This is ample to permit the pressure to drop to safe limits with the comparatively weak cartridge employed in this pistol.

The total movement of the slide is two and one-eighth inches during the entire recoil movement backward and of course the same distance forward.

Left side view of JAPANESE MODEL 94 showing breechblock in full recoil position.

A mechanical safety is included in the trigger assembly. This contains the disconnector to insure that the action is locked before the hammer can be released. As these weapons are of uniformly poor construction *this disconnector does not always function satisfactorily.*

As a result, pistols of this type often may be fired *before the slide is fully closed and locked.* As the cartridge is an essentially weak one, this is not as dangerous as would normally be the case. However, use of this pistol is *not* recommended. It should be considered entirely a curio or collection piece.

Another dangerous feature of this weapon is the fact that the sear is exposed for its full length on the outside of the left-hand side of the pistol. It is flush with the receiver, except when cocked; then it protrudes. When the weapon is cocked, if this sear is pressed in intentionally or inadvertently, the weapon will fire.

Loading: Press in the magazine release catch button mounted on the left side of the receiver behind the trigger guard and withdraw the magazine.

Load it as customary for automatic pistol magazines and insert in the handle, pushing in until it locks securely.

Push the thumb safety into the fire position, which is horizontal.

Grasp the cocking piece where it protrudes from the rear of the weapon and pull the slide back as far as it will go. This will compress the recoil spring and let the magazine spring force a cartridge up into line.

Release the slide and let it go forward to chamber the cartridge and snap the extractor head into the second groove in the cartridge case.

Pressing the trigger will now fire the cartridge, extract and eject the empty case, feed a new cartridge into the firing chamber and leave the weapon ready for the next pull of the trigger.

215

JAPANESE MODEL 94 field stripped. Note that breechblock is a separate unit designed to be assembled to the slide. Barrel has special lug to receive locking block.

Note that when this pistol is empty the slide stays open, being held open by the rising magazine platform. *However, there is no slide stop and the slide cannot be released until the empty magazine is withdrawn.* As this magazine must be withdrawn against the pressure of the recoil spring, two hands and considerable force are necessary to free it.

As in the case of the Italian Beretta, the hold-open device on this pistol is merely to notify you that the magazine is empty. Withdrawing the magazine lets the slide go forward; but after a new magazine has been inserted, the slide must be drawn back to permit it to go forward again before the weapon is once more ready to be fired.

Dismounting: 1. Draw the slide to the rear until it catches behind the magazine follower.

2. Grasp the pistol in the right hand with the thumb under the rear of the frame and the fingers over the slide.

3. Draw the slide back all the way and grasp it tightly with the right hand.

4. The slide is made in two pieces somewhat like the slide in the Savage pistol. The rear slide extension, or cocking piece is held in place by a trans-

verse locking block, which in turn is held in place by the firing pin, in its normal or rearward position.

5. Therefore, to remove the locking block, insert the left index finger into the hollow underside of the cocking piece and push the firing pin forward into the firing position.

6. The locking block may now be pushed out from the right to left. (As the locking block is rather small it may be necessary to complete its removal with the aid of a small stick or punch.)

7. The cocking piece is now free and may be removed directly to the rear.

8. Then with the left hand around the forward end of the slide, withdraw the magazine and ease the slide forward into the locked position.

9. A slight pressure of the left thumb on the muzzle will unlock the slide and the remaining compression of the recoil spring will push the slide off the frame. The recoil spring and bushing will come with it. The barrel and lock may be lifted up and out of the frame.

Any further dismounting of the pistol requires the use of a screw driver. The hammer and trigger are held in place by screws, the heads being visible on the left side of the frame.

The magazine catch is screwed together and staked, preventing its removal as well as the removal of an automatic safety, which blocks the trigger when the magazine is removed.

To reassemble this weapon, merely reverse the instructions given above.

Chapter 7

Caliber .32

.32 R. F. Short and Long

CARTRIDGE
Data

Except in .22 caliber, rimfire cartridges have been obsolete so long in the U. S. that any stocks of them located are unlikely to be fit for shooting. In the last two decades of the nineteenth century most manufacturers of the period produced models to use rim fire ammunition and large numbers of these weapons are still to be encountered.

Arms using these cartridges should be considered collection pieces only, though they are still used in Europe to some extent.

.32 R. F. Short and Long

MISCELLANEOUS
Weapons

Remington Rider. Cal. 32 Extra Short R.F. This obsolete pistol carried its cartridges in a tube below the barrel. They were fed to the loading platform by a spring within the tube. Pulling back the top loading spur ejected the empty, cocked the hammer, and reloaded the chamber.

Merwin Hulbert. Cal. .44 Rim Fire. Showing pistol open after unloading. Barrel and cylinder assemblies swing over to the right and are thrust ahead to unload. (Note: These revolvers were later made in several Center Fire calibers. The weapons themselves are obsolete, however).

218

CARTRIDGE
Data

.32 Colt Long and Short

32 Short Colt

32 Long Colt

.32 Short Colt

Bullet
80 Gr. Lub.

Muzzle Velocity in f.s.:	800
Vel. at 50 Feet:	783
Vel. at 150 Feet	750

Calculated Energy

Muzzle Energy in ft. lbs.:	117
Energy at 50 Feet:	109
Energy at 150 Feet:	100

Calculated Drop

At 50 feet:	.75 inch
At 150 Feet:	7.3 inches
At 300 Feet:	30.1 inches

Penetration at 15 Feet

7/8" soft pine boards	3

Length of Barrel in Which Tested

inches	4

Shell Case

Weight:	24.6 grains
Max. Length:	.650 inch
Outside Body Dia. at Head, Max.:	.318 inch
Outside Body Dia. at Neck, Max.:	.318 inch
Inside Mouth Dia. Max.:	.2995 inch
Volumetric Capacity to Base of Bullet in cubic inches:	.024

Bullet

Weight:	80 grains
Approx. Length:	.570 inch
Diameter Max.:	.314 inch
Area, Cross Sectional:	.0774 square inch
Shape:	Round Nose

Powder

Amount and type varies with different lots manufactured.

Cartridge

Approx. Length, Loaded:	1.015 inches
Approx. Total Weight, Loaded:	109.5 grains

.32 Long Colt

Bullet
82 Gr. Lub.

Muzzle Velocity in f.s.:	800
Vel. at 50 Feet:	783
Vel. at 150 Feet:	749

Calculated Energy

Muzzle Energy in ft. lbs.:	117
Energy at 50 Feet:	112
Energy at 150 Feet:	102

Calculated Drop

At 50 Feet:	.78 inch
At 150 Feet:	7.9 inches
At 300 Feet:	33.4 inches

Penetration at 15 Feet

7/8" soft pine boards	3

Length of Barrel in Which Tested

inches	4

Shell Case

Weight:	29.6 grains
Max. Length:	.916 inch
Outside Body Dia. at Head, Max.:	318 inch
Outside Body Dia. at Neck, Max.:	.318 inch
Inside Mouth Dia. Max.:	.3005 inch
Volumetric Capacity to Base of Bullet in cubic inches:	.038

Bullet

Weight:	82 grains
Approx. Length:	.560 inch
Diameter Max.:	.302 inch
Area, Cross Sectional:	.0716 square inch
Shape:	Round Nose

These are obsolescent cartridges. Early Colt revolvers were chambered for them, but they are no longer manufactured. They are center fire cartridges with rims. The cases are nearly the same diameter as the bullets and are crimped to the bullets, whose bases are of reduced diameter to enable them to enter the cases.

The Short uses an 82 grain bullet with a diameter of .313 inch with a heel of .299 and an overall length of .48 inch. The case measures .64 inch with head diameter of .315 inch. Overall length of the loaded cartridge is 1.05 inch. Powder may be either black or smokeless. Black powder load as reported by H. P. White Co. is 7.8 grains. Muzzle velocity about 805 feet per second.

The Long uses an outside lubricated lead bullet also, but the weight is 90 grains. Bullet diameter is again .313 but length is .513 inch. The case measures .793 inch with head diameter .316 inch. Overall length of the loaded cartridge is 1.193 inch. Powder charge (black) is 10 grains. Smokeless was also used, averaging about 2.0 grains Bullseye.

.32 Colt Long and Short

COLT
Various Models

Typical Early Colt for these cartridges. Later made for the 38 S&W.

Early models of Bisley, Bisley Target, (see Colt under Caliber .44-40 Winchester), Single Action Army (see Colt under Caliber .45 Colt), Pocket Positive (see Colt under Caliber .32 Colt New Police), Police Positive and Police Positive Target.

Note that *modern* Colt's will not use these cartridges. Only early arms on which the caliber is plainly stamped on the barrel will handle them.

.32 Colt Long and Short

MISCELLANEOUS
Weapons

This cartridge will fit any European black powder revolver Caliber .320. Webley & Scott manufacture pocket revolvers in this caliber as do several Belgian makers.

220

CARTRIDGE .320 Revolver
Data

This is a popular European model originally loaded only with black powder but in recent years also manufactured with a smokeless loading.

It is interchangeable with the .32 Short Colt. As manufactured for Continental use by AKT. Lignose in Berlin it used a 72 grain lead bullet with outside lubrication which had a diameter of .295 inch and a length of .498 inch. The case has a head diameter of .317, neck diameter of .313 inch and a length of .603. Overall length of the loaded cartridge was .938 inch. The load was 6.3 grains of black powder. Muzzle velocity was given as 575 feet per second. Striking energy at muzzle 59 pounds.

This cartridge as manufactured by ICI in England uses an 80 grain lead bullet and a load of either 6 grains of black powder or 2 grains of Revolver Neonite. Muzzle velocity is given as 550 feet per second, muzzle striking energy as 53.777 pounds.

WEBLEY AND SCOTT .320 Revolver
WP

These revolvers were made by Webley until 1934. The W. P. Hammer model is a standard hinge frame automatic extracting pocket revolver. It differs from similar American types chiefly in having the barrel lock mounted on the standing breech instead of on the barrel extension. Observe that it does not employ, however, the famous Webley stirrup lock as the weak cartridge does not require it. The lock (or catch) is attached to the upper end of the standing breech and snaps over the breech end of the barrel extension.

The cylinder has 6 chambers. Barrel length is 3 inches and weight empty is 17 ounces.

This revolver is also made in a "hammerless" model with the hammer fully enclosed to require double action firing.

Note: These arms are also chambered for the standard .32 S&W Short cartridge which is *not* interchangeable with the .320.

.32 Smith and Wesson

.32 Smith & Wesson
85 Gr. Lub.

Muzzle Velocity in f.s.:	720
Vel. at 50 Feet:	708
Vel. at 150 Feet:	684

Calculated Energy

Muzzle Energy in ft. lbs.:	98
Energy at 50 Feet:	95
Energy at 150 Feet:	88

Calculated Drop

At 50 Feet:	.91 inch
At 150 Feet:	8.8 inches
At 300 Feet:	36.8 inches

Penetration at 15 Feet

7/8" soft pine boards:	3

Length of Barrel in Which Tested

inches:	3

Shell Case

Weight:	27.5 grains
Max. Length:	.605 inch
Outside Body Dia. at Head, Max.:	.339 inch
Outside Body Dia. at Neck, Max.:	.339 inch
Inside Mouth Dia. Max.:	.313 inch
Volumetric Capacity to Base of Bullet in cubic inches:	.024

Bullet

Weight:	85 grains
Approx. Length:	.500 inch
Diameter Max.:	.314 inch
Area, Cross Sectional:	.0774 square inch
Shape:	Round Nose

Powder

Amount and type varies with different lots manufactured.

Cartridge

Approx. Length, Loaded:	.930 inch
Approx. Total Weight, Loaded	117.5 grains

This is perhaps the most widely used pocket revolver cartridge ever developed. The bullet is the same maximum diameter as the earlier .32 Short and Long Colt cartridges with their outside lubrication; but in this current S&W cartridge lubrication is provided in grooves near the base of the bullet protected by the case, and the case fits over the base of the bullet itself instead of over a cutback heel as in the earlier types. Because of this the cartridge case is of greater diameter at its mouth than in the earlier Colt cartridges. While the two look very much alike, the difference in case diameter is great enough (.023 inch) to prevent the S&W cartridge being used in weapons chambered for the Short Colt, and the S&W cartridge requires a shoulder in the chamber. A reduction in the size of the bore was necessary with the adoption of the S&W cartridge. Originally a black powder load, this cartridge was loaded in this country with both smokeless and black powder until 1940.

COLT
Various Models
.32 S and W

Pocket Positive, Police Positive and Police Positive Target models are chambered for this cartridge. See these models under Colt in Caliber .32 S&W Long- .32 Colt New Police for complete details.

HARRINGTON AND RICHARDSON
Various Models
.32 S and W

All H&R revolvers of hinge frame design are stamped ".32 S&W CTGE." The principal recent models are the Auto Ejecting Model, an exposed hammer design with 3¼, 4, 5 or 6-inch barrel and a 6 chambered cylinder; the Premier, a lighter model with 2, 3, 4, 5, or 6-inch barrel and a 5-chambered cylinder; and the Hammerless, a conventional enclosed hammer design which can be fired only double action and is intended for close quarters shooting. Barrel lengths and cylinder capacity are the same as for the Auto Ejecting Model. Weights run from 12 to about 18 ounces on these models.

H&R Solid Frame Non-Ejector Revolvers in various weights and lengths are also chambered for this cartridge. Some models are: the Vest Pocket, a 9-ounce revolver with a 1⅛-inch barrel and a spurless hammer; the Young America with 2, 4½ or 6-inch barrel, five chambers and standard spur hammer; the heavier American Double Action with a 6 chambered cylinder and the more streamlined Model 4.

HOPKINS AND ALLEN
Various Models
.32 S and W

American Hopkins & Allen hinge frame and solid frame non-ejecting types are no longer manufactured, millions are in use. Essentially they differ very little from the H&R and Iver Johnson types. One noteworthy characteristic of the H&A line was the so-called "Triple Action Safety" employed on their best models.

This was an efficient and simple safety device by which the hammer was made to operate on an eccentric instead of on a standard pivot. As in the case of the Iver Johnson, the firing pin was not attached to the hammer but was a separate unit mounted with its coil spring in the face of the standing breech. When the hammer was at rest its nose was on a shelf above the line of the firing pin. Thus no blow delivered to the hammer could be passed on to the firing pin.

In the first movement of the triple-action pull the cylinder was revolved in standard fashion and the hammer brought to the full cock position. The hammer at rest was in the upper position in its eccentric pivot, in which position if it slipped during cocking it could only strike its shelf. At full cock, however, it was in its lower or firing eccentric. Thus when it was released by trigger pressure it could deliver its blow directly to the firing pin— instead of to the lifter as in the Iver Johnson. The third action occurred when pressure on the trigger was released and the trigger moved forward under compulsion of its spring. This action automatically raised the hammer to the upper eccentric where the hammer nose was above the line of the firing pin.

A special barrel lock was mortised out to fit the standing breech post so that when the action was closed wedge-shaped dogs flew into corresponding grooves to give an unusually rigid joint which automatically took up wear.

.32 S and W   **IVER JOHNSON**
                                                        Various Models

All models of the hinged frame types manufactured by this company and chambered for the .32 S&W cartridge have 5-shot cylinders. They differ only in minor details. Barrel lengths may be 2, 3, 4, 5 or 6 inches. Finishes and styles of grips vary.

Conventional hammer and hammerless designs are manufactured in these low priced pocket revolvers. The barrel locking catch is on the barrel extension and locks down over a projection on the standing breech. Opening the weapon and bending the barrel down on its hinge automatically forces the extractor to rise and eject the cartridges simultaneously from all chambers. It then snaps back into place under the action of its spring.

Iver Johnson arms of this type, however, are noteworthy for their use of coil springs instead of flat springs. The use of a coil mainspring permits a simple adjustment of spring tension as can be seen from the sectional drawing.

The outstanding feature of these arms, however, is the famous "hammer-the-hammer" safety. This is a slogan developed from the fact that when the hammer is at rest, even striking it with a nail driving hammer cannot possibly fire a cartridge.

This safety is simple, positive and quite ingenious and it effectively prevents discharge except by pulling the trigger all the way through. In this arm a firing pin and spring are mounted in the standing breech directly ahead of the hammer. The hammer rests on the metal above the firing pin and never touches the pin directly at any time. A long steel arm called the "lifter" is connected to the trigger and engages with the hammer. As the hammer goes back and the trigger pivots on its axis pin, the hand or pawl attached to the trigger pushes up against the ratchet on the head of the extractor to turn the cylinder in standard fashion the distance of one chamber. Movement of the cylinder is made possible by the action of the trigger pulling the cylinder stop out of its notch in the cylinder during the period of revolution.

The backward movement of the hammer on its axis pin also results in the lifter being raised until its front side is against the head of the firing pin and its rear is in line with the hammer. Thus as the hammer reaches full cock and is caught and held by the sear (if being used single action) the lifter is in position to transmit a blow to the firing pin when the hammer falls. Should the hammer slip before reaching full cock, the lifter is carried down out of its line and the hammer can only strike the standing breech above the firing pin. When trigger pressure is released after firing, the trigger draws the hand and the lifter back to their positions of rest ready for the next pull. Iver Johnson solid frame non-ejector revolvers of conventional low priced design are also chambered for this cartridge in various barrel lengths.

BASIC MODEL DATA

REVOLVER: Iver Johnson Hinge Frame.
LENGTH: Average about 7¼ inches (with 3-inch barrel).
WEIGHT: 14 ounces (with 3-inch barrel).
TWIST: Right hand.
CYLINDER: 5 chambers in caliber 32 S&W (6 in caliber 32 S&W Long, 7 in caliber 22)
ACTION: Double (also made in hammerless).
EJECTION: Automatic as barrel is bent down on hinge.
FRAME: Hinged. Lock on barrel strap.
CALIBER: 32 S&W (also made for 32 S&W Long, 38 S&W and 22).

Left side cutaway to show all operating details. Note that mainspring is a coil spring and that separate firing pin and spring are mounted in the face of the standing breech. The hammer is engaged with the lifter which when the hammer is cocked is automatically raised in line with the firing pin. The hammer falls when the trigger is pulled and drives the lifter against the firing pin; at all other times the hammer is resting on the breech and cannot fire accidentally.

225

.32 S and W

S&W MODEL No. 1½ SINGLE ACTION .32 Caliber Center Fire Revolver. The revolver for which the famous .32 S&W cartridge was designed.

Ammunition: .32 S & W Short Center-fire Cartridge.
Manufacturing Dates: Feb. 1878-1892.
Number Manufactured: Approximately 97,500.
Serial Numbers: Numbered in separate series beginning at 1.

Finish: Blue or nickel	*Number of Lands:*	5
Barrel Lengths: 3", 3½", 6", 8", 10".	*Direction of Twist:*	Right
	Number of Chambers:	5

Note: Top break, automatic ejector. Butt was round. Weight with 3½" barrel about 12½ ounces.

The automatic ejectors in some early S & W revolvers worked on a rack-and-pinion principle. While the extractor head was set flush in the head of the cylinder, the extractor rod passing down through the cylinder axis pin was coupled to a rack, but in a manner which permitted the rod to revolve without turning the rack.

A toothed wheel in the frame-and-barrel joint engaged with the rack. As the barrel was swung down, the pinion revolved about an eighth of a turn, giving the cartridges time to clear the breechblock before the extracting movement began. The pinion was then caught and held by a pawl at the lower side, thereby forcing the rack to move and raise the extractor to lift and eject the cartridge cases from the chambers. When the opening movement was nearing completion, a projection formed ahead of the pinion, which struck against the head of the pawl and pushed it back. The pinion now revolved freely, permitting the compressed spring to draw the rack and extractor back to rest position ready for the cylinder to be reloaded, at the same time turning the pinion until it was properly aligned with the rack for the next opening movement.

While of somewhat complicated design, this automatic ejecting feature was an outstanding advance in the mechanics of firearms construction in its time.

226

SMITH AND WESSON
Safety

.32 S and W

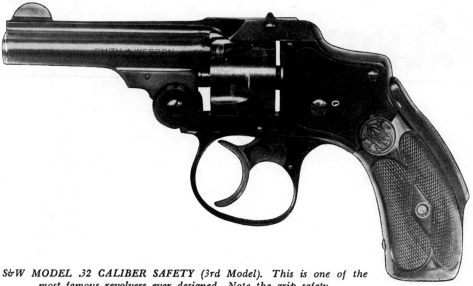

S&W MODEL 32 CALIBER SAFETY (3rd Model). This is one of the most famous revolvers ever designed. Note the grip safety.

Official Model Names: Model .32 Caliber Safety (First Model)
Model .32 Caliber Safety (Second Model)
Model .32 Caliber Safety (Third Model)

Ammunition: .32 Caliber S & W Short.

Manufacturing Dates: First Model—Feb. 1888—Sept. 1902.
Second Model—Sept. 1902—Oct. 1909.
Third Model—Oct. 1909-1937.

Number Manufactured: First Model—91,000.
Second Model—Approximately 80,000.
Third Model—Approximately 70,000.

Serial Numbers: All three models numbered consecutively in same series.

Finish: Blue or nickel.

Barrel Lengths: First Model—3" and 3½".
Second Model and Third Model—2", 3", also 3½" and 6" in Second Model.

Land Diameter:	.303-.304	*Direction of Twist:*	Right
Groove Diameter:	.312-313	*Diameter of Chamber:*	.3395-.3405
Number of Lands:	5	*Number of Chambers:*	5
Twist: One turn in	18¾"		

Model Changes: The First Model had a two-piece barrel catch that was operated by pushing down on knurled button at back of catch.

The Second Model had a T-shaped barrel catch with knurled buttons on each side to grip when lifting.

The Third Model had a front sight forged as an integral part of the barrel instead of being a pinned-in blade.

See S&W .38 Safety under .38 S&W.

.32 S and W

SMITH AND WESSON
Double Action

S&W MODEL 32 CALIBER DOUBLE ACTION REVOLVER (3rd MODEL).

Official Model Names: Model .32 Caliber Double Action First Model.
                          Model .32 Caliber Double Action Second Model.
                          Model .32 Caliber Double Action Third Model.
Ammunition: .32 S & W Short Cartridge.
Manufacturing Dates: First Model—Sept. 1880.
                         Second Model—1880-1889.
                         Third Model—1882-1889.
Number Manufactured: First Model—15.
                       Second Model—21,233.
                       Third Model—Approximately 21,000.
There are also Fourth and Fifth models of this arm. Production ceased in
1919. A total of over 327,000 of all models were made.
Finish: Blue and nickel.
Barrel Lengths: First Model—3″ only.
                  Second Model—3″.
                  Third Model—3″, 3½″, 6″, 8″, and 10″.

Land Diameter:	.303-.304	*Direction of Twist:*		Right
Groove Diameter:	.312-.313	*Diameter of Chambers:*	.3395-.3405	
Number of Lands:	5	*Number of Chambers*		5
Twist: One turn in	18¾″			

Notes: The Third Model differed from the Second Model principally in that
a spring-type stop was installed instead of the former rocker design.
The Fourth Model differed from the Third Model principally in that the rear
of the trigger guard was made to conform in shape to the trigger finger piece
instead of being a reverse curve. Also, the trigger stop and rear sear were
slightly redesigned so that action of the stop and sear was no longer exposed.

228

MISCELLANEOUS   .32 S and W

Weapons

Webley & Scott "WP" Models Hammer and Hammerless (See W&S under Caliber .320).

Belgian Bayard and German Pickert revolvers of all conventional designs will be found chambered for this cartridge. These arms are in the class of the H&R and Iver Johnson. Scores of nameless European types also are chambered for it.

Special Note: Any revolver chambered for the .32 Smith & Wesson Long Cartridge or for the .32 Colt New Police Cartridge will handle the .32 Smith & Wesson Cartridge.

.32 SMITH & WESSON LONG
98 Gr. Lub.

Muzzle Velocity in f.s.:	820
Vel. at 50 Feet:	803
Vel. at 150 Feet:	771

Calculated Energy

Muzzle Energy in ft. lbs.:	146
Energy at 50 Feet:	141
Energy at 150 Feet:	129

Calculated Drop

At 50 Feet:	.73 inch
At 150 Feet:	6.5 inches
At 300 Feet:	28.3 inches

Penetration at 15 Feet

7/8" soft pine boards	4

Length of Barrel in Which Tested

inches	4½

Shell Case

Weight:	27.5 grains
Max. Length:	.605 inch
Outside Body Dia. at Head, Max.:	.339 inch
Outside Body Dia. at Neck, Max.:	.339 inch
Inside Mouth Dia. Max.:	.313 inch
Volumetric Capacity to Base of Bullet in cubic inches:	.045

Bullet

Weight:	98 grains
Approx. Length:	.580 inch
Diameter Max.:	.314 inch
Area, Cross Sectional:	.0774 square inch
Shape:	Round Nose

Powder

Amount and type varies with different lots manufactured.

Cartridge

Approx. Length, Loaded:	.930 inch
Approx. Total Weight, Loaded:	137.5 grains

.32 Colt New Police

98 Gr. Lub.		Max. Length:	.920 inch
Muzzle Velocity in f.s.:	795	Outside Body Dia. at Head, Max.: .337 inch
Vel. at 50 Feet:	781	Outside Body Dia. at Neck, Max.: .337 inch
Vel. at 150 Feet:	754	Inside Mouth Dia. Max.: .3135 inch

98 Gr. Lub.

Muzzle Velocity in f.s.: 795
Vel. at 50 Feet: 781
Vel. at 150 Feet: 754

Calculated Energy

Muzzle Energy in ft. lbs.: 138
Energy at 50 Feet: 132
Energy at 150 Feet: 123

Calculated Drop

At 50 Feet: .80 inch
At 150 Feet: 7.4 inches
At 300 Feet: 30.5 inches

Penetration at 15 Feet

⅞" soft pine boards 3
Length of Barrel in Which Tested
inches 4

Shell Case

Weight: 34.5 grains

Max. Length: .920 inch
Outside Body Dia. at Head, Max.: .337 inch
Outside Body Dia. at Neck, Max.: .337 inch
Inside Mouth Dia. Max.: .3135 inch
Volumetric Capacity to Base of Bullet
in cubic inches: .022

Bullet

Weight: 98 grains
Approx. Length: .550 inch
Diameter Max.: .314 inch
Area, Cross Sectional: .0774 square inch
Shape: Blunt Nose

Powder

Amount and type varies with different lots manufactured.

Cartridge

Approx. Length, Loaded: 1.270 inches
Approx. Total Weight, Loaded: 137.5 grains

These cartridges are interchangeable. The principal difference between them lies in the fact that the S&W has a round nose bullet and the Colt bullet has a flat point which gives more effective stopping power.

.32 S and W Long

COLT

Pocket Positive (New Pocket)

General Description: Factory Model A. A pocket arm, built on a light .32 caliber frame with a curved stock—nearly uniform in cross section—and a partially rounded butt.

Ammunition: .32 Police Positive or S & W. .32 Long and Short Colt.

Manufacturing Dates: 1895 to 1943.

Serial Numbers: From Number 1.

Finish: Blue or nickel.

Barrel Length: .32 Pol. Pos. or S & W.: 2″, 2½″, 3½″, 6″; .32 Long and Short Colt, 2½″, 3½″, 6″.

Stocks: Rubber.

Bore Diameter: .305″—.001, all models.

Groove Diameter: .312″—.001, all models.

Rifling: (Left twist). 6 grooves. 1 turn in 16″.

Number of Shots: 6.

Action: Double.

Approximate Weight: 16 ounces with 2½″ barrel.

Over-all Length: 6½″ with 2½″ barrel.

Sights: Front: integral with barrel. Rear: a groove and notch in top of frame.

Note: Although bore dimensions are the same for the two cartridges, chamber dimensions are different. The Colt cartridge (both Long and Short—now obsolete) had a case and bullet of less diameter and used a hollow-base bullet which expanded sufficiently on firing to take the rifling. The original model had a square latch and solid firing pin. Refinements in design (probably about 1905) introduced a rounded latch, loose firing pin and a safety device, the Colt positive safety lock.

This model was fitted with the positive safety lock from serial Number 30,000 on.

.32 S and W Long

COLT

Police Positive

See Colt under Caliber .38 S&W.

.32 S and W Long

COLT

Police Positive Target (.32 Frame)

General Description: Factory Model H, center fire only. A light-frame target arm marking the beginning of a target-type revolver for general use (woods, trap line, etc.) rather than range use exclusively. (See Colt Police Positive Target Revolver, Factory Model G).

Ammunition: .32 Long and Short Colt. .32 New Police (Police Positive).

Manufacturing Dates: 1905 to 1925; originally not set up as a separate model, being produced concurrently with the New Police.

Serial Numbers: Number ending with 30,000; complete information not available.

Finish: Blue.

Barrel Length: 6″.

Stocks: Rubber.

Bore Diameter: .305″—.001, all models.
Groove Diameter: .312″—.001, all models.
Rifling: (Left twist), 6 grooves, 1 turn in 16″.
Number of Shots: 6.
Action: Double.
Approximate Weight: 19 ounces.
Over-all Length: 10½″.
Sights: Front: insert blade. Rear: drive in type.
Note: The two .32 cartridges in spite of similar barrel dimensions are not interchangeable. The Colt cartridge (now obsolete) used a smaller chamber and depended on the expansion of a hollow base to enable the bullet to take the rifling properly.
Note: Early models of the Colt Bisley and Single Action Army were also chambered for these cartridges. See these under Calibers .44-40 Winchester and .45 Colt respectively.

HARRINGTON AND RICHARDSON .32 S and W Long
Various Models

All late models of .32 Caliber will handle these cartridges as well as the short. (See H&R under Caliber .32 S&W).

IVER JOHNSON .32 S and W Long
Various Models

All comparatively late models where the cylinder contains 6 .32 caliber chambers will handle these cartridges. (Arms of this make in hinge frame models have only 5 chambers if bored solely for the .32 S&W cartridges.)

SMITH AND WESSON .32 S and W Long
Hand Ejector (1) First Model

S&W MODEL (I) .32 CALIBER HAND EJECTOR (1st MODEL). Note that this early type does not have the familiar thumb latch.

233

Ammunition: .32 S & W Long. This cartridge was designed for this gun.
Manufacturing Dates: 1896-1903.
Number Manufactured: 19,712.
Serial Numbers: From 1—19,712 in separate series.
Finish: Blue or Nickel.
Barrel Length: 3¼", 4¼", 6".

Land Diameter:	.303-.304	*Direction of Twist:*	**Right**
Groove Diameter:	.312-.313	*Length of Chamber:*	.886
Number of Lands:	5	*Diameter of Chamber:*	.3395-.3405
Lead:	18¾"	*Number of Chambers:*	6

Notes: This gun had two main features distinguishing it from the late .32 Hand Ejector Models: It did not have a barrel lug or locking bolt. The stop was installed in the top strap for the frame and operated by the action of the hammer when being cocked.

The Model (I) First Model was the first solid-frame, swing-out-cylinder revolver manufactured by Smith & Wesson.

.32 S and W Long   **SMITH AND WESSON**
                                                     Hand Ejector 1903

Official Model Names: Model (I) .32 Caliber Hand Ejector (Model of 1903).
Model (I) .32 Caliber Hand Ejector (Model of 1903-1st change).
Model (I) .32 Caliber Hand Ejector (Model of 1903-2nd Change).
Model (I) .32 Caliber Hand Ejector (Model of 1903-3rd Change).
Model (I) .32 Caliber Hand Ejector (Model of 1903-4th Change).
Model (I) .32 Caliber Hand Ejector (Model of 1903-5th Change).
Model (I) .32 Caliber Hand Ejector (Model of 1903-6th Change).

Ammunition: .32 S & W Long. This revolver will handle the .32 S & W Short, S & W Long, .32 Colt New Police (flat point), and .32 S & W Mid Range.
Manufacturing Dates: Model of 1903—January 1903—about Nov. 1904.
First Change—About Nov. 1904—Oct. 1906.
Second Change—About Oct. 1906-1909.
Third Change—About 1909.
Fourth Change—1910.
Fifth Change—1910—about 1917.
Sixth Change—About 1917 to date.

Serial Numbers: All models numbered in same series.
Finish: Blue or nickel.
Barrel Lengths: 3¼", 4¼", 6".
Principal Design Changes: Model of 1903 differed from First Model in that locking bolt was used, and a pivoting stop installed in bottom of frame.

First Change—Reciprocating stop.

Second Change—Rebound slide installed.

Third Change—Rebound slide key eliminated.

Fourth Change—Hand redesigned.

Fifth Change—Double action off hammer point instead of sear—extractor doweled and positioned by two pins—extractor rod knob solid on rod. From 1920 on, is the same as the Third Model Hand Ejector.

Sixth Change—Hammer block installed—heat-treated cylinders from 1920 on. Serial numbers from about 321,000.

Land Diameter:	.303-.304	*Direction of Twist:*	Right
Groove Diameter:	.312-.313	*Length of Chamber:*	.886
Number of Lands:	5	*Diameter of Chamber:*	.3395-.3405
Twist: One turn in	18¾″	*Number of Chambers:*	6

Sights: Front—fixed service type, 1/10″.

Rear—square notch cut in top of frame.

Note: Over-all length of latest (current) model with 6″ barrel is 10″. Weight with 3¼″ barrel—18 ounces. With 4¼″ barrel the weight is 18½ ounces. With 6″ barrel, 19¼ ounces.

SMITH AND WESSON   .32 S and W Long
Hand Ejector Third Model

Official Model Name: Model (I) .32 Caliber Hand Ejector (Third Model) Regulation Police. This arm is essentially the same as the Hand Ejector Sixth Change.

Ammunition: .32 S & W Long.

Manufacturing Dates: From 1920 to date.

Serial Numbers: Numbered in same series with .32 Hand Ejectors.

Finish: Blue and nickel.

Barrel Lengths: 3¼″, 4¼″, 6″; currently made in 2″, 3″, and 4″.

Land Diameter:	.303-.304	Direction of Twist:	**Right**
Groove Diameter:	.312-.313	Length of Chamber:	.886
Number of Lands:	5	Diameter of Chamber:	.3395-.3405
Twist: One turn in	18¾"	Number of Chambers:	6

Stocks: Formerly fitted with small square-butt regulation police stocks—could be fitted with oversize target stocks. Now normally found with rounded butt.

.32 S and W Long
SMITH AND WESSON
K-32 Hand Ejector First Model

Ammunition: .32 S & W Long.
Manufacturing Dates: Commercial production started in 1940.
Serial Numbers: Numbered in .38 Military & Police Series from about 690,000.
Finish: Blue only.
Barrel Length: 6".
Note: Similar to the Target version of the .38 Caliber Military & Police (Model of 1905—Fourth Change) except for chambering.

Land Diameter:	.303-.304	Direction of Twist:	**Right**
Groove Diameter:	.312-.313	Length of Chamber:	.886
Number of Lands:	5	Diameter of Chamber:	.3395-.3405
Twist: One turn in	18¾"	Number of Chambers:	6

Same as Model .38 Hand Ejector. Military & Police Model of 1905, 4th change Target.

.32 S and W Long
EUROPEAN
Various Models

Bayard and Pickert are the best of these. All makes and types previously covered may be found in these calibers, however. Spanish imitations of Colt and S&W revolvers are the poorest of these types.

**CARTRIDGE
Data**

.32-20 **Winchester**

.32 Win. (32-20)

100 Gr.		Max. Length:	1.285 inches
Muzzle Velocity in f.s.:	1030	Outside Body Dia. at Head, Max.:	.350 inch
Vel. at 50 Feet:	1011	Outside Body Dia. at Neck, Max.:	.3275 inch
Vel. at 150 Feet:	976	Inside Mouth Dia. Max.:	.310 inch
Calculated Energy		Volumetric Capacity to Base of Bullet	
Muzzle Energy in ft. lbs.:	271	in cubic inches:	.059
Energy at 50 Feet:	261	Bullet	
Energy at 150 Feet:	244	Weight:	115 grains
Calculated Drop		Approx. Length:	.645 inch
At 50 Feet:	.44 inch	Diameter Max.:	.312 inch
At 150 Feet:	3.9 inches	Area, Cross Sectional:	.0774 square inch
At 300 Feet:	18.2 inches	Shape:	Blunt Nose
Penetration at 15 Feet		Powder	
7/8" soft pine boards	6	Amount and type varies with different	
Length of Barrel in Which Tested		lots manufactured.	
inches	6	Cartridge	
Shell Case		Approx. Length, Loaded:	1.593 inches
Weight:	66 grains	Approx. Total Weight, Loaded:	192 grains

This cartridge was originally designed for the Winchester Model 1873 repeating rifle and was intended to use a load of 20 grains of the black powder then in use, hence the name .32-20. In actual practice when using black powder the load was generally well below 20 grains.

Colt issued revolvers chambered for the cartridge to permit the plainsman of those pioneer days to use the same ammunition in revolver and rifle.

Warning: High velocity .32-20 loads are intended solely for use in rifles. Before using .32-20 cartridges in any revolver read the box label carefully to make sure that the ammunition is standard revolver type. The high-velocity loads can be very dangerous in revolvers.

.32-20 Winchester   **BAYARD**
Revolvers

Bayard revolvers which are exact imitations of the Smith & Wesson swing-out cylinders are safe to use when chambered for the .32-20 revolver cartridge. Their finish, reliability, and accuracy are not as good as Colt and S&W arms.

.32-20 Winchester   **COLT**
Revolvers

Former models for this cartridge were the Single Action Army (see under Caliber .45 Colt), the Official Police (see under Caliber .38 S&W Special) and the Police Positive Special (see under Caliber .38 S&W Special).

.32-20 Winchester   **EUROPEAN**
Miscellaneous

See this heading under Caliber .38 S&W Special.

.32-20 Winchester   **SMITH AND WESSON**
Hand Ejector Winchester

Official Model Names: Model .32-20 Hand Ejector Winchester (First Model).
Model .32-20 Hand Ejector Winchester (Second Model, 1902)
Model .32-20 Hand Ejector Winchester (Model 1902-1st change)
Model .32-20 Hand Ejector Winchester (Model of 1905)
Model .32-20 Hand Ejector Winchester (Model of 1905-1st change)
Model .32-20 Hand Ejector Winchester (Model of 1905-2nd change)
Model .32-20 Hand Ejector Winchester (Model of 1905-3rd change)
Model .32-20 Hand Ejector Winchester (Model of 1905-4th change)

Ammunition: .32-20 Winchester Cartridge.

Manufacturing Dates: First Model—Mar. 24, 1899—1902.
Model of 1902—1902—Oct. 27, 1903.
Model of 1902, First Change—Oct. 27, 1903-May 1905.
Model of 1905—May 1905-Feb. 1906.
Model of 1905, First change—Feb. 1906—uncertain.
Model of 1905, Second change—Uncertain—Sept. 14, 1909.
Model of 1905, Third change—Sept. 14, 1909-April 20, 1915.
Model of 1905, Fourth change—April 20, 1915-1940.

Serial Numbers: Numbered consecutively in separate series.
Finish: Blue and nickel.
Barrel Lengths: 4", 5", 6", 6½", except on last two models for which 6½"-barrels were not made.

238

Land Diameter	.307-.308	Direction of Twist:	Right
Groove Diameter:	.312-.313	Diameter of Chamber	.328-.344-
Number of Lands:	5	.355	
Twist: One turn in	12"	Number of Chambers	6

Note: This model is practically the same as the Military & Police models and went through the same evolution of design changes. These will be covered under the Military & Police.

Note: This weapon is intended to use the *original* .32 Winchester Center Fire Cartridge, popularly called the .32-20. It should *never* be used with the high-velocity cartridge of the same caliber, which is loaded to pressures dangerous in revolvers.

Do not use .32 WCF ammunition in these revolvers unless the ammunition is from a reliable maker and the data on the cartridge box specifically state the contents may be used in revolvers.

For representative photographs, drawings and explanation of functioning see S&W under Caliber .38 S&W British, also Military & Police S&W models under Caliber .38 S&W Special. These are standard Smith & Wesson revolvers in swing-out cylinder, solid-frame models *only*.

.32 ACP

.32 AUTO

71 Gr. M.C.

Muzzle Velocity:	980
Vel. at 50 Feet:	956
Vel. at 150 Feet:	911

Calculated Energy

Muzzle Energy in Ft. Lbs.:	152
Energy at 50 Feet:	146
Energy at 150 Feet:	131

Calculated Drop

At 50 Feet:	.49 inches
At 150 Feet:	4.9 inches
At 300 Feet:	20.8 inches

Penetration at 15 Feet

5" Soft Pine Boards
Length of Barrel in Which Tested
4 inches

Shell Case

Weight:	42 grains
Max. Length:	.680 inch
Outside Body Dia. at Head, Max.:	.3375 inch
Outside Body Dia. at Neck, Max.:	.3365 inch
Inside Mouth Dia. Max.:	.3115 inch
Volumetric Capacity to Base of Bullet in cubic inches:	.021

Bullet

Weight:	74 grains
Approx. Length:	.475 inches
Diameter Max.:	.312 inches
Area, Cross Sectional:	.0763 inches
Shape:	M.C. Round Nose

Powder

Amount and type varies with different lots manufactured.

Cartridge

Approx. Length, Loaded:	.984 inches
Approx. Total Weight, Loaded:	122 grains

This cartridge was originally developed for use in the Browning Model 1900, the first truly successful pocket automatic pistol, manufactured by F. N. in Belgium. It is the most widely used and distributed automatic pistol cartridge made. Because its design and low power permit its use in unlocked pistols of light weight and low-cost construction, hundreds of types of blowback pistols have been designed to use this cartridge. It is generally known in Europe as the 7.65mm. Browning. While bullet weights, case measurements, and powder charges may vary slightly, for all practical purposes any European pistol of this caliber will handle U. S. ammunition.

Except for the Hungarian Frommer pistol which is fully locked, the American Savage which is insecurely locked, and the American Remington which was a delayed blowback, all automatic pistols of this caliber are unlocked types. The Schwarzlose is a blow-forward and all the others are elementary blowbacks. Note that in Europe cheap solid-frame revolvers were widely manufactured for this cartridge; this being possible because the cartridge case is not truly rimless but actually has a semi-rim on which the case seats in the chamber.

ALKARTASUNA   .32 ACP
Automatic

This pistol weighs about 34 ounces, has a 3⅝-inch barrel and measures 6⅜ inches overall. The capacity of the single-line box magazine is nine cartridges.

This is a cheap, heavy but very sturdily built .32 caliber automatic pistol of the straight blowback type with enclosed hammer. The design is essentially taken from the Colt .32 automatic, of which it is a very inferior copy. The magazine capacity is attained by having an unusually long grip holding an oversized magazine. A thumb safety is provided on the left side of the receiver which when turned up acts as a positive lock to prevent firing. The magazine release catch is at the rear in the bottom of the handle.

Weapons of this design may be found with the names of several Spanish makers or may be found with trade names stamped on them in lieu of the manufacturer's name. Under the name of the "Ruby automatic pistol," this weapon was a standard pistol in the French Army at the beginning of World War II.

In the period between the two World Wars huge quantities of this design were manufactured in Spain in varying qualities and under many brand names for American, Mexican, and South American export. They cannot be recommended for finish, accuracy, or general reliability.

The construction, operation, and takedown in general follow that of the

241

Colt .32 Automatic, though these Spanish arms seldom have the expensive grip safety.

The Alkartasuna was made by Alkartasuna Fabrica de Armas, Guernica, Spain.

.32 ACP	ASTRA
	Automatic

For representative photos and drawings of this Spanish automatic blowback pistol, see Astra under Caliber 9mm. Bayard Long. The smaller calibers differ essentially only in weight and length.

The Astra is one of the best of the Spanish pistols. The most popular of its models are those which are modifications of the Browning Model 1910.

Manufactured by Unceta y Cia, Guernica, Spain.

.32 ACP	BAYARD
	Old Model

This Belgian pistol is fully described under Bayard under Caliber .380 A.C.P. See also Bayard in the Identification Section under Caliber .32 A.C.P. This Bayard is one of the smallest pistols ever built for its cartridge and suffers from heavy recoil. It is not a particularly sturdy weapon. Magazines were of two sizes, six and eight shots. It was manufactured at Herstal, Belgium by Anciens Establissements Pieper.

.32 ACP	BAYARD
	1930

This model was introduced as a sturdier type than its predecessor. It, too, is a typical blowback with standard Colt-type slide and enclosed firing mechanism. Magazine capacity is six cartridges. A positive thumb safety is provided on the left side of the receiver to the rear of the trigger. See the Identification Section for other data. The 1930 was developed from a modification issued in 1923, the two being very much alike.

.32 ACP	BEHOLLA
	Automatic

For photograph and general data, see the Identification Section.

This pistol was originally manufactured in Germany by Becker & Hollander of Suhl, was widely used by the Germans in World War I and appeared again during the recent World War. (Note: This design was made in several factories and may be encountered bearing the manufacturing name of Leonhardt, Menta, or Stenda, who designed it.) It is the elementary blowback design with recoil spring housed below the barrel. Its one unusual characteristic is its system of barrel mounting which permits barrel removal by driving out a barrel locking pin through special holes in the slide.

.32 ACP	BERETTA
	1915

Berettas are the best of the Italian manufactured automatic pistols. See the

Identification Section for photos and descriptive data. For a description of the construction, takedown, and functioning of this model, see Beretta 1915 under Caliber .380 A.C.P. This is a simple blowback pistol with enclosed hammer, detachable box magazine and thumb safety.

Berettas are manufactured by the firm of Pietro Beretta, Brescia, Italy, one of the oldest arms manufacturers in the world.

BERETTA   **.32 ACP**
1931

BERETTA MODEL 1931 CALIBER .32 A.C.P. This was the official pistol of the Italian Navy. Note the insigne on the stock. It was also sold commercially. The spur projecting from the magazine is a finger rest.

The improved model with exposed hammer, more efficient slide, sturdier construction and automatic disconnector was originally issued in 1923. It was modified in 1931 and again in 1934.

This pistol weighs about 22 ounces, has a 3 5/16-inch barrel and measures 5¾ inches overall. Magazine capacity is seven cartridges. Except in dimensions it is identical with the .380 Caliber introduced in 1934. For additional

representative photographs, complete description of construction and functioning and working drawings see Beretta 1934 under Caliber .380 A.C.P.

This well-made and otherwise entirely reliable arm has an inefficient thumb
safety which locks the trigger but not the hammer or sear. This is not a positive safety and the pistol should not be carried with the chamber loaded and
hammer up and safety on. If the chamber is loaded it is safer to lower the
hammer to half cock when carrying the pistol.

.32 ACP   **BROWNING**
1900

*BROWNING 1900—the father of pocket automatic pistols. This is the basic type from
which all blowback pocket pistols draw their general principles of operation. It is obsolete
and currently rarely encountered. This pistol weighs about 22 ounces and measures about 6¾
inches overall. The barrel is 4 inches long. The magazine holds seven cartridges.*

This was the first successful pistol invented by John M. Browning. The
manufacturers, Fabrique Nationale, held an official jubilee to celebrate the
manufacture of the one millionth automatic pistol of this type at their factory
at Liege, Belgium in July, 1912.

This was the first commercially successful blowback pistol. It set the pattern
for most of the successful pocket automatic pistols since developed. This pistol
introduced the 7.65mm. Browning Automatic Pistol cartridge, which had been
developed from the unsuccessful Bergmann-Simplex. It was introduced into
the United States as the .32 Automatic Colt Pistol cartridge.

Basic Model Data

AUTOMATIC PISTOL: Belgian Browning 1900.

LENGTH: About 6¾ inches.

BARREL: 4 inches.

WEIGHT: 22 ounces.

MAGAZINE: Detachable box in handle. 7 cartridges.

OPERATION: Semi-automatic.

LOCK: Blowback, unlocked.

MAINSPRING: Leaf operating striker through lever.

DISCONNECTOR: Part of trigger bar design. Bar cannot engage with sear after firing until trigger is released and spring forces bar ahead.

TRIGGER: Transmits pressure through trigger bar across magazine well.

SAFETY: Thumbpiece on left side of receiver. Positively blocks striker movement.

INDICATOR: Upper arm of cocking lever protrudes through slide into line of sight when arm is *uncocked*.

RECOIL SPRING: Spiral with guide mounted in slide forging above barrel.

FIRING MECHANISM: Striker.

CALIBER: .32 A.C.P. (7.65mm. Browning).

NOTE: Early experimental models with minor manufacturing differences are sometimes encountered. These are largely war loot from special collections.

245

Construction. This pistol differs radically from every other design ever produced by John M. Browning. The slide forging houses the recoil spring and its guide in a tunnel above the barrel, while the barrel is held rigidly in the receiver by a locking lug. The forward section of the barrel is supported by the lower tubular section of the slide. The breechblock is a detachable screw-fastened unit which mounts in the slide above the line of the receiver. A lever is so mounted in the slide that during the opening motion of the slide the compressed recoil spring transmits pressure through its guide rod to this lever, causing its lower end, which is engaged with the striker, to force the striker back against its spring pressure until it is caught and held by the sear. The sear is supported by its leaf spring housed in the grip behind the magazine well, where the flat mainspring is also housed. The magazine is inserted in the handle and is the familiar sheet-metal box type, retained by a catch at the bottom of the handle. The trigger operates through a bar passing across the magazine well and in engagement with the sear and with the trigger leaf spring.

Operation. A loaded magazine is inserted in the handle and pushed in until the catch engages. The serrated breech piece is grasped and drawn back carrying the slide with it. This motion compresses the recoil spring which causes the guide to rock the cocking lever and force the lower end of the lever to carry the striker back tensioning its spring. At full cock the sear spring forces the sear into engagement with the striker. Meanwhile the upper end of the lever is forced down into a cut in the top of the slide clearing the line of sight. The slide is released to run forward under the pull of the recoil spring and chamber the top cartridge which the magazine spring has forced up into line during the opening slide stroke. Pressure on the trigger will now force the bar back against the sear. The sear forced out of engagement with the cut in the striker permits the mainspring leaf to act through a lever to drive the striker home to fire the cartridge. The rearward thrust of the gases against the head of the cartridge case is transmitted to the face of the breechblock starting the rearward movement to extract, eject, and recock, and to load up the recoil spring which will then pull the slide forward to reload from the magazine. The trigger bar cannot engage with the sear to fire the next shot until finger pressure is released, permitting the trigger leaf spring to push the bar and trigger ahead to point of sear engagement.

.32 ACP   **BROWNING**
                                                                     1910

This model weighs about 20½ ounces, has a 3½-inch barrel and measures about 6 inches overall. Magazine capacity is seven cartridges. For photograph of this striker-fired blowback pistol see the Identification Section. (Note: The D.W.M. pistol pictured in this section is an accurate copy of the Browning 1910 except for the stocks).

This pistol design has been widely imitated and modified. The 1935 catalog of the manufacturers, Fabrique Nationale, stated that over one million of this model had been sold at that time.

This arm differs radically from all the Brownings which preceded it. It was first marketed in 1912, but the factory designation is 1910.

Construction: Essentially the weapon is composed of the slide, barrel, magazine and receiver-and-frame assemblies. The receiver and frame are in one piece and incorporate the grip in standard fashion. This holds a grip safety, a manual thumb safety and a Browning disconnector. The barrel is locked into the receiver ahead of the magazine well by revolving it so that locking lugs on its underside mesh with mating grooves in the receiver well. The slide is of the rounded type surrounding the barrel and providing its own support at the front end. The recoil spring is mounted around the barrel and its front end is compressed by the slide during its rearward motion against a barrel abutment at the rear. The slide travels in grooves in the receiver.

A bushing retained by a bayonet-type lock is inserted in the front end of the slide around the barrel and serves as the forward resistance point for the recoil spring as well as a guide for it during compression.

The extractor, firing pin, and spring are mounted in the breechblock section of the slide. A point on the striker acts as the ejector to hurl the empty shell out of the weapon during the recoil movement of the slide.

The grip safety is so arranged that its upper end locks the disconnector preventing the trigger from being pulled when the grip safety is out. When the weapon is held firmly in the hand, the disconnector is freed, permitting the trigger to be pulled. When the thumb safety on the left side is pushed up, it locks the grip safety and prevents it from being moved to allow firing. An extension on the safety lever when it is in this position reaches into a cut in the slide to prevent the slide being opened.

This arm also has a magazine safety. When the magazine is withdrawn, a lever is forced by a spring against the grip safety preventing it from being pushed in, thus making it impossible to discharge the weapon. The slide however may be drawn back by hand to clear the chamber. Only one shot may be fired for each pull of the trigger. A positive disconnector is incorporated in the weapon and its connection with the trigger is broken when the slide moves away from the fully closed position.

Dismounting. (1) Remove the magazine and draw back the slide to check the firing chamber to be sure there is no cartridge there. (2) Holding the weapon in the right hand to force the grip safety in, push the slide back until the thumb safety catch can be thrust up to engage in the hold open notch on the slide. (3) Turn the barrel far enough to release its locking lugs from the receiver. (4) Holding the weapon firmly in the right hand, grasp the slide and push the thumb safety catch out of engagement to permit the compressed recoil spring to push the slide forward. (This arm has a striker and spring mounted under the slide. Care must be taken when the slide is removed to see that these units do not fly out.) (5) Push the slide and barrel assemblies straight ahead out of their guides in the receiver. (6) Twist the barrel to the left and let it go forward under the compression of the recoil spring around it. (7) Push in and turn the bushing around the muzzle of the barrel to unlock it from its grooves in the slide and withdraw it. (8) The barrel with the recoil spring around it may now be moved out of the front of the slide.

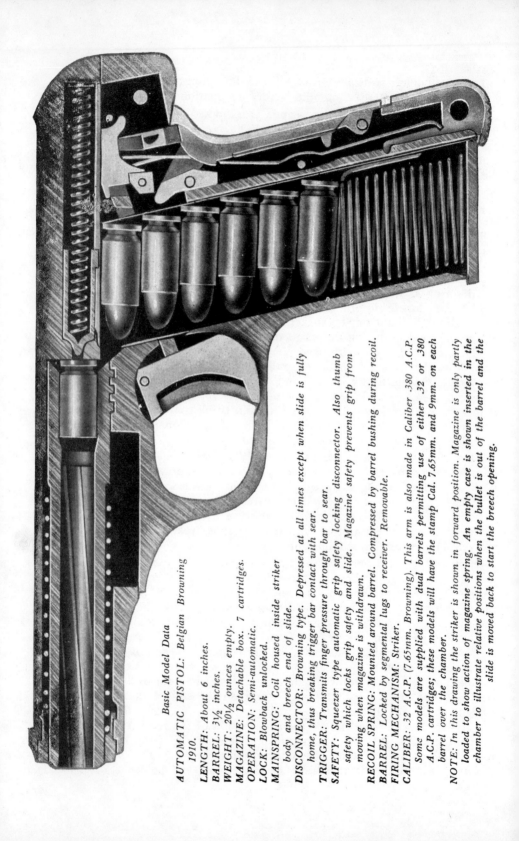

Basic Model Data

AUTOMATIC PISTOL: Belgian Browning 1910.

LENGTH: About 6 inches.

BARREL: 3½ inches.

WEIGHT: 20½ ounces empty.

MAGAZINE: Detachable box. 7 cartridges.

OPERATION: Semi-automatic.

LOCK: Blowback unlocked.

MAINSPRING: Coil housed inside striker body and breech end of slide.

DISCONNECTOR: Browning type. Depressed at all times except when slide is fully home, thus breaking trigger bar contact with sear.

TRIGGER: Transmits finger pressure through bar to sear.

SAFETY: Squeezer type automatic grip safety locking disconnector. Also thumb safety which locks grip safety and slide. Magazine safety prevents grip from moving when magazine is withdrawn.

RECOIL SPRING: Mounted around barrel. Compressed by barrel bushing during recoil.

BARREL: Locked by segmental lugs to receiver. Removable.

FIRING MECHANISM: Striker.

CALIBER: .32 A.C.P. (7.65nm. Browning). This arm is also made in Caliber .380 A.C.P. Some models are supplied with dual barrels permitting use of either .32 or .380 A.C.P. cartridges; these models will have the stamp Cal. 7.65mm. and 9mm. on each barrel over the chamber.

NOTE: In this drawing the striker is shown in forward position. Magazine is only partly loaded to show action of magazine spring. An empty case is shown inserted in the chamber to illustrate relative positions when the bullet is out of the barrel and the slide is moved back to start the breech opening.

BROWNING   **.32 ACP**
1922

This model is merely an enlarged version of the 1910 designed to provide greater sighting radius, better balance, and greater magazine capacity for use as a law enforcement pistol. It weighs about 25 ounces empty, has a 4½-inch barrel and measures 7 inches overall. Magazine capacity nine cartridges.

The barrel was lengthened in the interests of accuracy. To permit utilization of machinery in the factory, and make it unnecessary to provide new slides, an extension was provided for the forward end of the slide. It is fastened with a bayonet-joint lock which has a spring to prevent its working loose. The grip was lengthened to receive a longer magazine and a lanyard swivel was provided at the bottom of the grip.

This model also was made in Caliber .380 ACP (9mm. Browning Short). This design has been extensively imitated and modified, particularly in Spain and may be encountered under dozens of brand names.

CLEMENT   **.32 ACP**
Automatic

This Belgian blowback pistol is the basic type from which the American Smith & Wesson .35 Automatic Pistol was designed. (Under Caliber .35 Auto. see S&W). See the Identification Section for a photograph of the Clement. It weighs about 20 ounces, measures about 5.9 inches overall and has a magazine capacity of six cartridges.

Like the S&W the breechlock is not part of a heavy slide unit as in the Colt-Browning, but is a lightweight member extending back from the face of

249

BROWNING 1922: Note that this pistol is the same as the 1910 Model except for longer grip and barrel, and extension at forward end of slide. These pistols are occasionally found with specially matched barrels in 7.65 mm and 9 mm (32 and 380 A.C.P.) calibers. It is necessary only to switch barrels to change calibers in such pistols. The magazines will take either cartridge. Usually, but not always, these matched barrels bear both caliber stamps over the breech section which can be seen through the slide ejection port.

the cartridge chamber only. To facilitate cocking and loading the breechblock can be easily disengaged from the powerful recoil spring housed in the tunnel above the barrel proper in the barrel unit forging. See S&W for general construction and operating details of this unusual system. The Clement has a thumb safety on the left side of the receiver.

COLT   **.32 ACP**
Auto. Pocket

Official Model Name: Automatic Pocket .32 caliber.

General Description: A pocket or holster arm for home and personal protection combining safety with simplicity and convenience. In common with all modern Colt automatics, this pistol has a one-piece slide and breechblock fitted on the receiver from the front as a protection against the danger of slide blowing off to the rear as can happen with defective rear-mounted slides.

Ammunition: .32 A.C.P.

Manufacturing Dates: From 1903 to 1941, when it was discontinued.

Serial Numbers: From number 1.

Finish: Blue or nickel.

Barrel Length: 3¾"—present design with lug at muzzle end of barrel. 3¾"—

straight barrel assembled to arm with a barrel bushing. 4″—first model straight barrel assembled to arm with a barrel bushing.

Stocks: Rubber or checked walnut with medallion.
Bore Diameter: .305″—.001.
Groove Diameter: .312″—.001.
Rifling: (Left twist) 6 grooves, 1 turn in 16″.
Number of Shots: 8.
Action: Semiautomatic blowback.
Approximate Weight: 24 ounces.
Over-all Length: 6¾″.
Sights: Fixed. Front: swaged in slide. Rear: driven in place.
Note: First model barrel used to Number 72,000, 2nd model from there to

Number 105,050. A safety disconnector was incorporated at Number 468,097 preventing discharge of the arm with magazine withdrawn. This pistol has a hammer covered by the slide. It can be cocked only by rearward movement of the slide.

This pistol was designed by John M. Browning and appeared in Belgium in Caliber 9mm. (.380) Browning Long under the designation of Military Model 1903. The working drawing shown with the Browning 1903 (under Caliber .380 or 9mm. Browning Long) covers the Colt .32 and .380 Automatics for general purposes. Differences are minor.

The main parts of these pistols are the receiver, the barrel, and the slide. Except for caliber, the weapons are identical in construction. The receiver has guides to permit the slide to be mounted on it and to travel in it. The handle is hollow as usual to receive the cartridge magazine. The magazine is inserted in the handle from below and held there by the magazine catch at the bottom of the receiver. Pushing back the catch permits the magazine to be withdrawn from the handle.

The trigger is mounted in the trigger guard section of the receiver. It is a stirrup-type trigger with an arm passing across the receiver around both sides of the magazine.

The hammer, sear, disconnector, and mainspring, as well as the sear safety and trigger springs, are all mounted in the rear of the receiver behind the magazine well in the grip. Transverse recesses are provided in the receiver above the line of the trigger to receive the locking lugs on the barrel to retain the barrel in position.

The muzzle end of the barrel protrudes through its slot in the front end of the slide and is securely locked to the receiver (*but not to the slide*) at all times when the pistol is assembled. This is effected by locking lugs on its underside which lock securely into the recesses in the receiver.

The magazine is a standard tubular holder with perforations in both side walls to permit the number of cartridges in the magazine to be counted.

The rear end of the slide serves as the breechblock where it is machined out to receive the firing pin and extractor and to permit the hammer to swing up from the receiver. A niche cut in its underside on the left-hand side receives the point of the disconnector when the action is fully forward.

The front end of the slide is machined out to receive the barrel in its upper section while a tubular section extending back from the line below the muzzle to the tip of the receiver is used to accommodate the recoil spring and its plug and guide.

As the slide is mounted on the receiver grooves from the front, and the slide and breechblock are one solid unit, no powder gas can blow back.

This pistol is fitted with the famous Colt disconnector. This is a small vertical piece mounted on a pin just ahead of the sear in the receiver. When the weapon is fully closed, the upper end of this disconnector projects from the top of the receiver into a slot in the underside of the slide. When it is thus raised, this disconnector does not interfere with the operation of the trigger. *If the slide is moved back at all,* either manually or by recoil, this rearward action of the slide forces the top of the disconnector down into the receiver. In this position the lower arm of the disconnector prevents the movement of the trigger bar from operating the sear; hence the hammer cannot be released by the sear until the slide is fully forward against the face of the barrel.

Operation: As in all Colt automatic pistols, when a loaded magazine has been inserted in the handle, the slide must be grasped firmly at the rear end and drawn back as far as possible to cock the hammer and allow a cartridge to rise in line with the breechblock. This action also compresses the recoil spring. When the slide is released to go forward it chambers a cartridge, snaps the extractor over the extracting groove, and brings the disconnector slot in the slide in position where the spring from below can force the disconnector up into its niche, thus leaving the firing hookup ready for a pull of the trigger.

This being a straight blowback pistol without any form of locking device except the weight and inertia of the moving parts and the recoil spring, the slide starts back at the same time that the bullet starts down the barrel.

However, since the inertia of the moving parts is tremendously greater than that of the bullet, the bullet is out of the barrel before the action has opened enough to be dangerous.

The backward pressure of gases, exerted through the head of the cartridge case to the breechblock part of the slide, starts the action backwards. The extractor, caught in the extracting groove of the cartridge case, guides it in a straight line until it strikes the ejector. It is ejected through the port in the right side of the slide. At this point the magazine spring, forcing the follower and cartridges above it upward, brings the top cartridge into line for the breechblock to pick up on its forward movement.

Meanwhile the recoil spring (housed in the receiver and the lower section of the slide below the barrel) has been compressed against its stop and around its guide. The breechblock section of the slide has pushed back and run over the head of the hammer, rotating it on its axis pin in the receiver.

Note that this weapon differs from the .25 Colt automatic in that it is not a striker-operated weapon, but has a hammer which is fully enclosed by a recess in the rear of the slide and the receiver. *While it is called a hammerless weapon, it is actually a concealed-hammer pistol.*

The disconnector having been forced down by the slide, the sear can snap into engagement in the notch in the hammer and hold it in full-cocked position, but cannot permit its release until tension on the trigger has been released for an instant, thereby re-establishing trigger and sear contact.

The hammer spring or mainspring in this weapon is a long leaf spring housed in the grip section of the receiver and mounted on the lower end against the movable steel grip which provides an automatic safety in this pistol.

One end of the sear spring, which also functions the disconnector and the trigger, holds the magazine release catch in place. This spring has three leaves.

When the slide goes forward to chamber a cartridge, releasing the trigger for an instant permits *the disconnector leaf* of the spring to force the disconnector up, since a second arm of this spring forces the trigger ahead to a position where it can engage with the sear. The pistol is now ready for another shot.

Note that it is absolutely impossible to fire more than one shot for each pull of the trigger with this weapon. This is a necessary safety device. Also observe that this weapon cannot be fired until the breech is fully closed, as it might be dangerous if the weapon were otherwise constructed.

Dismounting: First remove the magazine by pushing back the magazine catch at the rear at the bottom of the receiver and withdrawing the magazine.

Check to be sure there is no cartridge in the firing chamber.

Push in the grip safety and draw the slide back to cock the weapon.

Now insert the left thumb through the trigger guard and grip the first finger up around the left-hand top of the slide.

Push the slide back with the right hand and then tighten the grip of the left hand to hold the slide in rearward position just short of fully retracted.

On the right side of the slide at its front end is an arrow with a perpendicular line at its point. Hold the slide back far enough that this perpendicular line on the slide is right against the edge of the receiver.

At this position, the barrel may be twisted to the left, so that the locking lugs on its lower surface will be revolved out of their locking recesses in the receiver. Note that the slide is machined out to permit the barrel to be revolved *at this point only.*

The slide, recoil spring, and barrel may now be moved forward off the receiver. Recoil spring and guide may now be lifted out of the slide.

Revolve the barrel back to its original position with its locking lugs pointing downward from the slide (when the slide is held in its normal position) and the barrel may now be pulled forward out of its seat in the slide.

The barrel may be removed for cleaning without taking the slide out as follows: Hold the slide back as indicated heretofore with the perpendicular line ahead of the arrow lined up with the receiver on the right-hand side of the pistol. Turn the barrel to the left as far as it will go. Then let the slide move forward slowly. When it is fully forward, the barrel may be revolved to its original position (as far to the right as possible) and drawn out of the front end of the slide.

Remove the stock screws and the stocks may be lifted off. Drifting out the various retaining pins will permit the removal of the grip safety, the hammer, sear, trigger, and disconnector mechanisms. The thumb safety may also be withdrawn from its slot in the receiver. The firing pin and spring may be removed from the receiver by drifting out the retaining pin.

Reassembling: Hold the slide so you can look down inside it and insert the barrel with the locking ribs up so you can see them. Twist the barrel one-quarter turn right or left so the locking ribs will fit into a recess prepared for them in the upper part of the slide. You will have to "feel" for this recess.

With the slide still held upside down, fit it to the front end of the receiver. Make sure that the forward end of the recoil spring enters the recess for it in the lower part of the slide. Push the slide to the rear until the perpendicular line in front of the arrow on the right side of the slide is lined up with the edge of the front end of the receiver.

Move the barrel carefully until it engages (meanwhile maintaining the slide in position) and when the lugs on the barrel are lined up with their recesses in the receiver, turn the barrel as far as it will go to the right. The barrel is then fully locked to the receiver and the slide may be allowed to go forward to its fully closed position.

If the firing mechanism has been dismounted, care must be taken in reassembling to see that the springs are inserted in proper position. The mainspring must be inserted so that its small lower arm faces toward the magazine well. The three-leafed spring must be inserted so that its lower single-piece end will press against the magazine catch directly ahead of the lower short arm of the mainspring. Its three upper arms must engage the disconnector, trigger, and sear. The disconnector is properly inserted when its upper end *curves toward the front.*

If the barrel has been withdrawn and the slide left on the receiver, reinsert the barrel as follows: Insert the barrel in the front end of the slide until the front end of its center guide band is just in the front end of the slide. Twist it one-quarter turn.

Then draw the slide back until the line ahead of the arrow is lined up with the front end of the receiver and twist the barrel as far as it will go to the right.

CZ   .32 ACP
1927

This Czech pistol usually bears the CZ mark of the Ceskoslovenska Zbrojovka, akc, SPOL factory, but WW II versions may have the name Bohmische Waffenfabrik A.G.Prague on the top of the slide. The pistol is a simple blowback design weighing about 25 ounces, measuring about 6 1/3 inches overall and having a magazine capacity of eight cartridges.

The CZ Model 1927 is a composite arm incorporating a modified Colt barrel-mounting system and a modified Mauser 1910 lockwork. It can hardly be classed as an improvement on either one, though it is a well made and well finished pistol.

Construction. The principal parts of this pistol are: (1) The receiver which

serves as the handle and contains the lockwork. Its extension forward of the trigger guard reaches to the end of the slide. Guides are provided in the top of the receiver for the slide travel. (2) The slide which forms the breechblock. It has a bushing at its forward end which also acts as a compressor for the recoil spring which is mounted on a rod-type guide in the receiver well below the barrel. (3) A Mauser-type removable side plate on the left side of the receiver which is tongued in and which protects the lockwork. (4) A shaped unit which seats in the receiver tube above the trigger guard and which is designed to receive and lock the segmental lugs on the barrel. This unit or lock (unlike the Colt where it is part of the receiver forging) is removable and when in position is retained by a pin passing through the receiver walls at its front end, and by the pressure of the recoil spring which abuts against it. The locking pin has a spring-held sliding head which retains it in position. (5) The lockwork. Except that it has an exposed hammer which barely protrudes from the slide (the Mauser 1910 uses a striker), the lockwork is much like the Mauser. The trigger is Mauser pattern. The sear bar runs under the removable side plate, its nose engaging in a bent (or cut) in the left side of the hammer, its tail pivoted to a cam-shaped disconnector. This disconnector rises into a niche in the underside of the slide when the slide is fully forward. Any rearward or opening movement of the slide will ride over the cam-shaped disconnector and break the trigger contact to prevent the arm being fired. A

coil spring below the disconnector forces it up. Pressure on the trigger pivots
it on its pin causing the nose to raise the disconnector and the tail of the
attached sear, thereby drawing the nose of the sear out of hammer engagement. The mainspring in this lockwork is a leaf spring attached to the inside
of the grip section of the receiver. When the hammer rolls back, its mainspring
notch in engagement with the top of the leaf tensions it. The sear spring is
a very small coil spring seated below the sear nose. The sear pivots on a
bushing. (6) The safety. This is a direct Mauser copy. Pushing down the
thumb catch on the left side of the receiver behind the trigger forces a safety
bar into contact with the rear of the sear positively preventing it from being
lowered out of engagement with the hammer. This thumb catch is fitted with
a spring, and pressing the small button below the catch releases it and removes
the safety bar. While this is a positive hammer and sear block safety, it has
the disadvantage that the release button is so small that it is difficult to release
it in a hurry.

As in the Beretta, the magazine follower rises and holds the slide open
when the last cartridge has been fired to warn that the weapon is empty.
Much force is necessary to withdraw the magazine. The slide then runs forward on an empty chamber. Thus, it is necessary to draw the slide back
manually to reload the firing chamber when a loaded magazine is inserted.

Dismounting. Pull back the slide. If the weapon is empty, the magazine
follower will hold the slide open. If there are any cartridges in the weapon,
work the slide back and forth until they are all ejected and the slide stays back.

When the slide is back, pressure is off the fixing pin which holds the barrel
unit locked to the slide and receiver. A milled thumbpiece mounted on the
frame or receiver directly above the front of the trigger guard on the left-hand
side of the weapon may now be slid down in a groove, if the projecting pin on
the right is pushed flush with the receiver. This thumbpiece and attached
barrel locking pin may then be withdrawn to the left.

While holding the slide firmly against spring pressure, press the catch in the
bottom of the handle and withdraw the magazine. As the magazine is with
drawn, the slide is free to go forward. Let it move forward slowly.

Draw the slide off the front of the receiver.

The mounting block for the barrel and the recoil spring and guide may
now be lifted off.

Remove the housing and slide the barrel out.

Remove the stock screws and take off the stocks. This will give further
access to the lockwork if necessary for further dismounting. The cover plate
on the left side of the grip may be worked up out of the receiver, exposing
the disconnector cam and sear lever and springs.

DREYSE   .32 ACP
1907

This German striker-fired blowback weighs about 24 ounces, has a 3.58-inch
barrel and measures about 6¼ inches overall. The magazine holds eight
cartridges. The arm is made of first-class materials and is a product of the

former great Rheinische Metallwaren & Maschinenfabrik of Sommerda. It is a most unusual design, costly to machine and not particularly efficient.

Construction and Operation. The barrel, slide, and recoil spring units are mounted in a forging hinged to the true receiver at the forward end of the trigger guard. The assembly is locked at the rear of the pistol by a spring latch when in firing order. The barrel is fastened securely in a tubular extension below the slide. The recoil spring is around the barrel, being held by a spring locked bushing at the forward end. This collar is engaged with the slide, so that as the slide goes back it compresses the recoil spring around the barrel. The rear section of the intricately machined slide serves as the breechblock; the extractor and the striker and spring are mounted in it. The rear of the striker passes through a hole when cocked to serve as an indicator.

The magazine is the standard box type inserted in the handle from below. A swinging thumb safety of standard pattern is mounted on the left of the receiver.

The recoil spring is particularly stiff, and the slide because of its unique construction must be drawn back by gripping it near the muzzle. This is necessary because the breechblock section of the slide is housed in the support forging and cannot be gripped; its rear emerges from the support forging during rearward travel. Gripping serrations are provided at the forward end of the slide.

The trigger pull is bad because of the peculiar lockwork which was intended as a safety feature. When the slide has been pulled back to cock the striker, pressure on the trigger does not free the sear from engagement directly as in other automatic pistols. Instead the sear draws the striker back against main-spring pressure until the striker bent escapes from the sear to let the main-spring drive the striker forward to fire. Note that while this somewhat duplicates the design of a double-action automatic, it actually will not cock the striker for firing. It is a supplementary pull which can take place only when the striker is cocked by drawing the slide back.

Ejection is through a small port in the right side of the support forging.

Dismounting. Pushing the catch at the top of the rear of the receiver frees the barrel and slide assemblies and as a unit they can be hinged open. The barrel bushing must be pushed in around the barrel far enough to permit the slide to be disengaged from the mounting lug on top of the bushing. The recoil spring can then be eased out. Raising the slide about 30 degrees will permit it to be drawn forward out of the support forging.

DWM   **.32 ACP**
Automatic

This striker-fired blowback pistol weighs about 20½ ounces, has a 3½-inch barrel and measures six inches overall. The magazine capacity is seven car-tridges.

It was manufactured by the Deutsche Waffen-und-Munitionsfabriken, orig-inal manufacturers of the famous Luger pistol.

It is a straight blowback weapon of the unlocked breech type, noteworthy only for the very fine finish, common to all products of that manufacturing company, and because of the excellent balance of the pistol. It is fitted with both a thumb and a grip safety. The magazine is inserted in the handle from below in standard fashion.

It may be recognized by the monogram "DWM" and German proof marks stamped on the slide. This pistol was never put into very extensive production, but occasional samples will be encountered which have been brought here from Europe by returning servicemen. Very few were ever imported into the country.

Essentially this is a German version of the Belgium 1910 Browning pistol.

.32 ACP   **FROMMER**
                                                                        Stop

The Frommer was, in .32 ACP, used by the Hungarians to some degree in World War I. After the war it was manufactured in the original .32 ACP caliber and also in .380 under the name of Frommer Stop. This model must not be confused with the elementary Frommer 1901 design which used the special short .32 Roth Sauer cartridge.

The Frommer Stop weighs about 22 ounces, has a 3⅞-inch barrel and measures 6½ inches overall. The magazine holds seven cartridges. A pocket model known as the Frommer Baby is mechanically the same but is shorter, lighter and has a five-shot magazine. (See the Identification Section). The Frommer differs radically from every other automatic pistol of low power (.32 ACP and

.380 ACP). The breech is fully locked until the bullet is out of the barrel. However, it should be noted that the locking system is totally unnecessary with these low-powered cartridges, and the design is expensive and fragile.

Construction and Operation. The locking system in this weapon is of unique design. It is the so-called long-recoil system, in which the barrel and bolt recoil locked together the full length of the cartridge case. When the barrel stops re-coiling, the *bolt is held to the rear while the barrel moves forward.*

The locking is positive and is brought about by lugs on a rotating bolt head which engage in recesses in the barrel extension. The bolt is held back by a catch to complete unlocking as the barrel moves forward.

Another unusual feature of this weapon is that return energy is stored by two coil springs above the barrel and the bolt. They are both compressed during the rearward action. The recoil spring proper pushes the barrel back to forward position. The lesser, or bolt spring, returns the bolt to its forward locking position.

Operation: This weapon is loaded in ordinary automatic-pistol fashion: insert a charged magazine in the handle from below, and push it in until it locks; pull back the knurled knobs on the bolt head just ahead of the hammer to draw the recoiling members as far as possible to the rear; then release the bolt, permitting it to run forward and load the firing chamber.

Observe that the barrel and the bolt are completely enclosed in a special barrel casing which, while it resembles the slide of the customary automatic pistol, *does not move.* The hammer is an external one of rather unusual shape.

As the trigger is pressed, it moves the sear lever back to contact the tail of

Bolt being drawn back to load firing chamber. Note that receiver is one piece and that bolt and guide rod move inside the receiver casing.

261

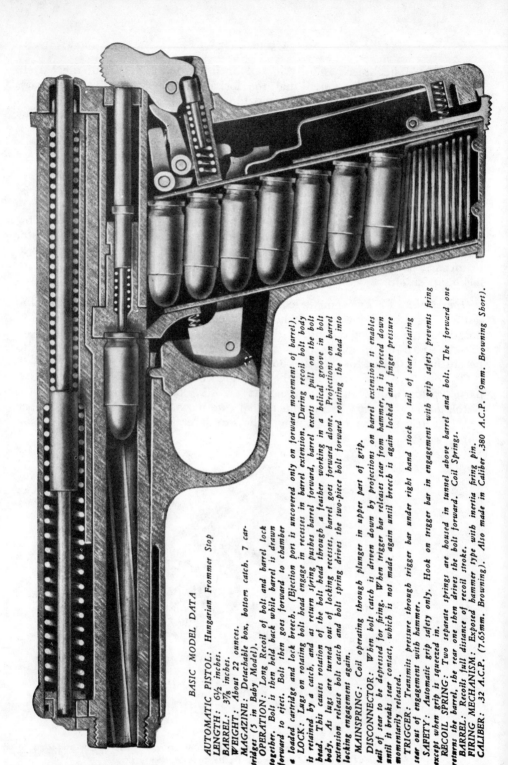

BASIC MODEL DATA

AUTOMATIC PISTOL: Hungarian Frommer Stop
LENGTH: 6½ inches.
BARREL: 3⅞ inches.
WEIGHT: About 22 ounces.
MAGAZINE: Detachable box, bottom catch. 7 cartridges (5 in Baby Model).
OPERATION: Long Recoil of bolt and barrel lock together. Bolt is then held back while barrel is drawn forward to eject. Bolt then goes forward to chamber a loaded cartridge and lock breech. (Ejection port is uncovered only on forward movement of barrel).
LOCK: Lugs on rotating bolt head engage in recesses in barrel extension. During recoil bolt body is retained by a catch, and as return spring pushes barrel forward, barrel exerts a pull on the bolt head. This causes rotation of the bolt head through a feather working in a helical groove in bolt body. As lugs are turned out of locking recesses, barrel goes forward alone. Projections on barrel extension release bolt catch and bolt spring drives the two-piece bolt forward rotating the head into locking engagement again.
MAINSPRING: Coil operating through plunger in upper part of grip.
DISCONNECTOR: When bolt catch is driven down by projections on barrel extension it enables tail of sear to be depressed for firing. When trigger bar releases sear from hammer, it is forced down until it breaks sear contact, which is not made again until breech is again locked and finger pressure momentarily released.
TRIGGER: Transmits pressure through trigger bar under right hand stock to tail of sear, rotating sear out of engagement with hammer.
SAFETY: Automatic grip safety only. Hook on trigger bar in engagement with grip safety prevents firing except when grip is squeezed in.
RECOIL SPRING: Two separate springs are housed in tunnel above barrel and bolt. The forward one returns the barrel, the rear one then drives the bolt forward. Coil Springs.
BARREL: Recoils full distance of recoil stroke.
FIRING MECHANISM: Exposed hammer type with inertia firing pin.
CALIBER: .32 A.C.P. (7.65mm. Browning). Also made in Caliber .380 A.C.P. (9mm. Browning Short).

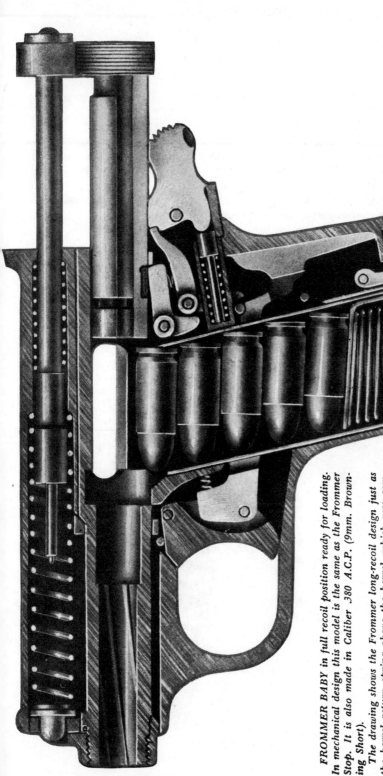

FROMMER BABY in full recoil position ready for loading. In mechanical design this model is the same as the Frommer Stop. It is also made in Caliber 380 A.C.P. (9mm. Browning Short).

The drawing shows the Frommer long-recoil design just as the barrel return spring above the barrel, which was compressed on rearward movement, has driven the barrel forward to unlock the bolt and eject the empty case. Projections on the barrel extension are about to force the catch out of engagement with the cut in the underside of the bolt body. The hammer has been ridden over and cocked by the bolt body and the sear is engaged in its hammer notch while the hammer has compressed the mainspring. The magazine spring has forced the follower to raise the cartridges in the magazine. The top one held by the folded over edges of the top of the box is ready to be driven into the chamber. The bolt body cannot turn, but as it moves forward it will impart a turning motion to the rotating bolt head, causing the head to turn and engage its two lugs in the locking recesses as the cartridge is fully chambered.

The rear spring, the bolt return spring, will now force the guide ahead to drive the bolt forward.

the sear. Continued pressure rotates the sear, releasing the hammer to fly forward and strike the firing pin to fire the cartridge. If the weapon is not fully closed, it cannot be fired, as the disconnector will prevent it. Disconnection also takes place, of course, during rearward recoil action to prevent more than one cartridge being fired for each pull of the trigger. As the sear lever moves back, a disconnecting pin forces it down until it breaks contact with the sear. This permits the sear to re-engage the hammer as the action compresses it.

At the moment of discharge, the bolt is locked securely to the barrel by lugs on its rotating bolt head engaging in recesses in the barrel extension. The locked unit travels back the full length of the cartridge and the bolt is caught and held to the rear by a catch as the recoil spring pushes the barrel forward. This action revolves the bolt head.

This weapon is complicated and expensive to manufacture. Its involved locking system is of no practical value, as the low-powered cartridges it uses can be used with equal safety and effectiveness in pistols of simple blowback design.

.32 ACP   **GECADO**
Automatic

This is a good German automatic of standard blowback design.

.32 ACP   **HARRINGTON AND RICHARDSON**
Automatic

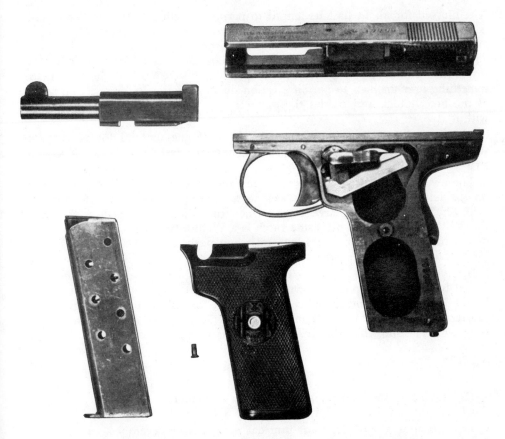

H&R DISMOUNTED. Upper line: Detail of barrel. Note cut on underside of squared section. The upper end of the trigger guard locks into this cut when the weapon is assembled to hold the barrel rigidly in place in the receiver.

Bottom view of slide showing details of striker and striker spring and receiver guides.

Receiver with stock and magazine removed to show action of grip safety whose upper end swings out of line of interference with trigger bar as the weapon is gripped in the hand and the lower pivoted end swings in.

Note connection of trigger and trigger bar. This is a striker-type weapon and does not have the conventional hammer. A projection on the striker catches on the sear which holds it back while compressing the recoil spring inside the striker tube.

This low-priced American blowback pistol is no longer manufactured but large numbers are in use. It weighs about 20 ounces, has a 3½-inch barrel and measures 6½ inches overall, and has a magazine capacity of eight cartridges.

The H&R is a modification of the British Webley & Scott design. It is noteworthy for its very fine takedown system which combines the good features of the rigid barrel with the ease of cleaning and replacement of the removable barrel. It is one of the simplest and potentially sturdiest designs ever conceived.

The principal parts are (1) the receiver which forms the handle and the receptacle for the magazine and also houses the lockwork; (2) the barrel which

265

is reinforced for about half its length to permit the slide to travel over it, and is provided with a notch on its underside to receive a locking lug which is an extension of the trigger guard forging; (3) the standard box magazine; and (4) the slide. The slide covers only about half the barrel length, terminating just ahead of the trigger guard. It is open on top forward of the breech for something over an inch to permit ejection during recoil. Its rear section serves as the breechblock and carries the extractor, striker and striker spring housed within it.

This is a true hammerless pistol. As the slide goes back it forces back the striker, compressing the striker spring in standard fashion. At full cock the striker is caught and held by the sear.

There is a conventional thumb safety of Webley type mounted on the receiver on the left side of the pistol, as well as an automatic squeezer safety in the grip which prevents discharge except when the pistol is gripped in the hand for deliberate fire. The magazine catch is a Webley-type button in the bottom of the handle. It is spring loaded and when pushed in releases the magazine for withdrawal from the bottom.

Dismounting is very simple. The top of the spring steel trigger guard is forced back and then pulled down to draw its lug out of engagement with the barrel. The barrel and slide are then pushed forward out of their guides in the receiver and separated. Removing the stocks gives access to the safety and trigger mechanism, while the striker and spring are readily eased out of the slide.

.32 ACP   JAGER
                                                                 Automatic

(Note: For assembled photo of this arm and data on its characteristics, see the Identification Section. For disassembled shot see next page.)

This pistol is one of the most unusual designs ever developed. It is in the class of weapon which can be manufactured in a small plant with a minimum of tools. It does not have a receiver in the ordinary sense of the word. When it is remembered that the receiver forging is the expensive part of any weapon, the simplicity of this design will be at once appreciated.

It is a standard blowback pistol without a lock and with the standard type magazine inserted from below into the grip. It is striker fired.

The barrel forging is provided with studs at either side of the chamber and on top above the chamber, as well as with a pierced lug below the chamber. The stamped side plates which take the place of the receiver are fastened to the barrel by these lugs passing through holes in the right- and left- hand side plates. The recoil spring is mounted in the top of the stamped slide. The upper lug above the barrel chamber locks this stamping together with the others to take the place of the receiver. The breechblock is inserted in the rear section of the slide but is an individual member. The back strap which carries the thumb safety and the front strap which carries the trigger and trigger guard are provided with suitable holes to permit them to be attached by screws.

The net effect is to produce a quite strong and serviceable pistol without the need for expensive machinery.

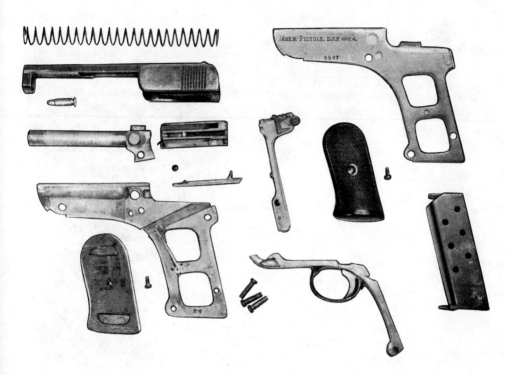

JAGER PISTOL PARTS. Recoil spring. Stamped top plate and slide. Note recess in roof of slide to accommodate guide locking lug on top of barrel. Recoil spring is mounted around the barrel and is compressed by the collar at the front end of the slide. Note locking lug at side of barrel which locks it to left-hand side plate and note hole in right-hand side plate which receives the lug on the opposite side of the barrel. The trigger bar directly below the breechblock forms the connection from the trigger to the striker which releases the latter for firing. The trigger is pinned to the front strap. The upper end of the front strap is retained within the side plates, while the bottom is screwfastened to the plates. The magazine is of standard seven-shot design.

IAG., JIEFFECO, KABA, KOMMER   .32 ACP
Automatics

These are good but undistinguished European blowback pistols. The IAG is Italian; Jieffeco is Belgium; the others German.

LANGENHAN (F.L. SELBSTADER)   .32 ACP
Automatic

This German blowback pistol weighs about 20 ounces, has 4 3/16-inch barrel, measures 6¾ inches overall and has a magazine capacity of eight cartridges.

Although most models of the pistol encountered bear the name Langenhan, these weapons are commonly known by the initials of the inventor, F.L. (Fritz Langenhan of Suhl). A word of warning is necessary because of the combina-

tion of the initials and the exterior similarity to the model 1900 Browning, which is commonly known as the "F.N." from Fabrique Nationale, the Belgian makers. While the F.N. (Browning 1900) is a striker-fired weapon of sturdy but complicated design, it is thoroughly safe and reliable. The F.L. (Langenhan), on the other hand, is an enclosed hammer design which, while made of good materials, *is inherently dangerous* because of its breechblock design. It was a substitute standard German pistol in World War. I.

A thumb safety is provided on the left side of the receiver.

Unlike most blowback pistols, in which the rear end of the slide forms the breechblock, the breechblock in this weapon is separate from the slide.

The recoil spring is mounted above the barrel in a tunnel in the slide. The slide fits over the breechblock by a hinged stirrup. This stirrup fits into a slot in the rear of the slide and also in a slot in the breechblock, and is secured by the large screw seen directly ahead of the milled surfaces above the receiver.

This weapon is loaded in standard blowback pistol fashion by inserting a loaded magazine in the handle; then gripping the milled finger surfaces and pulling back the slide and breechblock assemblies to compress the recoil spring, and permitting the magazine spring to lift a cartridge in line with the breechblock. Releasing the block permits the recoil spring to pull the assemblies forward chambering a cartridge and snapping the extractor over the case into the extracting groove.

The only really interesting feature of this weapon is the takedown, which is unusually simple. Loosen the screw which connects the slide, stirrup, and breechblock. Push the stirrup up. Slide and breechblock may then be slid off the pistol.

These weapons are dangerous because the screw will eventually wear and even with the low-powered cartridge used there is danger of the screw working out while the weapon is being fired. If this screw works out, the breechblock can be blown straight to the rear out of the receiver as the weapon recoils.

LITTLE TOM
Automatic

.32 ACP

This blowback automatic pistol was mainly manufactured by Wiener Waffenfabrik at Vienna, Austria. It is equipped with one of the simplest double-action systems used in any automatic pistols for cocking the hammer for the first shot. As in all blowback automatic pistols of its type, the magazine is inserted in the handle from below and it is necessary to draw the slide to the rear by hand and then let it go forward under tension of the recoil spring to load the firing chamber itself. The hammer may then be lowered with

269

the thumb. Pressure on the trigger, exactly as in the case of a double-action revolver, will then force the hammer back to full cock and trip it to strike the firing pin and discharge the cartridge in the chamber. From there on the slide as it is blown back by the rearward pressure of the gases in the cartridge case cocks the hammer and ejects the empty cartridge case on its rearward movement. On forward stroke it reloads. In case of a misfire, pulling the trigger will raise and trip the hammer for a second try.

While the design of this weapon is particularly interesting because of its simplicity, the pistol itself is very poorly and cheaply manufactured of very soft metals. It is safe with the standard .32 Colt Automatic Pistol cartridge which it uses but is not to be compared for reliability with American-made pistols of this type.

Construction: Some of the design features in this pistol follow closely those of the Italian Beretta. The principal parts of the pistol are the barrel (which is mounted in the manner of the Beretta, being retained in position by a lug on the lower side of the barrel below the chamber fastening in a niche in the receiver); the receiver which forms a handle in which the magazine is inserted and carries the lockwork and the tracks on which the slide functions; the slide carrying the firing pin and extractor; and a recoil spring and guide mounted in unusual fashion inside the receiver above the trigger guard and ahead of it.

A detachable side plate on the upper right-hand side of the receiver covers the lockwork and is retained in place by a fastening pin at the rear and by the screw which passes through the stock and the plate into the receiver at the forward end. The recoil spring is so mounted around its guide that when in position the rear end of the guide exerts pressure and functions as the trigger support spring.

Dismounting: (1) Draw the slide back and push the catch up into the second notch to hold it open. (2) Push the barrel from the muzzle end exactly as in the case of the Beretta to free it from its seating in the receiver and lift it up and out of the slide. (3) Withdraw the magazine and ease the slide forward. It will come off the receiver. (4) The recoil spring guide and the combination spring may now be lifted out of their seat in the receiver. (5) Removing the stock on the right hand side will permit the removable side plate to be pushed out of engagement and withdrawn from the receiver exposing the lockwork for further dismounting, if required.

.32 ACP

MAUSER
Pocket 1910

This is one of the best-finished pistols ever manufactured. It weighs about 20 ounces, has a 3.2-inch barrel, measures just over six inches and has a magazine capacity of eight cartridges.

This is a straight blowback pistol of the striker-fired type. It possesses several unusual design features worthy of attention.

Construction and Operation: The principal parts of this pistol are: (1) The receiver which forms the handle to receive the standard-type sheet-metal magazine from below and accommodates the lockwork and the safety mechanism.

M1910. The streamlined M1934 shown in Identification Section is the same mechanically.

It is machined to receive a removable steel side plate on the left side and to permit the slide to travel back and forth during recoil. A hollow extension forward of the trigger guard houses the recoil spring assembly and mounts the barrel.

(2) The barrel which is secured to the receiver by two lugs which are part of the forging. The rear lug seats deeply in a well in the tubular receiver extension. The forward lug is pierced to permit the barrel holder guide rod to pass through and lock it. This guide rod is inserted just below the muzzle and passes back under the barrel. It is fitted with a spring catch which when turned locks the unit securely. This guide rod also serves as the recoil spring guide.

(3) The slide. Its rear section serves as the breechblock and houses the striker assembly. It is cutaway on top forward from the breech to expose the barrel, as is necessary with the barrel removal system employed.

(4) The lockwork. This includes a striker with its own coil spring housed partly within it.

When the striker is cocked a pin protrudes through a hole in the rear of the slide as a warning device. The trigger has a catch which engages with a small interceptor block above it. The trigger spring is a folded leaf. The interceptor block is pivoted to the sear tail. When the slide is fully forward a spring forcing up against the interceptor raises it into a cut provided for it in the underside of the slide. In this position when the trigger is pressed it pivots and forces the interceptor up, and the interceptor in turn raises the tail of the sear. The sear (a long pivoted bar running from the interceptor across the magazine well under the side plate) pivots and its nose is drawn down out of engagement with its bent in the striker. The striker is driven forward by its spring to discharge the cartridge in the firing chamber. As the recoil drives the cartridge case and breechblock back, the slide rides over the interceptor

271

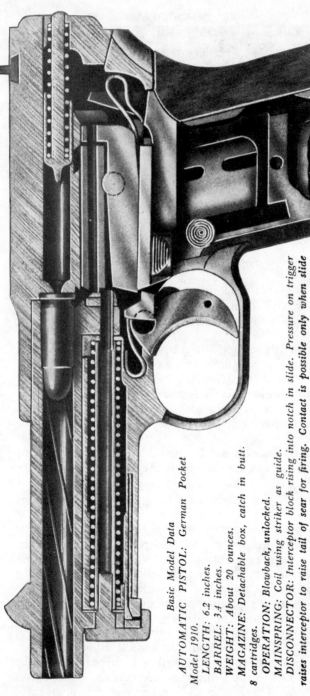

Basic Model Data

AUTOMATIC PISTOL: German Pocket Model 1910.

LENGTH: 6.2 inches.
BARREL: 3.4 inches.
WEIGHT: About 20 ounces.
MAGAZINE: Detachable box, catch in butt. 8 cartridges.

OPERATION: Blowback, unlocked.

MAINSPRING: Coil using striker as guide.

DISCONNECTOR: Interceptor block rising into notch in slide. Pressure on trigger raises interceptor to raise tail of sear for firing. Contact is possible only when slide is home and trigger has been permitted to go to full forward position under influence of trigger spring.

TRIGGER: Pivoted. Has a rear projection which raises interceptor when trigger is pressed. Return spring mounts above trigger.

SAFETY: Thumbpiece when pressed pivots lever to block sear. Released by pressure on button below thumbpiece. Magazine disconnector prevents firing when magazine is withdrawn.

RECOIL SPRING: Below barrel. Compressed around barrel holder guide.

BARREL: Removable. Locked securely to receiver by lug at rear seating in mounting hole and at front by barrel holder and guide.

SLIDE LOCK: Holds slide open when empty. Slide goes forward when magazine is inserted, as the magazine releases the catch automatically.

FIRING MECHANISM: Striker. Pin protrudes through rear of slide when striker is cocked. Sear is a pivoted lever whose tail is raised by the rising interceptor block acted upon by the trigger nose. Nose of **sear** engages in striker cut.

and pushes it down, thereby depressing the sear tail and breaking the trigger contact. The sear spring forces the sear nose up to catch and hold the striker at full cock. As the slide travels back the extractor draws the empty case out for ejection, and the magazine spring brings a cartridge up in line. The recoil spring, compressed during the rearward stroke, draws the slide forward to chamber a loaded cartridge. The trigger must be released momentarily before it can again act on the interceptor, thereby preventing the firing of over one shot for each trigger pull.

(5) The safety. A spring supported lever on the frame is pushed down to set the safety. Pushing the thumbpiece pivots the lever, forcing the rear end up until a beak on it engages in a cut in the striker and holds it securely. At the same time it blocks movement of the sear. The breech cannot be opened when the safety is engaged. Pushing in a small release button just below the safety thumbpiece frees it and its spring drives the thumbpiece up, thereby lowering the rear end of the safety out of sear engagement.

(6) The grip. This may be of wood or other material. It is one piece and is shaped to serve as right and left grip and back strap. It is retained by screws on either side.

Late models of both the .25 and .32 Mauser Pocket pistols are fitted with magazine disconnectors which prevent firing when the magazine is out of the pistol. This is a safety feature to prevent accidents from failure to clear the chamber when unloading. When the last shot has been fired, the slide stays open. Removing the magazine and then reinserting it will free the catch to let the slide run forward. This feature is a warning arrangement that the pistol is empty and a device to speed reloading.

Dismounting: (1) Press in the spring catch below the muzzle of the barrel and twist the head of the recoil spring guide pin out of engagement. (2) Pull the pin directly out to the front. (3) With magazine in the handle, draw the slide back until it is held open by action of the magazine on the catch. (4) Now raise the barrel up so that the locking pin on its under side comes up out of its locking hole in the receiver. The barrel may now be lifted out. (5) Withdraw the magazine and then while holding the slide firmly with the left hand, force the magazine back into the handle, as this action will release the slide catch. Now ease the slide forward out on its guides in the receiver. (6) Withdraw the magazine, and the slide may now be drawn completely off the receiver. (7) The recoil spring and the recoil spring guide tube may now be lifted out. (8) Twist the striker pin to free it from engagement and lift it and its spring out of their mounting in the receiver. (9) Remove the stock screw and work the stock off. (10) The side plate on the left side of the receiver may now be worked off. The trigger and sear arrangement with their components may be withdrawn from the receiver if necessary.

MAUSER   .32 ACP
H Sc

This double-action blowback automatic pistol is one of the most advanced forms of pocket pistol design. The arm weighs about 20½ ounces, has a

3⅜-inch barrel, measures 6½ inches overall and has a magazine capacity of eight cartridges.

This pistol is streamlined to minimize the danger of snagging on holster or clothing when being drawn. The shaping of the wood grip, the pitch of the pistol and the matted rib are all designed to help in fast, accurate shooting.

In most models the hammer is exposed, though only a small spur protrudes through the rear of the slide to provide a thumb hold when lowering the hammer on a loaded chamber. Various thumb safeties are encountered. The common form is a turning lever on the slide which raises the head of the firing pin vertically out of hammer alignment. A few pistols were made with fully enclosed hammers.

Construction and Operation: The principal parts of this pistol are: (1) The receiver. This forms the foundation for the wood grip, receives a box magazine from below in its well, is machined to hold the lockwork with a minimum of pins and no screws, has travel guides for the slide as well as a special escape slot to permit removal of slide at proper position. It forms the triggerguard and extends forward to within an inch of the muzzle. This front section houses a catch which is normally thrust up by its spring into the cut in the underside of the slide, and which serves to lock the slide so it cannot jump its guides. A stud is machined into the receiver below the barrel chamber and barrel lugs lock over it.

(2) The barrel. It is heavily reinforced about the chamber and is shaped

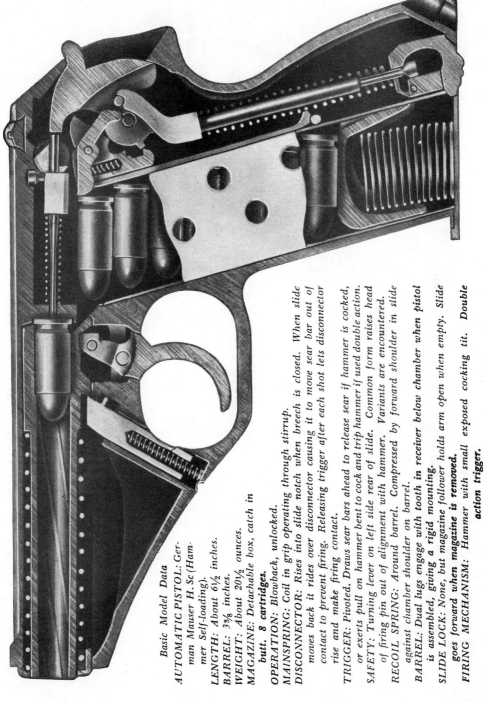

Basic Model Data

AUTOMATIC PISTOL: German Mauser H. Sc (Hammer Self-loading).

LENGTH: About 6½ inches.

BARREL: 3⅜ inches.

WEIGHT: About 20½ ounces.

MAGAZINE: Detachable box, catch in butt. **8 cartridges.**

OPERATION: Blowback, unlocked.

MAINSPRING: Coil in grip operating through stirrup.

DISCONNECTOR: Rises into slide notch when breech is closed. When slide moves back it rides over disconnector causing it to move sear bar out of contact to prevent firing. Releasing trigger after each shot lets disconnector rise and make firing contact.

TRIGGER: Pivoted. Draws sear bars ahead to release sear if hammer is cocked, or exerts pull on hammer bent to cock and trip hammer if used double action.

SAFETY: Turning lever on left side rear of slide. Common form raises head of firing pin out of alignment with hammer. Variants are encountered.

RECOIL SPRING: Around barrel. Compressed by forward shoulder in slide against chamber shoulder on barrel.

BARREL: Dual lugs engage with tooth in receiver below chamber when pistol is assembled, giving a rigid mounting.

SLIDE LOCK: None, but magazine follower holds arm open when empty. Slide goes forward when magazine is removed.

FIRING MECHANISM: Hammer with small exposed cocking tit. **Double action trigger.**

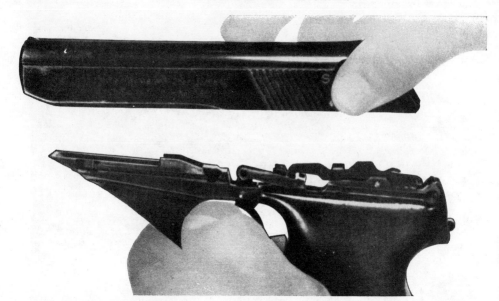

*DISMOUNTING THE MAUSER H. SC. The slide catch is being held in to lower the projection out of the path of the slide cut. The slide is pushed forward slightly, then drawn **back and up**.*

there to provide a compression shoulder for the recoil spring. Dual lugs on the bottom of the barrel below the chamber engage securely with the receiver projection when the arm is assembled.

(3) The slide. It is shaped to extend the full length of the weapon. Its muzzle end has a single hole—that for the barrel to emerge. The recoil spring is mounted around the barrel, its front end utilizing the slide as forward compression point, doing away with the necessity for special bushings. The slide is machined to travel in the receiver guides. The rear end of the slide has an ejection port on the right side, carries the extractor in its breechblock face, and is machined to carry the firing pin and spring. It is recessed behind the pin to enable the hammer to swing up and strike the firing pin. A slot in the rear of the slide permits the small cocking tit on the hammer to protrude and travel. The thumb safety mounted on the slide has a cutaway bolt mounted in a hole in the slide. In firing position the hammer can hit the head of the firing pin; but when the safety lever is turned down, the rear of the firing pin is raised into the slide out of alignment so the hammer cannot drive it ahead. (Note Variants of this system exist).

(4) The lockwork. This is one of the sturdiest of the double-action systems, though in many pistols of war manufacture parts are not too durable. Stampings were often substituted for the customary forged parts. The trigger is pivoted on a pin placed directly above it in the receiver. It is attached above the receiver by a link pin to a stamped bar on each side which extends back to the hammer mechanism. Pressure on the trigger draws these bars forward causing them to exert a pull transmitted to the lower surface of the hammer. The hammer pivots and through its stirrup compresses the coil mainspring

276

in the grip. At full cock the engagement with the hammer bent is slipped and the hammer driven forward by the mainspring. The magazine catch in the butt works off the mainspring.

(5) The magazine. Its follower rising in the path of the breechblock when the last shot has been fired will hold the slide open. However, when the magazine is withdrawn the slide runs forward and must be drawn back again over a loaded magazine to load the chamber. The magazine itself is the customary box type.

Safeties: Besides the thumb safety on the slide the pistol has a disconnector operating through the slide. When the slide is home and the breech fully closed a coil spring can force the disconnector up into a niche in the slide, thereby bringing the sear bar into position to trip the sear.

Dismounting: Hammer must be cocked and safety on S. While pressing in the slide catch in the trigger guard against its spring, push the slide forward the slight distance it will go, then move it back and up out of the receiver guides. The slide and barrel assembly come off together. Pushing the barrel forward against the recoil spring, lift up the breech end and ease it and the spring out of the slide. Removing the stocks gives access to all the lockwork.

MELIOR AND MENTA .32 ACP
Automatic

The Melior is an undistinguished Belgian blowback patterned after the 1910 Browning. Simply dismounted by removing wedge block from slide. Its thumb safety is on the receiver to the rear of the trigger on the left. See the Identification Section.

The Menta is a German pistol made during World War I and is identical with the Beholla. These two are fair weapons made from good materials.

MENZ .32 ACP
II

This very small blowback pistol was manufactured by August Menz of Suhl, Germany, and is modeled after his Lilliput 4.25 automatic pistol. It is a compact striker-fired weapon weighing about 19 ounces, measuring about 5 inches overall and with a magazine capacity of six cartridges. A thumb safety is provided on the left side of the receiver, and a signal pin protruding through the rear of the slide warns when the arm is cocked.

MENZ .32 ACP
Special

This is a double-action blowback which so closely resembles the Walther PPK that it will often be confused with it. It is very slightly heavier and longer than the Walther PPK, its magazine release catch is in the butt (the Walther is a button on the side of the receiver), its safety is a sliding thumb catch moving up and down in a slot in the slide just ahead of the rear sight (the Walther is a lever on the slide), the trigger guard takedown is modified, and it holds nine cartridges in the magazine—one more than normal in the Walther.

277

It is made of excellent materials. This pistol was also made in .380 A.C.P. (9mm. Browning) caliber and in a special center fire .22 caliber with inside primer which is not to be confused with the familiar .22 rim fire.

It bears the stamp "August Menz Waffenfabrik Suhl, P.B. Special" on the left side of the slide.

.32 ACP   **ORTGIES**
                                                                 Automatic

ORTGIES. The button on the receiver behind the stock is pushed in to force out the grip safety. When the weapon is gripped for firing, movable steel grip is squeezed in to remove the safety. The button must be pushed each time to reset it.

This striker-fired blowback pistol is a product of the Deutsche Werke at Erfurt, Germany. (See the Identification Section for characteristics).

The principal parts of this pistol are the receiver, the slide, the barrel, and the striker mechanism. It will be noted that there is no hammer in this weapon. It fires on the striker principle, as in the case of most high-power rifles.

This is a German-made weapon of good workmanship. Huge numbers of

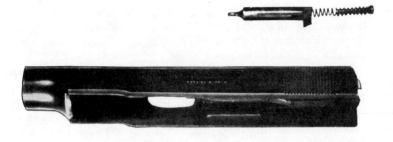

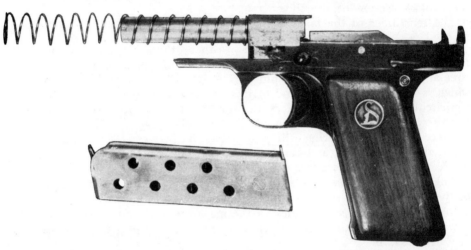

ORTGIES .32 AUTOMATIC DISMOUNTED. Note that mainspring is very small and seats in striker tube. The slide design in general has been adapted to most of the successful pistols of late pocket type, as has the recoil spring mounting system. Barrel is pinned rigidly to receiver.

these weapons were sold and distributed in the U. S. and throughout South America.

The slide is shaped to completely inclose the barrel and working mechanism. It is a straight blowback pistol in which the rear end of the slide forms the breechblock.

The recoil spring operates on the concentric principle, being placed around the barrel under the slide and compressed as the slide travels backwards in its grooves in the receiver.

The magazine is the standard box type inserted in the handle from below and the magazine catch is at the rear at the bottom of the weapon.

The pistol is fitted with a grip safety of unusual design. This grip safety does not operate until the small button on the left-hand side of the receiver near the trigger guard is pressed in. This causes the grip safety to spring out. When the weapon is firmly gripped, the grip safety is pushed in and the weapon will fire. Before the safety begins to operate, however, the button must again be pushed.

Dismounting: Unless you know where to start, this is probably the most difficult pistol to dismount that will ever be encountered. It is very simple when you know the trick; but is almost impossible to fathom unless you are familiar with it.

1. First, withdraw the magazine and draw back the slide to see that there is no cartridge in the firing chamber.

2. Then holding the pistol in the right hand push in the grip safety release button with the right thumb. While holding this in, with the left hand push the slide back about one-half inch and lift it up. It may be lifted off the receiver.

3. The striker pin and spring may be pushed forward and pulled out of the breechblock section of the slide.

The remainder of the takedown is quite simple.

Reassembling: In reassembling this weapon, there is also a trick to be remembered. In the top of the breechblock end of the slide is a small semi-circular cut. When the firing pin spring is pushed forward, a small stem which is inserted in the rear end of this spring can be pushed down into this semicircular cut where it will lock the spring into place to permit reassembly. If this spring is not locked into position the slide cannot be remounted on the receiver since the spring will project out the rear end. The slide must be replaced very carefully, and care taken to see that this spring and its rod do not leap out. Both pieces are so small that they can be easily lost.

The grips on this weapon are held in place by a spring catch on the rear of the receiver inside the magazine well.

Insert a screw driver or a stick in the magazine well and about halfway up it will strike against the spring catch and release the grips (stocks) which then may be lifted off.

.32 ACP   PICKERT
                                                                          Revolver

This German revolver usually bears the Arminius-head trademark on the stocks. With 2¼-inch barrel as pictured it measures about 5⅝ inches overall and weighs 17 ounces. These revolvers are made in a wide variety of weights, barrel lengths and finishes in both hammer and hammerless (enclosed hammer) styles.

Arminius model Pickerts are in a class with the American Iver Johnson and Harrington & Richardson revolvers. They are low-priced arms of good materials and manufacture and are very widely distributed throughout Europe. Those of .32 caliber are intended for the 7.65mm. Browning (.32 Colt Automatic Pistol) cartridge, but will also handle the .32 S&W short rimmed cartridges.

Semirim pistol cartridges may be used because the solid-frame design and swivel-mounted rod ejector permit the use of this type since empty cases are individually pushed out of the chambers by action of the rod inserted inside the case.

These revolvers have rebounding hammers. Firing pins are mounted in the frames. Thumb safeties are found in most models. Traps are usually provided in the butts to receive a special clip holding five semirim cartridges. While these revolvers usually have 6 chambers, the number may vary. Over 70 varieties of this brand have been marketed. The calibers are commonly .32 A.C.P., .25 A.C.P. or 5.5mm. (.22) Velo-Dog, though some chambered for the .38 S&W cartridge may be encountered.

PIEPER   **.32 ACP**
1909

This Belgian blowback is fairly well made of good materials. For photograph and general specifications see the Identification Section. This pistol is of interest purely because of its takedown system which was the forerunner of several of the latest European designs. Turning down a takedown lever on the left side of the receiver permits the barrel and breechblock assemblies to be pulled back and up off the receiver mountings.

RHEINMETALL   **.32 ACP**
Automatic

This is an undistinguished German pistol made of the best materials. It is of elementary blowback design and was not made in quantities. However, it should be noted that any product of this firm is a well-made and reliable arm. See the Identification Section for photograph and general specifications.

This was used as a French Service pistol for a while. It was originally manufactured in Spain by Gabilondo and Alkärtasuna and is described in this section under Alkärtasuna. This is a staunchly built pistol which is heavy for the weak cartridge employed. It is essentially an imitation of the Colt .32 A.C.P. without the grip safety.

.32 ACP

SAUER
Old Model

This is one of the best German-made pistols, though later designs by the same maker have long rendered the original model obsolescent. It is a standard blowback arm made by Sauer & Sohn of Suhl. It has a 3-inch barrel, measures 5⅞ inches overall and weighs about twenty-two ounces. Magazine capacity is 7 cartridges.

The design is quite unusual in its takedown system but is otherwise a standard blowback. The knurled block at the rear of the slide is held locked by the rear sight. When released and turned it may be withdrawn to permit removal of the slide and barrel assembly from the receiver by easing them forward. The recoil spring is of the concentric type which mounts around the barrel and requires neither guide nor bushing. This is a striker-fired pistol. The standard thumb safety is mounted on the left side of the receiver. Magazine release catch is in the butt.

.32 A.C.P. SAUER Old Model Blowback Striker-
Fired Automatic

SAUER   .32 ACP
1930

This model is a somewhat streamlined version of the original Sauer. The grip is shaped to fit the hand in a style later used in the Model 38. The 1930 version may be found with a signal pin which protrudes from the rear when the arm is cocked. It will also be found with slide and receiver made of light weight duralumin. General specifications are about the same as for the earlier model except that the duralumin model weighs somewhat less than fifteen ounces.

SAUER   .32 ACP
38 (H)

This is one of the most advanced forms of pocket automatic pistols. Originally designed as a pocket and police pistol in calibers .25 A.C.P., .32 A.C.P. and .380 A.C.P. it was issued as the Model H. In the .32 caliber it was adopted as a German substitute standard under the designation Model 38, and was widely used by air and tank forces of the Germans during World War II.

The barrel is about 3 1/3 inches long, the overall length is about 6¼ inches and the weight is about twenty-six ounces. Magazine capacity is 8 cartridges.

Construction and Operation: The principal parts of this pistol are the receiver, barrel, slide, lockwork, and magazine. (1) The receiver is forged to form the handle in which the lockwork is mounted and in whose well the

283

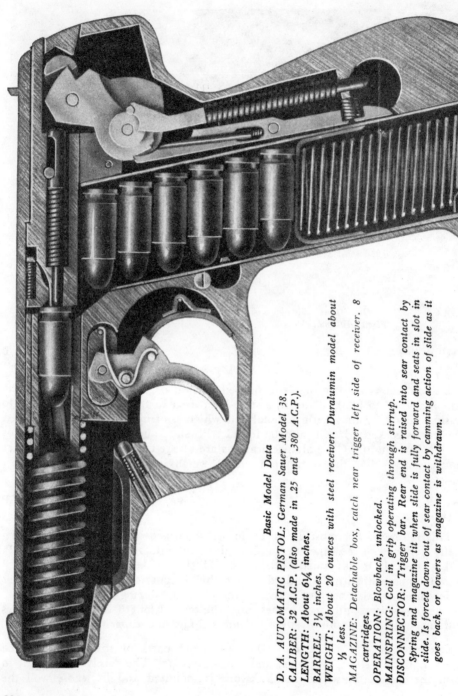

Basic Model Data

D. A. AUTOMATIC PISTOL: German Sauer Model 38.

CALIBER: 32 A.C.P. (also made in .25 and .380 A.C.P.).

LENGTH: About 6¼ inches.

BARREL: 3⅓ inches.

WEIGHT: About 20 ounces with steel receiver. Duralumin model about ⅓ less.

MAGAZINE: Detachable box, catch near trigger left side of receiver. 8 cartridges.

OPERATION: Blowback, unlocked.

MAINSPRING: Coil in grip operating through stirrup.

DISCONNECTOR: Trigger bar. Rear end is raised into sear contact by Spring and magazine tit when slide is fully forward and seats in slot in slide. Is forced down out of sear contact by camming action of slide as it goes back, or lowers as magazine is withdrawn.

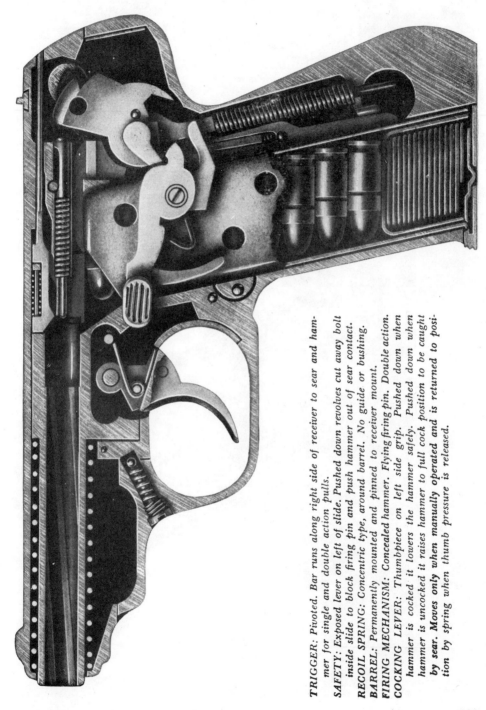

TRIGGER: Pivoted. Bar runs along right side of receiver to sear and hammer for single and double action pulls.

SAFETY: Exposed lever on left of slide. Pushed down revolves cut away bolt inside slide to block firing pin and push hammer out of sear contact.

RECOIL SPRING: Concentric type, around barrel. No guide or bushing.

BARREL: Permanently mounted and pinned to receiver mount.

FIRING MECHANISM: Concealed hammer. Flying firing pin. Double action.

COCKING LEVER: Thumbpiece on left side grip. Pushed down when hammer is cocked it lowers the hammer safely. Pushed down when hammer is uncocked it raises hammer to full cock position to be caught by sear. Moves only when manually operated and is returned to position by spring when thumb pressure is released.

SAUER MODEL 38 (OR H). Right-side view with loaded magazine in position and slide in full recoil. Solid surface on underside of slide has cammed trigger bar down out of engagement with sear. Slide has ridden over hammer after cocking it. Recoil spring is seen compressed between its seat in muzzle end of slide and barrel mounting shoulder. On forward strike slide will chamber a cartridge and trigger bar spring will force bar up into niche in slide, bringing hook into sear contact when pressure on trigger is released and trigger draws bar ahead.

magazine is inserted. It has an extension which forms the trigger guard and is machined to receive the forward bearing surfaces of the slide. A mount rising above the trigger position is provided as part of the receiver forging to house the barrel. The upper rear of the receiver is machined to receive the slide and guide its travel.

(2) The barrel is mounted in and pinned to the receiver and is intended to be removed only at the factory. The recoil spring positions around the barrel and is compressed against the receiver mounting. No bushing is needed as the forward end of the recoil spring seats in the muzzle end of the slide.

(3) The slide forms the breechblock at its rear in standard fashion and carries the extractor and the flying firing pin. A positive thumb safety is also mounted on the slide. Its lever is mounted on the left side. When the hammer is cocked, pushing the lever down will revolve the attached cutaway pin inside the slide to bring a solid surface into contact with the hammer. This not only blocks the hammer from reaching the firing pin but also forces the hammer back out of contact with the sear. The slide carries the sights and a matted rib and is milled out from the breechblock forward far enough to reach the end of the trigger guard extension to permit mounting it over the barrel from the front. It is machined to travel in the receiver guides and has an ejection port on the right side.

(4) The lockwork is one of the simplest and best double-action systems made, and is fitted with a unique external lever to permit lowering or raising the concealed hammer manually. The hammer is mounted in standard fashion on a pin in the rear of the receiver and has an attached strut which passes through the coils of the mainspring and through a compression shoulder in the bottom of the grip section of the receiver. The head of the hammer rises up into the cutaway section of the slide behind the firing pin and is completely enclosed. The trigger is pivoted in the receiver and is fitted with a long bar inset in the right side of the barrel mount and the side of the receiver wall. When the magazine is in the handle a small tit on the right side wall raises the rear of the trigger bar to bring it in contact with the cocking notch in the hammer. Pressure on the trigger will pivot that part and cause it to draw the trigger bar ahead in its guides. The bar will rotate the hammer on its axis pin, causing it to thrust the hammer stirrup down and compress the mainspring. When the hammer passes the cocked position the hook on the end of the trigger bar will slip its notch and permit the mainspring to drive the hammer forward against the firing pin.

It must be noted that as in all semi-automatic pistols the slide must be drawn back by hand to load the chamber for the first shot. This action cocks the pistol in standard fashion. As the slide starts back, a solid surface on the slide strikes the trigger bar which is rising into a disconnector cut and as it rides over it forces the bar down out of contact with the sear. Pressure on the trigger must be released before the bar can again come in contact with the sear to release it from its bent in the hammer. Should the cartridge in the chamber fail to fire, a second pull on the trigger will raise and drop the hammer for a second try at the cartridge in the firing chamber. Should that cartridge again fail to fire, it is necessary to pull the slide back by hand to eject it. (Note that this is unlike the double-action revolver in which the trigger pull not only raises and drops the hammer but also revolves the cylinder to bring a new cartridge under the firing pin).

A lever with an external thumbpiece is mounted under the left-hand stock where it is pivoted to the receiver. The thumbpiece is milled to permit a firm pressure to be exercised and is free to travel downwards in a cut in the grip. When the hammer is cocked this lever is at rest. If it is desired to lower the hammer with the chamber loaded, pressure on the thumbpiece will pivot the lever and bring its rear end into position to trip the sear at the same time that it engages with a projection attached to the lower surface of the hammer. This permits the hammer to be eased down exactly as in the case of an exposed hammer at the same time that it prevents the hammer from reaching the firing pin. A spring under the cocking lever will return it to rest position when thumb pressure is released. Pressure on the thumbpiece when the hammer is down will cause the rear of the lever to force up the hammer projection carrying the hammer back until it is at full cock and is caught by the sear. This system combines all the advantages of the concealed hammer (streamlining and the removal of projections which may interfere with quick drawing or with the line of sight) with the advantages of the exposed hammer (ability to carry chamber loaded with mainspring at rest and in complete safety).

(5) The magazine is the customary tubular steel box type. Its one unusual feature is the tit on the right magazine wall which forces the trigger bar up to make sear contact when the magazine is inserted, thereby functioning as a safety feature.

Dismounting: Pull down the slide lock catch from its position in the underside of the receiver just ahead of the trigger. This will bring its upper section below the line of the slide. With the hammer cocked, draw the slide back meanwhile exerting a lift on the rear end. The slide will clear its receiver guides and may be eased forward over the barrel. The recoil spring may be drawn off the barrel. Removing the magazine and the stocks will give access to the lockwork, all parts being exposed for easy removal and replacement. The barrel should not be removed from the receiver mounting.

Note: This model was manufactured during World War II in limited quantities with duralumin slide and receiver which materially lowered the weight.

Geco adapters were also made for practice work with these pistols. These adapters consisted of an insert barrel assembly and steel cases resembling .32 A.C.P. cartridges. 4mm. cartridges are inserted in the heads of the hollow adapter cases and the units are then placed in the magazine. When using these adapters it is necessary to draw the slide back to eject each case as it is fired, since the recoil is not sufficient to function the action.

Manufacturer: J. P. Sauer & Sohn, Suhl. (This firm was founded in 1751).

SAVAGE
1907

.32 ACP

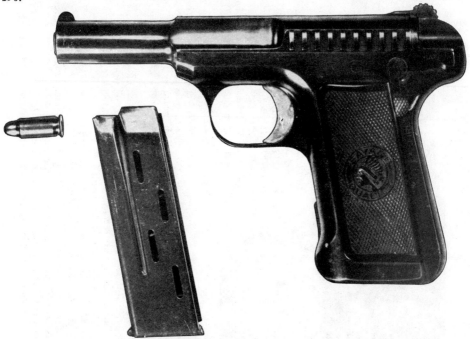

SAVAGE MODEL 1907 (exposed cocking spur model). Large capacity double stagger magazine extracted. Pistol uncocked.

Though patented in 1905 the first pocket model of this Savage .32 (.380 introduced in 1913) automatic was not introduced until 1907. The pistol shown has a 3¾ inch barrel, an overall length of about 6½ inches, weighs about 19 ounces empty and has a magazine capacity of ten cartridges. In these early models barrel and overall lengths, as well as weights, varied. Lengths and weights given are for representative specimens.

This is the earliest type of Savage pocket automatic pistol. While it has a burr-type exposed cocking piece, it does not have a conventional hammer. If the cocking spur is used to lower the striker which is attached to it, the point of the striker will impinge on the cartridge in the chamber. WARNING: This pistol should never be carried with a cartridge in the chamber except with the cocking spur back and the thumb safety applied.

SAVAGE
1915 Hammerless

.32 ACP

For photograph of this model see Savage under Caliber .380 A.C.P. This model was apparently made in very limited quantity since manufacture was stopped in 1927. Dimensions and weights are practically the same as on the exposed spur model.

The *enclosed* spur type (or so-called "hammerless" types) of the Savage pistol is provided with a grip safety. In this type a hook on the grip safety engages with the safety bar to prevent movement of the sear. Only when the

Basic Model Data

AUTOMATIC PISTOL: *American Savage 1907* exposed cocking piece.

LENGTH: About 6½ inches.

BARREL: About 3¾ inches.

WEIGHT: About 19 ounces.

MAGAZINE: Detached staggered box. **Catch** front bottom of handle. Capacity 10 cartridges.

OPERATION: Delayed blowback. Barrel is rotated 30 degrees to unlock lug from ceiling of slide by cam slot in slide. The breech opens nearly as fast as in unlocked types.

DISCONNECTOR: Trigger acting through bar can reach sear mounted in breechblock only when slide is closed and trigger is forward. No separate unit employed with this design.

TRIGGER: Mounted to move back in straight line to transmit pressure to sear. Does not pivot. A link and spring pivoted to it transmit pressure.

SAFETY: Turning coach up revolves bar unit inside receiver raising a bar into a sear notch to prevent sear movement.

RECOIL SPRING: Concentric type. Around barrel under slide.

MAINSPRING: Coil around striker.

BARREL: Removable. Retained by lower lug below chamber engaging in receiver cut while upper lug is in cam slot in slide.

FIRING MECHANISM: Striker type. Pivoted cocking lever attached to striker draws striker back to cock during recoil movement as lower arm bears against grip.

SAVAGE 1907 (Hammerless enclosed model) dismounted to show construction of slide, breech-block, barrel, and receiver.

pistol is firmly gripped in the hand ready for firing is this grip safety pushed in far enough to permit proper sear contact to allow the weapon to be fired.

SAVAGE   .32 ACP
1917

This model differs from earlier ones principally in the shape of the grip and in the screwed-on grips. The grip slopes at a steeper angle than in the previous models and is broader and thicker to provide a better hand hold.

It should be emphasized, however, that when the cocking piece is fully forward on Savage pistols the firing pin is protruding through the breechblock and resting against the face of the cartridge in the firing chamber. It is unsafe to carry them in this condition.

These pistols should be carried loaded with the thumb safety up or should be carried with the magazine loaded and the firing chamber empty. This last, of course, requires that the slide be pulled to the rear and released before the firing chamber is ready for a pull of the trigger.

SAVAGE 1917 with magazine extracted. Spur-type cocking piece is back showing striker is cocked. Thumb safety is applied.

The principal parts of this pistol are the receiver, the slide, the barrel, and the breechblock. Note that in this pistol the breechblock is not a machined part of the slide but is fitted into the rear end of it, and is equipped with guides to permit it to function in straight line as a prolongation of the slide.

The receiver is of unusual design. It has a hollow handle to receive the magazine inserted from below in the customary manner. The magazine release catch, however, is at the front end of the handle instead of the rear.

The receiver provides a great deal of space above the trigger guard to accommodate the unusual trigger mechanism. The barrel is heavily reinforced over the chamber. A small cam-shaped lug is machined on top of this reinforced section, fitting in a cam slot in the underside of the slide. At the lower rear end of the chamber another lug projects which rests in a slot provided for it in the receiver. This serves as a barrel stop and positioner.

The slide is tubular in shape and completely houses the barrel and breech. The front end of the slide, which is cylindrical in form, houses the barrel.

The recoil spring is of the concentric type wrapped around the barrel so that a guide is not necessary.

The lower rear section of the slide is open on the bottom and is provided with grooves to permit it to slide in the guides in the receiver. An ejection port is provided on the right side of the slide. A slot is provided on the underside of the rear top of the slide; and a lug in this slot retains the extractor in position. Rear sight is commonly a milled surface on the slide.

The breechblock is unique. It is tongued and grooved into the rear of the slide where it is fastened by twisting it a quarter turn from right to left. Guides are machined on its side which line up with the slide when the breechblock is in proper position so that it can travel back and forth with the slide.

The extractor is a separate piece which lies on top of the breechblock where it is retained by the lug already mentioned in the top of the slide.

The breechblock is machined to house the striker and the powerful striker spring, as well as a heavy lever which is pivoted near the center of the block. The lower arm of this lever ends in a lug with a rolling surface machined in.

This weapon does not have a hammer in the ordinary sense of the word. While on some models a cocking piece is visible on the outside and the striker can be drawn back to full cock by pulling back on this piece, it is *not* a hammer but is actually part of the striker mechanism. The lug end of the lever rests on the inside of the rear of the receiver when the weapon is uncocked. This lever provides the medium by which the weapon is cocked as the slide comes back. The upper end of the lever forms the cocking piece.

The trigger mechanism, which is housed in the receiver over the trigger guard, moves in a straight line, not on a pivot. Its upper end projects to the front where it is pivoted to a link provided with a spring plunger. The tail of this link acts as a trigger bar. It can come up to press against the tail of the sear when it is directly opposite the proper cut in the slide.

This feature provides a complete safety disconnection. It eliminates the need for a *separate* disconnector such as is provided in most other good automatic pistols. Only when the slide is fully forward in the closed position can this trigger bar push back to release the sear to permit the striker to go forward.

The sear is mounted in the front end of the breechblock with its front end resting on the upper surface in a groove machined into the breechblock. Here it can engage and hold the cocking bent on the front end of the striker.

The tail of the sear bears at right angles to the left, thence straight ahead on the left-hand side of the breechblock where it can engage the trigger bar when the slide is fully home. When the trigger is pressed the trigger bar moves the tail of the sear to the rear, elevating the nose of the sear to release the striker. The striker is driven forward to fire the cartridge and the striker lever swings down on its pivot until the lug at its lower end strikes against the inside of the receiver.

The sear spring, a very small coil spring mounted in a hole in the side of the breechblock, pushes the sear back to position.

The locking mechanism of this pistol is of the so-called "hesitation" or "delayed blowback" type. Searles, the inventor, claimed that the work of the bullet following the rifling resisted barrel rotation and helped keep the breech locked. However, German spark photographs comparing this pistol with a Colt blowback show clearly that the action opens quicker than the Colt, both slides starting back before bullets leave barrels.

When the slide is fully home, the small lug on the top of the barrel rests in a slot on the inside of the top of the slide. The last quarter inch at the rear of this slot is cut at a steep left-hand angle.

As the slide recoils when the weapon is fired, the barrel, whose anchor lug on the bottom is set in its niche in the receiver, is twisted from right to left until the cam lug on top of the barrel reaches a straight section of the groove on the inside of the slide.

The use of this delaying action (which is actually a weak lock) permits the use of lighter moving parts than is customary in weapons of this type.

The anchor lug as it is mounted in the slot in the receiver does permit a certain amount of rearward movement of the barrel during this twisting action; but the hesitation is long enough to permit a considerable drop in breech pressure before the slide and breechblock move far enough to rear to expose the ejection opening.

The trigger and sear mechanism in this weapon consist of a number of very small and very delicate pieces. Considerable care must be taken when dismounting the weapon to see that they are not lost or injured. Furthermore, the sear action is so delicate that a low trigger pull is dangerous, as it is possible, if sear engagement is not complete, to jar this weapon off very easily so that it will "maxim" (fire more than one shot on a single trigger pull.)

The thumb safety is at the upper left-hand side of the receiver. Pushing the outside lever *up* turns the squared pin of which it is a part, and which passes through a slot in the receiver. When the safety is applied, it engages in the recess in the slide. This prevents the slide from being pulled back. It also elevates a bar on the underside of the breechblock, forcing its nose to engage in a bent on the tail of the sear. This prevents the sear from being pushed back to release the striker.

This thumb safety is also used to hold the slide back when the pistol is being dismounted. When the slide is pushed all the way back, the thumb safety may be turned up to engage in a recess opposite the end of the ejection port. This locks it securely to permit turning the breechblock to remove it from the slide.

Operation: When the cartridge is discharged the backward thrust of gas against the inside of the head of the cartridge case transmits pressure to the breeckblock directly behind it.

Since the top barrel lug is fitted in its slot on the inside of the slide, when the slide starts its rearward motion it bears against this lug, and as the barrel anchor lug fastened in the receiver slot directly below prevents any appreciable movement to the rear, the groove in the slide acts to twist the barrel to the right until the lug enters the straight section of the slide groove. From then on the slide, with the breechblock firmly fastened in its rear end, recoils straight back on guides in the receiver.

The lower lug end of the cocking lever which is now resting against the inside of the receiver, is forced upwards as the rear end of the breechblock to which the lever is pivoted slides over the rear of the receiver. This upward movement of the cocking lever draws back the striker which is fastened to it and again engages the striker pin with the sear.

Meanwhile, the recoil spring around the barrel has been compressed by the rearward movement of the slide. The extractor mounted above the breechblock has carried the empty cartridge case back with it to strike it against the ejector which hurls it out the ejection port. The magazine spring has forced up the follower bringing a new cartridge into line for the forward movement of the breechblock to pick it up and chamber it.

In its forward movement the straight section of the slide slot runs straight ahead over the barrel lugs; but in its closing motion the angular section of the slots bears against the lug, compelling it to revolve the barrel to the left as the cartridge is chambered, and the extractor snaps into the extracting groove in the case.

When the trigger is pressed and the striker released, the long lever arm attached to the striker is thrown down into the well in the receiver.

Some types of this weapon are provided with a slide stop which holds the weapon open when the last cartridge in the magazine has been fired.

The slide release on these pistols is on the right-hand side of the receiver above and ahead of the trigger guard. When the weapon is empty, pressing this catch, which is quite small, will permit the slide to go forward. If a loaded magazine has been inserted, releasing this catch will automatically load the firing chamber ready for immediate use.

Dismounting: 1. Press the magazine catch at the forward front end of the handle section of the receiver. This will release the magazine which may be withdrawn from the bottom of the weapon.

2. Draw the slide back as far as it will go with the left hand while holding the grip securely with the right and, holding it in its rearward position, push the thumb safety up until it locks and holds back the slide.

3. Grasp the breechblock firmly and give it a half turn to the right. It may now be drawn straight to the rear out of its grooves in the slide.

4. While holding firmly to the slide, which is under compression of the recoil spring, ease down the thumb safety. As it comes out of engagement with the slide, the slide and recoil spring can be moved forward and withdrawn from the receiver.

5. The barrel may now be lifted straight up out of the receiver, as it is merely mounted in a recess there by an anchor lug on the bottom of the barrel. Normally the recoil spring will be around the barrel and will have to be removed from it.

6. Pushing back on the trigger will permit the rear end of the attached trigger bar to be lifted up. It may then be drawn out of engagement and the other trigger mechanism components lifted out of their well in the receiver. These parts are all very small and very delicate, and it is not advisable to remove them except when necessary for cleaning or for possible replacement.

7. If necessary, the axis pin of the cocking lever may be driven out to remove the mainspring, striker, and striker lever. The extractor may be lifted off the top of the breechblock. As the sear and extractor and their springs are very small and fragile, it is not advisable to remove them.

8. The magazine in this pistol, while of the standard box type, is wider than usual and is fitted with a special platform and spring to permit the

cartridges to stagger in double rows, the cartridges moving automatically first to one side of the magazine well then to the other. This staggered box gives greater magazine capacity. Naturally the thickness of the grip is also increased. However, in this weapon this is a distinct advantage as it makes for a firm grip and better instinctive pointing.

.32 ACP

SCHWARZLOSE
1908

SCHWARZLOSE 1908. This model does not have the squeezer safety shown in the drawing.
Both types are common.

This unique Austrian weapon is no longer manufactured.

It is a blow-forward type, the only one ever marketed successfully. That is to say, there is no locking device in the pistol, but instead of the slide moving to the rear as in the customary blowback, in this weapon the receiver and the rear breech face are a single solid unit, and the barrel itself (which is hooked up to a powerful recoil spring) moves forward as the pistol is fired.

The receiver not only acts as the handle for the pistol, with a hollow magazine well to permit insertion of the magazine from below in standard fashion, but also extends forward to provide a trigger guard and continues forward to the full length of the barrel.

The recoil spring and guide are mounted in this extension of the receiver over the trigger guard while the barrel directly above it travels forward in guides in the receiver.

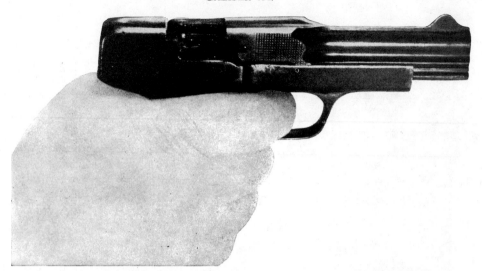

SCHWARZLOSE 1908 in full recoil position. The barrel has blown forward away from the solid receiver and the ejector on the barrel has hurled out the empty case. The recoil spring below the barrel has been compressed and is about to return the barrel to pick up and chamber a cartridge from the special magazine.

On some models a grip safety is provided in front of the handle directly below the line of the trigger guard. This is not present on all models.

A magazine release catch is provided in the form of a catch on the bottom of the receiver directly behind the magazine well.

To load this weapon, a loaded magazine is inserted in the handle and pushed in until it locks securely.

Then the milled finger grips on the rear of the barrel at the chamber end are gripped firmly and the barrel is moved directly forward.

As the barrel is pushed forward, it compresses the recoil spring below it and, when the barrel is released, the spring pushes the barrel back to pick up a cartridge, bullet end first, from the peculiar magazine.

In this type of pistol, the recoil is invariably excessive. This is to be expected in view of the fact that, whereas in the straight blowback type much of the rearward thrust of the gas inside the cartridge case is transmitted to the breechblock which carries the moving parts directly to the rear, in this type the rearward shock is transmitted through the rigid receiver to the hand.

Thus as the barrel goes forward, the bullet precedes it. The bullet is well out of the barrel before the barrel has moved forward far enough to expose much of the cartridge case gripped by the extractor behind it.

The general theory of the blow-forward action was that interposing a solid part of the receiver directly behind the cartridge case prevented any possible danger of a slide being blown back to injure the firer.

While it is impossible for good pistols of modern design of the blowback type to move too far during rearward action of the slide (since in all types a forward section of the slide abuts against the receiver and can only be mounted

Basic Model Data
AUTOMATIC PIS-
TOL: Austrian Schwarz-
lose 1908 Blow-forward.
    LENGTH: About 5½
inches.
    BARREL: About 4⅛
inches.
    WEIGHT: About 20 oz.

MAGAZINE: Detachable box. Catch in butt. Capacity 7 cartridges.

OPERATION: Blow-forward, unlocked.

MAINSPRING: Leaf in grip.

DISCONNECTOR: A rocking member mounted to barrel. Connects trigger to hammer only when action is closed.

TRIGGER: Acts across magazine well through barrel bar.

SAFETY: Squeezer type in front of grip. Also manual on left side of receiver behind trigger.

RECOIL SPRING: Coil with guide below barrel.

BARREL: Blows forward away from solid standing breech face of receiver under influence of rearward gas pressure within cartridge case. Carries ejector. Fulfills the function of slide except that it does not carry the breechblock.

FIRING MECHANISM: Hammer with attached firing pin as in revolver. Hammer is completely enclosed and this pistol is classed as a "hammerless" model.

on the receiver from the front), in some of earlier types where the slide was fastened (as in the case of the first Colt .38 automatic) by a bolt passing through the slide and receiver, the shearing of this bolt could permit the slide to be blown back to the rear.

However, even with a low-powered cartridge of the type of the .32 Colt automatic, the blowforward system was never really practical. Extraction and ejection were never very reliable and feeding jams were quite common.

The jar caused by the barrel moving forward and again by its return as it brings up against the face of the breechblock, added to the excessive recoil, makes this an unpleasant weapon to shoot.

Dismounting: Insert a short piece of wire in the hole drilled laterally near the end of the spring guide. Using the wire as a handle, pull the guide out until spring is completely compressed. Tilt the guide piece until it enters its bearing in the step machined for it in the bottom of the spring tunnel. The barrel will now slide off. Care must be taken to keep the spring from jumping out, as it is quite difficult to replace. Some models may be stripped by merely pushing barrel ahead, then forcing end of spring guide up, permitting assembly to come off forward.

These weapons may be found with the name Schwarzlose stamped on them. They may be found with or without grip safeties. They may be found with the stamp of the Schwarzlose machine gun on them. Or they may have the names of American, British, or South American importers who handled them.

This pistol is also unique in that the firing pin is an integral part of the hammer as is the case in early revolvers.

From 1908 to 1913 these pistols were widely sold throughout the world by a mail-order firm. They retailed at about $15. Essentially, however, they are of interest only to the collector, or to the police officer who may encounter them in the course of duty.

SHARPSHOOTER .32 ACP
Automatic

This exposed hammer pistol is of Spanish manufacture. It weighs about 28 ounces, has a 3¾-inch barrel and an overall length of 6½ inches. The magazine holds eight cartridges. This is another simple type of blowback automatic pistol. It is very heavy for the type of cartridge which it shoots. While the finish is poor, the weapon is well designed and is very strong. It is fitted with an outside hammer.

Its very unusual feature, however, lies in the fact that the barrel is hinged at the front end and the slide cut away on top of the barrel. By drawing the slide back far enough to bring the breechblock face away from the barrel chamber, then pushing up the barrel locking catch, it is possible to tip up the barrel for easy and speedy cleaning from the muzzle end.

Loading and operating is standard for pocket blowback pistols.

SHARPSHOOTER showing magazine withdrawn and barrel tipped down for loading chamber or cleaning.

.32 ACP

SMITH AND WESSON
Automatic

Official Model Name: Model .32 caliber Automatic Pistol.
Ammunition: .32 Automatic Pistol Cartridge.
Manufacturing Dates: Feb. 29, 1924-Mar. 13, 1937.
Serial Numbers Numbered in separate series starting at one.

Finish:	Blue	*Twist:* One turn in	12″
Barrel Length:	3½″	*Direction of Twist:*	Right
Land Diameter:	.303-.304	*Length of Chamber:*	.630
Groove Diameter:	.312-.313	*Diameter of Chamber:*	.338-.3435
Number of Lands:	6	*Capacity:*	7 shot

300

Note: This gun was made on the basis of the Clements patents purchased by Smith & Wesson in France. It had a fixed barrel and both front and back sights fixed instead of merely mounted. It proved an extremely expensive design from a manufacturing point of view and could not be sold successfully in competition with lower-priced pocket pistols.

The main parts of this pistol are the receiver, barrel, slide, and bolt.

The receiver forms the handle of the weapon and is hollowed out to receive the standard tubular type of box magazine.

A special finger-operated safety is mounted in the front side of the grip directly below the trigger guard. (The theory of locating the safety at this point is, that when so placed the weapon cannot be discharged accidentally when withdrawing hurriedly from a pocket or a holster, and gripping firmly enough to push in the regular grip safety. Merely grasping the weapon will not force in the safety to make the pistol ready for firing; a contraction of the hand around the handle *in normal shooting position* is necessary to force it in. In actual practice, as opposed to theory, the *standard type* of grip safety is simpler and just as positive.)

This weapon is fitted with an automatic magazine disconnector. When the magazine is withdrawn from the arm the trigger mechanism is not in contact with the sear, and so accidental discharge is prevented.

The barrel is securely fastened to the receiver. The theory here is that better grouping of shots can be obtained by a rigid, immovable barrel. In actual practice, however, any good automatic pistol will shoot very much closer than the ordinary user is able to hold.

The barrel is unusual in that there are guides on it to receive the slide.

The slide encloses the entire top of the pistol. Both sights are carried on the slide. They are of the thick, square Patridge type, very effective for quick lining up and rapid shooting at short distances.

As the slide travels directly in guides machined on the barrel, and as the sights are machined into the slide, permanent sighting alignment is assured.

The recoil spring is mounted in the slide in a groove on top of the barrel.

A very unusual feature of this weapon is found in the loading mechanism.

Standard types of automatic pistol require the use of considerable strength to pull back the slide to load the first cartridge into the chamber, since the backward movement of the slide must draw the recoil spring back and compress it fully (and in hammerless pistols must also cock the hammer and compress the mainspring). In the Smith & Wesson automatic pistol, pushing in a stud which projects through the slide directly above the grip on the left-hand side (this is the bolt release catch) frees the bolt from contact with the recoil spring. The bolt can be drawn to the rear, permitting the magazine spring below to force a cartridge up in line. Pushing the bolt forward with the fingers will strip the cartridge from the top of the magazine and chamber it. Releasing the bolt catch will let it snap back into place to hook up with the recoil spring.

While the slide may be retracted under spring tension by pulling directly back on the bolt *without releasing the bolt catch,* so that the loading follows that customary in blowback automatic pistols, it will be seen that this little release device makes loading so much easier that the device has some excellent advantages.

Operation: When a loaded magazine is inserted in the handle, the bolt release catch is pushed through to free the bolt from spring compression and it is drawn fully back. Drawing the bolt back cocks the hammer. The cartridge rises in the magazine to position in front of the bolt. Pushing the bolt forward will chamber the cartridge and permit the extractor to snap into the extracting groove in the case. Releasing the spring-loaded catch will permit the bolt to hook up to the recoil spring mounted in the slide. When the weapon is gripped firmly so that the finger safety below the trigger guard is pushed in, the trigger can make contact with the sear releasing the hammer to fire the cartridge in the chamber. The slide and bolt recoil together in the guides in the barrel and the receiver. This rearward action compresses the recoil spring, extracts and ejects the empty case, rides over and cocks the hammer and permits the cartridge to rise into the feed way. On forward motion as the bolt is pulled ahead with the slide by the recoil spring, it chambers a fresh cartridge and leaves the weapon in firing position.

Dismounting. First push the magazine catch at the rear bottom of the handle and withdraw the magazine. Then draw the bolt back to check that there is no cartridge in the firing chamber.

Grasp the weapon in the left hand, first finger through the trigger guard, hand around the barrel and slide so that the left thumb may push in the bolt release catch.

While holding the catch in, use a drift pin of a small screw driver to push down the slide stop plunger. This is housed in a hole on top of the slide directly behind the rear sight.

Continued pressure on the bolt release catch will now permit the slide to come forward off the guide.

Note that the bolt remains in place on top of the receiver. The bolt in this weapon is a moving section which in the ordinary automatic pistol would be part of the slide. It is a sliding member mounted directly against the firing chamber of the barrel and extending backward to the end of the receiver. The front breechblock (or bolt) end houses the extractor and firing pin. Directly behind this the bolt is hollowed out so that only an arm on each side, which is scored to permit good finger grasp, rides in the receiver grooves and lines up with the slide. The two arms going back from the breechblock are joined across the back of the pistol. The bolt assembly mounts over a locking stud rising from the rear of the receiver.

With the slide and recoil spring removed, the bolt and extractor may now be lifted off.

The stocks may be removed by unscrewing the retaining screw.

Further dismounting is not recommended.

Assembling: Insert the ejector on the left side on the top of the receiver. Place its round spring plunger against the bolt and press it into position, the notch should be to the right and the groove on the upper left corner must line up with the corner formed by the receiver and the barrel.

Replace the bolt, and make sure that it fits properly over the extractor. The hammer must be fully cocked before the block can be inserted. If the hammer is down, it prevents the block from going forward to its front position. To cock the hammer it will be necessary, first to insert the magazine in the handle, then pull the hammer back with the thumb. The magazine should then be removed.

Insert the slide spring in the slide. Holding the slide in the left hand, place the rear end of the slide on the pistol so the spring lies in the groove on top of the barrel.

Push the slide back on the pistol making sure the square tongues on the barrel engage with their grooves in the slide.

Tilt the slide a little to permit it to pass over the projection on the rear of the barrel which acts as an abutment for the slide spring.

Then press in the bolt release catch on the side of the weapon so the slide can pass it and continue to move forward until the slide reaches its latch pin.

While holding the slide in position with the left hand, push the latch pin (directly behind the rear sight) in with the thumbnail of the right hand. The slide will now go forward to its fully closed position.

This pistol, originally manufactured by Echeverria of Eibar, Spain, is an elementary blowback design weighing about 30 ounces, having a barrel 4.8 inches long and an overall length of about 7.5 inches. The magazine holds nine cartridges.

This is a very heavy weapon for the cartridge it shoots. It is manufactured by the best of the Spanish arms manufacturers and is a heavy-duty weapon which will stand hard usage. This was one of the weapons used by the French Army during World War II. The Star employs the magazine button release on receiver.

It is unusual in that the barrel is mounted very solidly to the receiver. The recoil spring is housed below the barrel and is compressed by the slide arms under the barrel which form part of the slide and breechblock unit.

The resemblance in design of this pistol to the American Reising will be noted at once. It also embodies some of the features of the very early Mann-licher pistols.

One good feature of the weapon is the solid thumb safety, though it is awkwardly placed on the extreme right-hand side at the rear of the slide. When turned, the lever revolves the bolt which passes through the slide turning its cutaway face and interposing a solid surface between the hammer and the firing pin so that it is impossible to discharge the weapon.

STAR
Model I

.32 ACP

This arm is a modified version of the Model 1919. It is a combination of features of the German and the Colt-Browning designs. The mainspring housing is arched to improve the grip, a Colt-type slide stop operated by the magazine platform is provided, and a disconnector and thumb safety rather resembling the Colt are incorporated. While the safety is more easily applied than in earlier models, it is not of the positive type employed in the Colt. Manufacturing shortcuts in the lockwork make this an inferior weapon.

STAR   .32 ACP
Model H
This arm is a further modification of the earlier designs. The slide is of conventional pattern but has a heavy external hammer unusual in so short an arm. The thumb safety operates through a lever on the receiver above the magazine release button. Weapons of this type are widely used in both exposed and concealed holsters by ranking officers in Europe. For general specifications see The Identification Section.

STEYR   .32 ACP
1909
This enclosed hammer blowback pistol was made in both Austria and Belgium. The Austrian variety is much the finer weapon from the standpoint of manufacture and reliability. It weighs about 23 ounces, has a 3½-inch barrel and measures about 6½ inches overall. The magazine holds seven cartridges.

305

STAR MODEL H

While it is a straight blowback automatic pistol in which only a powerful recoil spring and the weight of the moving parts keep its breech closed at the moment of firing, the weapon has a number of unusual features worthy of attention.

It will usually be found with the receiver stamped: "Oesterr. Waffenfabrik Ges. Steyr Austria." These pistols were also manufactured in Belgium by the firm of N. Pieper which worked very closely with the Austrian firm of Steyr. (Pieper designed the pistol). Steyr also controlled the Solothurn works in Switzerland after World War I. This firm, incidentally, was owned in the 1920's by the Rheinmetall firm in Germany, an organization which became one of the largest manufacturers of machine weapons in the world during World War II.

Early Steyr pistols of this type are not fitted with extractors. The back pressure of the gases inside the empty cartridge case is utilized not only to drive back the slide and operate the cocking mechanism, but also to blow the empty cartridge case back against the ejector which hurls it out of the pistol. (Later models have extractors as guides.)

Pushing the catch on the left side of the receiver, then drawing the slide back slightly, permits the barrel, which is hinged ahead of the trigger guard, to be tipped up for cleaning. (This excellent feature in a somewhat modified form was later incorporated in the Spanish Sharpshooter pistol and in the French LeFrancais pistol.)

While doing away with an ejector has advantages in that there are fewer parts, and less machining is required, there is a big disadvantage in that if the load happens to be weak or the recoil spring unusually strong, the gun may jam because of insufficient pressure within the empty case during rearward motion of the slide.

In case of a misfire the cartridge is usually seated rather firmly in the firing chamber because of the pressure delivered to it by the blow of the firing pin. Before this weapon can be fired again, it is necessary to tip up the barrel and pry or punch out the misfired cartridge. Pulling back the slide, since there is no extractor, has no effect on the misfired cartridge in the chamber; but merely serves to bring another cartridge up into line with it and hopelessly jam the weapon.

This weapon is designed so that it may be used as single-shot pistol by tipping the barrel down, which disconnects the heavy recoil spring from the slide. When the barrel is open, the slide may be pulled back to cock the hammer with a minimum of energy and then pushed forward to position again. Snapping the loaded barrel down into place hooks up the heavy spring mechanism to permit extraction and the development of energy for closing the slide. Initial recoil spring resistance in this weapon is four pounds but rises to ten pounds at completion of the full stroke, which is 1.48 inches.

Construction: The Steyr uses a forward pivoted barrel in which the recoil spring is mounted in a tube above it which is part of the barrel forging. The bolt can slide freely in the receiver but its backward movement is limited.

STEYR MODEL 1909

This pistol was invented by N. Pieper in Belgium. It was made in that country by Pieper, stamped with his name, at the same time that it appeared in Austria.

Oesterreichische Waffenfabrik at Steyr purchased manufacturing rights from Pieper. This firm also made the OWA pistol.

A somewhat modified type shown in the Identification Section was manufactured at the Steyr plant in 1934, and many were marketed under the name Steyr-Solothurn.

STEYR 1909 with magazine withdrawn, barrel tipped down for cleaning or loading chamber and breechblock drawn back to show distance of its travel in recoil.

When the joint pin is removed to lift off the barrel, the bolt can be slid forward out of the receiver. It cannot be blown off to the rear.

When the barrel is snapped into place, the hook at the end of the recoil spring tube above the barrel breech makes the connection between the recoil spring mounted over the barrel and the bolt which must then draw back the recoil spring and its guide in rearward travel.

This is a hammer weapon in which the hammer is enclosed in the receiver. The bolt, driving to the rear, rides over and cocks this hammer. When the hammer is cocked, a small pin projects from the rear of the action.

This pistol weighs 22 ounces. The bolt weighs 2.6 ounces. The recoil spring guide rod weighs an additional .7 of an ounce and must be considered as part of the recoiling member. Thus, it will be seen that the weight of the recoiling members is 3.3 ounces as against 8 ounces in the standard type of slide employed in the ordinary .32 automatic pistol.

Due to the general construction, the recoil of this pistol is considerably heavier than that of most .32 automatics.

.32 ACP   STOCK
                                                             Automatic

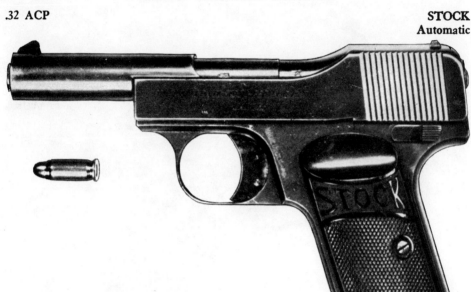

This German automatic is well made of excellent materials but of undistinguished blowback design. The barrel is 4 inches long, overall length is about 6¾ inches and weight is about 22 ounces. Magazine capacity is eight cartridges. The slide and breechblock are separate. To strip, lock the slide back with the safety. Pull the front end of the extractor and remove the breechblock by pressing at the rear. Press Safety Lever down and remove the slide from the front of the pistol. A standard thumb safety is provided on left side of receiver.

.32 ACP   WALTHER
                                                               4 (1910)

This model and its predecessor the Model 3 were the first .32 caliber automatics made by Walther. The Model 4 was the first really successful pistol made by this firm. It is an elementary blowback of unremarkable design. The barrel length is 3½ inches, overall length is 6 inches and the pistol weighs about eighteen ounces with empty magazine. The slide comprises the breechblock and is intricately machined to enclose the barrel and the recoil spring. An ejection port is provided on the left side of the slide, and firing this pistol is often disconcerting as empty cases are tossed out in line of vision of the right-handed shooter. This arm is not to be confused with the later Walther models, which are of superior design.

.32 ACP   WALTHER
                                                            PP and PPK

In 1929 the German firm of Karl Walther of Zella Mehlis introduced their double-action blowback Model PP (Police Pistol). Originally issued in .32

310

WALTHER
4 (1910)

.32 ACP

WALTHER MODEL 4, 1910.

WALTHER
PP and PPK

.32 ACP

THE WALTHER MODEL PP.

THE WALTHER PPK.

caliber, it was later manufactured for the .22 Long Rifle and also for the .380 A.C.P. cartridge. The barrel length is about 3⅞ inches, overall length about 6⅝ inches, weight about twenty-three ounces and magazine capacity 8 cartridges. This model was designed as a holster pistol and was widely adopted by police departments in Europe.

In 1931 a smaller model of the same arm was issued as the PPK (Police Pistol "Kriminal"—indicating an arm for use by detectives who carry their pistols concealed). This model has a 3¼-inch barrel, an overall length of about 6 inches, weighs about eighteen and a half ounces and has a magazine capacity of 7 cartridges.

As originally issued these pistols differed structurally only as required by their difference in size. Receivers were forged to shape the grip. In later models of the PPK, however, stocks are shaped to be attached to a pitched (instead of a curved) grip forging. Both forged and moulded grips are common in this model.

Originally the .32 and .380 calibers in both PP and PPK models used a spring-supported pin mounted in the slide above the firing pin as a loading indicator. These indicators were not used in the .22 caliber pistols because these used rim-fire ammunition, and to function properly the pin must float freely into the chamber above the firing pin when the chamber is empty; and the cartridge case head above the primer must have room to force the pin back when the chamber is loaded so the rear of the pin will project from the rear of the slide. On many war models of the PPK in .32 and .380 caliber, no indicator pins were provided.

As manufactured before World War II these Walthers were among the world's best finished pistols. War models usually have only a brush finish and usually show tool marks. Many of the last issue before the German collapse were poorly fitted and are not to be classed for reliability with earlier manufacture.

WALTHER PPK showing details of receiver, barrel mounting, slide, and trigger guard slide lock. Insert shows trigger connection with hook on trigger bar engaged in upper sear notch ready to pull it forward to release the hammer.

Among the standard accessories for both models were plastic magazine bottoms with finger spurs which added to the length of the grip for use by people with large hands, and detachable luminous sights (leuchtkorn) for night shooting by police and patrolmen. Limited quantities of both models were also made with lightweight duralumin slides and receivers which reduced the weight about one-third. Engraved presentation models were also common. When slides are made of duralumin, care must be taken not to attempt to blue them or bring them in contact with caustic compounds which will corrode them. Presentation models will be found made of a gold-colored alloy. Just how safe it is to fire these beautiful weapons is an open question although we know of one that fired several rounds of standard ammunition without apparent damage.

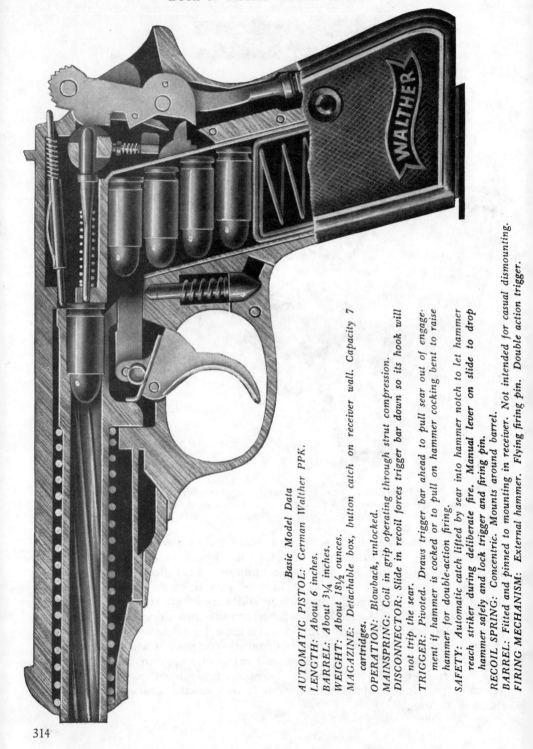

Basic Model Data

AUTOMATIC PISTOL: German Walther PPK.

LENGTH: About 6 inches.

BARREL: About 3¼ inches.

WEIGHT: About 18½ ounces.

MAGAZINE: Detachable box, button catch on receiver wall. Capacity 7 cartridges.

OPERATION: Blowback, unlocked.

MAINSPRING: Coil in grip operating through strut compression.

DISCONNECTOR: Slide in recoil forces trigger bar down so its hook will not trip the sear.

TRIGGER: Pivoted. Draws trigger bar ahead to pull sear out of engagement if hammer is cocked or to pull on hammer cocking bent to raise hammer for double-action firing.

SAFETY: Automatic catch lifted by sear into hammer notch to let hammer reach striker during deliberate fire. Manual lever on slide to drop hammer safely and lock trigger and firing pin.

RECOIL SPRING: Concentric. Mounts around barrel.

BARREL: Fitted and pinned to mounting in receiver. Not intended for casual dismounting.

FIRING MECHANISM: External hammer. Flying firing pin. Double action trigger.

Construction: The principal parts of both models are the receivers, slides, barrels, lockwork, and magazines. (1) Receivers may be forged to shape the grip—common in the PP—or may be pitched to receive molded stocks which determine the shape. The latter procedure is common in the PPK. A barrel mounting is part of the receiver forging, rising above the line of the trigger, while an arm extends forward from the mounting below the line of the barrel to receive and guide the front section of the slide. This arm has a cut in its underside to permit a projection on the end of the hinged trigger guard to pass up from below into the cut on the underside of the slide to lock that member when the pistol is assembled. The receiver is also machined behind the trigger seat to receive a trigger guard lock spring and plunger and is pierced to permit the trigger guard to be pivoted to it. The double-action lockwork is fitted in suitable cuts and the rear top of the receiver carries the slide travel guide grooves.

(2) The barrel is fitted to the receiver mounting which securely supports it and also reinforces the chamber. The concentric recoil spring mounts around the barrel and is compressed during recoil by its seating in the muzzle end of the slide against the shoulder of the barrel mount.

(3) The slide forms the breechblock at its rear end where it carries the firing pin and extractor—and in many models the floating chamber indicator pin. On the left side it is pierced to receive the thumb safety which has an external lever and an interior turning pin so machined that it locks over the firing pin and presses down the sear when the lever is pushed down. The ejection port is on the right side of the slide. The top of the slide is matted and carries the sights. The section forward from the breech face is milled out nearly to the muzzle to permit mounting the slide over the barrel from the muzzle.

(4) The lockwork is somewhat complicated but in well-made pistols is efficient, dependable and desirable. The hammer is external and is pivoted to the receiver by a pin. It acts through a strut to compress the mainspring which mounts around the lower section of the strut. The trigger is pivoted to a pin passing through a receiver hole and is hooked up to a long trigger bar on the right side of the receiver. A hook on the end of this bent trigger bar engages in the upper sear notch when the arm is ready to be fired; but if the slide is not fully home or the trigger has not been released, the hook is forced down into the lower notch in the sear where it cannot draw the sear forward to release the hammer. A pull on the trigger when the hammer is down and unlocked will draw the trigger bar ahead. This pulls the sear ahead on its pin causing the hammer cocking bent to be drawn ahead and up thereby raising the automatic safety tumbler out of the path of the hammer and rotating the hammer on its axis pin to compress the mainspring. As the sear slips out of the cocking bent the hammer falls. The ejector is mounted in the receiver behind the magazine opening.

(5) The magazine is the conventional box type with a button catch on the the right side of the receiver.

Safeties. An automatic safety is built into the lockwork in the form of a catch which blocks the hammer at rest from reaching the firing pin. This catch is lifted by a face on the sear as it is revolved by pull of the trigger bar. Only when the trigger is deliberately pulled can the sear raise the catch to the point where the hammer is cutaway to pass over the catch and hit the striker. If the hammer slips, the catch is below the hammer cut and will block the hammer fall. When the hammer is down this catch is in the path of the hammer at all times.

When the manual safety lever is pushed down it revolves the cutaway safety bolt attached to it, thereby bringing a solid steel surface in between the hammer and the head of the firing pin. Continued pressure forces the edge of this safety bolt to depress the sear. This drops the hammer safely on the steel bolt, meanwhile locking the sear and preventing trigger movement. Thus if the hammer is cocked and the safety lever is turned down it will drop the hammer violently but with complete safety on a loaded chamber and will lock the trigger to prevent the hammer from being affected by trigger pressure. If the safety is then pushed up, it will leave the weapon ready with loaded chamber for a double-action trigger pull to fire the first shot. Succeeding shots, of couse, function in the conventional semi-automatic fashion with the slide going back to cock the hammer.

Dismounting. Pull down the front end of the trigger guard and push it to the left. Withdraw magazine. Draw slide back with lifting motion until its rear end clears the guides. Ease slide forward over barrel mounting and off barrel (Do not remove barrel, as this is a factory job). Unscrew stock screw and remove stocks; this will afford access to all lockwork parts.

.32 ACP   WEBLEY AND SCOTT
                                                                  Metropolitan Police

This English automatic pistol weighs about 20 ounces, has a barrel 3½ inches long and an overall length of about 6¼ inches. This was the Official Metropolitan Police Model, the standard weapon of the London City Police and widely used throughout the Empire. (It has since been supplanted by heavier-caliber revolvers).

The .32 caliber differs from the .25 caliber only in size and sighting equipment. It has a front sight on the barrel and a rear sight at the extreme end of the slide. (The .25 is not equipped with sights, as it is felt they are unnecessary on a weapon which is primarily for close-quarters work). The hammer of the .32 caliber is shaped somewhat differently from the .25, but is equally difficult to cock rapidly. The name and address of the maker and the caliber are stamped on the slide above the trigger guard.

This caliber operates the same as the .25. It is a straight blowback weapon.

A thumb safety is provided on the receiver directly below the slide behind the trigger on the left side. When it is pushed down, the word "Safe" may be seen on the slide above it. The weapon cannot then be fired.

The magazine release catch is in the bottom of the handle at the rear of the magazine. It is pushed in to release the magazine. Except that it has an outside hammer of typical European design, there is nothing unusual about this weapon. It is a standard blowback type.

316

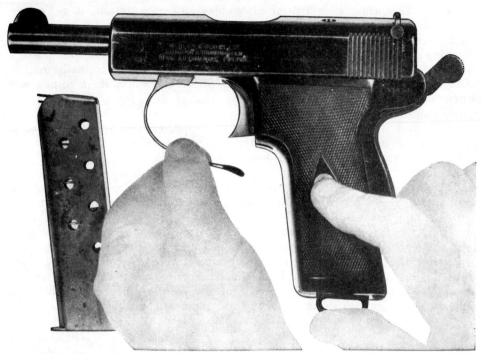

Webley & Scott quick dismounting system as used on their .32 Auto & 9mm M & P types. Spring trigger guard has been sprung up and out of engagement.

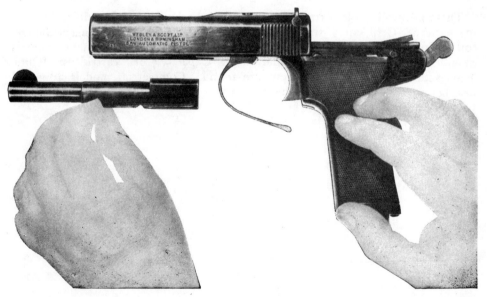

Barrel and slide have been pushed forward and barrel withdrawn. Note locking notch in barrel.

The recoil spring, as is typical of Webley automatic pistols, is a V-spring mounted under the right-hand grip of the pistol and connected with the slide by a lever. The slide going back pushes against this lever which compresses the V-spring to provide energy for the return motion. This type of spring is not as dependable as the coil spring, or as the lighter flat spring normally used in American pistols. Because of its position under the stock, these pistols will often be found with broken righthand stocks, as dropping or even seriously jarring them will crack the vulcanite stock.

The barrel is held on the receiver by the upper ends of the trigger guard. The slide acts as the breechblock, and also carries the firing pin and firing pin spring and extractor in its breech end.

The trigger is mounted on an axis pin with a coil spring behind it to act as a return spring functioning through a plunger. Pressure on the trigger is transmitted by a steel bar mounted across the left side of the receiver in line with the trigger. When the safety catch is applied, it pivots and pushes down this trigger bar (or trigger auxiliary lever as it is called) to break engagement with the sear which is hooked into the cocking notch on the hammer.

Pressing the trigger pushes the trigger auxiliary lever, which is in contact with the sear, to disengage it from the hammer notch and permit the coil spring mounted in the receiver ahead of the hammer to rock the hammer forward on its axis to strike the flying firing pin and discharge the cartridge.

.32 ACP   HUNGARIAN
                                                           Model 37

This pistol is commonly found in 9mm (.380 A.C.P.) caliber, but those in 7.65mm (.32 A.C.P.) are the same except for caliber.

These are well made, extremely sturdy blowback pistols of modified Browning pattern. Grip safety, small exposed hammer, finger spur on magazine, recoil spring and guide below barrel, slide stop release. Grip safety operates when hammer is cocked. No manual safety. Capacity 7 or 8 cartridges. Minor manufacturing and stock variations are found. Commercial models appeared just before the war. During the war many of these pistols were issued to German military personnel.

Chapter 8
Caliber .35

CARTRIDGE

Data

Manufacture of this cartridge has been discontinued in the United States. As originally issued it used a 96-grain bullet of unusual design. The nose section was metal patched and the base section was ordinary lead alloy. The theory of the design was that the point would not be deformed during automatic

loading and that the base would take the rifling more easily and injure it less than would a full-jacketed bullet. In actual practice the theory does not work very well. The bullet diameter is really the same as that of the standard .32 A.C.P. The designation .35 was given to distinguish it from the standard .32 auto. The muzzle velocity is about 809 feet per second and the striking energy approximately 110 foot pounds at muzzle.

.35 Smith and Wesson Auto

SMITH AND WESSON
Automatic

Official Model Name: Model .35 Caliber Automatic Pistol.
Ammunition: .35 S & W Automatic.
Manufacturing Dates: May 6, 1913-Jan. 27, 1921.
Serial Numbers: Numbered in separate series beginning at one.

Finish:	Blue and nickel	*Twist:* One turn in		12″
Barrel Length:	3½″	*Direction of Twist:*		Right
Land Diameter:	.310-.311	*Diameter of Chamber:*	Back:	.351
Groove Diameter:	.320-.321	*Capacity:*		7 shot
Number of Lands:	6			

35 S&W AUTO with magazine extracted, trigger guard lock pulled down and barrel partly raised to show position of separate breechblock and system of mounting.

The main parts of this pistol are the receiver, barrel, and bolt. Note that in this weapon there is no slide as the term is normally used in connection with blowback automatic pistols. There is a sliding member which is actually the bolt, or breechblock.

The receiver is hollowed out to receive the magazine from below. The lockwork is mounted in the rear of the handle section of the receiver directly behind the magazine well. A rear post rises above the rear of the grip section of the receiver and is fitted with a suitable hole to permit the rear of the barrel extension to be screwed to it.

The trigger guard is hinged to the receiver, but is not an integral part of it.

The bolt or breechblock has ribs on each side to the rear of the barrel to permit ease of grasp when the weapon is being cocked by hand for the first shot. Its rear end fits over the post which rises from the extreme rear of the receiver. Near its front end at the breech of the barrel it is fitted with a spring-loaded release catch. Pushing in this catch frees the bolt from contact with the powerful recoil spring. By this means, it is possible to disconnect the bolt from spring tension so it may be drawn to the rear and then pushed forward to cock the weapon and load the first cartridge without the usual heavy spring pull necessary in automatic pistols.

The barrel has an extension passing above the line of the bore from the breech back far enough to permit it to be hinged to the frame post rising from the extreme end of the receiver. The forward end of the barrel is clamped to the receiver by the trigger guard which is attached to it by a pin. When closed, the two parts practically form one piece. The lower end of the guard is sprung into a recess in the receiver below the trigger, where it is securely held. This guard can be unhooked from the receiver permitting the barrel to be swung up on its hinge at the rear of the receiver post to permit cleaning of the barrel from the muzzle or breech.

A positive finger safety is mounted in the handle of the receiver directly below the trigger guard. This acts as an automatic grip safety when the weapon is held in the firing position.

On the left side of the receiver behind and above the center of the stock, is a thumb-operated, wheel-type safety. When pushed into position, this engages with and locks the sear so the weapon cannot be discharged until the safety is pushed off deliberately.

A magazine release catch is provided at the rear of the bottom of the butt.

The magazine is the conventional steel box type inserted from below into the handle.

The bolt is operated by the recoil. It is attached to the bolt spring (or recoil spring) by a bolt rod and a bolt release catch. Its abutment is the receiver post at the rear.

The firing pin, extractor, and ejector are mounted in the bolt.

A special unit called the insert (because it is inserted in the rear of the receiver) has mounted in it the mainspring, mainspring plunger, and the manual safety. This insert is held in place by two screws which secure it in position.

The recoil spring is mounted in an extension above the barrel from the breech forward to the muzzle.

When the insert is removed, the entire lockwork is exposed. When it is replaced, care must be exercised to make sure that the lower end of the stirrup seats properly in its socket in the plunger.

As the barrel and receiver are very securely fastened together in this weapon, and only the bolt moves, in theory the accuracy should be considerably greater than in a weapon with a full-moving slide or with a moving barrel. In actual practice, however, no appreciable increase in accuracy can be noted.

The lockwork is unusually simple in this weapon.

The sear is pivoted to the hammer and when the hammer is cocked, the sear is carried upward and pressed forward into a cocking notch by the sear spring.

At the same time the mainspring is compressed as the hammer pushes down the stirrup, the lower end of which engages with the mainspring plunger carried in the insert.

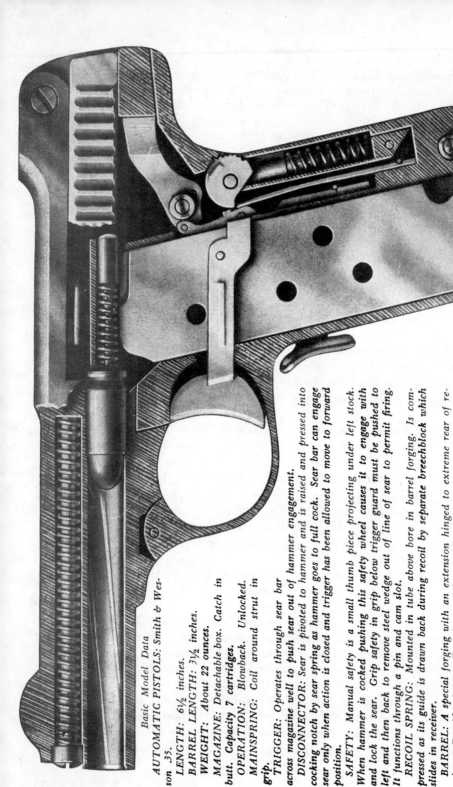

Basic Model Data

AUTOMATIC PISTOLS: Smith & Wesson .35.

LENGTH: 6½ inches.
BARREL LENGTH: 3½ inches.
WEIGHT: About 22 ounces.
MAGAZINE: Detachable box. Catch in butt. **Capacity 7 cartridges.**
OPERATION: Blowback. Unlocked.
MAINSPRING: Coil around strut in grip.
TRIGGER: Operates through sear bar across magazine well to push sear out of hammer engagement.
DISCONNECTOR: Sear is pivoted to hammer and is raised and pressed into cocking notch by sear spring as hammer goes to full cock. Sear bar can engage sear only when action is closed and trigger has been allowed to move to forward position.
SAFETY: Manual safety is a small thumb piece projecting under left stock. When hammer is cocked pushing this safety wheel causes it to engage with and lock the sear. Grip safety in grip below trigger guard must be pushed to left and then back to remove steel wedge out of line of sear to permit firing. It functions through a pin and cam slot.
RECOIL SPRING: Mounted in tube above bore in barrel forging. Is compressed as its guide is drawn back during recoil by separate breechblock which slides in receiver.
BARREL: A special forging with an extension hinged to extreme rear of receiver. Provides for recoil spring and has locking lug on under side.
FIRING MECHANISM: Concealed hammer.
CALIBER: .35 S & W Automatic.
SPECIAL FEATURE: This pistol does not have a slide. A separate breechblock shuttles from the breech between the receiver and the top of the barrel extension. A spring catch on the breechblock may be pushed in to disengage from the recoil spring to permit easy loading of chamber.

When the trigger is pressed it engages with the sear plunger releasing the sear from its notch.

The construction of this notch plate is unusual in that it is made of very high-carbon steel hardened to the point where there is practically no wear. This feature provides an absolutely even and nonchanging trigger pull.

The cocking notch has a very large surface which tends to reduce the friction of the pull-off to a minimum.

The manual safety, a small wheel-like affair mounted on the left side of the receiver to the rear of the stock, engages with, and locks the sear when pushed up. (A small directional arrow and the letter S etched on the frame show the direction to push the safety.) This safety is clumsy and not very practical.

The finger safety below the trigger guard requires two motions of the middle finger, first pushing the bar across and then pushing it inwards. While ordinarily this is done instinctively as the weapon is grasped, on occasion it may require conscious finger movement. This safety wedges a solid block of steel between the wall of the insert and the sear; firmly locking the sear into the notch in the frame.

When the safety is operated it causes the block to lift up above the sear by means of a pin in a cam slot. When the finger pressure on the safety is released, the block at once goes back to its original safe position.

Loading: The magazine release catch in the bottom of the rear of the butt is pushed to permit the magazine to be withdrawn. When a loaded magazine is inserted, it is pushed in until it locks securely in the handle.

The weapon is held in the right hand with the finger outside the trigger guard for safety, and the bolt grasped with the fingers of the left hand, the bolt release catch being pushed in. (This catch is on the forward left side of the bolt.)

Pressing in this release catch frees the bolt from the bolt spring and permits it to be drawn back with a minimum of effort while the magazine spring forces the cartridge up into line. Drawing the bolt to the rear pushes the hammer back to full cock.

While still retaining pressure on the release catch, push the bolt to its forward closed position with a quick thrust. Then release the catch. This motion strips a cartridge from the top of the magazine into the firing chamber and snaps the extractor into the extracting groove of the case. Releasing the catch permits it to spring out so that the bolt engages with the bolt lock spring.

Make sure that when the bolt is drawn to the rear, no pressure is applied to the trigger or to the automatic safety.

Firing: Make sure that the manual safety is off. (The milled portion must be rolled *downward.*)

Note that if this manual safety is on when the hammer is down, it will be released automatically as the bolt is pulled back to cock the weapon.

As you grip the pistol for firing, the middle finger must push slightly over and then back on the safety to force it back into the handle to make it ready to fire.

Note that this weapon (unlike the later Model .32 Smith & Wesson automatic pistol) does *not* have a magazine safety. When the magazine is withdrawn, this weapon may be fired if a cartridge remains in the firing chamber. Therefore, to unload it, first remove the magazine and then draw the bolt back to be sure that there is no cartridge remaining in the firing chamber.

This pistol may easily be used as a single-shot weapon by withdrawing the magazine, pressing in the bolt release catch and pulling the bolt back. As the bolt is not hitched up to the recoil spring at this time, it will stay back. A cartridge may be inserted directly in the firing chamber. Pressing in on the bolt release catch and pushing the bolt smartly forward will close the weapon and leave it ready for firing and automatic ejection of the cartridge.

Dismounting: First push back the magazine catch in the butt and withdraw the magazine.

Press in the bolt release catch and pull the bolt back and look in the chamber to be sure that there is no cartridge there.

The barrel is attached to the receiver at the rear by an interlocking hinge on the receiver post, and at the forward end by the trigger guard.

Pull out the trigger guard while holding firmly to the grip. (This will require a very strong pull).

The rear of the trigger guard will come out of its slot in the receiver and pulling up on it will free the attached barrel and permit it to be swung up on its hinge.

Unscrew the joint screw and the barrel can be removed from the receiver.

The bolt may now be lifted up and off over the receiver post.

Remove the two screws holding the insert and it can be withdrawn to expose the lockwork for dismounting or oiling.

The pivoted sear in this weapon does away with the need for several parts. It is a simple piece of design.

The stocks are removed by withdrawing the stock screws and sliding down out of the grip.

The recoil spring is mounted in a tube directly above the barrel. Unfastening the retaining screw above the barrel muzzle will permit withdrawal of the recoil spring if necessary.

Chapter 9

Caliber 9mm and .357

CARTRIDGE   **9mm. Japanese**
Data

This is a revolver cartridge of the standard rim type somewhat resembling the Smith & Wesson cartridge. The bullet is lead, despite the fact that this is a Japanese service revolver cartridge. The muzzle velocity is about 750 feet per second. This cartridge has never been manufactured outside of Japan and nothing manufactured in this country will chamber in revolvers intended for it.

JAPANESE   **9mm. Japanese**
26

This is a hinge-frame revolver wtih a breech locking catch of the type used in Smith & Wesson revolvers. It has a barrel about 4.7 inches long, measures about 9.4 inches overall and weighs about 36 ounces.

Construction and Operation: The loading and ejecting system follows that of the Smith & Wesson hinged-frame design. Lifting the barrel catch on the barrel extension frees the extension from the standing breech and permits the barrel to be hinged down on its axis pin. The extractor is forced up by cam action to automatically eject all cartridges or cases in the chambers. The cylinder, which has 6 chambers, may be unscrewed and withdrawn from its mounting, carrying the extractor unit with it.

The lockwork is unusual in that it follows somewhat the pattern of the Austrian Rast-Gasser. Pulling down the hinged trigger guard permits the left hand side plate to be swung out on its hinge above the handle. The stocks may then be removed. Opening the side plate exposes all the lockwork.

This is purely a double-action pistol which cannot be thumb cocked. There is no cocking bent to hold the hammer in rear position. Pulling the trigger revolves the cylinder, raises and slips the hammer to which the firing pin is attached. This was primarily a Japanese cavalry weapon and is incapable of truly accurate shooting by American standards.

9mm. Browning Long   CARTRIDGE
                                                                           Data

This is a European cartridge designed for use in the Browning Model 1903, the pistol design known in this country as the Colt .32 or .380. The cartridge is a semirim type which is intermediate in power between the .380 and the .38 Colt Automatic. Except for a very small quantity manufactured early in the century, this cartridge has never been manufactured in the United States. It is loaded with a 110-grain bullet and is usually full metal jacketed. The muzzle velocity may vary between 1,000 and 1,100 feet per second. Actual bullet diameter is .355 inch, case length is about .80 and over-all length of loaded cartridge is about 1 and 1/10 inches. The powder charge may vary from 4 to 6 grains depending on the type of powder used.

9mm. Browning Long   BROWNING
                                                                           1903

This pistol was manufactured in Belgium by F.N. from Browning patents. Except for minor differences the design is the same as the .32 Colt Automatic

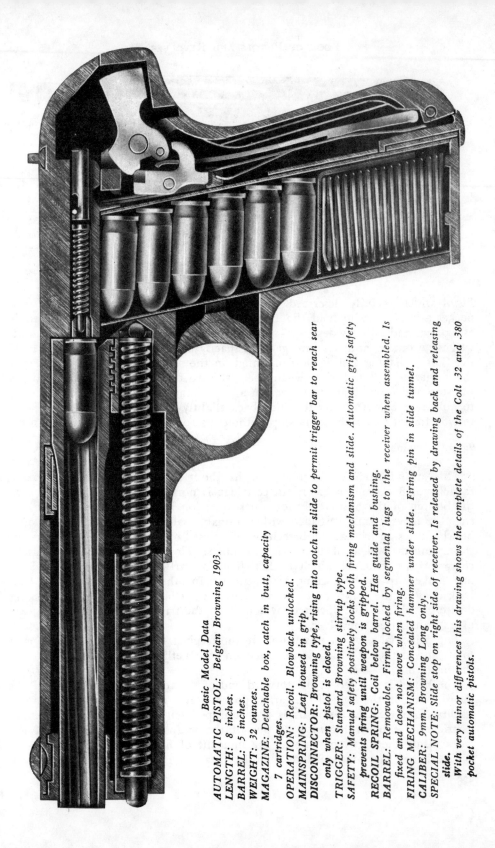

Basic Model Data

AUTOMATIC PISTOL: Belgian Browning 1903.

LENGTH: 8 inches.

BARREL: 5 inches.

WEIGHT: 32 ounces.

MAGAZINE: Detachable box, catch in butt, capacity 7 cartridges.

OPERATION: Recoil. Blowback unlocked.

MAINSPRING: Leaf housed in grip.

DISCONNECTOR: Browning type, rising into notch in slide to permit trigger bar to reach sear only when pistol is closed.

TRIGGER: Standard Browning stirrup type.

SAFETY: Manual safety positively locks both firing mechanism and slide. Automatic grip safety prevents firing until weapon is gripped.

RECOIL SPRING: Coil below barrel. Has guide and bushing.

BARREL: Removable. Firmly locked by segmental lugs to the receiver when assembled. Is fixed and does not move when firing.

FIRING MECHANISM: Concealed hammer under slide. Firing pin in slide tunnel.

CALIBER: 9mm. Browning Long only.

SPECIAL NOTE: Slide stop on right side of receiver. Is released by drawing back and releasing slide.

With very minor differences this drawing shows the complete details of the Colt 32 and 380 pocket automatic pistols.

Showing slide blown back. Recoil spring about to pull it forward.

Pistol which is fully described. While Colt manufactured this design as a pocket arm, F.N. who held the European manufacturing patents produced it as a police and military design. It has a 5-inch barrel, measures 8 inches overall, weighs 32 ounces and has a magazine capacity of 7 cartridges. It differs from the Colt in having a slide stop mounted on the right side of the receiver. As the magazine follower rises when the last cartridge has been fired, it strikes the stop and forces it up to engage in a cut on the right-hand side of the slide to hold it open. Drawing the slide back slightly will enable it when released to ride forward over the slide stop without use of the customary thumb piece.

9mm. Browning Long   **LeFRANCAIS**
Army

This arm, introduced in 1928, weighs about 2.2 lbs. and has a magazine capacity of 8 cartridges. A ninth cartridge is normally carried in the loop at the bottom of the butt, ready for quick insertion in the chamber; though the chamber may be carried loaded with reasonable safety. This is a conventional blowback design in that the breech is held closed only by pressure of the recoil spring and the weight of the moving members. However, it has several unusual characteristics, chief of which is that, like the early Roth pistols, the slide is not hooked up to the cocking arrangement. In other words, as the slide goes back it ejects the empty and reloads. However, it has no effect on the cocking device, which must be operated by a pull on the trigger exactly as in the case of a "hammerless" revolver.

The principal parts of this pistol are the receiver, the barrel which is hinged to it, and the slide which is mounted on it, together with the lockwork and the magazine.

The barrel is pivoted at the forward end of the receiver ahead of the trigger guard, much in the style of the earlier pocket Steyr. Like that earlier weapon in its first form, the Le Francais is not equipped with an extractor, the empty cartridge case being blown back out of the weapon by the pressure of the gases inside the cartridge case at the moment of firing.

The barrel fastening pin has a milled head and may be easily withdrawn.

A heavy lug is part of the barrel forging directly below the firing chamber, after the general style of the American Reising pistol, caliber .22. A notch on this lug is engaged by a spring catch which has a lever attached which protrudes through the right side of the receiver.

The rear section of the slide provides the breechblock and fits against the face of the chamber, while arms extend forward from it and are joined at their forward end just behind the barrel hinge.

The rear of the slide has thumbpieces to permit gripping for loading the pistol in standard automatic pistol fashion. However, the feature of the tip-up barrel design is intended to make loading easy. Withdrawing the magazine tips up the barrel for insertion of a cartridge directly in the chamber.

The striker and its compression spring are mounted in the breechblock section of the slide, the pin itself being provided with a lug which serves as a bent on which the sear can bear for firing. This striker is so placed in the breechblock that the bent can move forward a short distance against spring action. Behind this bent, the coil mainspring is wound around the thick rear section of the striker and is held under tension by a special collar as the striker is forced back by trigger pressure.

The recoil spring, which returns the action after the slide has been blown back, is also a coil and is positioned in the front end of the receiver directly below the rear of the trigger. A lever under the left stock is directly affected at its upper end by the slide arm as the slide moves to the rear, and turns on its pivot to draw up on a compressor attached to the recoil spring to provide energy for the return movement.

The eight-shot magazine is of the standard box type, being inserted from

THE LE FRANÇAIS ARMY MODEL. The insert shows the barrel automatically opening as the magazine is extracted. The barrel can also be operated by pushing the catch seen above the trigger.

329

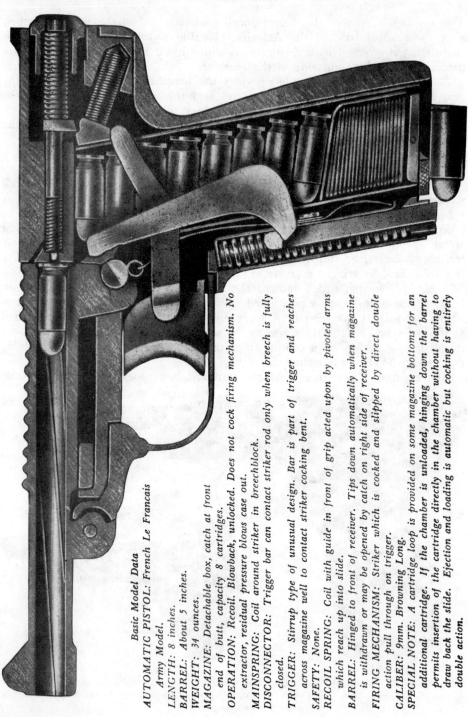

Basic Model Data

AUTOMATIC PISTOL: French Le Francais
    Army Model.
LENGTH: 8 inches.
BARREL: About 5 inches.
WEIGHT: 34 ounces.
MAGAZINE: Detachable box, catch at front
    end of butt, capacity 8 cartridges.
OPERATION: Recoil. Blowback, unlocked. Does not cock firing mechanism. No
    extractor, residual pressure blows case out.
MAINSPRING: Coil around striker in breechblock.
DISCONNECTOR: Trigger bar can contact striker rod only when breech is fully
    closed.
TRIGGER: Stirrup type of unusual design. Bar is part of trigger and reaches
    across magazine well to contact striker cocking bent.
SAFETY: None.
RECOIL SPRING: Coil with guide in front of grip acted upon by pivoted arms
    which reach up into slide.
BARREL: Hinged to front of receiver. Tips down automatically when magazine
    is withdrawn or may be opened by catch on right side of receiver.
FIRING MECHANISM: Striker which is cocked and slipped by direct double
    action pull through on trigger.
CALIBER: 9mm. Browning Long.
SPECIAL NOTE: A cartridge loop is provided on some magazine bottoms for an
    additional cartridge. If the chamber is unloaded, hinging down the barrel
    permits insertion of the cartridge directly in the chamber without having to
    draw back the slide. Ejection and loading is automatic but cocking is entirely
    double action.

below; but is unusual in that it is provided with a loop below the base plate in which an extra cartridge may be carried. The magazine release catch is in the lower front end of the magazine, the magazine itself being retained by a flat spring in the front section of the grip which connects directly with the tip-up lever for the barrel.

The trigger, its connecting bar and the sear are a single steel unit in this weapon. It is mounted in the receiver so it can slide back and forth freely; and does not require the use of pins or screws. A small coil spring mounted on the guide directly below the mainspring exerts forward pressure against the sear end of this piece, serving to return the trigger to forward position when the trigger is released between shots. This also serves as a disconnector, as when a shot has been fired, until the trigger is released the sear is too far back to permit engaging with the striker bent for the double-action pull necessary to fire the weapon.

Cooling fins are provided on top of the barrel, though their value is questionable. These do not appear in the pocket models, photographs of which will be found in the identification section at the rear of this book.

.The front sight is an integral part of the barrel forging, while the rear sight on the slide is offset somewhat to compensate for the slight movement of the muzzle as a weapon with a long double-action pull of this type is fired.

Operation. The magazine catch is pressed and the magazine withdrawn from the handle and loaded in standard tubular fashion customary in blowback pistols of the pocket type. When the magazine is withdrawn, the spring against which it has been exerting tension is free to act on the barrel lever and throw the barrel up away from the slide at its breech end. A cartridge is inserted in the barrel, the magazine is then inserted in the handle until it locks and the barrel is returned to position.

WEBLEY AND SCOTT
New Military and Police

9mm. Browning Long

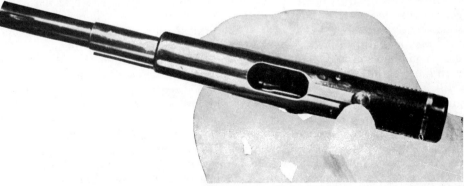

Top view showing pistol held open by follower rising after last shot has been fired. Pressing down the slide stop catch in the roof of the slide releases the slide.

This pistol measures 8 inches overall, weighs 32 ounces and has a magazine capacity of 8 cartridges. The takedown system and general design are those already described for the Webley & Scott under Caliber .32 A.C.P. This is

a straight blowback weapon and not to be confused with the Webley .455 Naval automatic pistol which has a fully locked breech, though in appearance the two are much alike.

The comparatively low power of the cartridge employed does not require a breech-locking system.

The magazine release catch is a spring-loaded button type catch and is mounted inside the front bottom of the butt.

The rearward thrust of the gases inside the empty cartridge case as the bullet goes down the barrel pushes the case back against the breechblock face of the slide to drive the slide to the rear against the tension of the recoil spring and to drive on back and cock the hammer. It then rides over, disconnects the trigger mechanism, and permits the magazine spring to lift a cartridge in line with the breechblock. On forward motion of the breechblock as the recoil spring pulls it ahead, a cartridge is stripped from the magazine into the firing chamber, and the extractor snaps over its head into the extracting groove as the slide reaches fully forward position.

Releasing the trigger permits connection to be made with the sear. Only one shot may be fired for each pull of the trigger, as this weapon has a positive disconnector. These arms may be encountered with or without grip safeties.

One feature of this pistol is the slide release catch. When the last shot has been fired, the magazine follower forces the slide catch up to hold the slide in open position. Inserting a loaded magazine, and then pressing the stud on top of the slide directly ahead of and in line with the rear sight, releases the catch and permits the compressed recoil spring to drive the slide forward and load the pistol.

CARTRIDGE
Data   9mm. Glisenti

While the over-all dimensions of this cartridge so closely resemble the 9mm. Luger that they will interchange in chambers, the Glisenti load is considerably lower in power than the German. Pistols designed for this cartridge should not be used with German or American ammunition. The Glisenti cartridge is identical in appearance with the truncated nose type of Luger cartridge. The designation Glisenti is a popular one for this cartridge.

BERETTA
1915   9mm. Glisenti

This pistol is described under Caliber .380 and differs only in bore and slight structural alteration. It has a buffer spring intended to cushion the recoil of the Glisenti cartridge. As this is a blowback arm it should never be used with high-pressure American and German ammunition.

GLISENTI
Army 1910   9mm. Glisenti

This was an official Italian service pistol in both World Wars. It has a 4-inch barrel, measures about 8¼ inches overall, weighs about 32 ounces and has a magazine capacity of 7 cartridges. Army models usually have stocks of wood, generally checkered. The Glisenti was developed from the 1906 Brixia and is quite similar to that arm.

The pistol is known as the Model 1910, but was patented in 1906 and was offered for test to the United States Ordnance Board in 1907. It was rejected early in the tests. While it chambers a cartridge identical in appearance and of the same general measurements as the German Luger cartridge, the

GLISENTI showing details of magazine construction, position of dismounting tool under stock, and weak construction of cutaway receiver. Spot polishing on hidden parts of foreign weapons is usually to cover tool marks or disguise soft metal.

Italian charge was normally about 25 per cent below the German.

Construction. This is a delayed blowback pistol and the lock is a prop-up design which will not stand up under heavy charges. The barrel and barrel extension are machined out of a single forging. The barrel extension is square in form to receive the breechblock which is likewise squared. The forward section of the extension is cut away just behind the barrel chamber to permit ejection. The lower forward end of the extension has two slots cut in it, one over the magazine and the other over a receiver slot through which the locking block swings up to engage in a cut in the under face of the breechblock.

While the barrel extension has the customary groove on each side to permit it to slide back and forth when the weapon is fired, only one (the one on the right-hand side) actually runs in the receiver. The left-hand groove slides in a light metal side plate which fits on the receiver on the left-hand side, and whose sole function is to protect the locking mechanism and the lockwork. As this side plate is held only by being hooked into a small recess on the rear of the receiver and retained in front by a small screw recoil even with the standard Italian ammunition very soon shakes the plate loose. This invariably induces jams.

334

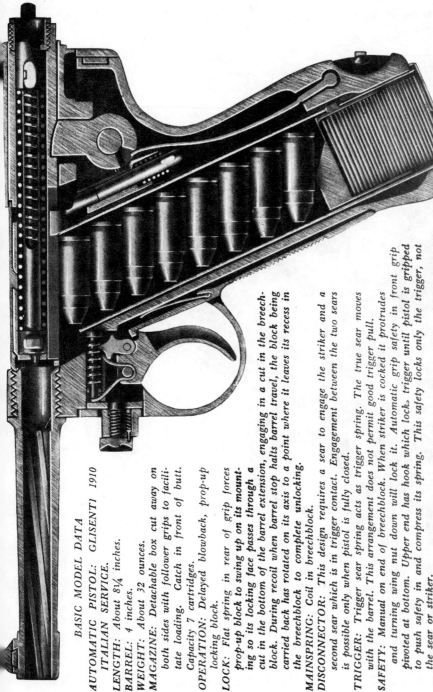

BASIC MODEL DATA

AUTOMATIC PISTOL: GLISENTI 1910
ITALIAN SERVICE.

LENGTH: About 8¼ inches.

BARREL: 4 inches.

WEIGHT: About 32 ounces.

MAGAZINE: Detachable box cut away on both sides with follower grips to facilitate loading. Catch in front of butt. Capacity 7 cartridges.

OPERATION: Delayed blowback, prop-up locking block.

LOCK: Flat spring in rear of grip forces prop-up block to swing up on its mounting so its locking face passes through a cut in the bottom of the barrel extension, engaging in a cut in the breechblock. During recoil when barrel stop halts barrel travel, the block being carried back has rotated on its axis to a point where it leaves its recess in the breechblock to complete unlocking.

MAINSPRING: Coil in breechblock.

DISCONNECTOR: This design requires a sear to engage the striker and a second sear which is in trigger contact. Engagement between the two sears is possible only when pistol is fully closed.

TRIGGER: Trigger sear spring acts as trigger spring. The true sear moves with the barrel. This arrangement does not permit good trigger pull.

SAFETY: Manual on end of breechblock. When striker is cocked it protrudes and turning wing nut down will lock it. Automatic grip safety in front grip pivoted at bottom. Upper end has hook which locks trigger until pistol is gripped to push safety in and compress its spring. This safety locks only the trigger, not the sear or striker.

RECOIL SPRING: Breechblock is driven forward by the coilspring with it; locking block is rotated up through 60 degrees by its flat spring; and barrel is returned by a separate barrel spring above the trigger.

BARREL: A unit with its extension. Travels back with breechblock and lock about ¼ inch before travel is halted.

FIRING MECHANISM: Striker type. A stud on its left side which travels in a cut in the breechblock and projects into a parallel groove in the barrel extension cocks it.

CALIBER: 9mm. Italian Service (Glisenti)

The drawing shows the Glisenti in unlocked position. Note that breech-block return spring winds around striker. A separate flat spring is required to function the swinging prop-up block. A small coil above the trigger sear is the barrel return spring.

Left side view showing all parts in full recoil position. Cam extending above magazine well is secondary sear on barrel. Stud projecting from receiver below barrel is side plate fastener. Key-shaped piece in front of magazine at bottom is a tool carried under the stock and used for removing striker unit.

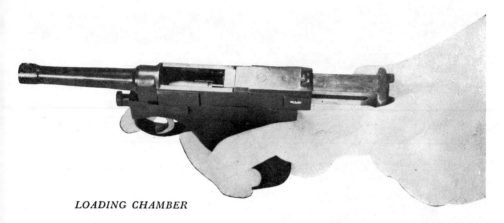

LOADING CHAMBER

The bolt is square to fit in the barrel extension and is provided with milled surfaces at its rear end which are used as finger grips to draw the bolt back for cocking. This bolt (or breechblock) is held by a square pin fitted with a spring catch which passes through the pistol and through a slot in the breechblock behind the coil main and recoil springs housed in the breechblock itself.

The extractor is of the flat-spring type and is mounted on the upper surface of the breechblock. There is a square stud on the left side of the striker which runs in a slot in the breechblock, but projects into a similar groove in the side of the barrel extension. When the weapon is cocked, this striker projects through the rear of the breechblock and may be locked by turning a winged bolt fastened about it.

Functioning. As the cartridge is fired, the barrel and barrel extension (which are a single unit) start back firmly locked to the bolt (or breechblock). The locking block is rotated on its axis to the rear to start the unlocking action. Since this block passes through a slot in the barrel extension to reach the locking notch in the underside of the breechblock, as it rotates it pushes against the barrel extension drawing it and the one-piece barrel to the rear.

After a short travel (just over ¼ inch) a stop on the barrel extension strikes against the rear of the receiver, which halts further travel. At this point the locking block has rotated far enough that it is withdrawn entirely from its notch in the underside of the breechblock, and the breechblock continues backwards under the momentum which has been imparted to it. The extractor on its upper face draws the empty cartridge case out of the firing chamber. The recoil spring, which is housed about the striker, is compressed during this rearward action to provide energy for the forward movement.

The lock is held down below the barrel extension as the flat surface of the breechblock riding back presses it down. The barrel extension is thereby prevented from moving forward until the notch on the under surface of the breechblock on return movement reaches the proper position to permit the stiff, flat spring compressed by the swinging block to reassert itself and force the block up through the recess in the barrel extension. The recoil spring

337

9MM. Brixia Model 1906.

housed around the striker pushes the breechblock itself forward to bring it to this position.

A separate barrel-return spring is necessary to force the barrel fully forward the last ¼ inch. This spring is mounted in a hole milled out of the barrel piece; it thrusts against a special shoulder on the receiver just ahead of the magazine. Since the complete forward thrust of the barrel cannot occur until the tip of the locking block has entered its notch on the lower surface of the breechblock, the feeding system is complicated. The cartridge is actually chambered before the barrel is in its fully forward position.

Because of this construction, actually two sears are required in this pistol. The normal sear is mounted inside the barrel extension; it is in the form of a cam which pushes back a stud on the striker and allows it to ride over under pressure of the mainspring. As this cam moves with the barrel, a second sear is provided which trips over the trigger itself when the barrel returns to complete firing position. When the trigger is fully forward, this second sear (which is on the trigger) can lift the tail of a regular sear to fire the weapon. As the trigger hookup is not made otherwise, no disconnector is necessary to prevent firing more than one shot for each pull of the trigger. Each sear is equipped with a small flat spring. The trigger sear spring also functions as the trigger spring.

Besides the manual safety at the rear of the breechblock, this pistol has an automatic grip safety placed in front of the handle below the line of the trigger guard. It is milled on its outer surface to give a firm grip. The lower end is a hook which engages in a recess in back of the trigger until it is pressed back when the pistol is firmly gripped. There is a small, flat spring mounted below it which forces it out when pressure is released. It will be noted that this is a trigger lock (as in the case of the Japanese pistol) and not a sear lock or striker lock. While it prevents the trigger from being pulled, it does not necessarily provide a positive safety against jarring off the sear.

The magazine is unusual in that it is open on both right and left sides and has grips attached to the magazine follower to permit them to be pulled down to facilitate loading.

COMPARISON DATA ON 9 mm LUGER (PARABELLUM) CARTRIDGES

The H. P. White Company, Ordnance Engineers, report the following results with various types of the 9 mm Luger cartridge as tested in a Walther P. 38 pistol with $4\frac{7}{8}''$ barrel:

(a) Remington Commercial	124 gr. bullet: Vel. 1193 fps.	Penetration 5″
(b) Western War Contract	115 gr. bullet: Vel. 1231 fps.	Penetration $4\frac{15}{16}''$
(c) German Govt. 1918	123 gr. bullet: Vel. 1207 fps.	Penetration $5\frac{19}{64}''$
(d) German Govt. 1941 (Pist.)	124 gr. bullet: Vel. 1242 fps.	Penetration $6\frac{3}{4}''$
(e) German Govt. 1941 (m.e.)	99 gr. bullet: Vel. 1391 fps.	Penetration $4\frac{31}{32}''$
(f) German Govt. 1943 (m.e.)	98 gr. bullet: Vel. 1385 fps.	Penetration $5\frac{25}{64}''$
(g) German Govt. 1944 (s.e.T)	91 gr. bullet: Vel. 1487 fps.	Penetration $4\frac{47}{64}''$
(h) Italian Govt. 1941 (Glisenti)	124 gr. bullet: Vel. 1050 fps.	Penetration $3\frac{37}{64}''$
(i) Italian M1938, 1942	115 gr. bullet: Vel. 1335 fps.	Penetration $4\frac{11}{16}''$

Velocities are 20 feet instrumental. Penetrations are in yellow pine 2″ planks at 25 feet. Lots b, e, f, g, and i gave greater recoil and muzzle flash than most pistol loads. Because of the wide variety of loads available in 9mm Parabellum, especially military loads, it is advisable to use caution in firing military loads in pistols of doubtful reliability.

9mm. Luger

9mm. Luger

115 Gr.

Muzzle Velocity in f.s.:	1150
Vel. at 50 Feet:	1112
Vel. at 150 Feet:	1050

Calculated Energy

Muzzle Energy in ft. lbs.:	365
Energy at 50 Feet:	343
Energy at 150 Feet:	305

Calculated Drop

At 50 Feet:	.38 inch
At 150 Feet:	3.6 inches
At 300 Feet:	16.8 inches

Penetration at 15 Feet

7/8″ soft pine boards	10.0

Length of Barrel in Which Tested

inches	4

Shell Case

Weight:	61.5 grains
Max. Length:	.752 inch
Outside Body Dia. at Head, Max.:	.394 inch
Outside Body Dia. at Neck, Max.:	.380 inch
Inside Mouth Dia. Max.:	.352 inch
Volumetric Capacity to Base of Bullet in cubic inches:	.030

Bullet

Weight:	125 grains
Approx. Length:	.615 inch
Diameter Max.:	.355 inch
Area, Cross Sectional:	.0989 square inch
Shape:	Conical

Powder

Amount and type varies with different lots manufactured.

Cartridge

Approx. Length, Loaded:	1.155 inches
Approx. Total Weight, Loaded:	194 grains

This cartridge was originally designed for the German Luger Automatic pistol. In the course of World War II it became the most widely used pistol and submachine gun ammunition in existence. This cartridge may be encountered in a wide variety of loads and with flat-point or round-nose bullets.

9mm. Luger

**ASTRA
400**

The ASTRA blowback 600 is chambered for this cartridge specifically. Its big brother the ASTRA 400 (see under Cal. 9mm Bayard Long) will use most round nose bullet 9mm Luger cartridges.

BROWNING
1935 (High Power)

9mm. Luger

9mm Browning High Power as made in Canada.

This is the last pistol designed by John M. Browning. Mr. Browning designed the pistol in 1925-26, and applied for a patent in that year. U. S. Patent No. 1,618,510 was granted on February 22, 1927, three months after his death. The pistol was called the 1935 Model, which is the year it was introduced formally. Browning intended it as an improved form of his famous locked-breech design.

In World War II it was extensively used by German SS troops. It was manufactured in Belgium before the war. During the war it was manufactured in Canada for use by Chinese, Greek, Canadian and British troops.

This pistol has a 4⅝-inch barrel, an over-all length of 7¾ inches, weighs about 32 ounces empty and has a double-line magazine which holds 13 cartridges. While the pistol follows the general outline of the .45 Colt Automatic it is mechanically quite different.

Construction. The receiver forms the grip and has a semicylindrical hollow for the slide as well as a slide abutment. A cam is riveted to the receiver to function the barrel nose which serves instead of the swinging link of the Colt type. The receiver is suitably machined to receive a slide stop, firing mechanism, and magazine with catch.

The lockwork is decidedly unusual. The trigger is pivoted and is provided with a lever which it thrusts straight up to contact a sear lever in the slide. It does not reach across the magazine well; instead, a sear lever runs the length

341

of the underside of the slide and is pivoted near its center. The trigger is provided with a spring and a magazine safety and its spring which is positioned so that withdrawal of the magazine moves the trigger lever out of line of the sear lever. This system of trigger leverage accomplishes the purposes of a disconnector.

The barrel is reinforced at the breech and has two locking ribs on top which engage in recesses in the slide in standard Browning custom. However, the bottom of the barrel below the breech is machined to form a feeding ramp for the cartridges and also a nose in which the guiding slot is controlled by a cam riveted in the receiver. The rear of the barrel is forced back and down on this nose to unlock instead of on a swinging link.

The slide forms the breechblock at the rear. The front end of the slide has a recess for the barrel muzzle and has a solid face below which serves as the seat for the recoil spring (this design dispenses with the need for barrel bushings and plugs). There is a central hollow for mounting. The slide is suitably grooved to travel in the receiver and has an ejection opening on the right side. In the ceiling of the slide are the recesses to receive the barrel locking lugs. The sear lever is mounted in the slide in the breechblock section as is the extractor. The recoil spring is mounted around its guide as an assembly. The magazine is the customary removable type. The follower is designed to raise the slide stop in standard Browning fashion when the pistol is empty.

Operation. At the instant of firing the barrel is locked to the slide by its ribs. As the slide starts back carrying the barrel with it, the sear lever in the slide moves away from the trigger lever. The lower part of the notch on the barrel nose contacts the cam in the receiver. This draws the rear end of the barrel down unlocking it from the slide and halting its motion. The slide continues to the rear to cock and ride over the hammer. The empty case drawn back by the extractor hits the ejector and is thrown out the ejection port. The rearward travel of the slide compresses the recoil spring around its guide. Rearward movement is halted when the slide stop hits the receiver stop.

The recoil spring reasserts itself to force the slide forward causing it to strip the top cartridge from the magazine and feed it into the chamber. The barrel is forced up and ahead by the breechblock and returned to firing position with its ribs engaging in the recesses in the slide due to the action of the cam in the receiver on the upper part of the notch of the barrel nose.

The trigger lever is raised up and ahead of the sear lever in a notch in the slide, thus preventing more than one shot being fired per trigger pull. When the trigger is momentarily released, its spring forces it back into position bringing the trigger lever directly below the tail of the sear lever.

When the trigger is pressed, it raises the trigger lever which forces up the tail of the sear lever in the slide. The sear lever pivots and its nose is brought down into contact with the sear mechanism in the top of the receiver ahead of the hammer. This pushes the sear out of engagement with the hammer notch and permits the mainspring to rotate the hammer to strike the firing pin and discharge the cartridge.

When the magazine is withdrawn, the safety lever is forced out into the

Top: COLT (U. S. ARMY MODEL 1911AI(-BROWNING PATENT) Field Stripped.
Bottom: The 1935 Browning made in Canada field stripped for comparison.

343

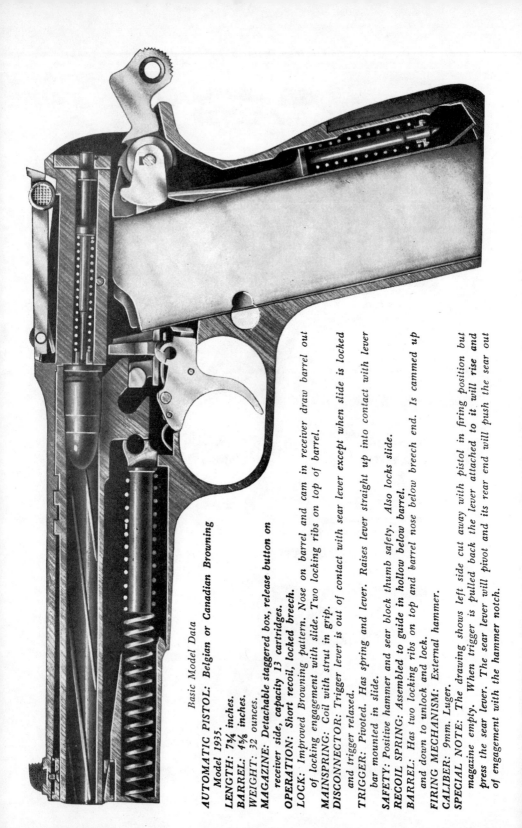

Basic Model Data

AUTOMATIC PISTOL: Belgian or Canadian Browning Model 1935.

LENGTH: 7¾ inches.

BARREL: 4⅝ inches.

WEIGHT: 32 ounces.

MAGAZINE: Detachable staggered box, release button on receiver side, capacity 13 cartridges.

OPERATION: Short recoil, locked breech.

LOCK: Improved Browning pattern. Nose on barrel and cam in receiver draw barrel out of locking engagement with slide. Two locking ribs on top of barrel.

MAINSPRING: Coil with strut in grip.

DISCONNECTOR: Trigger lever is out of contact with sear lever except when slide is locked and trigger relaxed.

TRIGGER: Pivoted. Has spring and lever. Raises lever straight up into contact with lever bar mounted in slide.

SAFETY: Positive hammer and sear block thumb safety. Also locks slide.

RECOIL SPRING: Assembled to guide in hollow below barrel.

BARREL: Has two locking ribs on top and barrel nose below breech end. Is cammed up and down to unlock and lock.

FIRING MECHANISM: External hammer.

CALIBER: 9mm. Luger.

SPECIAL NOTE: The drawing shows left side cut away with pistol in firing position but magazine empty. When trigger is pulled back the lever attached to it will rise and press the sear lever. The sear lever will pivot and its rear end will push the sear out of engagement with the hammer notch.

magazine well by its spring. It is so attached to the trigger lever that it forces the trigger lever out of line of the sear lever to prevent firing until the magazine is returned to position.

Dismounting. (1) Press catch and remove magazine. (2) Draw slide back and push thumb safety up into second notch in slide. (3) Press up slide stop and it may be drawn out the left side of the receiver. (4) Hold the slide firmly and press the catch out of engagement. Remove slide and barrel assembly from the front. (5) Grasp the head of the recoil spring guide and push toward the muzzle to release the head of the guide from the barrel. It may then be removed. (6) The barrel may then be drawn out from the breech end. Care should be taken in removing the barrel. (7) Removing the stocks will give access to the lockwork. Slide assembly may be dismounted by starting with removal of firing pin in standard Colt fashion.

DREYSE   9mm. Luger
Military

This was one of the earliest blowback weapons designed to use a powerful cartridge, and was introduced in 1909 or 1910. While in exterior appearance it closely resembles the .32 Dreyse Automatic Pistol intended to shoot the low powered .32 automatic cartridge, its design is more involved because of the necessity of providing a heavy recoil spring. The principal parts of this pistol for the most part resemble very closely those of the .32 Dreyse Automatic. It consists essentially of the receiver which forms the grip, a heavy slide mounted in the receiver to which it is hinged and which encloses the barrel, a recoil spring mounted around the barrel inside the heavy slide, and a sliding breechlock mechanism.

The recoil spring is held by a collar fitted with a spring catch which is very difficult to operate. It is fully described under .32 Dreyse Automatic Pistol.

A lug is mounted midway on the top of the barrel. A slide cocking lever projects from the slide. When it is pulled upward, it disengages from the recoil spring lug below. This permits the slide to be pulled back, compressing *only the striker;* lifting it off the recoil spring lug disengages it from the recoil spring on the same general theory that the .35 Smith and Wesson Automatic was designed so that the slide could be withdrawn free of tension to permit easy loading.

When the slide is pushed forward to chamber a cartridge, this lever is pushed forward and it compresses the mainspring. Its lug inside the slide is now engaged with the recoil spring lug and the slide is held firmly forward.

Operation: When a loaded magazine is inserted in the handle and the loading lever is pulled out to disengage the slide from the recoil spring, the

Cocking lever unlocked and drawn all the way back for loading the chamber. Note breech-lock protruding at rear.

slide is drawn back and then pushed forward to chamber a cartridge. Folding in the lever locks it ready for firing.

Pressure on the trigger releases the striker in standard fashion to go forward in the breechblock and fire the cartridge in the chamber. During slide movement, the striker is compressed and caught and held by the sear, and the empty cartridge case is extracted from the firing chamber and struck against the ejector which hurls it out the very narrow port on the right side of the pistol.

Unlike the Spanish Astra, these 9mm. Dreyse pistols were never very successful. It is possible during firing for the slide cocking lever to be blown loose from its lug, which may produce dangerous results. It is not recommended that pistols of this type be used; particularly in view of the fact that they were manufactured for the original 9mm. Luger cartridges and will not stand the shock of modern high velocity ammunition.

LUGER   **9mm. Luger**
Army, Navy Auto

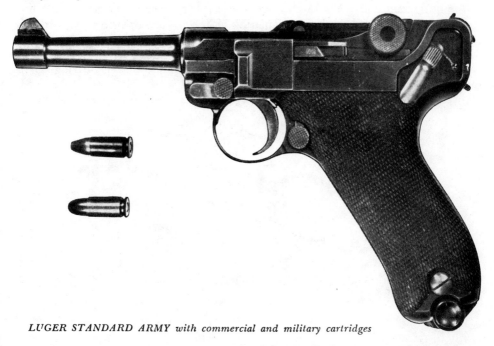

LUGER STANDARD ARMY with commercial and military cartridges

The Luger pistol is rather unique in construction. Its design has **never** been commercially imitated. The receiver in this weapon really is comprised *of two sections.* The first is the movable section into which the barrel is screwed. This part has two side pieces extending backwards, in which are housed the breechblock, toggle-joint links, and the firing pin and sear assemblies. The second receiver unit is the standard non-recoiling one comprising the grip and housing, the trigger unit, recoil spring, and the magazine. The barrel and the first receiver unit slides backward and forward in the second receiver unit, which acts as a frame.

The bolt is fitted into grooves on the inner side of the two receiver arms coming back from the barrel. A flat claw extractor is mounted in the upper front end of the breechblock. When the firing chamber is empty the extractor is flush with the top of the block. When a cartridge is in the chamber the extractor is hooked into the extracting groove in the cartridge case and the extractor rises above the face of the breechblock, where it can be seen or felt.

The firing pin and its coil spring are housed in the bolt. The left side of the bolt, or breechblock, is cut away to permit a projection on the side of the firing pin to emerge. When the weapon is cocked, this projection is held back by the sear, having been drawn back and cocked by the claw at the front end of the link as it buckled up during the rearward motion.

The breechblock is supported in the firing position by links hinged to it. At the rear, the links are hinged to the two arms of the sliding portion of the receiver. A center pin joins the two links together. The center of this middle pin, which connects the breechblock and the toggle joint, lies *below the center of the other two pins when the breech is closed.* This prevents the toggle joint from bending or the breech from opening at the instant of firing.

A swivel is pivoted to the bottom end of the rear link and this hangs down inside the grip, where it is hooked up to the recoil spring.

The magazine is made of sheet metal and has the customary cartridge platform or follower. The magazine spring is unusual in that it is a spiral spring. (Since 1943, German magazines, in many instances, have done away with this

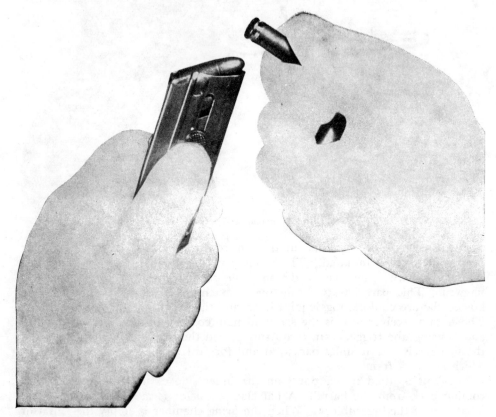

Loading the Luger magazine.

spiral spring and replaced it with a zigzag spring of simpler design.) The magazine bottom may be wood, metal, or plastic.

On grip-safety models, a thumb safety catch is pivoted to the frame on the rear left side. When its rear end is pressed up, its front end is lowered and hooks in front of a projection on the automatic safety catch to prevent the pistol being fired until the safety is pushed off. This is the universal thumb safety system on *all early models* of the Luger, both military and commercial, which have grip safeties. If the weapon is a later model with only the thumb safety, the safety is *pulled back* to engage; and is pushed forward to disengage.

The automatic grip safety, which projects to the rear of the grip, is operated when the weapon is held firmly in the hand. (It is not used on later German army models). Its top end prevents the sear from being disengaged from the projection on the firing pin unless the grip is held firmly.

The sear action (which hooks up the trigger with the firing mechanism) *works laterally in this pistol instead of vertically as in most other weapons.* It works on the left side of the firing pin.

The sear proper is located on the outside of the receiver, below the lower part of the knurled knob of the toggle joint. When the safety lever is pulled back, its locking arm is thrust up through a slot in the receiver directly opposite the sear and the cocked firing pin. This keeps the sear engaged with the spur on the firing pin. It is therefore impossible for the firing pin to be released to go home to strike the cartridge.

Loading: Push the checkered stud of the magazine release catch on the left side just behind the trigger. This will permit the magazine to be withdrawn from the grip.

Pull down the checkered metal button protruding from the right side of the magazine, which is attached to the magazine follower. This will compress the follower against the spring below it and permit cartridges to be inserted easily into the magazine. The overlapping lips of the magazine will prevent the cartridges from flying out.

The loaded magazine is then pushed up into the grip until the slot cut in it engages with the magazine catch and is held fast.

Holding the weapon in the right hand with the finger outside the trigger guard, grip the knurled knobs of the toggle joint with the left hand and draw upward and backward as far as possible, and release sharply. As the toggle joint bends, drawing the breechblock (which is fastened to it) directly to the rear in its guides, the claw on the lower end of the toggle link, pressing against the projection on the firing pin, draws the firing pin back until it is caught and held by the sear, snapped into place by its flat spring. Meanwhile, the swivel attached to the rear link has drawn up and compressed the powerful recoil spring housed in the grip. The energy stored up in this spring pulls the action forward when the knurled knobs are released.

The recoil spring forces the barrel and the sliding part of the receiver forward and straightens out the toggle joint, thus forcing the breechblock home against the face of the firing chamber. The breechblock, meanwhile, has picked up a cartridge from the top of the magazine and driven it into the firing chamber,

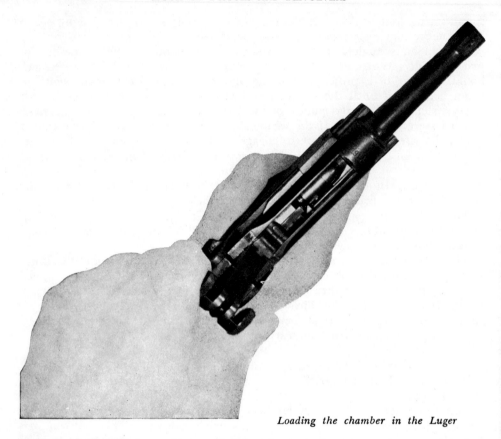

Loading the chamber in the Luger

and the extractor has snapped up and over the extracting groove in the cartridge case. The weapon is now ready to fire.

Firing: The trigger is hooked up to a rocking engagement bar on the inside of the side plate directly above it. Pressing the trigger rocks this arm to force back the sear until it springs out of engagement with the firing pin, which is then driven ahead by its spring to fire the cartridge in the chamber.

Recoiling action: The barrel and the components locked with it in the sliding section of the receiver all recoil together for a distance of about one-quarter of an inch. In this pistol, this not only gives the bullet time to pass out of the barrel but also permits the breech pressure to drop to absolute zero. *There is no residual pressure in this weapon when it starts to open.* The opening is performed entirely by the momentum imparted to the breechblock at the instant of firing. (In many automatic pistols, residual pressure in the barrel as the bullet leaves actually starts the extraction of the empty cartridge case. The design of the Luger pistol is so efficient that the actual extraction is done entirely by the extractor itself.)

The knurled cheeks of the toggle joint, after this short travel, strike curved

350

Basic Model Data

AUTOMATIC PISTOL: German *Luger.*

LENGTH: 8¾ inches.

BARREL: 4 inches.

WEIGHT: 30 ounces.

MAGAZINE: Detachable box with depressing button on follower. Thumb release catch on left side. Capacity 8 cartridges.

OPERATION: Short recoil. Rising toggle joint.

LOCK: Breechblock is securely locked to barrel and receiver by a toggle joint whose center is below the line of the barrel and breechblock. After short recoil the joint is broken as bosses ride up ramps on the receiver.

MAINSPRING: Coil in breechblock.

TRIGGER: Sear is set horizontally in receiver and striker is cocked directly on it. When trigger is pressed a right-angular trigger lever mounted on side plate pushes a plunger in front of sear. Sear is rotated to release striker.

DISCONNECTOR: As barrel and sliding section of receiver are driven forward by recoil spring, sear plunger is thrust in by upright trigger lever arm. Pistol cannot be fired until trigger is released permitting trigger lever to move out and let sear plunger move into position.

SAFETY: Thumb safety prevents striker from being released. Early models have grip safety also.

RECOIL SPRING: Coil in grip hooks up to breechblock by bell crank lever. (Early models have flat spring).

BARREL: Screwed into barrel extension. Travels back a short distance locked to the breech-block.

FIRING MECHANISM: Striker.

CALIBER: 9mm. Luger (also made in Caliber 7.65mm. Luger). Pistol is shown with left side cut away with chamber loaded and striker cocked ready for firing.

Luger in full recoil. Magazine spring has brought a cartridge in line ready for loading stroke. Recoil spring is ready to close action. Lever on toggle has cocked striker.

The Luger was designed as a completely recoil operated pistol. Used with original pistol ammunition, there was no remaining pressure in the barrel when the pistol unlocked. Modern ammunition has been stepped up considerably in power and velocity, hence in the average Luger shooting today extraction and ejection is not entirely by momentum but is assisted as in other auto pistols by small gas pressure in the chamber after the bullet is out of the barrel.

Occasional Lugers will be found with special safety to prevent firing when magazine is withdrawn, with silencer or grenade launching attachments, or other unusual features. These represent custom built devices, not standard features.

Lugers bearing the Dutch word "Rust" instead of the German "Gesichert" for safe are part of a special lot made for the Netherlands Government by Vickers. The Japanese captured many of these from Dutch East Indian troops, and many were in turn "liberated" by American soldiers from the Japs.

ramps machined into the stationary receiver, which throws the joint out of line and buckles the links upwards. These links fold exactly like a jackknife and rise above the line of the receiver. The empty cartridge case, striking against the ejector, is tossed out of the top of the pistol.

The magazine spring forcing up the cartridges resting on the follower pushes the next cartridge up into line to be picked up on forward motion of the breechblock.

Meanwhile, the small hooked arm at the front end of the first link of the toggle joint pushes back against the firing pin projection passing through the slot in the breechblock, to draw the firing pin back to full cock as the joint collapses.

The initial recoil of the barrel and sliding part of the receiver, (which have been stopped by the barrel striking its barrel stop in the receiver proper after about one-quarter inch of locked travel), together with the continued recoil of the breechblock and the buckling of the toggle joint, cause the swivel attached to the rear link and hooked to the recoil spring inside the grip, to compress the recoil spring to its fullest extent.

When the recoil energy is exhausted, this recoil spring pulls the swivel down to snap back to its original position. This action straightens out the toggle joint which, in turn, thrusts the breechblock forward in its guides. The breechblock drives the cartridge from the top of the magazine ahead of it into the firing chamber and snaps the extractor into place.

It is necessary to release the trigger slightly to permit the coiled spring mounted behind it to force it forward before contact is made with the sear and firing pin to permit firing another shot.

In weapons of this type having a grip safety, the pistol is provided *with a special safety sear* which rises automatically in place when pressure is released from the grip. *No modern Lugers are equipped with this grip safety.*

When the last cartridge has been fired in this weapon, as the breechblock passes back over the magazine follower, the follower pushes against a stop which forms part of a lever pivoted in the receiver proper parallel with the breechblock. This stop holds the breechblock in rearward position. The magazine is extracted and a new magazine inserted. Then the toggle joints (which are buckled at this point) are drawn slightly back to release them from the stop. The recoil spring then drives the locking assembly forward to load a cartridge and lock the action.

When the last shot has been fired, and the action is open, the action cannot be closed *while an empty magazine is in place.* Either a loaded magazine must be inserted, or the action may be closed when the empty magazine is drawn down far enough that the follower is not in contact with the lever of the stop.

Dismounting: The simplest way to dismount this pistol is to insert an empty magazine and then draw the toggle joints back and up until the pistol stays open. Then remove the magazine by pressing the magazine release catch on the left side of the receiver just behind the trigger. Directly ahead of the trigger on the left-hand side is a checkered locking bolt. It fastens the locking plate,

353

which is tongued in. Turn this bolt down as far as it will go. Holding firmly onto the toggle joint, pull back slightly and ease it forward to let the recoil spring push the action down. As the barrel and moving section of the receiver go forward, they will push the trigger plate out of engagement. The trigger plate with its attached rocking trigger engager may now be lifted off. The barrel, the sliding section of the receiver, and the parts mounted therein may now be slid off directly to the front. The trigger and the small coil spring set into its slot in back of the trigger, may now be lifted directly out of the receiver. Push the large locking pin at the rear of the sliding receiver (it locks the rear link to the receiver) from the right and draw it out to the left. Buckle the knobs of the toggle joint slightly. This is necessary to lift them clear of the ramps in the sliding receiver. The breechblock and toggle mechanism may now be withdrawn out of the guides in the inside of the sliding receiver. With a screw driver, push the end piece at the rear of the breechblock inward until it can be twisted a quarter turn to the left. The end piece, firing pin spring, and firing pin may now be withdrawn. Extractor and extractor spring may be drifted out if necessary.

Assembly: To reassemble this weapon, merely reverse the stripping procedure. When inserting the breechblock, be sure it fits properly into its guides in the sliding receiver before pushing it forward flush against the barrel. It will be necessary again to buckle the knurled members slightly to permit insertion of the locking pin at the rear. When it is in place, force the toggle down to full-locked position. To be sure that the recoil spring action is properly hooked up, it is necessary to hold the barrel and breech mechanism upside down, with its attached recoil spring swivel resting flat against the action. The two engaging arms at the end of the swivel must point to the rear. These arms catch into the split lever in which is mounted the recoil spring. Holding the grip section of the receiver also upside down, line it up at the rear so the barrel and sliding section of the receiver may be pushed back into the grooves. Push the barrel and sliding receiver back as far as they will go, then turn the pistol right side up. The swivel will then drop down in proper position behind the magazine well, and its link will drop down so that the projecting arms pass below and under the recoil spring lever. Insert an empty magazine. Now pull the toggle joint back and up by its knurled knobs, and the tension of the spring will tell if the swivel and the recoil spring lever are in proper engagement. If they are, the action will be held open in full-recoil position under spring tension as the magazine follower forces up the stop. *This recoil spring engagement is the only trick in reassembling the Luger.* The trigger cover plate may now be replaced, making sure that its rearward tongued section is properly inserted. Turning the trigger plate locking catch back to locked position completes the reassembly. Remember that it is necessary to remove the magazine or insert a loaded magazine before the action can be closed.

German Government Model Lugers

Model 1904: (also the Model '04-'06 which came later). This is the Marine model officially adopted by the German Navy in 1904. Until the period of

LUGER NAVY

World War I, this always appeared with a grip safety. Toward the close of the war it was manufactured without this safety.

Model 1908: This was officially adopted by the Ordnance Board for the German Army. D.W.M. made up this model especially for the Army because of objection which had been raised to the necessity for, and value of, the grip safety of the regular Model '04-'06.

Long pistol Model 1908: Several years later this special model with an 8-inch barrel and a sliding adjustable sight mounted on the barrel was adopted by the German Government during World War I. It was used with the 32-round magazine.

All these pistols bore the year of manufacture stamped on the receiver directly ahead of the breechblock. They also carried the German government eagle, proof marks, and serial numbers.

None of these numbers ever run very high. The official reason given for this was that numbers would run so high that it was preferable to start a new series each month. A different letter of the alphabet was added to the end of the number for each month.

On German Army pistols, the last two numerals of the serial number were stamped on each individual part. These two numbers were also prominently stamped on the outside so that they could be readily seen.

Commercial pistols, on the other hand, while also numbered, usually had the numbers hidden so they would not injure the appearance of the pistol.

All postwar models of commercial manufacture have the lug at the bottom of the rear of the grip for attaching to a shoulder stock, with the sole exception of the special Swiss model.

Many pistols marketed in the United States after the war were reconditioned government models. In many instances they were provided with barrels of different length. These were not issued from the factory so equipped, however.

Because of such assembly procedures, freak Lugers will often be encountered.

355

Luger with long barrel, detachable stock, loader and special 32-shot snail magazine

When such weapons are found with barrels of more than eight inches, functioning trouble will almost invariably occur as the standard cartridges were not intended to function in these weapons.

The 7.65 mm. Luger carbine with 12-inch barrel (often quoted as 11¾-inch barrel) manufactured before the war used a special cartridge with approximately one-seventh greater powder charge than the standard pistol cartridge. The cartridge case was always *black*.

The breech pressure in these cartridges reached as high as 40,000 pounds per square inch. The velocity of the long barrel approached 2,000 feet per second.

Most of the parts in Luger weapons are interchangeable. Changing the barrel and recoil spring, and in some instances the magazine, will permit transforming one caliber to another. (Also see Luger under Caliber 7.65 mm. Luger.)

MAUSER FOR THE 9MM. LUGER CARTRIDGE, shown with clip of cartridges. Hammer is at full cock.

Pistol fastened to holster stock.

Mechanically and in appearance the above pistol is the same as the Mauser 7.63mm. It is however chambered and altered to accommodate the 9mm. Luger Service cartridge. The figure 9 carved or painted on the grips provides a quick identification for this model, which was issued during World War I and was never in commercial production by Mauser. (See under Cal. 7.63mm.)

RADOM 9mm. Luger
Automatic

Barrel Length:	4¾″	*Magazine Capacity:*	8 shots
Over-all Length:	7¾″	*Caliber:* 9 mm. Luger or Parabel-	
Weight:	29 ounces	lum	

Construction: The Radom is a Polish variant of the original Browning-Colt Government Model 1911 automatic pistol.

It is modified in line with the changes by John M. Browning for his improved version of the old reliable Colt automatic pistol.

This weapon was made at the Radom arsenal in Poland under the direction of engineers from the Belgian Fabrique Nationalé plant, which manufactured

This is the early-WW II pistol. To speed up manufacture during the War, the Germans eliminated many features at different times. Hence this P. 35 as the Germans called it may be encountered minus hammer release, hold open device, or any combination of those features. Stocks also vary. Late manufacture was poorly finished and fitted.

the Browning weapons under patent permission in Europe before the War.

This pistol was put into extensive use by the Germans and most specimens encountered will be found to have German proof marks.

Basically this pistol is a combination of our 1911 .45 Colt automatic and the improved 1935 F. N. High-Power Browning. Various manufacturing and design changes have been made in the weapon, however.

Its general over-all appearance and construction resemble the Colt .45 Model 1911 quite closely. However, the grip has a better pitch and the hang and balance have been improved.

The magazine release catch button on the left side of the receiver and the single-line tubular box magazine are essentially the same as in earlier models.

The slide stop is the typical Colt-Browning design, operated by a step on the magazine platform as the last cartridge is fired. It acts to force the slide stop up into engagement in the notch in the slide to hold the slide back. When a new magazine is inserted, pressing down the slide stop will let the slide run forward on the compression of the recoil spring below the barrel to strip a cartridge from the top of the magazine and chamber it.

At first glance this weapon seems to have the typical Colt thumb-lock safety. However, this piece is not actually a thumb safety. It is really a hold-open device, which may be pushed up when the slide is drawn back to engage in a notch cut in the left side of the slide. It is necessary to lock the slide at this point when dismounting it.

From an American standpoint, the hammer on this weapon is not efficient.

This style of rounded hammer, together with the common burr, has been in vogue for years in Europe (as witness the Mauser 7.63 mm. automatic pistol which was in continuous manufacture until WW II). It is simpler to manufacture than the standard type of hammer so familiar to us, and in theory is helpful in quick-cocking the weapon by thrusting the head of the hammer against the side of the leg (or against the saddle when firing from horseback. It must be remembered that when this pistol was designed the Polish Army placed great importance on their cavalry.)

While the general construction and functioning of this weapon is practically identical with that of the Colt, the various innovations need description.

Mounted on the slide on the left-hand side directly below the rear sight is a thumbpiece. When the hammer is at full cock, pressing down on this thumbpiece revolves a cutaway bolt inside the slide. The first movement of this bolt pulls the firing pin into its recess in the breechblock, compressing its spring far enough to remove it from the line of the hammer when the hammer falls. As the thumbpiece is pushed further down against spring tension, it interposes a solid bolt between the firing pin and the hammer. Then it makes sear contact which releases the hammer and permits the mainspring to drive the hammer forward without any possibility of its striking the firing pin to discharge the cartridge. By this somewhat involved procedure, it is possible to lower the hammer with a cartridge in the firing chamber without danger of the hammer slipping and discharging the cartridge.

Instead of the familiar bushing in the front end of the slide as in the Colt, the front end of the Radom slide has a large hole to permit emergence of the barrel muzzle; but the section below it is solid except for a very small hole which permits the recoil spring guide (which is just a round, thin rod in this pistol) to project through as the slide goes back. This removes the necessity for both the barrel bushing and the recoil spring plug familiar to us.

The recoil spring is mounted about its guide, the two being assembled as a unit to simplify the takedown. The guide extends the full distance from its rear position against the barrel nose lock forward to its emergence hole in the front end of the slide.

When the slide starts back, the recoil spring guide rod protrudes through this hole. The spring itself is supported at its forward end by a sturdy collar which thus prevents the spring from entering the guide hole. This is forced back by the slide to compress the spring around the guide to store up energy to return the slide to forward position when rearward travel is completed. It will also be observed that this type of recoil spring is kinkproof.

The barrel is locked at the top into the slide by locking ribs on top of the barrel fitting into corresponding recesses in the underside of the slide exactly as in the Colts and Brownings. However, it *does not have the swinging link of the Colt design.* Instead, it is fitted with *a special barrel lug machined below the firing chamber end of the barrel.* This is in accordance with the last design of John M. Browning, later incorporated in the 1935 Browning High-Power pistol.

As the slide and barrel recoil locked together during the moment of high breech pressure, the rearward motion cams this barrel nose down into a re-

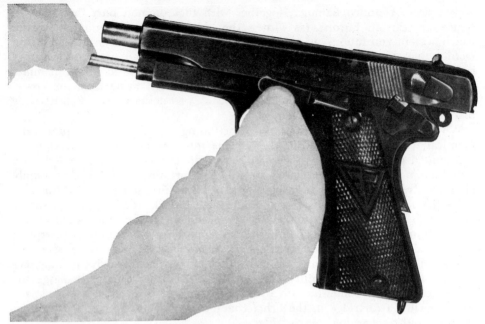

Removing the slide stop pin

cess prepared for it in the receiver. This lowering of the rear end pulls the locking ribs out of engagement and permits the slide to travel to the rear by itself. The barrel is stopped in its rearward travel by striking against its abutment in the receiver. The slide with the empty cartridge case gripped by the extractor travels back to extract and eject in standard fashion.

When the lower part of the slide abuts against the extension of the receiver, forward of the trigger guard, the rearward travel of the slide is stopped, after having ridden over and cocked the hammer.

The compressed recoil spring now reasserts itself and drives the slide forward to strip a cartridge from the top of the magazine, chamber it, and as the breech face of the slide strikes the barrel chamber, the barrel is pushed forward and upward on its ramp in the receiver. As the lugs on top of the barrel lock into place in their slots in the underside of the slide, the barrel nose is resting firmly on top of the receiver to complete the locking action.

As there is no link on the barrel, the lug is shaped to permit the slide stop pin to pass by it and complete the positive locking of barrel, receiver, and slide.

Dismounting: While dismounting and reassembling operations on this weapon are simple, they involve several tricks which must be known.

First, the thumbpiece which looks like a thumb safety. Actually this is part of the takedown system. Remove the magazine.

The slide must be pushed back until its rearmost notch in the slide is in line to permit the thumbpiece on the receiver to be pushed up to catch and hold it.

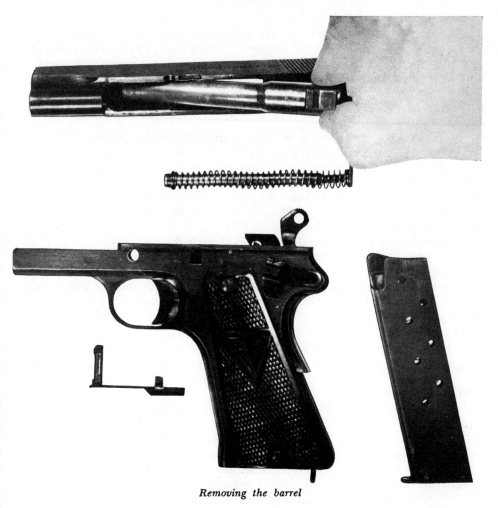

Removing the barrel

The recoil spring guide now protrudes through its hole in the front end of the slide below the line of the barrel. Pulling this guide forward takes the tension of the recoil spring off the slide stop pin.

The slide stop pin is now loose and if the pistol is tipped over on its left-hand side, slight pressure on the protruding part of the pin at the right will push it out the left side of the receiver.

Holding firmly to the slide, press down on the slide hold-open catch and ease the slide and barrel assemblies forward off their guides in the receiver.

The recoil spring and its guide may now be lifted out the rear of the slide. The barrel may be lifted up by the barrel nose and withdrawn from the rear of the slide. (Note that it does not slide forward out of the front end.) Removing the stocks exposes the action for further dismounting. Observe that this weapon is fitted with the Colt-Browning type of old stirrup trigger.

361

Assembling: Assembling the weapon is also somewhat tricky.

The barrel is inserted from the rear and dropped into place so that the lugs on its top fit into their locking recesses in the slide. The recoil spring and guide are then inserted and the assembly held upside down while the receiver is slid on from the rear.

The slide is pushed back far enough to permit the thumb slide lock to be pushed up into place to lock it. Lower hammer and retain trigger pressure to lower disconnector.

The recoil spring guide must be pulled forward to release tension before the slide stop pin can be inserted from the left side of the receiver.

This weapon is fitted with a customary positive disconnector which prevents more than one shot from being fired per pull of the trigger and prevents firing the weapon until the slide is home and the action fully locked.

The automatic grip safety prevents the weapon from being fired unless it is held securely in the firing hand.

In general it may be pointed out that although this pistol is crude in workmanship when judged by American standards, it is of simple and sturdy design with excellent balance and good instinctive pointing features.

The cartridge it uses is quite pleasant to shoot in a weapon of this weight. In view of the fact that so many Luger loads are now available, only a weapon of the husky design of this Radom pistol is safe to use with the higher-powered 9 mm. cartridges.

9mm. Luger   WALTHER
                                                              P38

This pistol was originally introduced by Walther as the H. P. Model. Under the official designation of P-38 it was made by several German factories during World War II with several design changes.

Construction: This is a short-recoil weapon. The barrel and slide recoil together a short distance fully locked together during the moment of high breech pressure. Then a falling block is cammed down to unlock them as the barrel strikes its stop and the slide continues to the rear to function the action.

The main parts of this weapon are the receiver, barrel, slide, lock, and lockwork.

The receiver handle is hollowed out to receive the magazine inserted from below in conventional manner.

The magazine catch is at the bottom of the butt to the rear. It must be pushed back to release the magazine to permit it to be withdrawn from the pistol.

The receiver extends forward over the trigger guard which is a part of the receiver forging. The locking block which rises and falls to lock and unlock the barrel and slide is housed in a lug which is part of the barrel forging below the chamber and is unlocked by camming down into a recess in the receiver above and ahead of the trigger. At the forward end of this receiver extension on the left-hand side is a locking lever with a bolt which retains the slide in place at its forward end.

The hammer and lockwork are contained in the receiver behind the magazine

well. A coil mainspring in the grip functions through the use of a hammer stirrup.

The barrel is fitted with a special machined lug below the firing chamber, in which the locking mechanism is housed, into which the lock is cammed up to allow projections on its sides to engage with the slide for locking.

The slide travels in suitable guides in the receiver. It extends only to the end of the receiver extension, leaving the barrel exposed ahead of it. It is also cut away from the breech forward about half the exposed barrel length.

The front sight is a blade dovetailed into a band around the barrel. It may be adjusted laterally. The rear sight is a block with a U-notch mounted on the slide.

Two recoil springs are mounted in the receiver extending backward from the breech. There is a spring and a guide fitted into the slots cut for them in the sides of the receiver, one on each side. They are compressed as the slide goes to the rear to furnish energy for the forward motion.

A thumb safety is provided on the left side of the slide. If the pistol is cocked, pushing this safety lever down to the safe position turns the stem of this lever and locks the firing pin. It then operates a trip on the left side of the hammer which moves the sear to release the hammer. The sear is rotated in this raised position which prevents the trigger bar and trigger from returning to the forward position.

When the lever is pushed up to the firing position, the sear is released from the trip and the trigger bar and trigger return to their normal positions. The firing pin is also unlocked.

If the safety lever is adjusted when the hammer is down, the trip prevents the sear from rotating sufficiently to slip from the hammer catch and the weapon cannot be fired by pulling the trigger. This position can be instantly recognized because the trigger will be halfway back.

If the hammer is cocked and this safety lever is pushed to the safe position, the hammer will swing forward on its pivot but will not drive the firing pin, as the moving lever locks it before the hammer strikes. The trigger will now be fully back so it is impossible to pull it.

If the slide is drawn back while the catch is in the safe position, the hammer will not stay cocked but will move forward with the slide. Since the firing pin is locked, this permits chamber loading without normal cocking.

The firing pin is also locked by a safety stop in the bolt. It cannot be driven forward by the hammer until it is released by a lever, which forced upward by the sear, in turn forces up the safety stop. The slide must be fully forward to permit this lever to force up the safety stop against its spring.

A positive disconnector is incorporated in this weapon. As the slide recoils it forces down the trigger bar from its engaging point with the sear. Thus only when the slide is fully forward and locked can the weapon be fired.

This weapon is fitted with a double-action mechanism which permits the pistol to be carried with a cartridge in the firing chamber and with the hammer down ready for action. Instead of thumb cocking the hammer or drawing back the slide as is customary in standard automatic pistols, just pulling the trigger straight to the rear as in the case of double-action revolvers will raise and trip the hammer and fire the cartridge; if the firing chamber is loaded. As in all automatic pistols, the chamber must be manually loaded for the first shot.

The extractor in this weapon is a spring-loaded claw on the left side of the bolt. The bolt or breechblock is an integral part of the slide in this weapon.

The ejector is an arm pivoted vertically on the rear axis pin on the right side center of the receiver. It is kept raised by the magazine. Ejection is to the left.

When the last cartridge has been fired, the magazine follower pushes up against a projection on the inside of the receiver which raises the lever on the outside of the receiver. This lever moves up and engages in the notch in the slide.

If a loaded magazine is inserted, pushing down the slide release permits the recoil spring to drive the slide forward to load the weapon ready for instant firing, as in the Colt Government Model.

The locking system in this weapon is unusual. A locking block is hinged by a spring to the underside of the barrel. There are projections on each side of it at the top which engage in recesses cut in the slide to receive it. A sliding plunger is mounted in the forward face of the barrel lock lug in line with this block. After the barrel and slide have recoiled together about one-quarter of an inch, this plunger strikes a forward face on the receiver thrusting it forward to cam down the locking block and release the slide.

The recoil springs and their guides are fitted in guide grooves at the top of the receiver. There is one on each side. These are compressed between two projections at the forward end of the slide and the ends of the guide grooves.

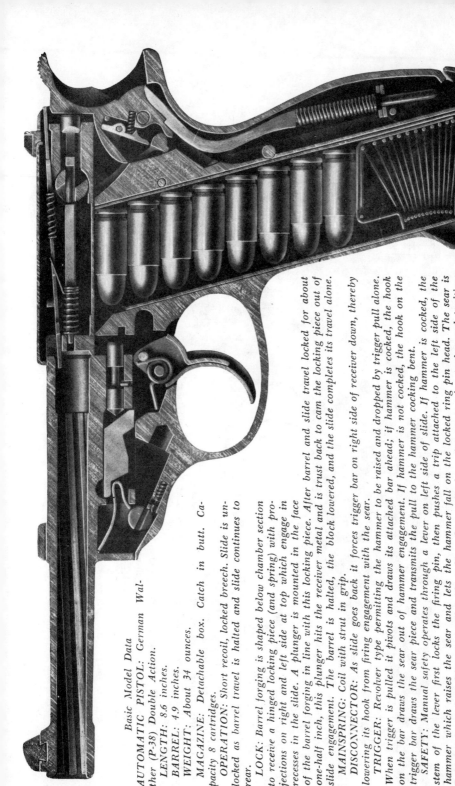

Basic Model Data

AUTOMATIC PISTOL: German Walther (P-38) Double Action.

LENGTH: 8.6 inches.

BARREL: 4.9 inches.

WEIGHT: About 34 ounces.

MAGAZINE: Detachable box. Catch in butt. Capacity 8 cartridges.

OPERATION: Short recoil, locked breech. Slide is unlocked as barrel travel is halted and slide continues to rear.

LOCK: Barrel forging is shaped below chamber section to receive a hinged locking piece (and spring) with projections on right and left side at top which engage in recesses in the slide. A plunger is mounted in the face of the barrel forging in line with this locking piece. After barrel and slide travel locked for about one-half inch, this plunger hits the receiver metal and is trust back to cam the locking piece out of slide engagement. The barrel is halted, the block lowered, and the slide completes its travel alone.

MAINSPRING: Coil with strut in grip.

DISCONNECTOR: As slide goes back it forces trigger bar on right side of receiver down, thereby lowering its hook from firing engagement with the sear.

TRIGGER: Revolver type permitting the hammer to be raised and dropped by trigger pull alone. When trigger is pulled it pivots and draws its attached bar ahead; if hammer is cocked, the hook on the bar draws the sear out of hammer engagement. If hammer is not cocked, the hook on the trigger bar draws the sear piece and transmits the pull to the hammer cocking bent.

SAFETY: Manual safety operates through a lever on left side of slide. If hammer is cocked, the stem of the lever first locks the firing pin, then pushes a trip attached to the left side of the hammer which raises the sear and lets the hammer fall on the locked ring pin head. The sear is held in elevated position preventing the trigger bar and trigger from returning to forward position. If the safety lever is turned when the hammer is down, the trip blocks the sear from rotating far enough to slip the hammer catch.

Mechanical safety in slide positively locks firing pin at all times except when hammer is fully

cocked and trigger deliberately pulled. When slide is fully forward, an arm on the right side of receiver can be raised by the sear as the hammer goes back. This arm forces the mechanical safety bolt up against spring opposition until it frees the firing pin.

RECOIL SPRINGS: Two coil spring with guides are mounted in guide grooves, one on each side of receiver; and are compressed between twin projections in forward end of slide and their receiver seats.

BARREL: Specially machined to permit guided travel of one-half inch. Carries locking block and unlocking plunger arrangement below chamber.

FIRING MECHANISM: External hammer normal (An enclosed hammer model was made in limited quantities.)

CALIBER 9MM. LUGER: (Pistole 08 German cartridge).

Special Features: Loading indicator. A spring controlled pin in slide which floats into chamber when there is no cartridge there, and is thrust back when chamber is loaded so its end projects through slide.

Slide stop. Lever on left side pressed up by magazine platform when magazine is empty holds breech open. Pushing thumb piece releases slide.

Left side view cut away to show details of breech lock in unlocked position and barrel lock (at forward end of drawing). Slide sectioned to show automatic firing pin block in slide and details of hammer and sear mechanism in compressed position.

Drawing shows right side of Walther cut away to show *locking block* forced *up* into engagement. *Detail of trigger bar and its contact with sear connection may be seen. Any rearward movement of slide forces the bar down so its hook drops too low in the cut to pull the sear. Arm attached to hammer is forced up and supported by sear bar and raises automatic safety out of path of firing pin when hammer is at full cock. This prevents accidental discharge if hammer slips when being cocked. Right hand recoil spring and guide are shown.*

Top detail drawing shows position of recoil springs and systems of mounting in slide. Also loading indicator pin.

Another unusual feature of this weapon is a cartridge indicator. This is a floating bar fitted with a spring mounted in the slide above the line of the firing pin. When at rest it floats through the face of the breechblock end of the slide into the firing chamber. When there is no cartridge in the chamber, the rear end of this pin is below the surface of the rear of the slide. However, when the chamber is loaded, this pin is lifted by the head of the cartridge and is forced back into the slide so that it protrudes through the end. When this rod can be seen or felt (in the dark) above the line of the firing pin, there is a cartridge in the chamber.

Dismounting: 1. Pull the slide back to fully open position. If the magazine is empty, the weapon will stay open.

2. Push back the magazine release catch in the butt and withdraw the magazine.

3. Push the safety catch down so it is in the safe position.

4. Turn down the slide lock lever (at the left side of the forward end of the receiver above the trigger guard).

5. Keeping the slide under control with one hand, push down the slide release catch and let the slide and barrel move to the front under pressure from the recoil springs.

6. Press the trigger, and the slide and barrel may now be pushed forward off the receiver.

7. The locking plunger protrudes below the chamber of the barrel. Push this forward and it will force the white metal locking block out of its seat below the barrel. This unlocks the barrel from the slide.

8. Pull the barrel straight forward out of the slide. This will come out better if the slide and barrel are held upside down. If the stock screw is withdrawn, the stocks may be lifted off the receiver. If the removable deck on top of slide is raised at the front it can be slid forward to expose firing and indicator pins and thumb safety.

Assembling: 1. When putting this weapon together, first insert the white metal locking block in the barrel assembly if it has been removed. Make sure that the lugs on each side of it line up with the wide ribs on the lug below the barrel and that the flat spring inside is properly compressed.

2. Press the barrel assembly into the slide as far as it will go. This is best done while holding the units upside down. Push the locking block into its locked position.

3. *Make sure that the hammer is fully forward.* In the receiver directly ahead of the hammer are two flat steel pieces which must be pressed down below the level of the bearing surfaces on the receiver. Check to see that the recoil springs are securely mounted in their guides in the receiver.

4. Check the safety catch on the slide to be sure it is in the safe position. Hold the locking block securely to keep the slide and barrel locked together. Start the slide back in the guides on the receiver and hold the locking block up into place as the barrel also is slid on with the slide.

5. Insert an empty magazine in the handle until it locks. Push the slide back

as far as it will go and the magazine follower will push up the catch and hold it open.

6. Turn the slide locking lever back to its horizontal or locked position. Push down the slide release catch and the action will close.

Remember that while this weapon can be loaded in the chamber while the weapon is on safety, it cannot be fired until the safety on the slide is pushed into "off" position.

If you wish to lower the hammer while there is a loaded cartridge in the firing chamber in this pistol, it is merely necessary to push the safety lever on the slide to the safe position. The hammer will automatically go forward in somewhat startling fashion; but the firing pin is locked and cannot move. (Some models use the PPK type lock which blocks hammer from firing pin head.) Pushing the safety to the fire position now leaves the weapon safe to carry but ready to fire by pulling straight through on the trigger. The recoil of the weapon will eject, cock the hammer, and reload for succeeding shots in standard fashion.

While this is one of the most advanced automatic pistols designed in existence, the double-action system is quite complicated. In field service it has proved to be remarkably sturdy, however.

It has the advantage that if the cartridge in the chamber fails to fire, merely pressing the trigger will drop the hammer for a second time and the cartridge may then discharge.

Special Note on Walther Pistols

It must be noted that the quality of all German pistols declined rapidly during the last two years of World War II as a result of our bombing and the German use of slave labor.

This decline is particularly noticeable in the finish and the fitting of these pistols. Numerous design changes and manufacturing short-cuts were employed, particularly in the firing and safety mechanisms. A comparison of an individual pistol with the drawings shown, therefore, may disclose differences, notably in the construction of the sear and the right hammer arm which elevates the automatic firing pin lock in the slide. At least one instance has been reported of accidental firing of a P38 when the hammer was dropped on a loaded chamber by use of the thumb safety. An examination of the locking bar on that particular safety disclosed that the section normally locking the firing pin was extremely thin and had apparently crystallized and broken off within the slide. Accidents of this nature are impossible with Walthers embodying the PPK type lock where the safety as it is applied interposes a surface between hammer and firing pin, rather than just locking the pin itself.

Use of the thumb safety on the slide to lower the hammer on a loaded chamber, therefore, cannot be recommended unless the pistol is of pre-war Walther quality or has been checked to find the specific type and condition of safeties employed.

9mm. Bayard Long   CARTRIDGE
                                                                        Data

This cartridge was originally designed for the Bergmann Bayard. It is very popular in Spain but is little known in the United States. The case while appearing to be straight is actually slightly tapered, as in most Bergmann designs to facilitate extraction. This cartridge is not manufactured in the United States and no American weapon is designed to use it. The bullet is full jacketed weighing about 125 grains and measuring .355 inch. The case is rimless. The over-all length of the cartridge is about 1.30 inch. The muzzle velocity is about 1115 feet per second and muzzle striking energy about 360 foot-pounds.

As originally issued, the 9mm. Bayard Long cartridges used the 135-grain bullet and the muzzle velocity of about 1050 feet per second.

In recent years however the velocity and consequent striking energy of this cartridge have been stepped up considerably.

9mm. Bayard Long   ASTRA
                                                                         400

This straight blowback unlocked breech automatic is unusual in using high-powered automatic pistol cartridges, and in that the magazine and chamber designs are such that cartridges of different lengths will chamber in and operate it. While originally designed for the 9mm. Bayard military cartridge, it will also handle satisfactorily the 9mm. Steyr military automatic pistol cartridge, the .38 Colt automatic pistol cartridge; most of the various 9mm. Parabellum (Luger) type cartridges when they have round nosed bullets, and the semi-rim Browning 9mm. Long which is even shorter than the Luger.

Basic Model Data

AUTOMATIC PISTOL: Spanish Astra Model 400.
LENGTH: 8.7 inches.
BARREL: About 6 inches.
WEIGHT: About 35 ounces.
MAGAZINE: Detachable box, catch in butt, capacity 8 cartridges.
OPERATION: Blowback unlocked.
MAINSPRING: Coil with strut in grip.
DISCONNECTOR: Colt type operated by slide.
TRIGGER: Stirrup type operating across magazine well.
SAFETY: Manual thumb safety and automatic grip safety.
RECOIL SPRING: Mounted around barrel in tubular slide.
BARREL: Mounted securely to receiver by segmental lugs in Browning fashion.
FIRING MECHANISM: Internal hammer covered by slide.
CALIBER: 9mm. Bayard Long Note: this weapon is so chambered that it will handle the 38
    A.C.P. 9mm. Steyr and 9mm. Luger cartridge interchangeably. Best results are obtained
    with the 9mm. Bayard Long).
Drawing shows left side cut away and magazine partly loaded. Hammer is fully cocked.
    Trigger bar is cut away. In building the gun a hole is bored in the rear end of the slide
    to permit drilling the serf for the firing pin. This hole is afterwards plugged.

The weapon itself is well made of good materials and is reasonably well finished. While it does not compare with the best American, British, and German makes, it is still a reliable pistol.

Construction: This pistol is essentially an oversized model of the Campo Giro Model 1913-16. The receiver forms the handle into which the magazine is inserted. The lockwork which includes a Colt-type disconnector and a concealed hammer are also mounted in the receiver. The receiver is provided with tracks to guide the movement of the slide backward and forward; and close fitting special recoil spring collar and concentric recoil spring minimize sideplay. When the weapon is dismounted, care must be taken not to injure the tracks. In the hollow of the receiver above and ahead of the trigger the receiver is machined to receive the barrel and lock it firmly, mounted in the manner familiar to those who have handled the .32 Colt automatic pistol. The slide is of the somewhat cylindrical type of the Savage autoloading pistol. It is machined out of a solid block of metal and is provided with guides suitably machined to travel in the tracks on the receiver. The recoil spring is mounted around the barrel under this slide and is compressed by a collar at the forward end as the slide moves to the rear when the weapon is fired. The rear section of the slide forms the breechblock and contains the firing pin and extractor. The sights are also machined into the slide. The barrel is solidly mounted to the receiver by teeth below the chamber locking into recesses in the receiver.

A slide stop is provided, being positioned on the right side of the receiver. When the last cartridge has been fired, a step on the magazine follower forces up against the inside of this catch bringing it up to engage in a notch on the underside of the slide and hold it open.

The magazine release catch is mounted on the left side of the pistol at the bottom of the grip. Pressing it in releases the magazine and permits it to be withdrawn from the handle. The weapon has the elementary Colt type of magazine disconnector which, when the magazine is withdrawn prevents the trigger from being pulled.

The common automatic disconnector of the Colt-Browning type rises into the path of the slide. It is forced down by a bevelled surface on the slide as the slide moves to the rear and breaks the sear and trigger bar engagement so that trigger pressure cannot release the hammer. Only when the slide is fully forward and the breechblock against the face of the cartridge in the chamber can this disconnector rise under the pressure of its spring into the notch prepared for it in the underside of the slide and thus complete the firing arrangement.

Instead of the thumb slide release provided on the Colt military pistols, the slide on this weapon is released from the open position by drawing back slightly on the slide itself and releasing it to go forward and ride over and depress the slide stop.

The thumb safety is mounted on the receiver on the left side directly behind the trigger. Pushing it up to its engagement notch in the slide locks the weapon manually. This thumbpiece also acts to hold the slide back for dismounting when it is pushed up as the slide is held retracted. A grip safety which functions automatically and is patterned after the standard Browning type is also incorporated.

Dismounting: (1) Withdraw magazine and check firing chamber. (2) Use bottom of magazine to press in the knurled muzzle collar with one hand, while using thumb of hand holding pistol to turn the collar, always keeping it under control. The collar will turn the recoil spring guide collar with it out of slide engagement. (3) Ease out spring with guide and lock collar and remove from pistol. (4) Push the slide back until the barrel can be turned to disengage its locking teeth from the receiver. (5) Slide and barrel may be pushed forward off receiver and separated. (6) Extractor and firing pin assemblies may be removed by driving out their respective pins if necessary. (7) Removing stocks gives access to holding pins which permit removal of lockwork if necessary.

Note: The design of the recoil spring guide and barrel makes special buffers unnecessary on current pistols. The chamber section of the barrel is heavily reinforced, the forward end of the reinforce acting as rear compression point for the heavy recoil spring. The cylindrical guide around the barrel has a separate collar, the two turning into the locking engagement in the slide. The guide also serves as forward compression point for the recoil spring. The front end of the spring is guided, and while being compressed it is so fully suported that spring kinking often encountered with the ordinary concentrically mounted spring does not occur with the Astra guide.

The Model 400 is well balanced and recoil is not excessive, though ejection is forceful when used with high pressure loads. This pistol has won many European awards for accuracy. This model must not be confused with the Model 600. The barrel of the 400 is stamped "9mm. & 38". The receiver of the 600 is stamped "9mm. Parabellum." The 600 is designed only for 9mm. Luger cartridges and is shorter and somewhat lighter than the 400.

All current Astra pistols are machined from fine steel forgings, and are well fitted and finished. They are manufactured by Unceta Y Compania S. A. at Guernica, Spain.

9mm. Bayard Long

BERGMANN
Bayard 1910

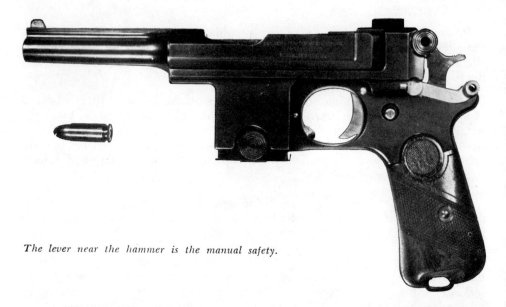

The lever near the hammer is the manual safety.

This is one of the earliest successful military autoloading pistols. The barrel length is about 4 inches, over-all length about 10 inches, weight about 36 ounces and magazine capacity either 6, 8, or 10 cartridges.

First patented by Theodore Bergmann in 1903, it was officially adopted as a Danish side arm in 1910. Since then it has seen extensive police and military use in Greece and in Spain. The model illustrated was manufactured by Anciens Establissements Pieper at Herstal, Belgium; but both receiver and grips bear the name Bayard, which is the Pieper trademark.

A weapon of the same general design but with a grip shaped in more

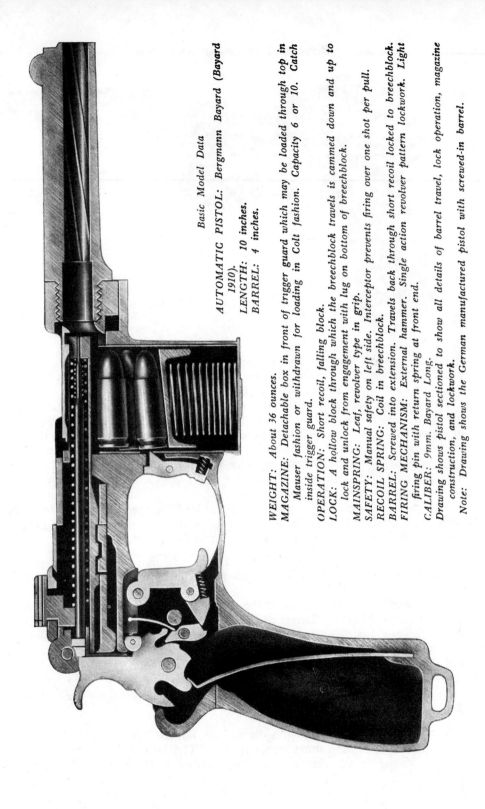

Basic Model Data

AUTOMATIC PISTOL: Bergmann Bayard (Bayard 1910).
 LENGTH: 10 inches.
 BARREL: 4 inches.

WEIGHT: About 36 ounces.
MAGAZINE: Detachable box in front of trigger guard which may be loaded through top in Mauser fashion or withdrawn for loading in Colt fashion. Capacity 6 or 10. Catch inside trigger guard.
OPERATION: Short recoil, falling block.
LOCK: A hollow block through which the breechblock travels is cammed down and up to lock and unlock from engagement with lug on bottom of breechblock.
MAINSPRING: Leaf, revolver type in grip.
SAFETY: Manual safety on left side. Interceptor prevents firing over one shot per pull.
RECOIL SPRING: Coil in breechblock.
BARREL: Screwed into extension. Travels back through short recoil locked to breechblock.
FIRING MECHANISM: External hammer. Single action revolver pattern lockwork. Light firing pin with return spring at front end.
CALIBER: 9mm. Bayard Long.
Drawing shows pistol sectioned to show all details of barrel travel, lock operation, magazine construction, and lockwork.
 Note: Drawing shows the German manufactured pistol with screwed-in barrel.

Breechblock in full recoil position

standard revolver fashion and with a somewhat differently shaped hammer was manufactured under the Bergmann patents in Germany. This type was the predecessor to the type used by Denmark.

The German variety of the Bayard was issued in a leather holster with a steel frame, so designed that it could be attached to the handle of the pistol to convert it to a carbine. This type of weapon was widely sold by the Germans under the name of Mars to shoot a special 10mm. Mars cartridge. Magazines of 6-shot or 10-shot capacity were provided for this pistol. These weapons may be loaded with a clip from the top exactly as in the case of the Mauser military 7.63mm.

The shoulder stock and carrying case provided for the Belgian Bayard somewhat resembled that for the Mauser. It is of quite different design from the German, which was made by Bergmann at Gaggenau.

Comparison of Belgian and German Types. Belgian type weighs 2 pounds, 4 ounces. German type weighs 2 pounds. Barrel and over-all lengths are practically identical.

Barrel and barrel extension of the Belgian model are a single piece as in the case of the Mauser. Barrel of the German type is screwed into the extension. Belgian barrel in some instances measures ⅛″ less than the German.

The Belgian uses the Pieper system of rifling: 6 grooves with narrow lands and left-hand twist. German rifling is 4 broad grooves, right-hand twist, lands practically the same diameter as the grooves.

Parts for the German and Belgian makes are not interchangeable although they are similar in design in most cases.

Construction: The Bergmann Bayard in all its forms is a locked breech pistol operating on the short recoil system. The bolt or breechblock securely locked to support the cartridge in the chamber at the instant of firing by a

376

rising and falling block, mounted in the barrel extension, through which the breechblock travels.

The lockwork in this Bayard is extremely simple. It is constructed along the lines of that in a standard single-action revolver. However, it is provided with an interceptor (or disconnector) to prevent over one shot being fired for each pull of the trigger.

The magazine in this pistol is detachable. The magazine catch is in the front end of the trigger guard. Pushing it in permits withdrawal of the magazine from the bottom. The magazine as normally issued has a capacity of 6 cartridges, caliber 9mm. Bayard long.

An external hammer of good design is provided on this weapon. As the firing pin is of the flying type in which the pin is supported by a coil spring and is shorter than the length of the breechblock in which it is mounted, it is necessary for the hammer to strike a full blow in order to drive the pin ahead far enough to strike the cartridge in the firing chamber and then be pulled back into the breechblock by its spring. Because of this feature, it is safe to carry this weapon with a cartridge in the chamber and the hammer lowered. However, a thumb safety is provided at the upper left side of the receiver.

The receiver cover-plate is held by a spring catch which is easily removed to permit cleaning of the lockwork.

Functioning: When the hammer falls it drives the flying firing pin ahead to fire the cartridge, as the bullet passes down the barrel, the barrel and breechblock move to the rear firmly locked together.

The bolt, which is square section, rides inside a hollow square block which has a vertical movement of about ⅛th of an inch. This hollow block is mounted in a slot in the barrel extension; and when the weapon is closed, a lug and a recess on each side of the lug fits in and locks two mating recesses on the bottom of this square block.

When the weapon is closed, this square block rests *on the receiver.* Immediately behind it a recess is machined to a depth of about ⅛", and is shaped to receive the bottom side of the block.

As the barrel and breech assemblies recoil locked together, the square block engaged with the lug on the underside of the bolt rides back with them. This keeps them firmly locked together.

The rear of the receiver is machined to receive the barrel extension and the upper surface of the block, which is beveled. Therefore, during recoil this beveled surface of the block coming in contact with the roof of the tunnel at the rear of the receiver forces the block down.

When the weapon is in full recoiling position, the block is resting in the shallow recess machined into the receiver for it. This, of course, frees the bolt lug from its recess in the bottom of the square bolt block; and the bolt is free to move rearward under the momentum imparted to it to extract and eject the empty cartridge case and compress the recoil spring which is mounted around the striker or firing pin within the bolt.

The magazine spring forces a cartridge up into line as the bolt clears the head of the magazine opening and the compressed recoil spring drives the action forward to chamber a new cartridge.

The extractor, a flat leaf spring mounted on top of the bolt, snaps into the extraction groove in the cartridge case as the cartridge is chambered.

The ejector in this weapon is milled out of the receiver and runs in a groove in the lower surface of the bolt.

When this 9mm. pistol is of German manufacture the barrel is only screwed into the barrel extension and is detachable from it. The *barrel extension* provides the chamber for the cartridge.

9mm. Bayard Long   **MISCELLANEOUS**
       Weapons

Various imitations and modifications of the Colt-Browning locked breech design similar to the .45 Colt automatic pistol have been manufactured in Spain to take the 9mm. Bayard cartridge. The best known is the Star which is described and pictured under Caliber .45 ACP (this arm is also manufactured in Caliber 7.63mm. Mauser).

Another Spanish modification of the Colt using the Bayard cartridge is the Llama. This make usually has a barrel protruding a half-inch or more from the slide. It closely resembles in external lines the .45 Colt auto. None of these pistols are well finished or fitted by American standards.

CARTRIDGE
Data
9mm. Steyr

This was the official Austrian pistol cartridge. It was never manufactured in the United States. It resembles the 9mm. Bayard Long very closely. Steyr cartridges usually come packed in clips of 8. The jackets originally were steel though alloy was later employed. Bullet weight averages about 116 grains and diameters .355 inch. The case is rimless and measures about .90 inch. The over-all length of the loaded cartridge averages about 1.30 inch. The muzzle velocity varies between 1050 and 1200 feet per second in various makes. Striking energy is in the neighborhood of 370 foot-pounds.

STEYR
Military
9mm. Steyr

This famous pistol is Austrian. It has a 5-inch barrel, measures 8½ inches over-all, weighs about 33 ounces and has a built-in magazine loaded customarily with a clip through an opening in the top of the slide. This arm is often referred to as the Steyr-Hahn (hammer Steyr). It is one of the most powerful automatic pistols in existence. Originally introduced in 1911, it was noted for the positive breech locking effected by the short recoil and 60 degree turn of its barrel with its four heavy lugs. It introduced a bullet which was actually steel jacketed and was famous for its penetration. The Steyr was the official pistol of the Austrians in World War I and was also used extensively in the Balkan areas.

The one weakness is in the barrel. It is rather thin and may crack near the muzzle end. This defect should be looked for before using the weapon.

Most examples of this pistol encountered will have the manufacturing mark

379

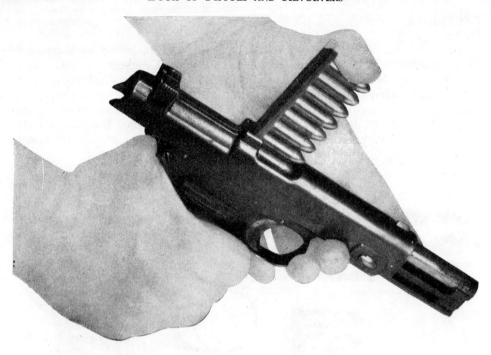

Osterreiche Waffenfabrik, Steyr on them. This arm was adopted by the Rumanian and Chilean Government in addition to the Austrians.

Loading: The loading system in this weapon differs from others and requires a special knowledge. When the weapon is empty, pulling the slide back by hand as far as it will go enables the magazine follower to rise in line with the breech-bolt face of the slide and hold the pistol open. *However, it cannot be loaded in this position.* The slide must be drawn further back and the thumb safety on the left-hand side of the receiver must be turned up until it catches and locks in the hold-open slot cut for it in the left side of the slide.

A clip loaded with eight cartridges is then inserted in the magazine or clip guides which are machined into the top of the slide. These cartridges are then stripped down by the thumb into the magazine. If no clip is available, cartridges may be inserted singly, since they are retained in place at the top by a spring-operated lip on the left side.

When cartridges have been inserted and the clip removed, pressing the catch out of engagement with the slide will permit the recoil spring to drive the slide forward and the breech face will strip the top cartridge out of the magazine and chamber it.

Unloading: This weapon is unusual in that it is not necessary to work the slide back and forth a number of times in order to empty the magazine. The

380

Basic Model Data

AUTOMATIC PISTOL: Austrian Steyr.

LENGTH: 8½ inches.

BARREL: 5 inches.

WEIGHT: 33 ounces.

MAGAZINE: Built into butt. Loaded through top. Capacity 8 cartridges.

OPERATION: Short recoil. Locked breech.

LOCK: Barrel and slide are locked together for short rearward travel by two curved ribs on barrel engaging in slide recesses. Helical guide slot in receiver acts on bottom curved barrel lug causing it to revolve barrel out of locking engagement and permit slide to travel to the rear to cock and eject. A fourth barrel lug is a stop for barrel.

MAINSPRING: Vertical leaf spring in grip.

DISCONNECTOR: Forced down on rearward movement of slide moves trigger bar out of sear engagement.

TRIGGER: Pivoted. Draws trigger bar to pull leaf spring forward to release hammer.

SAFETY: Thumb catch on left side locks hammer and slide.

RECOIL SPRING: Coil with guide in receiver tube below barrel.

BARREL: Has travel, stop and locking lugs. Recoils a short distance with slide.

FIRING MECHANISM: External hammer.

CALIBER: 9mm. Steyr. (Some World War II conversions use 9mm. Luger cartridges).

SPECIAL FEATURE: To load this weapon the slide must be drawn back and the safety catch pushed up into the second slide notch. Cartridges are then stripped into the magazine through the top of the action. If the catch on the side is pressed the magazine spring will expel all cartridges from the magazine. The follower holds the action open but not ready for loading when the last shot has been fired.

Drawing shows left side cut away exposing lockwork. Slide is cut away to show system of lug locking and travel.

Right side view with action cut away to show function of trigger and trigger bar, method of slide overriding hammer, and system of recoil spring compression and barrel support. Action is in full recoil position. Detail shows barrel sections with helical ribs and guide rib. Clip section shows side and front of special loading clip.

magazine which is not detachable but is an integral part of the butt, is fitted with a device to make speedy unloading simple.

The slide is drawn back by hand to eject the cartridge in the firing chamber and is held back while the locking catch is turned up to lock into the slide and hold it back. Pressing down the release catch on the left-hand side of the receiver above the line of the trigger will pull the locking lip away from the top cartridge in the magazine and permit the magazine spring to drive the follower up and force all the cartridges in the magazine out of it. Unless this motion is controlled by holding a hand over the ejection port, the loaded cartridges will all be hurled up and out of the gun a distance of several feet.

Construction and Operation: The slide in this weapon travels backwards and forwards in grooves in the receiver in standard automatic pistol fashion. The locking system, however, is unique. At the moment of discharge, the barrel and the slide are securely locked together by locking lugs on the barrel which are engaged with corresponding recesses in the underside of the slide.

A torque effect is set up in this weapon as the bullet, passing down the bore, tends to twist the barrel firmly in its locked position.

The barrel is revolved out of locking engagement as the slide goes back, and the locking slots on the slide rotate the barrel until its lugs are disengaged from those slots. Once free of the engagement, the barrel stops its motion but the slide continues on rearward.

The recoil spring, a coil spring, is mounted directly below the barrel in an extension of the receiver. A compressor at its forward end is driven back by a block passing through the slide and receiver-guide slots from left to right, much as in the case of the first Colt .38 Automatics. As this piece goes back as a unit of the slide, it forces the compressor back to store energy in the recoil spring.

Note: There is a short recoil of barrel and slide in this weapon until the barrel is stopped against its stop in the receiver, and the cammed surface on the barrel, traveling in the cam rib in the receiver, twists the barrel to the left to unlock it from the slide.

The extractor is a strong claw in the top of the bolt and is split to form its own spring. It withdraws the empty case as the slide goes to the rear.

The cartridge case strikes the ejector which, in this weapon, is the top piece of the disconnector, and is ejected from the weapon.

The rear of the slide forces back and runs over the hammer to rotate it on its axis and bring it to full-cock position.

The magazine spring forces the next cartridge into line and, as the compressed recoil spring reasserts itself, pulls the slide forward to strip a cartridge from the magazine and load it in the firing chamber.

The sear in this weapon is a bent on the rear face of a heavy vertical spring. The spring is hooked at its top to engage a stud on the trigger bar.

During rearward motion, or when the weapon is not fully closed, the disconnector is forced down and carries the trigger bar with it, leaving the sear free to catch the hammer.

When the trigger is pressed, the trigger bar is pulled forward and it, in turn, pulls the leaf spring forward to free the hammer, permitting it to be driven forward by the compressed hammer spring to strike the flying firing pin and discharge the cartridge.

Safety: The thumb safety mounted on the left-hand side of the rear of the receiver in this weapon, securely locks the hammer when it is pushed up into engagement. This feature, together with the positive disconnector, assures complete mechanical safety.

Special Note on Steyr-Hahn Pistols

During World War II Austrian factories converted many of these pistols to shoot the standard German P-08 (9mm. Luger) cartridge.

These conversions can be recognized by the stamp "P-08" on them.

9mm. Steyr   MISCELLANEOUS
                                                   Weapons

No pistol except the Steyr is chambered for this cartridge. However, it will function in the Spanish made Astra Model 400. Spanish imitations of the Colt .45 Auto will also use it when chambered for 9mm. Bayard Long. The Steyr cartridge is also used in some European submachine guns, notably the Steyr-Solothurn.

CARTRIDGE
Data

.357 S&W Magnum

.357 Magnum

.357 Magnum Met. P. Super-X

Bullet
158 Gr.

Muzzle Velocity in f.s.:	1430
Vel. at 50 Yards:	1230
Vel. at 100 Yards:	1110

Calculated Energy in Ft. Lbs.

Muzzle Energy:	717
Energy at 50 Yards:	530
Energy at 100 Yards:	430

Mid-range Trajectory

At 50 Yards:	.6 inch
At 100 Yards:	2.8 inches

Penetration at 15 Feet

7/8" soft pine boards:	12 inches

Length of Barrel in Which Tested

inches	8⅜

Shell Case

Weight:	81 grains
Max. Length:	1.290 inches
Outside Body Dia. at Head, Max.:	.379 inch
Outside Body Dia. at Neck, Max.:	.379 inch
Inside Mouth Dia. Max.:	.358 inch
Volumetric Capacity to Base of Bullet	
in cubic inches:	.056

Bullet

Weight:	158 grains
Approx. Length:	700 inch
Diameter Max.:	.359 inch
Area, Cross Sectional:	.101 square inch
Shape:	Blunt Nose

Powder

Amount and type varies with different lots manufactured.

Cartridge

Approx. Length, Loaded:	1.520 inches
Approx. Total Weight. Loaded:	256 grains

Muzzle Velocity in f.s.:	1430
Vel. at 50 yards:	1230
Vel. at 100 Yards:	1110

Calculated Energy in Ft. Lbs.

Muzzle Energy:	717
Energy at 50 Yards:	530
Energy at 100 Yards:	430

Mid-range Trajectory

At 50 Yards:	.6 inch
At 100 Yards:	2.8 inches

Penetration at 15 Feet

7/8" soft pine boards:	12 inches

Length of Barrel in Which Tested

inches	8⅜

Shell Case

Weight:	81 grains
Max. Length:	1.290 inches
Outside Body Dia. at Head, Max.:	.379 inch
Outside Body Dia. at Neck, Max.:	.379 inch
Inside Mouth Dia. Max.:	.358 inch
Volumetric Capacity to Base of Bullet	
in cubic inches:	.057

Bullet

Weight:	158 grains
Approx. Length:	.765 inch
Diameter Max.:	.359 inch
Area, Cross Sectional:	.101 square inch
Shape:	Conical

Powder

Amount and type varies with different lots manufactured.

Cartridge

Approx. Length, Loaded:	1.590 inches
Approx. Total Weight, Loaded:	256 grains

This cartridge was pioneered by Smith & Wesson. The general specifications of the case are the same as the .38 S&W Special except that the case is longer. This precludes its use in revolvers not designed for it. It should be emphasized that this is one of the most powerful revolver cartridges in existence, and that it is unsafe to alter revolvers of earlier design or lighter weight than S&W Magnum or Colt New Service or S.A. Army types to chamber it. However, any cartridge which will chamber in a revolver designed for the .38 Special can be used in one chambered for the .357 Magnum.

.357 S&W Magnum   **COLT**
                                                                  Miscellaneous

Colt Single Action Army, New Service, and Shooting Master (New Service Target) Models are made for the .357 Magnum cartridge. For specifications see these models under Cal. .45 Colt. For representative drawings and description, see Colt 1917 Revolver under Caliber .45 A.C.P.

.357 S&W Magnum   **SMITH AND WESSON**
                                                              .357 Magnum

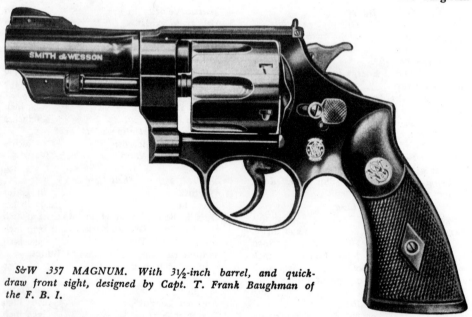

S&W .357 MAGNUM. With 3½-inch barrel, and quick-draw front sight, designed by Capt. T. Frank Baughman of the F. B. I.

The gun with registration Number 2 was presented to Mr. Philip B. Sharpe of South Portland, Me., an authority on handloading, who, together with Smith & Wesson's engineers and Mr. Merton A. Robinson of the Winchester Repeating Arms Co., developed the original .357 S & W Magnum load.

More complete specifications will be found later, in Part II. These specifications will be of interest to gunsmiths who often do custom work on this gun, or make custom rifles. The figures include the different dimensions of the Model 19.

Note: To prevent the magnum cartridge from being used in revolvers incapable of standing its power, the new cartridge was made with a case .135" longer than the standard to prevent it from chambering.

Hence, while the .357 Magnum will successfully chamber all the earlier cartridges which fit .38 Specials and the .38-44's, the overall length of the .357 Magnum cartridge is too great to permit it to be inserted in earlier revolvers. A few old .38 Special guns have chambers without a shoulder in the cylinder and will take .357 Magnum cartridges. They are generally safe with standard .38 Specials that develop less than 15,000 psi pressure. They are apt to blow up if fired with .357 Magnum cartridges, that develop breech pressure in the 45,000 psi range. The guns are quite dangerous with high pressure loads. Incidentally, the .357 Magnum is one of the very few revolvers whose caliber is actually what it is called.

To get the maximum velocity with this cartridge it is necessary to use the 8⅜-inch barrel. With shorter barrels, figure velocity approximately as follows: For each inch less down to six inches in barrel length, subtract 40 feet per second. For each inch thereafter down to 3½ inches, subtract 50 feet per second.

SMITH AND WESSON   **.357 S&W Magnum**
.357 Magnum Hand Ejector

*S&W .357 MAGNUM with 8¾-inch barrel for maximum range and velocity. **Insert shows** details of matted rib and rear sight.*

Ammunition: .357 S & W Magnum and all .38 Specials.
Manufacturing Dates: From April 1935.
Serial Numbers: Numbered in same series with .44 Hand Ejector Models.
Finish: Blue or nickel.
Barrel Lengths: Originally any length from 3½" to 8¾"; extreme length later cut to 8⅜", and standard lengths set at 3½", 5", 6", 6½", 8⅜".
Notes: The Magnum is similar in appearance to the .38-44, but different materials are used, minor dimensions changed, and the chamber lengthened for the .357 S & W Magnum cartridge. This was the first modern center-fire revolver equipped with recessed-head cylinder. Checkered top strap and

checkered rib full length of barrel. Front and rear tangs grooved. Concentric circular cuts on sides of hammer reduce friction.

At first, besides serial numbers, each Magnum was individually registered and had a registration number stamped in the yoke cut of the frame above the fitting number. Due to expense, this procedure was discontinued in 1940. The gun with registration number 1 and serial numbers, 45,768, was an 8¾" blue Magnum and was presented to J. Edgar Hoover, Director of the Federal Bureau of Investigation, on May 10, 1935. Although the Magnum was not adopted as the standard equipment of the F.B.I., it became extremely popular with F.B.I. agents who generally preferred the 3½" gun with the Baughman Quick-draw Front Sight mounted on a King Plain Ramp.

S&W have redesigned their safety as shown. The side plate was altered, a steel safety bar operating on an eccentric was added, and a hammer cut for the bar top was made below the firing pin. In this new construction, a steel bar blocks passage of the firing pin except when the hammer is released from full cock by deliberate trigger pressure.

For practical purposes this is a positive safety. However, the only truly accident-proof revolver hammer safeties are those found in the low priced, discontinued, Iver Johnson, "Hammer-the-Hammer" revolver and the obsolete Hopkins & Allen type eccentric system.

Chapter 10

Caliber .38

.38 S&W, S&W S.P., and Colt N.P.

The .38 S&W S.P.

.38 Colt New Police		.38 Smith & Wesson	
150 Gr. Lub.		*145 Gr. Lub.*	
Muzzle Velocity in f.s.:	695	Muzzle Velocity in f.s.:	745
Vel. at 50 Feet:	684	Vel. at 50 Feet:	733
Vel. at 150 Feet:	662	Vel. at 150 Feet:	709
Calculated Energy		*Calculated Energy*	
Muzzle Energy in ft. lbs.:	161	Muzzle Energy in ft. lbs.:	179
Energy at 50 Feet:	154	Energy at 50 Feet:	173
Energy at 150 Feet	145	Energy at 150 Feet:	162
Calculated Drop		*Calculated Drop*	
At 50 Feet:	1.0 inch	At 50 Feet:	.86 inch
At 150 Feet:	9.6 inches	At 150 Feet:	8.1 inches
At 300 Feet:	38.4 inches	At 300 Feet:	36.8 inches
Penetration at 15 Feet		*Penetration at 15 Feet*	
7/8″ soft pine boards	4	7/8″ soft pine boards	4
Length of Barrel in Which Tested		*Length of Barrel in Which Tested*	
inches	4	inches	4
Shell Case		*Shell Case*	
Weight:	62.5 grains	Weight:	62.5 grains
Max. Length:	.755 inch	Max. Length:	.775 inch
Outside Body Dia. at Head, Max.:	.3865 inch	Outside Body Dia. at Head, Max:	.3865 inch
Outside Body Dia. at Neck, Max.:	.3855 inch	Outside Body Dia. at Neck, Max.:	.3885 inch
Inside Mouth Dia. Max.:	.3585 inch	Inside Mouth Dia. Max.:	.3585 inch
Volumetric Capacity to Base of Bullet		Volumetric Capacity to Base of Bullet	
in cubic inches:	.034	in cubic inches:	.034

.38 Colt New Police (Cont.)

Bullet

Weight:	150 grains
Approx. Length:	.635 inch
Diameter Max.:	.359 inch
Area, Cross Sectional:	.101 square inch
Shape:	Blunt Nose

Powder

Amount and type varies with different lots manufactured.

Cartridge

Approx. Length, Loaded:	1.180 inches
Approx. Total Weight, Loaded:	215 grains

.38 Smith & Wesson (Cont.)

Bullet

Weight:	145 grains
Approx. Length:	.635 inch
Diameter Max.:	.359 inch
Area, Cross Sectional:	.101 square inch
Shape:	Round Nose

Powder

Amount and type varics with different lots manufactured.

Cartridge

Approx. Length, Leaded:	1.180 inches
Approx. Total Weight, Loaded:	209 grains

.38 Smith & Wesson Super Police

200 Gr.

Muzzle Velocity in f.s.:	630
Vel. at 50 Feet:	623
Vel. at 150 Feet:	611

Calculated Energy

Muzzle Energy in ft. lbs.:	176
Energy at 50 Feet:	171
Energy at 150 Feet:	164

Calculated Drop

At 50 Feet:	1.4 inches
At 150 Feet:	10.8 inches
At 300 Feet:	45.8 inches

Penetration at 15 Feet

7/8" soft pine boards	5

Length of Barrel in Which Tested

inches	4

Shell Case

Weight:	62.5 grains
Max. Length:	.775 inch
Outside Body Dia. at Head, Max.:	.3865 inch
Outside Body Dia. at Neck, Max.:	.3855 inch
Inside Mouth Dia. Max.:	.3585 inch
Volumetric Capacity to Base of Bullet in cubic inches:	.023

Bullet

Weight:	200 grains
Approx. Length:	.815 inch
Diameter Max.:	.359 inch
Area, Cross Sectional:	.101 square inch
Shape:	Round Nose

Powder

Amount and type varies with different lots manufactured.

Cartridge

Approx. Length, Loaded:	1.240 inches
Approx. Total Weight, Loaded:	266 grains

This cartridge was originally designed for Smith & Wesson hinged-frame revolvers. It has come to be one of the most widely distributed cartridges in commercial use. In many forms and slight variations it is known under different names. With round-point bullet it is called the .38 S&W. With flat-point bullet it is called the .38 Colt New Police. With a bullet some 50 grains heavier (about 200 grains) it is known as the S&W Super Police. It is an official cartridge of the British Armed Forces used in their revolvers designated Pistol, Revolver No. 2 MK. 1, MK. 1*, and MK. I**.

The construction of the case prevents it from being used in any revolver chambered for the .38 Smith & Wesson Special cartridges. The S&W is too large in diameter to chamber in the .38 Special; while the .38 Special is too long to chamber in weapons designed for the .38 S&W.

COLT   .38 S&W, S&W S.P., Colt N.P.
Police Positive (.38 Frame)

The only modern Colt revolvers which will accommodate this cartridge are the Police Positive and Bankers' Special Models. Description of the Police Positive model follows. For details on the Bankers' Special see note below. General appearance and functioning of all Colt models (except the Single Action Army) are practically identical.

General Description: Factory Model C. A police-type revolver of medium weight, on a .38 caliber frame, modern design in limb work using modern medium-power ammunition with safety and efficiency.

Ammunition: .38 Police Positive. .32 Police Positive. .22 L.R.

Manufacturing Dates: 1905 to 1945.

Serial Numbers: From Number 1 to 22,000 on present frame.

Finish: Blue and Nickel.

	.38 Pol. Pos.	*.32 Pol. Pos.*	*.22 L.R.*
Barrel Length:	2″	2½″	2″ Bankers Special
	4″	4″	
	5″	5″	
	6″	6″	6″

Stocks: Rubber; checked walnut with medallion (both narrow and wide butt).

	.38 Pol. Pos.	*.32 Pol. Pos.*	*.22 L.R.*
Bore Diameter:	.347″—.001	.305″—.001	.215″—.001
Groove Diameter:	.354″—.001	.312″—.001	.222″—.001

Rifling: (Left twist). 6 grooves. 1 turn in 16″. 22, 1 turn in 14″.

Number of Shots: 6.

Action: Double.

Approximate Weight: .38 caliber 4″ barrel: 20 ounces.

Over-all Length: 10½″ with 6″ barrel.

Sights: Fixed. Front: integral with barrel. Rear: groove with notch in top strap.

Note: Brought out first in .38 caliber with a narrow butt, this gave way to a wide-butt frame at about Number 300,000. Subsequent to 1926 changes included a top strap having a matted surface with a square cut rear sight notch of the Patridge type, a checked trigger, and chambering for the .32 Police Positive cartridge.

The "Banker's Special" is a variation of this model (in .38 and .22 calibers) developed originally for the Railway Mail Service and designed primarily for guard, messengers, tellers, etc. Besides a 2″ barrel The "Banker's Special" has a shortened ejector rod, and a rounded butt and rounded stocks in caliber .22.

ENFIELD   .38 S&W, S&W S.P., Colt N.P.
British Service No. 2 Mk 1

The barrel length is 5 inches, over-all length 10¼ inches, weight is about 27½ ounces and cylinder capacity is 6 cartridges. This is a revolver of the

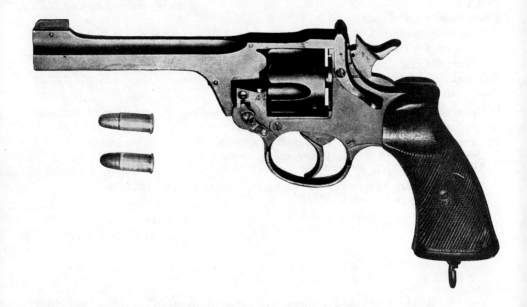

Webley pattern—hinged-frame with the lock mounted in stirrup form on the standing breech, controlled by a V-spring mounted on the outside of the right-hand side plate, and snapping down over the barrel extension to lock the revolver for firing.

Construction and Operation: The principal differences between this revolver and the earlier Pistol, Revolver No. 1 Mark VI (See under Cal. .455) aside from caliber are the type of cylinder catch and the mechanical safety arrangement. In this revolver as the trigger is pressed the trigger catch lowers the cylinder stop from the cylinder recess. The lifting pawl (or hand) is attached to the trigger and as it is lifted it engages with a tooth on the head of the extractor and rotates the cylinder clockwise. The trigger nose engages with the hammer catch and rotates the hammer on its axis pin, thereby compressing the long arm of the mainspring below the hammer end. The mainspring lever bears on a shoulder on the lifting pawl to compress the short arm of the mainspring. A safety stop rises opposite the cut in the hammer. As the nose of the trigger slips off the hammer catch (or bent) when the arm is being fired double action, the compressed long arm of the mainspring drives it ahead to strike its loose firing pin against the cartridge in line. Meanwhile the cylinder stop rises to engage in the cylinder recess immediately above it, preventing too much rotation. The cylinder is held securely locked in line with the barrel in the fired position by the cylinder stop, by the right side of the lifting pawl engaging the extractor tooth, and by the stop on the pawl.

The short arm of the mainspring forces the mainspring lever down and a shoulder on the latter strikes the rebound arm on the hammer and rotates the hammer backwards. This action draws the firing pin back into the standing

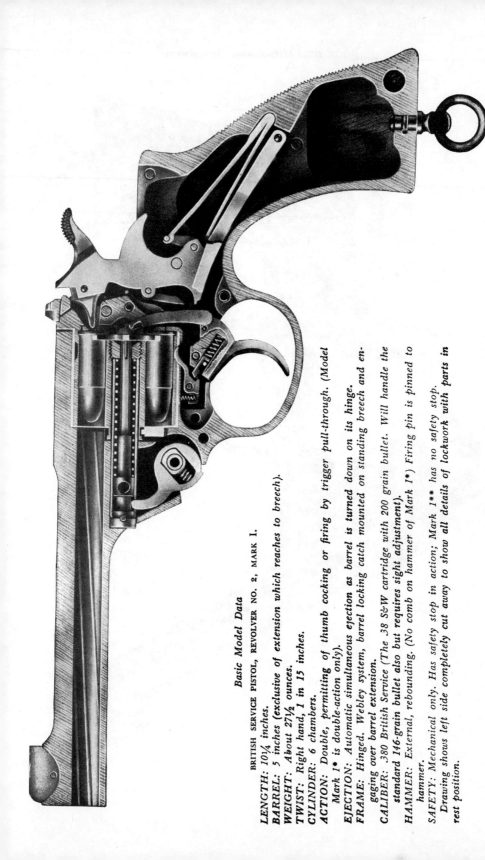

Basic Model Data

BRITISH SERVICE PISTOL, REVOLVER NO. 2, MARK I.

LENGTH: 10¼ inches.
BARREL: 5 inches (exclusive of extension which reaches to breech).
WEIGHT: About 27½ ounces.
TWIST: Right hand, 1 in 15 inches.
CYLINDER: 6 chambers.
ACTION: Double, permitting of thumb cocking or firing by trigger pull-through. (Model Mark I* is double-action only).
EJECTION: Automatic simultaneous ejection as barrel is turned down on its hinge.
FRAME: Hinged. Webley system, barrel locking catch mounted on standing breech and engaging over barrel extension.
CALIBER: .380 British Service (The .38 S&W cartridge with 200 grain bullet. Will handle the standard 146-grain bullet also but requires sight adjustment).
HAMMER: External, rebounding. (No comb on hammer of Mark I*) Firing pin is pinned to hammer.
SAFETY: Mechanical only. Has safety stop in action; Mark I** has no safety stop.
Drawing shows left side completely cut away to show all details of lockwork with parts in rest position.

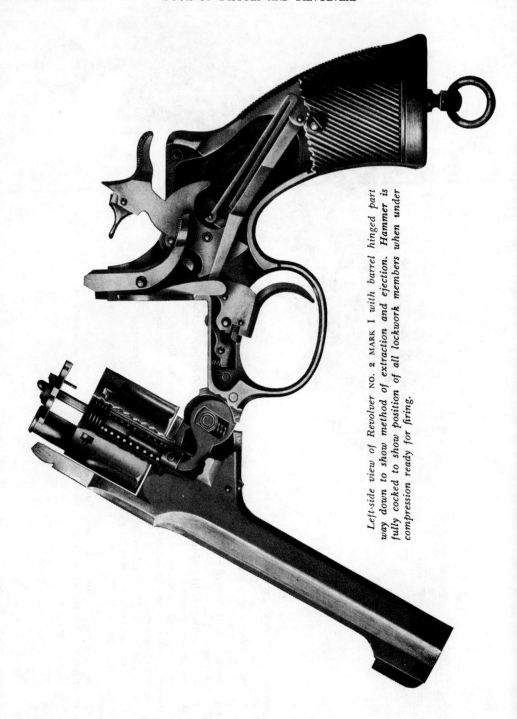

Left-side view of Revolver NO. 2 MARK I with barrel hinged part way down to show method of extraction and ejection. Hammer is fully cocked to show position of all lockwork members when under compression ready for firing.

394

breech and serves as a safety feature by keeping the firing pin out of contact with cartridge except at instant of complete hammer fall.

The long arm of the mainspring lever bears on the shoulder on the pawl and thereby returns the trigger to forward position when trigger pressure is released. The trigger nose engages the hammer bent or catch and the trigger catch engages the cylinder stop leaving the revolver ready for the next trigger pull.

Loading. Note stirrup lock which differentiates British from American hinged-frame revolvers.

Loading and Unloading: When the stirrup lever on the left side of the revolver is pushed it pivots the lever and draws the upper locking section back out of engagement over the barrel strap (or extension). When the barrel is turned down on its hinge a step on the extractor lever strikes the metal of the receiver (or frame) causing the lever to revolve. The curved arm of the lever is engaged with the extractor nut, hence it forces the extractor up out of its well in the cylinder and compresses its spring. The head of the extractor raises all the cartridges it is supporting and ejects them from the revolver. The lever is forced inward by the barrel where it strikes it until it is clear of the frame. At that point the compressed spring draws the extractor back into its seat.

Should the barrel not be fully closed after extraction or loading, the top of the hammer hitting the barrel catch will either snap it in place or block hammer movement. It is therefore impossible to fire a revolver with Webley lock unless it is fully closed and locked.

Dismounting: First push the barrel catch on the left side of the frame down as far as it will go to release the barrel lock. Bend the barrel down to open it and extract any cartridges which may be in the cylinder.

At the forward end of the frame just ahead of and below the cylinder is a cylinder catch retainer. (Officially this is called the lever cam cylinder fixing screw.) Unscrew this a few turns and it will release the lever. Push the lever up and the cylinder may be lifted up off its axis pin. Unscrew the extractor nut and the extractor and its spring may be lifted up out of the cylinder.

Unfasten the screw which passes through the stock from the left-hand side and fastens the right-hand stock also. The stocks may now be removed.

Unscrew the fixing screw which holds the barrel catch from the left-hand side and withdraw it. The V-spring which actuates this catch is mounted on the right side of the frame and may now be lifted off. The barrel catch may also be lifted off. The four screws which hold the retaining plate on the left side of the frame may now be unscrewed and the side plate lifted off. The top of the pawl (the hand which turns the cylinder) may now be levered back and lifted out.

The mainspring may be unhooked from the hammer swivel and removed, and knocking out the mainspring auxiliary pin permits removing the auxiliary. The hammer may now be rotated to the rear and removed and then the trigger and safety stop may be lifted out.

If necessary, the cylinder stop and its spring may now be removed. As this spring is very easily distorted, these units should never be withdrawn unless necessary.

Unscrewing the joint pin screw on the right side of the pistol will permit pushing the joint pin out with the cam lever to the left. This permits the barrel to be removed from the frame. If the barrel is taken out, the extractor lever in the barrel axis will also come out. Be careful *not to lose* this.

To remove the recoil plate, remove the screw and drive the plate out from left to right.

Assembling: Assembling this pistol is merely a matter of reversing the dismounting procedure. The one little trick that is necessary to remember is that the mainspring auxiliary should be raised slightly so that it rides on top of the pawl axis pin.

.38 S&W, S&W S.P., Colt N.P.   **ENFIELD**
                                                          Service No. 2 Mk 1*

This is a modification of the Mark I intended for quick drawing and close-quarters shooting, particularly in Commando operations. There is no bent on the hammer to permit it to be held at full cock when drawn back by thumb as in the case of the Mark I. This arm has a hammer without cocking spur to prevent snagging on holster. It can only be fired double-action.

.38 S&W, S&W S.P., and Colt N.P.   **HARRINGTON AND RICHARDSON**
                                                                Revolvers

H&R revolvers of the solid-frame nonejector type and those of the hinged-frame hammer and hammerless types already covered under Caliber .32 S & W are chambered in various barrel lengths and weights for this cartridge. Except that they are invariably chambered for 5 cartridges only, they differ from the other calibers only slightly in weights and ranges of barrel length. Barrels may run from 2 to 6 inches. Grips may be of any style or variety. The name of the manufacturer will be found on all H&R revolvers.

ENFIELD BRITISH SERVICE NO. 2 MARK I.

IVER JOHNSON   .38 S&W, S&W S.P., Colt N.P.
Revolvers

All Iver Johnson types of revolvers already described under calibers .22 Long Rifle and .32 S&W have been manufactured for the .38 S&W cartridge. These include the solid-frame nonejector and the hinged-frame in both hammer and hammerless models.

HOPKINS AND ALLEN   .38 S&W, S&W S.P., Colt N.P.
Revolvers

Hopkins & Allen revolvers while no longer manufactured are very widely distributed. In styles and quality they approximate the H&R and IJ. The types are described under caliber .32 S&W. These of S&W caliber differ only in weights. They are invariably found chambered for 5 cartridges. Types are solid-frame nonejector in which empty cases must be pried or punched individually out of chambers; and hammer and hammerless (enclosed hammer) hinged-frame models.

SMITH AND WESSON   .38 S&W, S&W S.P., Colt N.P.
Double Action

Official Model Names: Model .38 Caliber Double Action (First Model)
                      Model .38 Caliber Double Action (Second Model)
                      Model .38 Caliber Double Action (Third Model)
                      Model .38 Caliber Double Action (Fourth Model)
                      Model .38 Caliber Double Action (Fifth Model)
                      Model .38 Caliber Double Action (Perfected)
Ammunition: .38 S & W Cartridge.
Manufacturing Dates: First Model—1880.

397

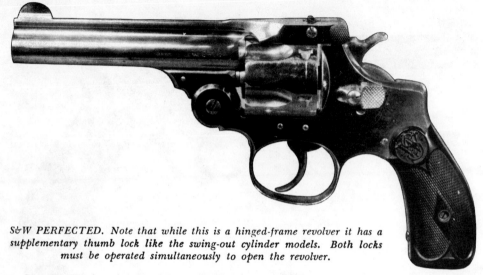

S&W PERFECTED. Note that while this is a hinged-frame revolver it has a supplementary thumb lock like the swing-out cylinder models. Both locks must be operated simultaneously to open the revolver.

Manufacturing Dates: Second Model—1880-1884.
Third Model—1884-1889.
Fourth Model—1889-1909.
Fifth Model—1909-1911.
Perfected—Jan. 1909-1920.

Number Manufactured: First Model—4,000.
Second Model—94,000.
Third Model—103,700.
Fourth Model—216,600.
Fifth Model—14,707.
Perfected—59,400.

Serial Numbers: The first five models were numbered consecutively in a single series—the Perfected was numbered in a separate series.

Finish: Blue or nickel.

Barrel Lengths: First Model—3¼".
Second Model—3¼", 4", 5", 6".
Third Model—3¼", 4", 5", 6", 8", 10".
Fourth Model—Same as Third.
Fifth Model—Same as Third and Fourth.
Perfected—Same as Third, Fourth, and Fifth.

Land Diameter:	.350-.351	*Twist:* One turn in	18¾"
Groove Diameter:	.360-.361	*Direction of Twist:*	Right
Number of Lands:	5	*Diameter of Chamber:*	.388-.389
		Number of Chambers:	5

Note: This was the first double-action Smith & Wesson Revolver and introduced the basic principles of Smith & Wesson's high-speed double-action lockwork. It was an immediate favorite and became extremely popular on the Western frontier as a light, hideaway gun.

Model Changes: The Second Model is very much like the First Model but the side plate was made irregular in shape, with curved edges to strengthen the frame walls.

The Third Model differed from the Second in that the rocker type cylinder stop was replaced by the ordinary hammer and sear actuated type. The half-cock notch was also modified.

The Fourth Model differed from the Third Model in that the latch notch on the sear was moved to reduce the weight of the single-action pull.

The Fifth Model differed from the Fourth Model in that the front sight was forged as an integral part of the barrel instead of being pinned in. The barrel catch was also redesigned.

The Perfected differed from the Fifth Model considerably. The gun was redesigned so that the bolt, operated by a thumbpiece on the left side of the frame, had to be pushed forward before the barrel catch could be lifted. It used the same lockwork parts as the Model I .32 Hand Ejector (Model of 1903), Third, Fourth, and Fifth Changes.

SMITH & WESSON   .38 S&W, S&W S.P., Colt N.P.
Safety

Official Model Names: Model .38 Caliber Safety (First Model).
                                Model .38 Caliber Safety (Second Model).
                                Model .38 Caliber Safety (Third Model).
                                Model .38 Caliber Safety (Fourth Model).
                                Model .38 Caliber Safety (Fifth Model).

These guns are also known as the Safety Hammerless—the New Departure—and popularly as the Lemon Squeezer.

Basic Model Data

REVOLVER: S&W Safety Hammerless Model Hinge Frame.

LENGTH: 7½ inches (with 3¼ inch barrel).

BARREL: Lengths vary (see S&W Text).

WEIGHT: About 18 ounces with 3¼ inch barrel.

CYLINDER: 5 Chambers only in this Caliber.

ACTION: Double only. Hammer is completely enclosed within frame.

EJECTION: Automatic, all chambers are cleared as barrel is hinged down.

FRAME: Hinged. Lock on barrel strap.

CALIBER: 38 S&W (Also manufactured for 32 S&W).

SAFETY: Automatic squeezer safety in grip prevents firing unless weapon is securely held in firing position.

SPECIAL NOTE: Drawing is cut away to show all details of lockwork and Safety. Note that action is shown in position with trigger back ready to slip the hammer. When the hammer falls, the block behind the hammer will be automatically forced in its path to prevent it from rising again if pressure on the grip is released. This drawing was prepared to show position of parts when trigger is being pulled and grip squeezed in.

Ammunition: .38 S & W Cartridges.
Manufacturing Dates: First Model—Jan. 1887-1888.
Second Model—1888-1890.
Third Model—1890-1898.
Fourth Model—1898-1907.
Fifth Model—1907-1940.
Number Manufactured: First Model—5,000.
Second Model—37,500.
Third Model—73,500.
Fourth Model—Approximately 104,000.
Serial Numbers: All models numbered consecutively in same series.
Finish: Blue or nickel.
Barrel Lengths: First and Second Models—3¼″, 4″, 5″, and 6″.
Third and Fourth Models—3¼″, 4″, 5″, 6″.
Fifth Model—2″, 3¼″, 4″, 5″, 6″.

Land Diameter:	.350-.351	Direction of Twist:	Right
Groove Diameter:	.360-.361	Length of Chamber:	.724
Number of Lands:	5	Diameter of Chamber:	.388-.389
Twist: One turn in	18¾″	Number of Chambers:	5

Notes: This was the first safety hammerless revolver, and is still considered the safest gun of its type.

Though the grip safety of the S & W Hammerless has not been imitated extensively in other revolvers, it has been used widely in automatic pistols, shotguns, and light machine guns.

Besides its safety feature, this model has another advantage as an undercover gun—it can be fired from a pocket in an emergency without any risk of jamming the action by having the hammer catch. Too, its ingenious action has a definite hesitation just before the hammer falls so that the trigger can be drawn back quickly and held at this point until the gun is carefully sighted. The final pull-off is almost the equivalent of single-action fire.

Note: While the "squeezer" type of safety was first produced on a successful *commercial* scale by S & W, the *principle* itself was used on several hand-made weapons during the flint- and percussion-lock periods.

Model Changes: First Model—barrel catch was a Z-bar operated by pushing bar inserted in top strap from left to right.
Second Model—minor internal changes—also, instead of Z-bar barrel catch, the Second Model was opened by pushing down on checked thumbpiece protruding from rear of top strap of barrel.
Third Model—Minor changes, including new barrel catch consisting of checked flat thumbpiece on top of frame. When thumbpiece was pushed down it released barrel and also blocked hammer to prevent discharge unless barrel was completely closed.
Fourth Model—Minor changes, including T-shaped barrel catch with knurled buttons on each side.
Fifth Model—Practically the same as the Fourth Model ex-

cept that the front sight is forged integrally with barrel
instead of being a pinned-in blade.

.38 S&W, S&W S.P., Colt N.P.

SMITH & WESSON
Regulation Police

Ammunition: .38 S & W Regular. This revolver will handle the .38 S & W,
the .38 S & W Super Police, the .38 Colt New Police, and
the new .38 British Service cartridges.

Manufacturing Dates: From Feb. 6, 1917 to date.

Serial Numbers: From 1 on in separate series.

Finish: Blue or nickel.

Barrel Lengths: 4".

Design Changes: Hand slot redesigned about Serial Number 4801 to improve
carry up. Square-notch rear sight and flat-top front sight from about 29,966 on.
Heat-treated cylinders from about 20,000.

Land Diameter:	.350-.351	*Direction of Twist:*	Right
Groove Diameter:	.360-.361	*Length of Chamber:*	.724
Number of Lands:	5	*Diameter of Chamber:*	.388-.389
Twist: One turn in	18¾"	*Number of Chambers:*	5

Sights: Square-notch rear-cut in the top of the frame. 1/10", solid service-
type front sight.

Note: Observe that the cylinder in this weapon is chambered to take only
five cartridges. The revolver weighs 18 ounces.

.38 S&W, S&W S.P., Colt N.P.

SMITH & WESSON
38/200 British Service—K-200

Ammunition: .38 S & W Regular.

Manufacturing Dates: April 1940-1945.

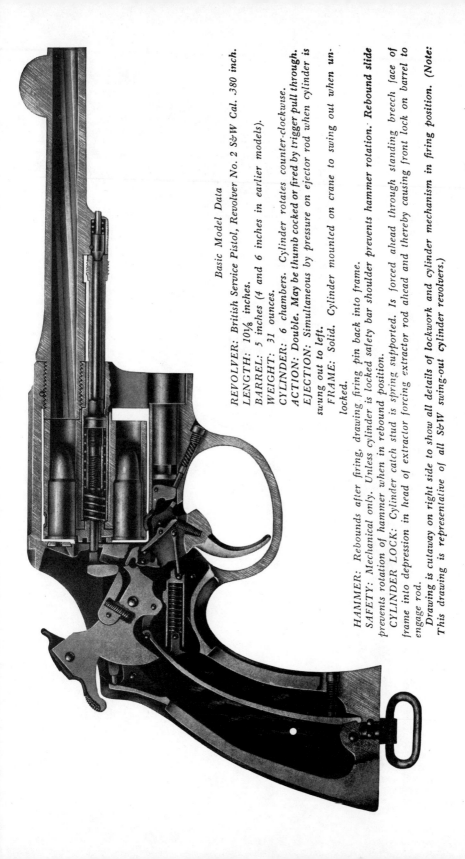

Basic Model Data

REVOLVER: *British Service Pistol, Revolver No. 2 S&W Cal. .380 inch.*
LENGTH: *10⅛ inches.*
BARREL: *5 inches (4 and 6 inches in earlier models).*
WEIGHT: *31 ounces.*
CYLINDER: *6 chambers. Cylinder rotates counter-clockwise.*
ACTION: *Double. May be thumb cocked or fired by trigger pull through.*
EJECTION: *Simultaneous by pressure on ejector rod when cylinder is swung out to left.*
FRAME: *Solid. Cylinder mounted on crane to swing out when unlocked.*

HAMMER: *Rebounds after firing, drawing firing pin back into frame.*
SAFETY: *Mechanical only. Unless cylinder is locked safety bar shoulder prevents hammer rotation.* **Rebound slide** *prevents rotation of hammer when in rebound position.*
CYLINDER LOCK: *Cylinder catch stud is spring supported. Is forced ahead through standing breech face of frame into depression in head of extractor forcing extractor rod ahead and thereby causing front lock on barrel to engage rod.*

Drawing is cutaway on right side to show all details of lockwork and cylinder mechanism in firing position. (Note: This drawing is representative of all S&W swing-out cylinder revolvers.)

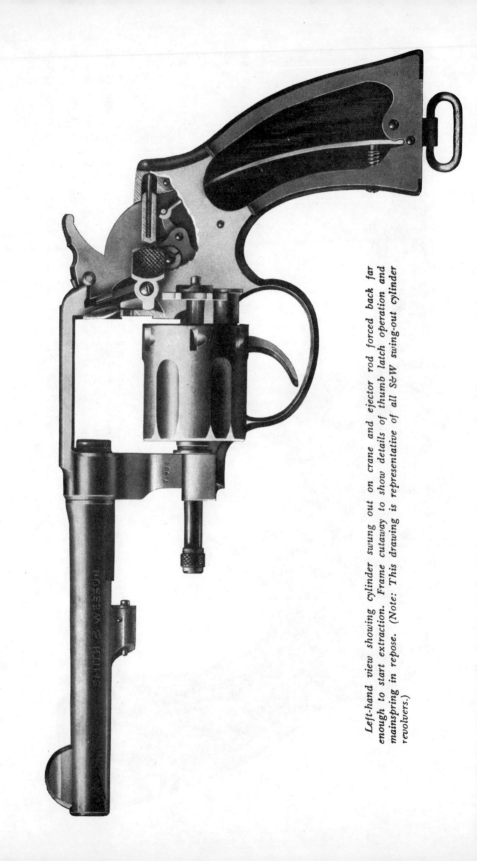

Left-hand view showing cylinder swung out on crane and ejector rod forced back far enough to start extraction. Frame cutaway to show details of thumb latch operation and mainspring in repose. (Note: This drawing is representative of all S&W swing-out cylinder revolvers.)

Number Manufactured: Approximately 890,000.

Finish: Brush polish blue from April 1940–April 1942 (4″, 5″, 6″ barrels)
Sandblast blue finish from April 1942 (5″ barrels only)

Barrel Lengths: 4″, 5″, 6″.

Shape of Butt: Square.

Stocks: Checkered walnut stocks with S & W monograms from April 1940–
Jan. 1, 1942. Smooth, uncheckered walnut stocks without monograms from
Jan. 1, 1942. All guns equipped with lanyard swivels.

Land Diameter:	.350-.3512	*Direction of Twist:*	Right
Groove Diameter:	.3595-.3612	*Length of Chamber:*	.724
Number of Lands:	5	*Diameter of Chamber:*	.388-.389
Twist: One turn in	18¾″	*Number of Chambers:*	6

Note: This was an official British Service Revolver together with the British-
made Enfield hinge frame which shoots the same cartridges.

SMITH & WESSON   .38 S&W, S&W S.P., Colt N.P.
.38/32 Terrier

Ammunition: .38 S & W Regular. This weapon uses the .38 S & W, .38
S & W Super Police, .38 British, and .38 Colt New Police Cartridges. It *must
not be confused* with weapons shooting the .38 S & W Special cartridge, which
is much more powerful and will not chamber in it.

Manufacturing Dates: October 1936.

Serial Numbers: Numbered in same series with .38 regulation Police model

Finish: Blue and nickel.

Barrel Length: 2″.

Land Diameter:	.350-.351	*Direction of Twist:*	Right
Groove Diameter:	.360-.361	*Length of Chamber:*	.724
Number of Lands:	5	*Diameter of Chamber:*	.388-.389
Twist: One turn in	18¾″	*Number of Chambers:*	5

Stocks: Round-butt grips or small square-butt regulation Police stocks.

Note: This revolver is often referred to as the ".38-32/2," meaning .38 caliber on a .32 frame with a two-inch barrel. It weighs only 17 ounces and measures 6¼ inches overall.

This is a powerful close-quarter weapon in which the recoil is not excessive. It is capable of very effective and accurate shooting at all reasonable pistol ranges. It is designed to afford enough room between trigger guard and stock to give ample gripping surface for average hands.

.38 S&W, S&W S.P., Colt N.P.   WEBLEY
Mark II, III, IV

The most modern and widely distributed of the Webley pocket revolvers are the Mark III .38's. One type of this revolver which employs all the patented Webley items of stirrup fastening, hollow-cylinder-axis mounting, lockwork, and cylinder fastening, is made with a six-shot cylinder to use the .38 Smith & Wesson cartridge or the new British .380 service cartridge (which is the same case as the .38 Smith & Wesson but with a heavier bullet). This weapon with a three-inch barrel weighs one pound and three ounces. It is also furnished in a four-inch barrel weighing one ounce more.

The Mark II .38 Police and Military model, with a larger and fuller hand grip, weighs one pound and four ounces when supplied with the four-inch barrel.

The Mark IV .38 Target model comes equipped with a six-inch barrel and weighs one pound and eight ounces. This model has a bead front sight and an adjustable wind gauge rear sight.

This weapon uses either the standard .38 Smith & Wesson cartridge with the 145-grain bullet, or the special British service cartridge, caliber .380, with a 200-grain bullet and 2.8 grains of powder. The muzzle velocity of the latter load is about 600 feet per second and the muzzle energy about 160 foot-pounds.

The weight of the Mark IV with five-inch barrel is one pound ten ounces (about one pound lighter than the .455). The theoretical shocking power as originally computed was practically the same as that of the .455. This theory has worked out so well in actual battle practice that British manufacturers now concentrate on this caliber.

It is to be remembered that the lock work and cylinder lock in this new Mark IV differs from that of all other Webley types.

MISCELLANEOUS   .38 S&W, S&W S.P., Colt N.P.
Weapons

This cartridge has never been greatly favored in Europe and comparatively few revolvers used there have ever been chambered for it. Large quantities have been made in Spain, however, for *export* to the United States, Mexico, and South America. The best are of only fair manufacture, while many are made of cast steel and are actually dangerous.

.38 Long and Short Colt

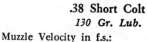

.38 Short Colt		.38 Long Colt	
130 Gr. Lub.		*150 Gr. Lub.*	
Muzzle Velocity in f.s.:	770	Muzzle Velocity in f.s.:	785
Vel. at 50 Feet:	758	Vel. at 50 Feet:	772
Vel. at 150 Feet:	734	Vel. at 150 Feet:	748
Calculated Energy		*Calculated Energy*	
Muzzle Energy in ft. lbs.:	171	Muzzle Energy in ft. lbs.:	205
Energy at 50 Feet:	165	Energy at 50 Feet:	199
Energy at 150 Feet:	155	Energy at 150 Feet:	187
Calculated Drop		*Calculated Drop*	
At 50 Feet:	.8 inch	At 50 Feet:	.8 inch
At 150 Feet:	7.0 inches	At 150 Feet:	7.2 inches
At 300 Feet:	38.0 inches	At 300 Feet:	31.0 inches
Penetration at 15 Feet		*Penetration at 15 Feet*	
7/8″ soft pine boards	4	7/8″ soft pine boards	6
Length of Barrel in Which Tested		*Length of Barrel in Which Tested*	
inches	6	inches	6
Shell Case		*Shell Case*	
Weight:	58 grains	Weight:	63.0 grains
Max. Length:	.763 inch	Max. Length:	1.035 inches
Outside Body Dia. at Head, Max.:	.379 inch	Outside Body Dia. at Head, Max.:	.379 inch
Outside Body Dia. at Neck, Max.:	.379 inch	Outside Body Dia. at Neck, Max.:	.378 inch
Inside Mouth Dia. Max.:	.3575 inch	Inside Mouth Dia. Max.:	.3585 inch
Volumetric Capacity to Base of Bullet		Volumetric Capacity to Base of Bullet	
in cubic inches:	.043	in cubic inches:	.051
Bullet		*Bullet*	
Weight:	130 grains	Weight:	150 grains
Approx. Length:	.550 inch	Approx. Length:	.700 inch
Diameter Max.:	.375 inch	Diameter Max.:	.359 inch
Area, Cross Sectional:	.110 square inch	Area, Cross Sectional:	.101 square inch
Shape:	Round Nose	Shape:	Round Nose
Powder		*Powder*	
Amount and type varies with different lots manufactured.		Amount and type varies with different lots manufactured.	
Cartridge		*Cartridge*	
Approx. Length, Loaded:	1,200 inches	Approx. Length, Loaded:	1.360 inches
Approx. Total Weight, Loaded:	191 grains	Approx. Total Weight, Loaded:	219 grains

Both of these cartridges are obsolescent. The .38 Short Colt is one of the earliest of the .38 Caliber center fire cartridges. The bullet weight is 125 or

130 grains lead and is outside lubricated. The .38 Long Colt, also a development of the early days, is an evolutionary step in the development of the superbly accurately .38 S&W Special and .38 Colt Special cartridges which followed it.

As the .38 Long Colt was an official United States service cartridge for some time, very large numbers of Colt and Smith & Wesson revolvers are in existence which will handle these cartridges but which will not take the later .38 Specials. The .38 Short Colt and .38 Long Colt cartridges may, however, be used in all revolvers chambered for the .38 S&W or Colt Special cartridges.

COLT   **.38 Long and Short Colt**
New Army, Navy, Marine

THE COLT NEW ARMY AND NAVY   *THE COLT D.A. MARINE CORPS*

General Description: This model on a .41 caliber frame (solid) introduced the swing out cylinder with simultaneous ejection and was the basis from which the modern Colt design was developed.

Ammunition: .32/20*, .38 L.C., .41 L.C., .38 Special.

Manufacturing Dates: 1889-1908.

Finish: Blue or Nickel.

	.32/20	.38 L.C.	.38 Special
Barrel Length:	3″	3″	6″
	4½″	4½″	
	6″	6″	

Stocks: Plain walnut; rubber. Checked walnut in the Marine Corps.

	.32/20	.38 L.C.	.38 Special
Bore Diameter:	.305″-.001	.350	.395″-.001
Groove Diameter:	.312″-.001	.357	.402″-.001

Rifling: (Left twist) 6 grooves. 1 turn in 16″.

Number of Shots: 6.

Action: Double.

Approximate Weight: About 34 oz.

Over-all Length: About 11″ with 6″ barrel.

---

* Model 1889 Navy and Model 1905 Marine not made in .32/20.

Sights: Fixed. Front: integral with barrel. Rear: groove and notch in top of frame.

Note: The original model had no bolt (or bolt cuts on the outside of the cylinder) until 1892 when a double bolt was incorporated. In 1889 this model was purchased for the Navy as a standard side arm and in 1892 it was adopted as a standard side arm by the United States Army. The New Navy and New Army differed only in markings and in stocks (as specified in Government contracts) but the New Navy was fitted with hard rubber stocks. In 1905 the New Marine Corps was first produced, differing only in having a rounded butt. Shipments of this design ran into 1910 although the production of the New Service (which really superseded the older model) began in 1909.

.38 Long and Short Colt   **COLT**

Officer's Target—New Army Frame

General Description: A target arm developed on the New Army frame with the same limb work (hand finished, however) and left hand revolution of the cylinder. This model was one of the first to allow fine adjustment of both front and rear sights by a lead or adjusting screw (as well as having a binding screw).

Ammunition: .38 Long Colt. .38 Special.

Manufacturing Dates: Began late in 1903. Went out of production during 1908.

Serial Numbers: From Number 1 to 300,000, concurrent with New Army.

Finish: Blue.

Barrel Length: 6".

Stocks: Checked walnut (no medallion).

Bore Diameter: .347"−.001. (See Note.)

Groove Diameter: .354"−.001. (See Note.)

Rifling: (Left twist). 6 grooves. 1 turn in 16".

Number of Shots: 6.

Action: Double.

Approximate Weight: 32 ounces.

Over-all Length: About 11".

Sights: Target. Front: adjustable for elevation. Rear: (with screw) for windage.

Note: Square latch—limb work similar to New Army. No drawings are available showing barrel dimensions for the .38 Long Colt. A hollow-base bullet was used and the best information available indicates a probable bore of .358" with a groove diameter of .365" although a groove diameter of .3605" was mentioned in print in 1904. (Probabilities are that at least three sets of dimensions were in use from 1889 to 1910).

The .38 Long Colt came into disrepute in the war in the Philippines (1898-1900) because of its inability to stop savage Moros. It is of considerable historical and design importance. Because of its lack of manstopping qualities—a lack which many feel could have been remedied by improving the cartridge design—the .38 Long doomed the medium-sized cartridge for U. S. Army use. It was supplanted by the .45.

In February, 1945, officials of the Colt factory unearthed a rare range plug bearing the date 9/1909 for this weapon. Its diameter is .349, which indicates a probable bore of .350 plus; with a groove diameter of .357 plus. A sample barrel of the same period checks at about these figures.

In the recent war Great Britain on a basis of field experience switched from .455 to .38 caliber. When it is remembered that every major fighting power except the U. S. is currently equipped with pistols and revolvers of .38 caliber or less, the significance of the original .38 Long Colt becomes at once apparent. The deep hollow-base bullet it fired was intended to expand enough when fired to take the rifling even though the bore diameter exceeded the bullet diameter.

SMITH AND WESSON
Hand Ejector M&P—First Model

.38 Long and Short Colt

Ammunition: .38 Long Colt or U. S. Service Cartridge—also some made commercially chambered for the .38 S & W Special, which was designed for this gun after the failure of the U. S. Service cartridge to stop the Moros in the Philippine fighting (1899).

Manufacturing Dates: Mar. 24, 1899-1902.

Number Manufactured: 21,000—including 2,000 for the U. S. Navy and 1,000 for the U. S. Army.

Serial Numbers: Started Military & Police numbering series in which all succeeding models have been numbered.

Finish: Blue and nickel.

Barrel Lengths: 4", 5", 6", 6½".

Shape of Butt: Round only.

Note: This was the first of the Military & Police series and did not have a locking bolt under the barrel.

Number of Lands:	5	*Number of Chambers:*	6
Direction of Twist:	Right		

CARTRIDGE
Data

.38 S&W Special, Colt Special

.38 Special

158 Gr. Lub.

Muzzle Velocity in f.s.:	870
Vel. at 50 Feet:	858
Vel. at 150 Feet:	833

Calculated Energy

Muzzle Energy in ft. lbs.:	266
Energy at 50 Feet:	261
Energy at 150 Feet:	247

Calculated Drop

At 50 Feet:	.6 inch
At 150 Feet:	6.1 inches
At 300 Feet:	24.6 inches

Penetration at 15 Feet

7/8" soft pine boards 7

Length of Barrel in Which Tested

inches 6

Shell Case

Weight:	62.5 grains
Max. Length:	1.155 inches
Outside Body Dia. at Head, Max.:	.379 inch
Outside Body Dia. at Neck, Max.:	.379 inch
Inside Mouth Dia. Max.:	.358 inch
Volumetric Capacity to Base of Bullet in cubic inches:	.063 inches

Bullet

Weight:	158 grains
Approx. Length:	.760 inch
Diameter Max.:	.359 inch
Area, Cross Sectional:	.101 square inch
Shape:	Round Nose

Powder

Amount and type varies with different lots manufactured.

Cartridge

Approx. Length, Loaded:	1.540 inches
Approx. Total Weight, Loaded:	227 grains

.38 Special Metal Piercing Super-X

150 Gr. M.P.

Muzzle Velocity in f.s.:	1175
Vel. at 50 Feet:	1140
Vel. at 150 Feet:	1083

Calculated Energy

Muzzle Energy in ft. lbs.:	460
Energy at 50 Feet:	433
Energy at 150 Feet:	391

Calculated Drop

At 50 Feet:	.35 inch
At 150 Feet:	3.3 inches
At 300 Feet:	14.6 inches

Penetration at 15 Feet

7/8" soft pine boards 11

Length of Barrel in Which Tested

inches 5

Shell Case

Weight:	62.5 grains
Max. Length:	1.155 inches
Outside Body Dia. at Head, Max.:	.379 inch
Outside Body Dia. at Neck, Max.:	.379 inch
Inside Mouth Dia. Max.:	.358 inch
Volumetric Capacity to Base of Bullet in cubic inches:	.064

Bullet

Weight:	150 grains
Approx. Length:	.725 inch
Diameter Max.:	.359 inch
Area, Cross Sectional:	.101 square inch
Shape:	Round Nose

Powder

Amount and type varies with different lots manufactured.

Cartridge

Approx. Length, Loaded:	1.540 inches
Approx. Total Weight, Loaded:	221 grains

<table>
<tr><td colspan="2">.38 Special Super-Match</td><td colspan="2">.38 Special</td></tr>
</table>

.38 Special Super-Match		.38 Special	
158 Gr. Lead		*158 Gr. M Pt.*	
Muzzle Velocity in f.s.:	845	Muzzle Velocity in f.s.:	870
Vel. at 50 Feet:	833	Vel. at 50 Feet:	858
Vel. at 150 Feet:	810	Vel. at 150 Feet:	833
Calculated Energy		*Calculated Energy*	
Muzzle Energy in ft. lbs.	251	Muzzle Energy in ft. lbs.:	266
Energy at 50 Feet:	242	Energy at 50 Feet:	261
Energy at 150 Feet:	230	Energy at 150 Feet:	247
Calculated Drop		*Calculated Drop*	
At 50 Feet:	.7 inch	At 50 Feet:	.6 inch
At 150 Feet:	6.4 inches	At 150 Feet:	6.1 inches
At 300 Feet:	26.7 inches	At 300 Feet:	24.6 inches
Penetration at 15 Feet		*Penetration at 15 Feet*	
7/8" soft pine boards	7	7/8" soft pine boards	7.5
Length of Barrel in Which Tested		*Length of Barrel in Which Tested*	
inches	6	inches	6
Shell Case		*Shell Case*	
Weight:	62.5 grains	Weight:	62.5 grains
Max. Length:	1.155 inches	Max. Length:	1.155 inches
Outside Body Dia. at Head, Max.:	.379 inch	Outside Body Dia. at Head, Max.:	.379 inch
Outside Body Dia. at Neck, Max.:	.379 inch	Outside Body Dia. at Neck, Max.:	.379 inch
Inside Mouth Dia. Max.:	.358 inch	Inside Mouth Dia. Max.:	.358 inch
Volumetric Capacity to Base of Bullet		Volumetric Capacity to Base of Bullet	
in cubic inches:	.061	in cubic inches:	.066
Bullet		*Bullet*	
Weight:	158 grains	Weight:	158 grains
Approx. Length:	.760 inch	Approx. Length:	.700 inch
Diameter Max.:	.359 inch	Diameter Max.:	.359 inch
Area, Cross Sectional:	.101 square inch	Area, Cross Sectional:	.101 square inch
Shape:	Round Nose	Shape:	Round Nose
Powder		*Powder*	
Amount and type varies with different lots manufactured.		Amount and type varies with different lots manufactured.	
Cartridge		*Cartridge*	
Approx. Length, Loaded:	1.540 inches	Approx. Length, Loaded:	1.540 inches
Approx. Total Weight, Loaded:	227 grains	Approx. Total Weight, Loaded:	227 grains

.38 Special Super—M.M.R.

148 Gr. Cl. Cut

Muzzle Velocity in f.s.:	770
Vel. at 50 Feet:	753
Vel. at 150 Feet:	720

Calculated Energy

Muzzle Energy in ft. lbs.:	195
Energy at 50 Feet:	188
Energy at 150 Feet:	172

Calculated Drop

At 50 Feet:	.8 inch
At 150 Feet:	7.9 inches
At 300 Feet:	33.1 inches

Penetration at 15 Feet

7/8" soft pine boards	7

Length of Barrel in Which Tested

inches	6

Shell Case

Weight:	62.5 grains
Max. Length:	1.155 inches
Outside Body Dia. at Head, Max.:	.379 inch
Outside Body Dia. at Neck, Max.:	.379 inch
Inside Mouth Dia. Max.:	.358 inch
Volumetric Capacity to Base of Bullet in cubic inches:	.037

Bullet

Weight:	148 grains
Approx. Length:	.660 inch
Diameter Max.:	.358 inch
Area, Cross Sectional:	.101 square inch
Shape:	Blunt Nose

Powder

Amount and type varies with different lots manufactured.

Cartridge

Approx. Length, Loaded:	1.190 inches
Approx. Total Weight, Loaded:	216 grains

.38 Special Super Police

200 Gr. Lub.

Muzzle Velocity in f.s.:	745
Vel. at 50 Feet:	737
Vel. at 150 Feet:	722

Calculated Energy

Muzzle Energy in ft. lbs.:	247
Energy at 50 Feet:	241
Energy at 150 Feet:	231

Calculated Drop

At 50 Feet:	.9 inch
At 150 Feet:	8.0 inches
At 300 Feet:	32.7 inches

Penetration at 15 Feet

7/8" soft pine boards	7.5

Length of Barrel in Which Tested

inches	6

Shell Case

Weight:	62.5 grains
Max. Length:	1.155 inches
Outside Body Dia. at Head, Max.:	.379 inch
Outside Body Dia. at Neck, Max.:	.379 inch
Inside Mouth Dia. Max.:	.358 inch
Volumetric Capacity to Base of Bullet in cubic inches:	.055

Bullet

Weight:	200 grains
Approx. Length:	.815 inch
Diameter Max.:	.359 inch
Area, Cross Sectional:	.101 square inch
Shape:	Round Nose

Powder

Amount and type varies with different lots manufactured.

Cartridge

Approx. Length, Loaded:	1.630 inches
Approx. Total Weight, Loaded:	271 grains

These cartridges are among the most accurate ever developed. They are interchangeable and may be used in any revolver chambered for the .38 Special or in revolvers chambered for the .357 Magnum, which is merely an over-length variety of the .38 Special.

The heavy-duty loads of the .38-44 and .38 Special High Velocity type should not be used in early patterns or lightweight types of .38 Special revolvers. Although they will chamber, their use should be confined to revolvers on .44 or .45 frames.

The ballistic data preceding was specially developed by the Western Cartridge Company for this book and the names given the different types are strictly trade names. All other major cartridge manufacturers produce a wide range of cartridges in .38 Special caliber under various trade names. The ballistics for the same load types are very much alike.

.38 S&W Special, Colt Special

COLT
Army Special

General Description: A holster arm (built on a .41 caliber frame) replacing the New Army and New Navy but of a different design including right-hand revolution of the cylinder.

Ammunition: .32/20. .38 Special. .41 Long Colt.

Manufacturing Dates: July 10, 1908 until replaced by Official Police about March 1, 1928.

Serial Numbers: From Number 300,000—continuing numbers from the New Army model.

Finish: Blue or Nickel.

Barrel Length: 4", 4½", 5", 6", all calibers.

Stocks: Rubber.

416

	.32/20	.38 Special	.41 Long Colt
Bore Diameter:	.305″—.001	.347″—.001	.395″—.001
Groove Diameter:	.312″—.001	.354″—.001	.402″—.001

Rifling: (Left twist). 6 grooves. 1 turn in 16″. All calibers.
Number of Shots: 6. All calibers.
Action: Double.
Approximate Weight: 4″ barrel, 32 ounces.
Over-all Length: About 11¼″ with 6″ barrel.
Sights: Fixed. Front: integral with barrel. Rear: groove with notch in top of frame.
Note: The frame of this model was slightly heavier than that of the New Army, the latch rounded, a loose firing pin used and the limb work adapted from designs developed in the New Service model.

COLT
Official Police (Model E)   .38 S&W Special, Colt Special

General Description: A holster arm on a .41 caliber frame. A continuation of the Army Special with refinements in design including checked walnut stocks, checked trigger, a square cut rear sight notch of the Patridge type and a matted, dull-finished top strap.
Ammunition: .32/20. .38 Special. .22 L.R. (from 2/11/1930).
Manufacturing Dates: About March 1, 1928 to date.
Serial Numbers: Continued with numbers of Army Special at about Number 520,000.
Finish: Blue (Standard in .22 L.R.) or Nickel.

	.32/20	.38 Special	.22 L.R.
Barrel Length:	4″	2″	6″
	5″	4″	
	6″	5″	
		6″	

Stocks: Checked walnut plastic.

	.32/20	.38 Special	.22 L.R.
Bore Diameter:	.305″—.001	.347″—.001	.215″—.001
Groove Diameter:	.312″—.001	.354″—.001	.222″—.001

Rifling: (Left twist). 6 grooves. .32/20 and .38, 1 turn in 16″. .22 L.R., 1 turn in 14″.
Number of Chambers: 6.
Action: Double.
Approximate Weight: With 6″ barrels: .38, 34 ounces. .22, 38 ounces.
Over-all Length: 11¼″ with 6″ barrel.
Sights: Fixed, with many special widths supplied up to .125″.
Note: Many of this model have been produced in .38 caliber with a heavy 6″ barrel, weighing approximately 38 ounces. In .22 caliber this model first used a conventional cylinder, then a design with a recessed head. For the rim-fire cartridge, adaptations include a recoil plate and a hammer with a solid or fixed firing pin. When fitted with a 2″ barrel most arms shipped have had a rounded butt.

.38 S&W Special, Colt Special

COLT
Commando

General Description: An adaptation of the Colt Official Police revolver to Government specifications to care for the needs of peace officers, etc., under wartime conditions. Production limited to Government orders.

Ammunition: .38 Special.

Manufacturing Dates: From November 12, 1942-1945.

Serial Numbers: From Number 1.

Finish: Blue on sandblasted surface.

Barrel Length: 4"; 2".

Stocks: Plastic.

Bore Diameter: .347"—.001.

Groove Diameter: .354"—.001.

Rifling: (Left twist). 6 grooves. 1 turn in 16".

Number of Shots: 6.

Action: Double.

Approximate Weight: With 4" barrel, 32 ounces. With 2" barrel, 30 ounces.

Over-all Length: 9¼" with 4" barrel.

Sights: Fixed.

.38 S&W Special, Colt Special

COLT
Officer's Target

For details see under Cal. .22 L.R. For working drawings and description of mechanism see under Caliber .45 A.C.P.

.38 S&W Special, Colt Special

COLT
Police Positive Special (Mod. D)

General Description: A square-butt arm on a .38 caliber frame designed to allow the use of ammunition as powerful as the .38 Special (including high-speed loads) with a minimum of weight. This combination has a wide appeal to watchmen, messengers, guards and peace officers.

Ammunition: .32/20, .38 Special, .32 Colt New Police and S&W.

Manufacturing Dates: From 1907.

COLT .38 OFFICERS' MODEL TARGET REVOLVER WITH HEAVY BARREL

COLT .38 DETECTIVE SPECIAL (POLICE POSITIVE SPECIAL)

Finish: Blue or Nickel.

	.32/20	.38 Spcl.
Barrel Length:	4″	2″
	5″	4″
	6″	5″
		6″

Stocks: Rubber. Checked walnut with medallion (both wide and narrow butt plates), plastic.

	.32/20	*.38 Spcl.*
Bore Diameter:	.305"—.001	.347"—.001
Groove Diameter:	.312".—.001	.354"—.001

Rifling: (Left twist). 6 grooves. 1 turn in 16".
Number of Shots: 6.
Action: Double.
Approximate Weight: .38 with 4" barrel: 22 ounces.
Over-all Length: 8¾" with 4" barrel.
Sights: Fixed. Front: integral with barrel. Rear: groove and notch in top strap.

Note: Since introduction, this model with no change in its basic design, has acquired many refinements. The rubber stocks gave way to checked walnut, the narrow butt was followed by a wider, fuller butt allowing a better grip; current design calls for a checked trigger. The front sight is wider while the top strap is now matted with a dull finish and the rear sight notch is of the square cut Patridge type.

The Detective Special, dating from 1926, is a development of this model. To meet the peculiar need of detectives and peace officers not in uniform this frame was fitted with a 2" barrel and a shortened ejector rod. Following this a rounded butt with checked walnut stocks to match became standard. As first produced, it had a square butt.

.38 S&W Special, Colt Special   **COLT**
                                                       Miscellaneous

New Service, Shooting Master and S. A. Army. See under Cal. .45 Colt for photos and data.

.38 S&W Special, Colt Special   **SMITH AND WESSON**
                                                  Hand Ejector M&P 1902

Official Model Name: Model .38 Hand Ejector Military & Police (Second Model, 1902).
Model .38 Hand Ejector Military & Police (Model of 1902—First Change).
Ammunition: .38 S & W Special.
Manufacturing Dates: Model of 1902—1902—Oct. 27, 1903.
First Change—Oct. 27, 1903—May 1905.
Number Manufactured: Model of 1902—About 14,000.
First Change—About 28,645.
Serial Numbers: Numbered in the Military & Police series.
Finish: Blue and nickel.
Barrel Lengths: 4", 5", 6", 6½".
Shape of Butt: Model of 1902—Round butt only.
Model of 1902—First Change—Round butt and also Square butt from Nov. 18, 1904 on.

S&W .38 CAL. HAND EJEC. M&P (2ND MOD., 1902)

Design Changes: The Model of 1902 differed from the First Model principally in that the locking bolt was installed under the barrel.

Model of 1902—First Change—differed principally in that the outside diameter of the barrel was increased at the rear.

Land Diameter:	.346-.3472	*Direction of Twist:*	Right
Groove Diameter:	.3555-.3572	*Length of Chamber:*	1.105
Number of Lands:	5	*Diameter of Chamber*	.380-.381
Twist: One turn in	18¾″	*Number of Chambers:*	6

SMITH AND WESSON   .38 S&W Special, Colt Special
Hand Ejector M&P 1905

Official Model Name: Model .38 Hand Ejector Military & Police (Model of 1905).

Model .38 Hand Ejector Military & Police (Model of 1905—First Change).

Model .38 Hand Ejector Military & Police (Model of 1905—Second Change).

Model .38 Hand Ejector Military & Police (Model of 1905—Third Change).

Model .38 Hand Ejector Military & Police (Model of 1905—Fourth Change).

Ammunition: .38 S & W Special. The following cartridges may be used in all these weapons: .38 Short Colt and .38 Colt Special; .38 S & W Special, .38 S & W Special Mid Range, and .38 S & W Special Super Police.

Manufacturing Dates: Model of 1905—May 1905-Feb. 1906.

First Change—Feb. 1906, Uncertain.

Second Change—Sept. 14, 1909, Uncertain.

Third Change—Sept. 14, 1909-Apr. 20, 1915.

Fourth Change—Apr. 20, 1915.

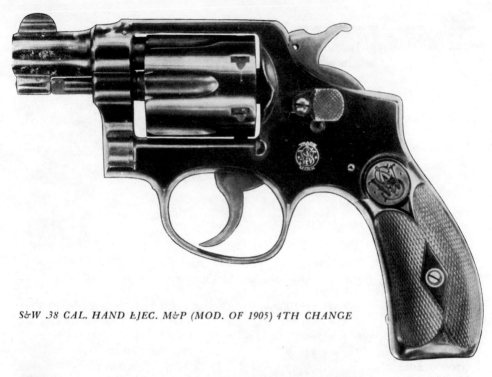

S&W .38 CAL. HAND EJEC. M&P (MOD. OF 1905) 4TH CHANGE

S&W HAND EJEC. M&P (MOD. OF 1905—4TH CHANGE)

Serial Numbers: All models numbered in same series.

Finish: Blue and nickel.

Barrel Lengths: 4″, 5″, 6″, 6½″ on all models except the **Fourth Change** which had 2″, 4″, 5″, 6″ barrels and Model 1905 which had 4″, 5″, and 6½″ barrels.

Shape of Butt: Round and Square.

Principal Design Changes: Model of 1905—Reciprocating—stop design.

First Change—Rebound slide installed.

Second Change—Rebound slide key eliminated; extractor doweled and positioned by two pins.

Third Change—Double action off hammer point instead of sear; extractor knob solid with rod instead of screwed on.

Fourth Change—Chaffing pins removed from hammer and trigger; only one extractor positioning pin used.

Changes in the Model of 1905-Fourth Change: First hammer block (leaf spring operated by plunger pushed back by rear face of hand) installed in square-butt service guns beginning April 20, 1915. Installed in round-butt service guns beginning July 1, 1926. Installed in target guns beginning June 2, 1926.

Second hammer block (leaf spring operated by ramp on hand) installed in all types from December 1926.

Square service sights with flat top strap instead of thin front blade and U-notch rear sight introduced April 1, 1922. This was the first revolver made with this type of service sight which was quickly adopted by other leading manufacturers.

Grooved front and rear butt tangs on target guns beginning August 14, 1923.

Grooved finger piece on trigger for all models beginning August 14, 1923.

First 2-inch gun made about July 1933.

Heat-treated cylinders from 1919 on.

Model .38 Hand Ejector Military & Police revolver is the largest-selling quality revolver ever made—over 2,500,000 have been manufactured to August 1959.

Land Diameter:	.346-.3472	*Direction of Twist:*	Right
Groove Diameter:	.3555-.3572	*Length of Chamber:*	1.105
Number of Lands:	5	*Diameter of Chamber:*	.380-.381
Twist: One turn in	18¾"	*Number of Chambers:*	6

Note: Weight of .38 M & P square butt with 6" barrel is 31 ounces. Overall length 11⅛". The .38 M & P target model is 32¼ ounces. The .38 M & P round butt with 6" barrel measures 10⅞" overall and weighs 30½ ounces.

SMITH AND WESSON
.38 S&W Special, Colt Special
.38/44 Hand Ejector

Official Model Name: Model .38/44 Caliber Hand Ejector. Service gun known as .38/44 Heavy Duty. Target gun known as .38-44 Outdoorsman.

Ammunition: Chambered for the .38 S & W Special, .38 Short Colt and .38 Colt Special, .38 S & W Special Mid Range, and .38 S & W Special Super Police cartridges. In 1931, in cooperation with Remington Arms Co. and Mr. Elmer Keith, a special high-powered cartridge called the .38-44 S & W Special was developed for this gun. During the late 1930's, the .38-44 designation was dropped and these heavy loads became generally known as the .38 Special Hi-Speed.

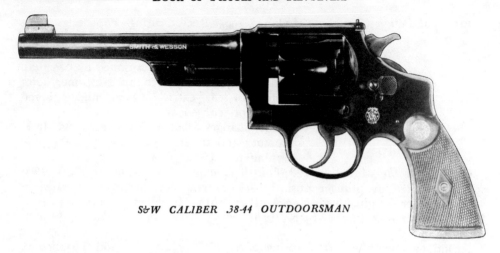

S&W CALIBER .38-44 OUTDOORSMAN

Manufacturing Dates: From April 1, 1930-1941.

Serial Numbers: Numbered in the .44 Hand Ejector Series from about 35,037 on.

Finish: Blue or nickel.

Barrel Lengths: Service gun, 5″, 6½″. Target gun 6½″.

Land Diameter:	.346-.347	*Direction of Twist:*	Right
Groove Diameter:	.356-.357	*Length of Chamber:*	1.105
Number of Lands:	5	*Diameter of Chambers:*	.380-.381
Twist: One turn in	18¾″	*Number of Chambers:*	6

Sights: On Heavy Duty Model—Square-notch rear, cut in top of frame, 1/10″ service-type solid front sight.

On Outdoorsman Model—Square-notch rear, adjustable for elevation and windage. 1/10″ or ⅛″ Patridge front sight.

Weight: Heavy Duty Model with 5″ barrel and over-all length of 10⅜″ weighs 40 ounces. Outdoorsman Model with 6½″ barrel and over-all length of 11¾″ weighs 41¾ ounces.

Note: The designation ".38-44" here means a revolver to shoot .38 Special cartridges, built on the frame of the S & W heavy .44 caliber target revolver.

Where the standard .38 S & W Special cartridge today develops a muzzle velocity of 870 feet per second and a muzzle striking energy of 266 foot pounds, the .38 S & W Special Hi-Speed (or .38 S & W Special-X as Western Cartridge Company designates it) has a muzzle velocity of 1175 feet per second and a striking energy at the muzzle of 460 foot pounds.

Because of this terrific increase in power, these Hi-Speed cartridges should not be used in lighter-frame revolvers.

Also, because of this increased power, the rear sight on the Outdoorsman Model—which is adjustable—is fitted with a special setscrew just ahead of the adjusting screw. Without this setscrew to hold it firmly in place, the adjusting screw would soon be jarred loose from its setting by the shock of the explosions.

The standard .38 S & W cartridges may be used in this model with the same sight adjustment as the Hi-Speed cartridges up to about 20 yards. For shooting a greater distance, the lower-powered .38 S & W Special cartridges will require more elevation of the sights than will the Hi-Speeds, because of the great variance in velocities.

The Outdoorsman will safely handle the entire range of ammunition for which it is chambered from low to ultra-high power.

SMITH AND WESSON .38 S&W Special, Colt Special
S&W Hand Ejector Operation and Construction

Note: Except for manufacturing details as noted under the individual models, this section covers generally all S & W swing-out-cylinder-type revolvers.

The four principal parts of this revolver are the frame, cylinder assembly, barrel, and the action (or lockwork).

The barrel is screwed into the solid frame by a right-hand thread. A pin is driven laterally through the frame when the barrel is seated and engages in a U-notch in the top surface of the barrel to lock and align it properly.

The cylinder has six chambers bored about a central axis. The extractor assembly passes down through the center of the cylinder.

The front sight is machined on the barrel. It is semicircular in shape, has a square section front and a flat top. The rear sight is a square notch cut in the rear of the top strap of the frame directly in front of the hammer.

A detachable side plate is fitted on the right-hand side of the frame. It is held in position by four screws. Removing these screws permits the plate to be lifted off for cleaning, stripping, and assembling. The front side plate screw also holds the yoke (the crane on which the cylinder is swung out of the frame).

Cocking the revolver, either single or double action, revolves the cylinder enough to align a cartridge chamber with the barrel.

There are no manual safeties on this weapon. When the cylinder is closed, the revolver is ready to be fired.

Operation: Push forward the thumbpiece on the left side of the frame below the hammer. This forces the attached bolt forward so that its nose presses through its hole in the frame behind the cylinder and forces the center pin mounted in the extractor rod ahead.

This pressure is transmitted to the center pin and pushes the locking bolt *at the front end* back into its mounting lug on the bottom of the barrel just ahead of the frame. This disengages it from the extractor rod.

While this pressure is maintained on the thumbpiece, the cylinder is free and can be pushed out on the swinging yoke or crane. Press from the right side and it will swing out to the left.

When the cylinder is open in this weapon, the bolt spring holds the bolt forward and the rear portion of the bolt engages under the rear edge of the hammer to prevent the revolver from being cocked. This built-in safety feature prevents the revolver from being fired unless the cylinder is fully closed and locked.

The cylinder is loaded with six cartridges and then is pressed back into the

425

frame. As the center pin spring has more tension than the bolt spring, pushing the cylinder in forces the end of the center pin back into the slot in the frame thereby pushing the bolt itself completely back into the frame.

At the same instant, the locking bolt engages in the *head* of the extractor rod to assist in locking and aligning the cylinder when the cylinder is turned by the lifter which is called the "hand" during cocking.

Thus when the cylinder is fully closed, the rear portion of the bolt is forced back out of engagement with the rear edge of the hammer, permitting the weapon to be cocked and fired.

Single-action firing: When the hammer is pulled back with the thumb to its full extent, the bent of the trigger is engaged with the front end of the lower part of the hammer. This action also revolves the cylinder *the distance of one chamber.* It also tensions the mainspring.

Pressing the trigger releases the bent of the trigger from the bent of the hammer and permits the hammer to be driven forward under tension of the mainspring. The rebound slide permits the hammer to fall fully and strike the cartridge.

Double-action firing: The full sequence of the locking and revolving action is as follows:

As the trigger is pressed its upper edge engages the sear and lifts the hammer until the bent of the trigger comes in contact with the bent of the hammer. The hammer continues to rise until it is almost in full-cock position, when it disengages from the trigger and falls under the pressure of the mainspring.

As the trigger goes back, the rebound slide is pushed to the rear to a point where a lug on the top surface of the rebound slide is back far enough to keep the lug on the hammer from coming in contact with it. This permits the hammer to fall forward its entire distance and fire the cartridge in the chamber.

While the trigger is cocking the hammer, a lug on the upper front edge of the trigger engages in the slot in the cylinder stop forcing it downward against the pressure of the cylinder stop spring and plunger.

This pulls the nose of the cylinder stop out of the notch in the cylinder directly above the bottom of the frame, freeing it so the cylinder can be rotated.

The "hand" pivoted to the trigger swings on its pin and is pressed through its slot in the frame to engage in the ratchet on the head of the extractor.

This action rotates the cylinder from *right to left* the distance of one chamber for each pull of the trigger, as the tip of the hand forces up against the ratchet on the head of the extractor.

There is an inclined ramp machined on the hand. This engages the lug on the hammer block. As the hand moves upward, this inclined ramp forces the hammer block out of its resting place between the forward face of the hammer and the frame. This removes the obstruction, *which is a safety,* and permits the hammer to fall and strike the cartridge. Note that this arrangement *positively prevents the cartridge from being fired unless the trigger is deliberately pulled through the entire length necessary.* If the hammer slips while being cocked it is impossible for it to strike the cartridge.

The trigger continues its movement to the rear and the cylinder stop is released from the trigger. The trigger stop spring reasserts itself, forcing the nose of the cylinder stop upward through the bottom of the frame into the recess in the cylinder ready to receive it. This point is reached when the hand has turned the cylinder far enough to align the cartridge chamber with the barrel.

Observe that when the hammer falls, the cylinder stop is locking the cylinder firmly from below while the hand engaged with the ratchet is locking it from above; this serves to keep the axis of the firing chamber in alignment with the axis of the barrel bore.

As finger pressure on the trigger is released, the rebound slide spring presses against the rebound slide to force the trigger ahead to firing position.

The lug on the top edge of the rebound slide bears against the lug on the lower edge of the hammer; this pushes the hammer back into the frame until the firing pin is withdrawn within the frame itself.

The inclined ramp on the hand permits the hammer block to move forward into position between the front face of the hammer and the frame, when the hand is pulled downward by the trigger.

Unloading: The cylinder is swung out to the left on its crane or yoke and the head of the extractor rod is pushed directly to the rear.

As the teeth of the extractor are engaged behind the rims of the cartridges in the cylinder this action lifts them up out of the chambers and ejects them. This pressure by the hand on the extractor rod also compresses the spring wound around the rod so that when the pressure is released, the spring pulls the extractor back into place. The extractor teeth fit into the recesses machined in the top face of the cylinder for them. The fixing pin attached to the cylinder, which serves to keep the extractor in perfect alignment at all times, seats in the hole drilled for it in the head of the extractor.

Dismounting: The only dismounting that should normally be done to this weapon by the amateur is removing the side plate screw to permit removing the side plate for oiling and cleaning.

For the benefit of the gunsmith, however, the following instructions are given:

1. The front side plate screw on the right side of the frame is also the cylinder locking screw. Its end is filed. This is to identify it so that when the weapon is reassembled the proper screw may be inserted in this particular hole.

2. Swing the cylinder out to the left and holding the cylinder by its rear end, pull the yoke (or crane) forward and it will disengage from the frame.

3. Partially unscrew the stock screw from the left. When it is free from the right-hand stock, bend it slightly and push back against the right-hand stock which will then come off the frame. (This prevents marring the frame as will occur if you pry the stock off.) Now push the left-hand stock screw from the inside and the left stock will come off.

4. The three remaining side plate screws are removed and the pistol held with the side plate uppermost, tapping lightly on the rear tang of the frame

with a wooden block will jar the side plate off. If the plate is pried off the frame, it will usually be scratched or marred.

5. The *strain screw* is inserted in the grip on the inside surface near the bottom. Unscrew this and the mainspring against which it presses may be lifted out of its base in the bottom of the grip and then disengaged from the top engagement with the hammer.

6. Pull the trigger about halfway back and the hammer may be lifted off the hammer stud.

7. Driving out the sear pin will permit the removal of the sear and sear spring from the hammer.

8. Driving out the stirrup pin will permit removal of the stirrup from the hammer.

9. Lift the rebound slide and spring until the rear section clears the rebound slide stud. This should be done with a screw driver. The blade should be placed vertically in the rear of the rebound slide alongside the stud; and upward leverage applied by using the inside of the rear tang of the frame as the resting point (or fulcrum). This is advisable so that when the rebound slide and the spring come up above this stud, the head of the screw driver will keep the spring from jumping out of the slide.

10. Draw the hand to the rear out of its slot and the complete trigger and hand assembly may be lifted off the trigger guard.

11. Pull the hand off the trigger. (When reassembling this unit, the *rear* of the hand lever must be pushed upward above the pin on the hand before the hand is reinserted into the trigger.)

12. Punch out the hand lever pin and remove the hand lever and spring.

13. Punch out the trigger lever pin and remove the trigger lever.

14. Press the cylinder stop down into the frame and lift off the stop stud. While this may be done with a screw driver without removing the cylinder stop screw, spring and plunger, it will usually be found simpler to remove the parts first and then shake the stop until it falls off its stud.

15. Remove the screw in the thumbpiece. Then push the bolt to the rear and lift it out. The bolt plunger and spring may now be withdrawn.

16. Plunger and spring must be removed carefully, as they are free to fly out of the bolt as soon as it is lifted from the frame. They are easily lost.

17. Loosen the extractor rod and the cylinder assembly may be dismounted. (When reassembling this unit, note that the extractor spring is tapered and *be sure the large end goes on the extractor first.* If you cannot determine easily which is the larger end, roll the spring on a level surface and observe which end travels further.)

18. Driving out the locking bolt pin from its lug under the barrel will permit the locking bolt and spring to be withdrawn.

19. The barrel cannot be removed except by a competent gunsmith or armorer in a properly equipped shop.

If the barrel retaining pin is drifted out of its seat in the forward end of the frame, and the frame is properly supported in a clamp or vise, the barrel may then be unscrewed from the frame.

Again it should be emphasized that this is normally a factory job. Even the most skilled mechanics at the factory with the most modern of equipment must give long and careful attention to proper alignment of barrel in order to assure proper accuracy.

COLT AND SMITH & WESSON
Miscellaneous Weapons
.38 S&W Special, Colt Special

The Smith & Wesson .357 Magnum Revolver (and Colt Revolvers for the .357 cartridge) will handle all .38 Special loads. The .357 Magnum cartridge is really a .38 Special caliber, with the case up to .135" longer, to prevent it being used in .38 Special revolvers. Some old .38 Special guns have chambers bored completely through the cylinder without a shoulder. These revolvers are apt to be wrecked if .357 Magnum loads are fired in them.

EUROPEAN
Revolvers
.38 S&W Special, Colt Special

The Belgian firm of Bayard manufactured imitations of standard .38 S&W swing-out cylinder revolvers for this cartridge. While decidedly inferior in workmanship and finish to American makes, these are reliable revolvers which have been officially proofed.

German firms, notably L. Loewe, manufactured revolvers for this cartridge principally in hinged-frame imitations of S&W revolvers. These arms while of good material and workmanship should not be used with modern high-velocity ammunition because of the comparatively weak type of lock employed.

Spanish manufacturers have produced enormous quantities of revolvers for this cartridge in imitations of Colt S.A. Army and swing-out cylinder and of S&W hinged-frame and swing-out cylinder models. They have also produced various modifications including a double action resembling the Colt S.A. Army in appearance and ejection.

.380 ACP

.380 Automatic

.380 AUTOMATIC

95 Gr. M.C.

Muzzle Velocity in f.s.:	970
Vel. at 50 Feet:	944
Vel. at 150 Feet:	896

Calculated Energy

Muzzle Energy in ft. lbs.:	199
Energy at 50 Feet:	187
Energy at 150 Feet:	168

Calculated Drop

At 50 Feet:	.5 inch
At 150 Feet:	5.0 inches
At 300 Feet:	21.6 inches

Penetration at 15 Feet

7/8" soft pine boards   5.5

Length of Barrel in Which Tested

inches   3¾

Shell Case

Weight:	51.8 grains
Max. Length:	.680 inch
Outside Body Dia. at Head, Max.:	.374 inch
Outside Body Dia. at Neck, Max.:	.373 inch
Inside Mouth Dia. Max.:	.3555 inch
Volumetric Capacity to Base of Bullet	
in cubic inches:	.031

Bullet

Weight:	95 grains
Approx. Length:	.460 inch
Diameter Max.:	.356 inch
Area, Cross Sectional:	.0995 square inch
Shape:	Round Nose

Powder

Amount and type varies with different lots manufactured.

Cartridge

Approx. Length, Loaded:	.984 inch
Approx. Total Weight, Loaded:	150.5 grains

This cartridge was originally introduced in Europe by F. N. of Belgium as the 9mm. Browning Short. It is extensively used in Europe, where it is usually known by the original name. In Italy it is a popular military cartridge under the name of 9mm. Corto. The European varieties differ from the American only very slightly and will chamber and usually function satisfactorily, while American ammunition may be used in all European types designed for the 9mm. Browning short cartridge. This is a desirable automatic pistol cartridge because the weapons in which it is generally used weigh practically the same as those designed for the less effective .32 A.C.P. cartridge. This may be classed as the smallest truly effective autoloading pistol caliber for general service.

ASTRA   .380 ACP
300

   For photograph and specifications of this model, see the Identification Section.   For working drawing see Astra under Caliber 9mm. Bayard Long, as
this light model is a smaller version of the heavy army type.   This is the best
of the Spanish modifications of the Browning designs.

BAYARD   .380 ACP
Automatics 1911, 1923 and 1930

   The Bayard was produced by one of the best European manufacturers, the
Anciens Establissements Pieper at Herstal, Belgium.   It was patented in Belgium in 1905-07. The original model has a 2¼-inch barrel, measures 4⅞ inches
overall, weighs 17 ounces.
   This weapon is noteworthy as being the smallest, most compact, and lightest
.380 caliber automatic pistol ever built.   In the .380 caliber the magazine
capacity is 6 cartridges (this weapon was also made in .32 caliber with a magazine capacity of 6 cartridges). It is a straight blowback pistol fitted with a
powerful recoil spring to hold the breech closed at the instant of firing.   The
magazine release catch is in the bottom of the grip.   The name Bayard appears
on each hard rubber grip. A thumb safety is provided on the left-hand side of

the receiver. When drawn back it exposes the word "SUR" (safe). When the thumbpiece is pushed forward to cover this word, the weapon is ready to fire.

An unusual feature of this weapon is the barrel which is bored in the front part of the receiver directly above the line of the trigger guard.

This weapon is loaded as is the conventional Colt by inserting a loaded magazine in the handle then pulling the slide back and releasing it to chamber the first cartridge and cock the gun. It is fitted with the usual disconnector to prevent firing more than one shot for each pull of the trigger.

The recoil in this pistol is very great and a special buffer arrangement is used to cushion the shock. The front sight locks the slide. Pushing it back and raising it slightly permits it to be removed from the slide together with the slide spring. The slide may then be drawn back fully and lifted out of its guide out of the receiver.

The 1923 and 1930 modifications of this model are somewhat heavier and of better construction. (See Identification Section for photos and details.)

While large numbers of these weapons were imported into the U. S., the weapon is much better known in Europe and in Central and South America than it is in this country.

BERETTA 9mm.   .380 ACP
1934

This is simple blowback weapon of excellent design and very fine workmanship. No locking device is necessary on a weapon of this size when used
with this cartridge.

Construction: The main parts of this pistol are the receiver (which extends
forward well beyond the front of the trigger guard and which is provided with
guides to receive the slide), the slide, lockwork, and the barrel.

The handle of the receiver is hollowed out to receive the magazine which is
inserted from below in standard fashion.

The magazine catch is at the bottom of the butt at the rear.

A lanyard swivel is provided just above the butt catch on the left side of
the receiver.

The magazine is unusual in that it has a finger spur protruding from the
front end to permit a better grip for those with large hands.

The barrel is solidly mounted. A lug on its underside fits down into a well
recessed for it in the receiver. Its forward end is supported by a slide which
is cut away at a point directly behind the front sight all the way back to the

point at which it becomes the breechlock of the weapon, extending from the firing chamber backwards.

A very simple and effective lockwork system is provided in this weapon.

The mainspring is a coil spring housed in the grip behind the magazine well.

A thumb safety is mounted on the left side of the receiver directly above the line of the trigger. Rotating it to the rear sets it on safe. When in the safe position, a small green ball or dot is usually discernible on the side of the receiver. When the safety is pushed forward so it is in the fire position, a red ball is exposed as a warning of danger. The colors wear off in time, hence this warning system is not infallible.

The hammer is of the exposed type and of poor shape for speedy cocking.

The front sight is a part of the slide. The rear sight is mounted in the slide. No adjustment is possible.

The recoil spring and its guide are housed in the receiver and in a small abutment below the front end of the slide.

This weapon is fitted with a positive and simple disconnector which prevents the trigger from hooking up with the sear to release the hammer until the slide is in the fully forward position.

Operation: The functioning is standard for the blowback type of automatic pistol. The slide is driven to the rear by pressure of gases inside the empty cartridge case as the bullet goes down the barrel. Pressure transmitted to the breechblock face of the slide, pushes the slide back to ride over the hammer and cock the weapon, the sear catching in the cocking notch to hold it. The slide rides over the disconnector to disconnect the trigger from the sear mechanism.

The recoil spring is compressed as its rod protrudes through the hole in the front end of the slide below the line of the barrel and the spring itself is pushed back on this rod which is supported in a recess in the rear of the receiver.

The extractor carries the empty cartridge case back with it to strike against the ejector, which hurls it out of the weapon.

The magazine spring forces the next cartridge up into line with the breechblock as the slide travels back over the top of the magazine.

As the slide is pushed forward by the expanding recoil spring, the breechblock face strips a cartridge from the magazine and loads it in the firing chamber where the extractor snaps over its head.

When the breechblock reaches its fully forward position and the trigger is released, the disconnector can rise under spring pressure into its slot in the underside of the slide. This completes the hookup between trigger and hammer to permit firing the next shot.

When the last shot has been fired, the magazine follower rises to hold the weapon open. When the magazine is withdrawn, (and it requires considerable force and the use of both hands to pull it out) the slide is freed and runs forward automatically to close on the empty chamber.

When a new magazine is inserted, it is necessary to draw the slide fully to the rear and release it before the chamber is again loaded for firing.

The manual safety on this weapon is not really secure, as it locks the trigger

Basic Model Data

AUTOMATIC PISTOL: Italian Beretta 1934.

LENGTH: 6 inches.

BARREL: 3½ inches.

WEIGHT: 20 ounces.

MAGAZINE: Detachable box, catch in rear of butt, capacity 7 cartridges.

OPERATION: Blowback unlocked.

MAINSPRING: Coil in butt operating through hammer strut.

DISCONNECTOR: Elevation on trigger bar depressed as slide opens to move away from sear.

TRIGGER: Stirrup type acting across magazine well.

SAFETY: Thumb safety on receiver. Does not block hammer.

RECOIL SPRING: Mounted with guide in receiver below barrel.

BARREL: Mounted securely in receiver by lug and supported by slide. Removable.

FIRING MECHANISM: External hammer. Flying firing pin in breechblock.

CALIBER: 380 A.C.P. (9mm. Short). Also as the Model 1935 made for 32 A.C.P.

Drawing shows left side completely sectioned to show parts in repose.

Slide cut away to show detail of barrel mounting and recoil spring operation. Parts in full recoil. Note that disconnector arm is forced down by slide breaking trigger engagement with sear which is holding hammer at full cock.

BERETTA barrel removal.

but does *not* lock the hammer. Thus it is possible, with the safety catch on, to draw the hammer back to full cock with the thumb. No pistol is really safe to carry fully cocked with a cartridge in the firing chamber unless the hammer is positively blocked.

The Beretta disconnector, on the other hand, *is* a positive device. Its upper tongue protrudes through the grip on the left side of the receiver and rises into and moves backwards in a groove in the underside of the flange on the left side of the slide as the trigger is pressed. When the slide is not fully forward, this connector tongue cannot rise but can only move backward. This disconnects the trigger from the sear which holds the hammer at full cock.

Dismounting: First, remove the magazine. Then draw the slide back and glance in the chamber to check that it is empty.

2. Turn the safety catch up to the rear or "safe" position.

3. Hold the pistol in the right hand. Push the slide back as far as it will go, using the left hand. When it is in its fully rear position, it will force the safety catch to jump up into a notch on the lower edge of the left side of the slide. This will hold the slide in rear position.

4. Holding the pistol firmly in the right hand, with the heel of the left hand

437

push the barrel straight to the rear to disengage its locking lug from the recess in the receiver. It may now be lifted up by its breech end out of the long slot in the top of the slide.

5. Still holding the pistol in the right hand, grip the side of the slide firmly with the left hand and with the left thumb push the safety catch down to the fully forward or "fire" position. This will release the slide and permit it to come forward on the receiver guides and off to the front.

6. The recoil spring and its rod may now be removed.

7. The safety catch can be shaken out of the left side of the receiver.

8. Removing the stocks will expose the lockwork for cleaning or necessary repairs. This pistol is so sturdy that it will seldom need repairs.

Assembling: First, replace the safety catch and turn it to its rear or "safe" position.

2. Replace the recoil spring and its rod, making sure that the collar on the rod is to the rear in the receiver well.

3. Start the slide onto the receiver from the front end and push it steadily back. When it is in the fully rear position, the safety catch will engage in the notch in the side of the slide and will thereby hold the slide back.

4. Replace the barrel by inserting the muzzle through the top of the opening in the slide and push it forward until the lug below the firing chamber section of the barrel engages in its recess in the receiver.

5. Holding the pistol securely in the right hand, grip the slide firmly with the left hand and with the left thumb push the safety catch to the firing position. This will permit you to ease the slide forward under tension of the recoil spring.

6. Holding onto the hammer, press the trigger to lower it. Inserting the magazine completes the assembly.

.380 ACP   **BROWNING**
1910 and 1922

The Browning Model 1910 for the .380 cartridge is the same in every way as the .32 Caliber model already described except for bore and the following specifications: Magazine capacity 6 cartridges and weight empty is 20 ounces. The Browning Model 1922 for this cartridge is the same as the pistol already described for the .32 cartridge except for the following differences: Magazine capacity is 8 cartridges, weight empty is 24⅛ ounces, and bore of course is different. (See Identification Section for photos.)

.380 ACP   **COLT**
Auto Pocket (Model M)

General Description: A pocket or holster arm for home and personal protection similar in design to the Colt Automatic Pocket .32 but using a cartridge with a bullet with a larger cross section and greater weight.

Ammunition: .380 A.C.P.

Manufacturing Dates: From 1908 to 1941, when it was discontinued.

Serial Numbers: From Number 1.

Finish: Blue or Nickel.

Barrel Length: 3¾"—present type with lug at muzzle end of barrel. 3¾"—straight barrel assembled to arm with a barrel bushing.
Stocks: Rubber or checked walnut with medallion.
Bore Diameter: .349"—.001.
Groove Diameter: .356"—.001.
Rifling: (Left twist). 6 grooves. 1 turn in 16".
Number of Shots: 7.
Action: Semiautomatic blowback.
Approximate Weight: 24 ounces.
Over-all Length: 6¾".
Sights: Fixed. Front: swaged in slide. Rear: driven in place.
Note: The straight barrel was used to Number 5,291. A safety disconnector was incorporated from Number 92,894 preventing discharge of the arm with the magazine withdrawn.

COLT   .380 ACP
Note

The working drawing showing the Browning Model 1903 under Caliber 9mm. Browning Long effectively covers the Colt .32 and .380 pistols. The differences are very slight and are described under the Browning.
For representative photograph see Colt under Caliber .32 A.C.P.

CZ (9mm. SHORT)   .380 ACP
Model 24

This Czech pistol was manufactured by Ceska Zbrojovka, Prague. For representative photograph see CZ 1927 under Caliber .32 A.C.P. The lockwork of the .380 (9mm. Short) is the same as that described for the .32 Caliber. However, while the smaller caliber is a straight blowback, the .380 has a fully locked breech. This pistol operates through short recoil with a turning barrel lock which is a modification of the Austrian Steyr system. The barrel is provided with two rear lugs which lock into slots in the slide when the action is closed. A third barrel lug near the forward end engages in a slotted steel block removably mounted in the receiver tube below the barrel and retained when the weapon is assembled by the locking pin which passes through the receiver. As the force of the recoil drives the barrel and slide to the rear the bottom barrel lug runs in the helical slot in the block which twists the barrel through 30 degrees until the upper lugs disengage from their recesses in the slide. The barrel stops and the slide continues on to compress the recoil spring and perform the functions of ejection and cocking in standard fashion.
While this is an interesting and secure design, it is entirely unnecessary in a pistol using this cartridge.

CZ (9mm. SHORT)   .380 ACP
Model 38

The Model 38 is blowback operated. Upon the functioning of the cartridge, the slide is forced back against the recoil spring which is mounted under the barrel, compressing the spring. During its travel to the rear, the slide cams the hammer down, cocking it, and the extractor draws the empty cartridge case out of the chamber following which the case is thrown out by the ejector.

The Model 38 differs from the earlier Czech Service pistols—Model 22, Model 24, and Model 27—in that it has a double-action trigger mechanism. The trigger mechanism is, however, merely a modification of that used on the earlier Czech pistols which were patterned on the Mauser Model 1910 pocket pistol (Taschen Pistole). Disassembly of the Model 38 is also similar to the earlier Czech pistols in having a slide-dismounting catch on the left side of the receiver and a removable plate on the left side to expose the trigger mechanism for cleaning and repair. It does not, however, have an easily dismountable barrel, as do the earlier models. The front end of the barrel is permanently attached to a movable collar which is pinned to the receiver. After the slide is dismounted, the barrel is examined and cleaned by tipping it up from the rear.

.380 ACP   **FROMMER**
                                                                  Automatic

This long-recoil locked-breech pistol is the same in every way except bore and slight difference in weight as the Frommer already described under Caliber .32 A.C.P.

.380 ACP   **ORTGIES**
                                                                  Automatic

This German manufactured pistol has a barrel 3¼ inches long, an over-all length of 6½ inches, weighs 22 ounces and has a magazine capacity of 7 cartridges. Except for bore it is in other respects identical with the Ortgies already described under Calibers .25 A.C.P. and .32 A.C.P. The slide will usually be found bearing the stamp Deutsche Werke Aktiengesellschaft Werke Erfurt—Ortgies Patent. This is a well-made and well-finished weapon very widely distributed in North and South America. It is inferior in design to the best American and German products.

REMINGTON
51

.380 ACP

This pistol was designed by J. B. Pedersen who also designed the "Pedersen Device," for converting the Springfield rifle to a semi-automatic weapon using a special short .30 caliber cartridge toward the end of World War I. The development and manufacture of this device was discontinued with the termination of the war. He is also the designer of the Pedersen automatic rifle.

While this weapon is sometimes classed as a locked-breech type, it is also considered by many a *hesitation* or *delayed blowback*. The barrel itself is rigidly fixed but the breechblock is in two parts, both of which recoil together for a short distance.

The grip safety in the Remington is of the type used in the Colt pistol. This weapon was introduced in 1918 and was discontinued in 1934 because the introduction of firearms laws made manufacture economically unsound.

Construction: The main parts of this pistol are the receiver, slide, barrel, and breechblock. Note that unlike the Colt and Webley types, where the breechblock is a part of the slide itself, the breechblock in this weapon *is a separate entity*, composed of two parts.

The recoil spring is of the concentric type, mounted around the barrel within the slide. Its front end rests against the inner face of the slide at the muzzle end. Mounting the recoil spring around the barrel, while it requires extra machining of the slide, does away with the necessity for recoil spring bushings and recoil spring guides.

There is a base lug on the bottom of the barrel which fits in a recess in the receiver above the trigger guard, where it is securely positioned by a split pin which can be removed when required.

During the rearward motion of the slide, the shoulder of the recoil spring housing inside the slide abuts against this lug.

This positioning of the recoil spring, together with the shape of the slide and the pitch of the grip, assures very little disturbance of aim when firing, as the rearward thrust of the mechanism is quite low and is just above the line of the trigger finger.

Length: 6⅝"

Weight: 21 ounces

Magazine Capacity: 7 shots

Safety: Grip Safety; thumb safety on rear left of receiver (which also acts as a cocking indicator since it cannot be put in place if the hammer is not cocked); and magazine disconnector safety which prevents the weapon from being fired when the magazine is out of the handle.

Sights: Blade front, square notch rear, mounted on top of the slide which is milled.

The lockwork is mounted in the space between the magazine well and the back strap of the butt.

The spiral mainspring is compressed by the long stirrup attached to the hammer.

The trigger bar is the standard stirrup type. The trigger is not pivoted but slides back along planes to engagement with the sear tail. A plunger-type disconnector operated by the slide as it recoils breaks the engagement of the trigger and sear tail after each shot until the trigger is released and the slide goes forward to the fully closed position where the disconnector can rise into its place in the underside of the slide.

The trigger arrangement in this weapon is the one point of complaint in it. Its design makes for a rather heavy trigger pull.

The grips are detachable and slide up from dovetailed slots in the handle section of the receiver.

Functioning: As the cartridge in the firing chamber is discharged, and the bullet moves down the barrel, the backward thrust of gases against the head of the cartridge case on the inside forces the case back against the face of the movable breechblock. This breechblock is mounted in the rear of the slide. After a rearward travel of about three-sixteenths of an inch, this movable section of the breechblock is brought into contact with holding recess in the receiver.

During this rearward travel it has, of course, passed on energy in the form of a quick thrust to the main body of the slide.

As the slide is free to move backwards along guides on the receiver, it lifts the breechblock out of its temporary engagement with the receiver. The coil spring around the barrel is compressed. The breechblock and slide continue back together.

Extraction, ejection, cocking of the hammer, and feeding of the new cartridge into line for stripping into the firing chamber are all accomplished in conventional manner.

The extraction recess where the barrel and the breechblock faces meet is normally covered by the slide in fully forward position. It is only exposed as the breech opens. This feature keeps dirt out of the action very effectively.

It is evident that the initial action of extraction is brought about by the force of the gases in the cartridge case forcing back against the inside head of the case itself.

However, the secondary extraction and the ejection of the case are brought about by the action of the breechblock and the slide as they travel to the rear under the influence of the thrust imparted to them.

When this weapon was designed, hundreds of experiments were made with hand molds to determine the correct shape, length, and pitch to provide the most nearly perfect average grip.

With the sole exception of the Luger, and the German Walther P38, the Walther PPK, Sauer-38 and Mauser H Sc (all foreign developments) this Remington 51 is probably the best-balanced, most-instinctive-pointing pistol ever made.

Stripping: 1. Remove magazine.

2. Pull back slide, cocking gun.

3. Pull slide back about one-fourth of an inch to align cutout on left side of slide with barrel holding pin. Remove barrel holding pin from left side.

4. Pull back slide sufficiently to allow finger grip on end of barrel. With grip safety depressed pull forward on barrel removing barrel and slide.

The rest of the stripping on the assembly is performed with the underside of the slide held upward. These operations are greatly simplified if the slide is held snugly in a vise.

5. With the right hand, catch a fingernail under the extreme rear end of the breechblock. With the left thumb on the rear of the barrel projection, slide the barrel forward against the spring tension. (This operation is facilitated by inserting a drift pin through the hole in the barrel projection.) At same time tilt the breechblock up from the rear and move it forward, removing the breechblock. Tip up the slide assembly allowing the firing pin spring and firing pin to drop out of the muzzle.

6. Move the barrel forward against the spring tension sufficiently to allow the recoil spring bushing to clear the recesses on each slide of the slide. Tip the barrel up just enough to hold the bushing under tension against the rear end of the slide recesses. Pull the barrel to the rear and up, removing the barrel, recoil spring bushing, and recoil spring.

Assembly: 1. Replace the recoil spring and recoil spring bushing. Have the recoil spring under tension and held so by having the recoil spring bushing tilted slightly upward and held against the rear end of the recesses in the slide.

2. Insert the barrel so that rear end just clears the breechblock—holding the projection on the slide. Push rear end of the barrel downward into proper alignment in the slide.

3. With the barrel moved forward, insert the firing pin in the forward end of the breechblock-holding projection. Place the firing pin spring on the front end of the firing pin.

4. With the barrel moved forward, place the forward end of the breechblock over the front end of the firing pin spring and move the breechblock to the rear and down at the rear end, allowing the breechblock to fall into position around the breechblock-holding projection.

5. Allow the barrel to move to the rear being sure that the barrel projection is aligned in the center of the slide in proper relationship with the breechblock.

6. Replace the slide on the forward end of the receiver until the rear end of the slide strikes the disconnector. Depress the grip safety, push down the disconnector, and continue to push the slide to the rear until it is in proper alignment.

7. Pull back the slide. Align the cutout in the slide with the hole in the left side of the receiver and replace the barrel holding pin. Replace the magazine and pull the trigger.

.380 ACP   **SAVAGE**
1915

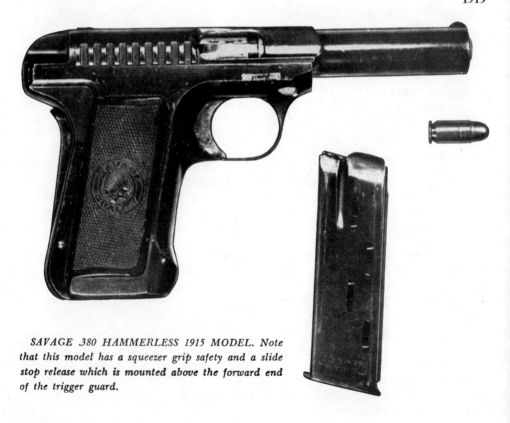

SAVAGE .380 HAMMERLESS 1915 MODEL. Note that this model has a squeezer grip safety and a slide stop release which is mounted above the forward end of the trigger guard.

446

THE SAVAGE LINE

.45 Auto. 1911
.25 Auto. 1914-15
.45 Auto. 1908-09

.380 ACP 1917
.32 ACP 1917

.32 ACP 1915 Inclosed Cocking Piece, Grip Safety
.32 ACP 1907
   Exposed Cocking Piece

Savage semi-automatic pistols of the three types described under Caliber .32 A.C.P. were also manufactured for the .380 cartridge. They differ only in barrel lengths, weights, magazine capacity, and bore. The 1907 models had barrels measuring about 4¼ inches, over-all length about 7 inches and weight about 21 ounces. Magazine capacity 9 cartridges. The 1917 model weighs about one ounce more.

.380 ACP **SAUER**
Automatic

The Sauer automatic pistols already described under Caliber .32 A.C.P. were also manufactured in .380 Caliber, differing only in bore and slightly in weight.

CARTRIDGE
Data

.38 ACP

.38 Auto Super-X

130 Gr. M. C.	
Muzzle Velocity in f.s.:	1300
Vel. at 50 Feet:	1238
Vel. at 150 Feet:	1140
Calculated Energy	
Muzzle Energy in ft. lbs.:	488
Energy at 50 Feet:	443
Energy at 150 Feet:	375
Calculated Drop	
At 50 Feet:	.3 inch
At 150 Feet:	2.9 inches
At 300 Feet:	13.2 inches
Penetration at 15 Feet	
⅞″ soft pine boards	10
Length of Barrel in Which Tested	
inches	5

Shell Case	
Weight:	67.5 grains
Max. Length:	.900 inch
Outside Body Dia. at Head, Max.:	.384 inch
Outside Body Dia. at Neck, Max.:	.384 inch
Inside Mouth Dia. Max.:	.3585 inch
Volumetric Capacity to Base of Bullet in cubic inches:	.048
Bullet	
Weight:	130 grains
Approx. Length:	.575 inch
Diameter Max.:	.359 inch
Area, Cross Sectional:	.101 square inch
Shape:	Round Nose
Powder	
Amount and type varies with different lots manufactured.	
Cartridge	
Approx. Length, Loaded:	1.280 inches
Approx. Total Weight, Loaded:	206 grains

The .38 A.C.P. cartridge was designed for Browning's first high-powered pistol, the Colt .38 Automatic Sporting Model, which was patented in 1897, and was first issued in 1900. Two years later the modified Colt .38 Automatic Military Model for this cartridge made its appearance. However, the .38 caliber had fallen into military disrepute because of the poor performance of the .38 Long Colt in the Philippines, so this superior Automatic cartridge was neglected for years in favor of larger calibers. When Colt finally developed a pistol of the 1911A1 Government Model type to use the .38 Automatic cartridge it was possible to step up the ballistics appreciably, and the cartridge has since become very popular with seasoned pistol shooters.

This is a semirim cartridge. It has the highest velocity and hardest striking energy of any autoloading pistol cartridge manufactured in the United States.

.38 Auto

COLT
Sporting

*1899 Type Colt Automatic, predecessor to the 1900
Type and the Sporting Type.*

This was the first high-powered automatic pistol of Browning design ever marketed. Browning produced many experimental models before the Sporting Model was designed, one of the first being a full-automatic pistol which emptied so rapidly that it could not be controlled.

General Description: A holster arm. Probably the first successful automatic pistol in commercial production in quantity. The rear sight worked as a manual safety; pushing it down blocked the hammer from striking the firing pin.

Ammunition: .38 A.C.P. Modern high-velocity cartridges should *not* be used.

Manufacturing Dates: From 1900 to June 2, 1908.

Serial Numbers: From Number 1.

Finish: Blue.

Barrel Length: 6″.

Stocks: Plain walnut.

Bore Diameter: .349″−.001.

Groove Diameter: .356″−.001.

Rifling: (Left twist). 6 grooves. 1 turn in 16″.

Number of Shots: 7.

Action: Semiautomatic, recoil operated. Locked breech.

Approximate Weight: 35 ounces.

Over-all Length: 9″.

Sights: Fixed.

Note: This model bears an initial patent date of 1897. Numerous experimental samples were produced prior to commercial production. The barrel was attached to the receiver with 2 links, and engaged the slide with transverse ribs at the top of the breech end, engaging corresponding cuts in the slide. Originally brought out with a steel firing pin, later changed to bronze; many of the first shipments were converted.

COLT .38 ACP

Military (Model L Mil.)

General Description: A holster arm developed from the .38 Sporting Model and designed for military use. Magazine capacity was increased by one round and a lanyard loop added. The grip was also made larger, with a square butt; a slide stop holding the slide back after the last shot was incorporated.

Ammunition: .38 A.C.P. Modern high-velocity cartridges should *not* be used.

Manufacturing Dates: From 1902 to December 11, 1928.

Serial Numbers: From Number 11,000.

Finish: Blue.

Barrel Length: 6″.

Stocks: Rubber and plain walnut.

Bore Diameter: .349″—.001.

Groove Diameter: .356″—.001.

Rifling: (Left twist). 6 grooves. 1 turn in 16″.

Number of Shots: 8.

Action: Semiautomatic, recoil operated. Locked breech.

Approximate Weight: 38 ounces.

Over-all Length: 9″.

Sights: Fixed.

Note: Manufactured under patent dates of 1897 and 1902. This model was brought out to use a bronze firing pin. A "flying" pin (shorter than the distance from hammer to primer) was introduced on this model; the only time the pin touches the primer is when the fall of the hammer drives it ahead. The spring around the pin pulls it back into the breechlock as the primer is struck.

COLT .38 ACP

Pocket (Model L Pock.)

While this pistol is no longer manufactured, it was widely distributed. In view of the system of slide mounting, it is not advisable to use modern high-velocity ammunition in these old pistols. The comparatively weak slide locks in early pistols have been known to shear off and let the slide fly back when used with high-velocity ammunition. Care should, therefore, be taken to use only ammunition which is specified by the manufacturer as being for the ".38 Automatic." Modern ammunition is intended for the .38 *Super* Automatic with its improved slide mounting which makes it impossible for the slide to be blown off the receiver.

General Description: Designed as a more convenient arm than the earlier Sporting and Military models, it used the 7-shot magazine and a rounded smaller butt at first and had no slide stop.

Ammunition: .38 A.C.P. Modern high-velocity cartridges should *not* be used.

Manufacturing Dates: 1903 to November 29, 1927.

Serial Numbers: From Number 16,000. Above Number 30,000 on The Pocket and the Military ran concurrently.

Finish: Blue.

Barrel Length: 4½″.

Stocks: Rubber.

451

Bore Diameter: .349″—.001.
Groove Diameter: .356″—.001.
Rifling: (Left twist). 6 grooves. 1 turn in 16″.
Number of Shots: 7.
Action: Semiautomatic, recoil operated. Locked breech.
Approximate Weight: 32 ounces.
Over-all Length: 7½″.
Sights: Fixed.

Note: Patent dates of 1897 and 1902 appear on this model. A bronze firing pin was used. Early models had rounded hammers, later ones used the more easily cocked spur type.

.38 ACP   **COLT**
Military & Pocket—Construction & Operation

Construction: The principal parts of this pistol are the receiver, barrel, slide, lockwork, and magazine.

The receiver has guides suitably machined to permit the slide to travel back and forth and a magazine well in the grip to permit insertion of the magazine from below. The trigger guard is formed as a part of the receiver and a place for the lockwork is provided in the rear. The top of the receiver extends forward from the handle almost to the muzzle. The barrel is attached to it by short swinging links at front and rear end. The links are attached to both barrel and receiver by link pins. Both links are the same length, hence as the barrel goes back in recoil the links carry it downward in a place parallel to its original position. The receiver section below the barrel provides a tubular seating for the recoil spring. A plug held in place by the forward link pin seals the tube at the front.

The rear of the slide forms the breechblock. The forward section is hollowed out to act as a cover over the top and side of the barrel, and has an ejection opening on its right top side. The firing pin and spring, the extractor and the ejector are all mounted in the rear breechblock section of the slide; while the ceiling of the forward tubular section is machined with recesses to receive three barrel lugs.

A transverse mortise in the front end of the receiver extends through the recoil spring seating. Corresponding recesses in the slide permit the insertion of the slide lock. This piece passes through the sides of the slide and the mortise thereby locking the slide to the receiver. The recoil spring and its guide rest in the tubular receiver section behind the slide lock. When the lock is in place a recess on its rear surface supports the front end of the recoil spring guide (follower). At the chamber end the recoil spring rests against a stiff coil intended to absorb shock.

The barrel has three transverse ribs on its top, and when the pistol is ready for firing the barrel is upright on its links with its ribs locked securely into the ceiling of the slide.

The lockwork is extremely simple. It consists of a stirrup trigger whose arms cross the sides of the magazine well, a flat trigger spring in the grip, a sear mounted with a disconnector, a hammer and leaf mainspring. The magazine is the standard steel-box type with its follower and spring.

Operation: When the pistol is cocked and ready to fire the upright disconnector (which is mounted with the sear) is raised up and its rounded head seats in a niche in the underside of the slide. At this point the trigger stirrup can push the sear out of engagement with the hammer. Any movement of the slide rides over and depresses the head of the disconnector, thereby lowering it to break the trigger stirrup contact with the sear.

Upon discharge the barrel and slide start back locked together as the gases inside the cartridge case thrust the case back against the breechblock. The barrel swings down on its twin links, pulling the barrel ribs out of their recesses in the slide. Barrel movement stops, and the slide continues to the rear to eject, cock, and compress the recoil spring.

As the slide goes back the slidelock (which crosses from side to side of the slide at its front end) forces the recoil spring follower back to compress the recoil spring. (Note: This is the one weak point of design. If the slidelock crystallizes it can shear and let the slide fly off. All modern Colt pistols using heavy cartridges have tubular abutments below the barrel to prevent this.) As the recoil spring reacts to drive the slide forward and chamber a cartridge, the breechblock strikes the barrel and raises it up on its swinging links until its ribs engage in the slide recesses.

Dismounting: Push in the plunger below the muzzle and remove the slide lock. The slide assembly can now be drawn off to the rear of the receiver. Removing the stocks affords access to the lockwork. The barrel may be removed by driving out the link pins.

453

.38 ACP

COLT
Super Auto (Model O38)

COLT 38 SUPER AUTOMATIC. Ribs in magazine identify it as for the 38 Auto Cartridge

General Description: A holster arm of the military type built to the same design as the Colt .45 Automatic Government model. This adaptation made possible the use of a higher-velocity .38 A.C.P. cartridge loaded to give 1300 f.s. from a 5″ barrel with a 130-gr. bullet and a muzzle energy of 488 ft.-lbs.

Ammunition: .38 A.C.P.

Manufacturing Dates: From January 3, 1929 to date.

Serial Numbers: From Number 1.

Finish: Blue.

Barrel Length: 5″.

Stocks: Checked walnut—no medallion.

Bore Diameter: .349″—.001.

Groove Diameter: .356″—.001.

Rifling: (Left twist). 6 grooves. 1 turn in 16″.

Number of Shots: 9.

Action: Semiautomatic, recoil operated. Locked breech.

Approximate Weight: 39 ounces.

Over-all Length: 8½″.

Sights: Fixed. Front: swaged in slide. Rear: driven in top rear of slide.

Note: This model was also available in two target models the serial numbers of which are concurrent with the standard arm. Both these arms have hand-finished actions and differ only in sighting equipment. The Super Match (fixed) has a fixed rear sight with a square cut notch of the Patridge type driven in a dovetail slot in the top rear of the slide, while the Super Match (adjustable) has a rear sight of the target type, adjustable for both elevation and windage. In both arms the front sight is of the ramp type with a serrated face, swaged in the slide.

The .38 Super is the same as the .45 Government Model in appearance, operation, functioning, dismounting, general design, weight, and length. However, the slide and receiver assemblies of the .38 Super will not interchange with those of the .45 Government because of structural modifications required by the difference in the cartridge case diameters (case lengths are the same), by the fact that the .38 Auto has a semirim case. The mouth of the case is crimped into a cannelure on the bullet, hence no forward shoulder is provided in the chamber. When the .38 Auto cartridge is seated in the chamber it is supported by the narrow rim (classed as semirim) of its case resting on a shoulder formed by the projecting lip at the top of the barrel.

Since the .38 Auto barrel has a smaller outside diameter at the muzzle than the .45 Auto, a special barrel bushing is required. The slide is machined differently at the point where it meets the barrel lip, since the .38 Auto lip is shorter than that of the bigger caliber. The extractors and firing pins are also necessarily different and cannot be interchanged. While the outside dimensions of the two magazines are the same, the sides of the .38 Auto are ribbed so as to constrict the interior space to hold the smaller cartridge. These ribs identify the magazine at sight.

The receivers and lockwork of the two calibers are the same except for the ejectors. The ejector in this design is a steel finger rising from the receiver to which it is securely pinned directly behind the magazine well. The slide is grooved to travel back over the ejector so the empty cartridge case carried back by the extractor hits the ejector and is tossed out the ejection port. The .38 Auto ejector is broader than the .45 Auto, hence will not permit slide travel in the Government Model slide. Conversely, since the narrow .45 Auto ejector is placed to let the rim of its case strike properly, it will not permit travel in the .38 Auto slide.

WEBLEY AND SCOTT .38 ACP
Automatic

This pistol was never extensively manufactured and will seldom be encountered. It is essentially a small, modified version of the official British Navy service type W&S .455 Self-Loading pistol (see under Cal. 455 S.L. for operating and construction details). The locking system, dismounting system, safety, and recoil mechanism follow the .455 S.L., but the .38 has an enclosed hammer. Magazine capacity is 8 cartridges.

MISCELLANEOUS .38 ACP
Weapons

Several Spanish modifications of the Colt .45 Government Model are also chambered for the .38 Super Automatic cartridge. Many of these pistols are of poor materials and of poorer workmanship. They are manufactured generally for Mexican and South American trade. Those bearing the name Star or Llama are the better makes. None are in a class with American pistols. The Astra Model 400 (see under Cal. 9mm. Bayard Long) is so chambered that it will handle the .38 Auto cartridge reasonably well, though its own cartridge is somewhat shorter in over-all length. When it is remembered that the .38 Auto chambers on its semirim while the Bayard chambers on its case mouth, the ingenuity of the design is evident.

CARTRIDGE
Data

.38 Winchester CF (.38-40)

.38 Winchester (38-40)

180 Gr. S.P.

Muzzle Velocity in f.s:	975
Vel. at 50 Feet:	959
Vel. at 150 Feet:	929
Calculated Energy	
Muzzle Energy in ft. lbs.:	380
Energy at 50 Feet:	368
Energy at 150 Feet:	345
Calculated Drop	
At 50 Feet:	.5 inch
At 150 Feet:	4.8 inches
At 300 Feet:	20.0 inches
Penetration at 15 Feet	
7/8" soft pine boards	6
Length of Barrel in Which Tested	
inches	5

Shell Case

Weight:	87.5 grains
Max. Length:	1.305 inches
Outside Body Dia. at Head, Max.:	.465 inch
Outside Body Dia. at Neck, Max.:	.417 inch
Inside Mouth Dia. Max.:	.399 inch
Volumetric Capacity to Base of Bullet	
in cubic inches:	.116

Bullet

Weight:	180 grains
Approx. Length:	.600 inch
Diameter Max.:	.401 inch
Area, Cross Sectional:	.126 square inch
Shape:	Blunt Nose

Powder

Amount and type varies with different lots manufactured.

Cartridge

Approx. Length, Loaded:	1.593 inches
Approx. Total Weight, Loaded:	284 grains

This cartridge derives its name from the fact that it was originally designed to be loaded with 40 grains of black powder. Winchester developed the cartridge for use in its lever action 1873 rifle, and Colt adapted it to the Single Action Army (or Frontier Model) revolver. The two arms were intended to supplement each other and enable the plainsmen to carry one type of cartridge for both weapons.

This is a bottle-necked cartridge. The actual mouth diameter is .399 inch, making the caliber nearer .40 than .38. This cartridge, therefore, will not chamber in any other variety of .38 caliber revolver than the ones designed for it.

It must be noted that modern .38-40 cartridges are of two different loadings. Those loaded for revolvers may also be used in rifles; but those loaded for rifles should not be used in revolvers. The .38-40 rifle cartridges develop pressures which may blow up a revolver. This ammunition should be used in revolvers only when the manufacturer's box label says it is intended for such use.

.38 Winchester CF (.38-40)   **COLT**
                                                              Miscellaneous

The New Service Model and the Single Action Army Model were made in this caliber (see under Caliber .45 Colt). The obsolete Double Action Army and Bisley Single Action models were also made in this caliber and thousands are still in use throughout the world.

No other American manufacturer makes revolvers for the .38-40 cartridge. S&W manufactured only 275 of their No. 3 Model in this caliber. Imitations of the S&W hinged-frame revolver made in this caliber by L. Loewe in Germany are well made of excellent materials, but even the standard .38-40 revolver load is too powerful for sustained use in any hinged-frame revolver. Belgian and Spanish imitations of the S&W hinged-frame design should not be used in this caliber.

Chapter 11
Caliber 10.35mm to .44

CARTRIDGE 10.35mm. Italian Service
Data

This cartridge is not manufactured in the United States. However, revolvers chambered for it have been brought to this country by returning soldiers. The bullet diameter is .422 inch. It is of lead, usually jacketed. Bullet weighs about 177 grains. Over-all length of cartridge is about 1.26 inches. Cartridge weighs about 290 grains, average, when loaded. The original load was about 17 grains of black powder. It is also commonly knowns as the 10.4mm.

ITALIAN 10.35mm. Italian Service
Revolvers

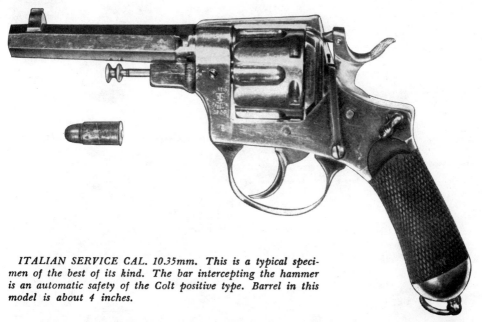

ITALIAN SERVICE CAL. 10.35mm. This is a typical speci-men of the best of its kind. The bar intercepting the hammer is an automatic safety of the Colt positive type. Barrel in this model is about 4 inches.

All Italian service revolvers stem from the Army Model of 1872, a solid-frame double-action revolver of rod-ejector type based on the Delvigne and Chamelot design with Schmidt improvements. (This lock very closely followed that of the American Allen Pepperbox.)

The first model introduced was manufactured by Glisenti at Brescia, and original specimens were carried by the Italians in World War II. This original model (still manufactured during the 1930's) has a 6.3-inch barrel, measures 11 inches overall, is rifled with 4 concentric grooves with twist of 1 turn in

459

ITALIAN SERVICE MODEL 1889. Note countersunk chambers.

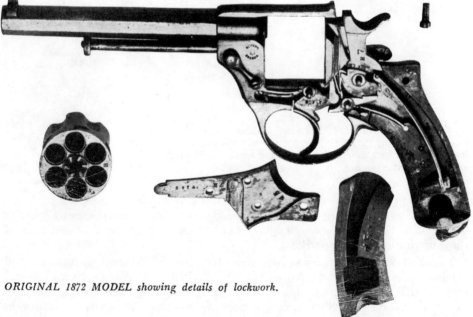

ORIGINAL 1872 MODEL showing details of lockwork.

ITALIAN SERVICE. Folding trigger type. Note that this incredibly crude revolver was manufactured in 1926.

9.84 inches, and has a cylinder with 6 chambers. The chambers are worthy of note, being countersunk to protect the weak cartridge heads. Thus we see in 1872 a cylinder development which was acclaimed in recent years as a great development in revolver design. The loading gates on the various Italian revolvers usually are hinged to be drawn back rather than swung out to load.

Most models have rod ejectors mounted below the barrels on a collar in such fashion that the ejector rod can be swung to the right and then pushed into the cylinder to force out the fired case. None of these have Colt-type return springs: the rod must be manually withdrawn. Pulling the rod out of the frame permits prying out the cylinder axis pin for cylinder removal in standard fashion.

At least sixty varieties of this revolver, some with folding triggers, are known. Frames may be made of forged steel, cast steel, brass and in some instances of an unusual type of hardened copper plates. These revolvers were made in small shops or on contract and the actual source of manufacture is often difficult to trace. Those bearing the Glisenti stamp are usually the best finished.

All the revolvers have rebounding hammers. Many have a rising steel bar operating inside or outside the lock plate on the left side, which is actually the forerunner of the famous "Colt positive lock." Only when the hammer is fully cocked and the trigger completely retracted is this locking bar lifted high enough to clear the hammer so that the firing pin can hit the cartridge. The firing pins are pinned to the hammers—a development which the United States and the British were comparatively late in adopting. The left lock plate is customarily held by a screw with an external lever. Revolving the lever pushes the plate off exposing all the lockwork for cleaning or repairs.

461

.41 Long and Short Colt

.41 Long Colt

200 Gr. Lub.	
Muzzle Velocity in f.s.:	745
Vel. at 50 Feet:	735
Vel. at 150 Feet:	716
Calculated Energy	
Muzzle Energy in ft. lbs.:	247
Energy at 50 Feet:	235
Energy at 150 Feet:	223
Calculated Drop	
At 50 Feet:	.9 inch
At 150 Feet:	8.1 inches
At 300 Feet:	33.4 inches
Penetration at 15 Feet	
7/8" soft pine boards	3
Length of Barrel in Which Tested	
inches	6

Shell Case	
Weight:	73 grains
Max. Length:	1.130 inches
Outside Body Dia. at Head, Max.:	.4105 inch
Outside Body Dia. at Neck, Max.:	.409 inch
Inside Mouth Dia. Max.:	.386 inch
Volumetric Capacity to Base of Bullet	
in cubic inches:	.059
Bullet	
Weight:	200 grains
Approx. Length:	.760 inch
Diameter Max.:	.387 inch
Area, Cross Sectional:	.117 square inch
Shape:	Round Nose
Powder	
Amount and type varies with different lots manufactured.	
Cartridge	
Approx. Length, Loaded:	1.410 inches
Approx. Total Weight, Loaded:	280 grains

Either Short or Long may be used interchangeably in revolvers designed for the .41 Long Colt cartridge. The .41 Long is still manufactured though no American revolvers have been made in this caliber for many years. The Short Colt used a 160-grain lead bullet with outside lubrication. The loaded cartridge measured about 1.10 inches over-all. Originally the powder was black but in later manufacture smokeless was employed. Muzzle velocity was about 670 feet per second, muzzle energy about 160 foot-pounds.

The .41 Long was also originally made with outside lubricated bullet and black powder load. The bullet and case were of the same diameter. As currently loaded with inside lubricated bullet, the bullet diameter is the diameter of the inside of the case (.387 "instead of .410"). For this reason the .41 Long bullet is cast with a hollow base to encourage expansion so as to take the rifling properly when the gun is fired.

COLT
Miscellaneous

No American revolvers are now made in this caliber. The .41 was long a favorite revolver in the West and Southwest and was manufactured in several models. From 1877 to 1912 the Colt Double Action Model, popularly called the Lightning, was made with rounded "bird's-head" butt and 2½- and 3½-in. barrels. This model did not have an ejector. The New Army, New Navy and Colt Army Special models with swingout cylinders and simultaneous hand ejectors were all chambered for this cartridge, as were the S.A. Army and the Bisley rod-ejector types. Manufacture has been discontinued.

Spanish imitations of the Colt types have been extensively produced, and must not be confused with the genuine Colt products.

11mm. French Service 1873

CARTRIDGE
Data

This obsolescent cartridge, while not generally known here, is a popular French type and revolvers for it formed part of the French armament in World War II. The cartridge measures about 1.16 inches overall. The lead bullet measures about .611 inch in length, diameter is .449, bullet weighs about 180 grains. Powder charge varies from 10 to as much as 15 grains of black powder.

11mm. French Service 1873

FRENCH SERVICE
1873

This revolver is no longer manufactured but large numbers still exist. It measures 9½ inches overall, has a barrel about 4 1/5 inches long, weighs 2.7 pounds and has a cylinder with 6 chambers. The rifling is 4 grooves concentric, one turn in 13.78 inches. The Model 1873 is a solid-frame revolver of heavy and rigid construction. The lockwork is the Chamelot-Delvigne which is one of the sturdiest systems ever developed. This is a double-action revolver with rod ejector. The rod is locked at its head and is so mounted that it can be thrust up into the cylinder to eject the cartridges. The loading gate opens to the rear. The left side plate may be removed to give access to the lockwork.

German Service 1883

French Service 1873

11mm. German Service

CARTRIDGE
Data

This cartridge was manufactured only in Germany and is almost entirely unknown in the United States. The cartridge measures about 1.20 inch overall, uses a black powder load of about 20 grains, and has a lead bullet of .428 inch diameter weighing about 260 grains.

11mm. German Service

GERMAN SERVICE
1883

This revolver is typical of the German product during the last part of the 19th century. The Germans advanced from revolvers of this type to the most modern automatic pistol designs. Revolvers of this pattern were encountered by our troops in the closing days of World War II when the Germans were using any arms obtainable. From the American viewpoint, they are strictly to be classed as souvenirs.

CARTRIDGE   **.44 Colt**
Data

This is an obsolete black-powder cartridge used early in the 1870's in Colt revolvers. The cartridge is described here merely to prevent confusion on the part of anyone who might connect it with current manufacture. It differs considerably from the S&W .44 American, although its ballistics are practically the same. The cartridge measures 1.5 inches, overall with case length being 1.08 inches, case head diameter .483 inch, case body diameter .451 inch; bullet length is .66 inch, bullet diameter is .444 inch and bullet weight 210 grains.

CARTRIDGE   **.44 Webley, .44 Bulldog**
Data

These cartridges are very much alike, the Webley having a heavier bullet and better ballistics. These cartridges are no longer made in England. Both were originally designed for short pocket revolvers of the solid-frame, non-ejector type popularly called "Bull Dogs."

The Webley measures 1.11 inch overall, has a 200-grain lead bullet, a charge of 18 grains of black powder or its equivalent in smokeless powder, develops a muzzle velocity of about 715 f.p.s. with short barrel and a muzzle energy of about 140 foot-pounds. Actual bullet diameter is about .436 inch.

The Bull Dog measures .95 inch overall, has a 170-grain bullet, a charge of 15 grains of black or its equivalent in smokeless powder, develops a muzzle velocity of about 450 f.p.s. with short barrel and a muzzle energy of about 80 foot-pounds. Actual bullet diameter is about .440.

CARTRIDGE   **.44 S&W AMERICAN**
Data

This cartridge is obsolescent. It was developed in 1869 to replace the rim-fire calibers S&W had been using in their first automatic ejecting revolvers. While it very closely resembles the .44 Russian which followed it, it differs considerably in bullet specifications.

The cartridge measures 1.43 inches overall. Case head diameter is .502 inch, case body diameter is .437 inch, case length is .90 inch. The bullet measures .70 inch, has a diameter of .434 inch and weighs 218 grains. The powder charge was originally 25 grains of black powder. Later loadings of semismokeless and smokeless vary in charge. Original velocity was given at 650 feet per second at muzzle, while muzzle energy was listed as 200 foot-pounds. England's great gun house, Parker-Hale, listed British Kynoch cartridges of this caliber in their 1938 catalog.

SMITH & WESSON   **.44 S&W American**
SA American No. 3

Official Model Names: Model No. 3 .44 Caliber Single Action American (1st Model).
Model No. 3 .44 Caliber Single Action American (2nd Model).
Ammunition: .44 S & W American Center Fire cartridge.
Manufacturing Dates: 1870-1873.
Number Manufactured: Approximately 30,000.

S&W MODEL No. 3 .44 CAL. SINGLE ACTION AMERICAN (2nd MOD.)

Finish: Blue or nickel.
Barrel Length: 8″; some made in 5½″, 6″, 6½″, and 7″.

Land Diameter:	.417-.419	*Length of Chambers:*	
Groove Diameter:	.429-.431		Straight chamber
Number of Lands:	**5**	*Diameter of Chamber:*	**.442**
Twist: One turn in	**20″**	*Numbers of Chambers:*	6
Direction of Twist:	**Right**		

Notes: This was the first revolver manufactured with an automatic ejector.
The First Model and Second Model differed in several minor details, including the changing of the cylinder stop from hammer actuation to trigger actuation.

While curiously there is no exact record of the number of the American Model made, there is an ordnance record of 1,000 having been ordered by the U. S. Army. They were delivered early in 1871.

These weapons had square grips. The cartridges for them were originally manufactured at the Frankford Arsenal, and used Martin's pocket primer.

Before the development of the .44 S&W American Center Fire Cartridge, these revolvers were manufactured in at least one other caliber known to collectors. This was the .44 Henry Rim Fire.

General Description: A heavy target arm with a hand-finished action differing essentially from the regular Bisley only in having a flat top frame, hand-finished limb work and target-type sights.

Ammunition: See table below.

Manufacturing Dates: 1894 to 1912.

Serial Numbers: Concurrent with the Bisley and Single Action Army (Model P).

Finish: Blue (standard).

Barrel Length: 7½″; also made in 3″, 4″, 4¾″, and 5½″ in other calibers.

Stocks: Rubber.

Bore Diameter: See table below.

Groove Diameter: See table below.

Rifling: (Left twist). 6 grooves. 1 turn in 16″.

Number of Shots: 6.

Action: Single.

Approximate Weight: 42 ounces.

Overall Length: 12½″.

Sights: Target type. Front: insert blade. Rear: driven in dovetail cut.

Note: Bisley (England) was in 1896 the focal point of formal small-arms competition—hence its use to denote a target model.

Ammunition:	*.32/44*	*.32 L.C.*	*.32 Pol. Pos.* *(S & W)*	*.38 Pol. Pos.* *(S & W)*
Bore Diameter:	*	.305″—.001	.305″—.001	.347″—.001
Groove Diameter:		.312″—.001	.312″—.001	.354″—.001

Ammunition:	*.38 L.C.*	*38/44*	*.44 Russ.* *(& Spcl.)*	*.45 Colt*	*.455 Eley*
Bore Diameter:	†	*	.420″—.001	.445″—.001	.445″—.001
Groove Diameter:			.427″—.001	.452″—.001	.452″—.001

* Definite information not available on these calibers of the time they were available in this model.

† This cartridge when it became obsolete probably used a bore of .350 with a corresponding groove diameter of .357.

467

.44 S&W Russian

LOEWE
Revolvers

The firm of Ludwig Loewe of Berlin manufactured very large quantities of imitations of the S&W Russian for the Czar's government. These revolvers are common in many sections of Europe. The revolvers are of good materials and workmanship and differ only in minor externals.

.44 S&W Russian

SMITH AND WESSON
Russian

Ammunition: .44 S & W Russian Center-fire Cartridge.
Manufacturing Dates: 1870-1878.
Number Manufactured: About 215,000.
Serial Numbers: Numbered in separate series beginning at one.
Finish: Blue is standard.
Barrel Length: 6½″; may also be found in 6″, 7″, and 8″.

Land Diameter:	.417-.419	Direction of Twist:	Right
Groove Diameter	.429-.431	Diameter of Chamber:	.458-.459
Number of Lands:	5	Number of Chambers:	6
Twist: One turn in	20″		

Butt Shape: Round butt, saw-handle grip.
Trigger Guard: Bow guard with fingerpiece for third finger.

Notes: These guns were made principally for the Russian Imperial Army and were also sold commercially. An improved version of the Russian was officially known as the Model No. 3 .44 Caliber Single Action (New Model).

The Russian is one of the most famous of military sidearms. Smith & Wesson's entire facilities were tied up for five years making these guns.

One English and two types of Russian inscription were used for stamping the Company's name and patent dates on top rib of barrel.

Note: The story behind this gun is that a Russian Grand Duke, in this country to purchase weapons for the Imperial Russian Army, went on an extended hunting trip with William Cody—the famous Buffalo Bill of history and legend—and was so impressed with the performance of the S & W .44's which were part of Buffalo Bill's armament that he placed an order with the manufacturers for many revolvers.

At that time the order was one of the choicest plums any manufacturer could ask for; and for the next five years S & W worked steadily without a care in the world—no sales problems, no financial problems.

During those years the West was opening up in a big way and the demand was constantly expanding for reliable weapons; and it was then that the Colt Company had its golden opportunity to develop the home market.

For those five years of steady employment filling a foreign order, Smith & Wesson paid the price of forfeiting all the publicity, all the glamour, and all the legends that went with the opening up of the West.

The name and fame of the Colt spread far and wide; and the quality of the Colt line expanded its prestige to the point where Colt became for a time the largest manufacturer of first-class revolvers in the world.

Smith and Wesson, the only other first-line revolver makers to survive in this country, has the most modern revolver and pistol plant in the world. Their production presently greatly exceeds Colt's.

SMITH AND WESSON .44 S&W Russian
No. 3 Single Action

S&W MODEL No. 3 .44 CAL. SINGLE ACTION (NEW MODEL)

Official Model Names: Model No. 3 .44 Caliber Single Action Revolver (New Model)

Model No. 3 .44 Caliber Single Action Revolver "Frontier"

Model No. 3 .32-44 Single Action Target Revolver.

Model No. 3 .38-44 Single Action Target Revolver.

Model No. 3 .38 Single Action Revolver.

469

Ammunition: New Model—.44 S & W Russian.
.450 Webley.
Frontier—.44-40 Winchester Rifle cartridge—Model 1873.
.32-44—.32-44 S & W Center Fire cartridge.
.38-44—.38-44 S & W Center Fire cartridge.
.38 S.A.—.38-40 Winchester Rifle cartridge.

Manufacturing Dates: New Model—1878-1908.
Frontier—1885-1908.
.32-44—1887-1910.
.38-44—1887-1910.
.38 S.A.—1900-1905.

Number Manufactured: New Model—38,796.
Frontier—2,000.
.32-44—4,333.
.38-44—Uncertain.
.38 S/a—Uncertain.

Serial Numbers: Each Model numbered in a separate series.
Finish: Blue and nickel on all models.
Sights: All types made with both service and target sights except the .32-44 and .38-44, which were exclusively target revolvers.
Notes: These guns were a development of the military Russian Model and are all essentially the same gun. They did not have the saw-handle grip of the Military Russian and were usually fitted with a bow trigger guard without finger piece for the third finger.

As a target revolver, the New Model was the first handgun which proved that a short-barrel arm could be a really accurate weapon. The Bennett Bros. and Chevalier Ira A. Paine were among the outstanding shooters who used this gun. Between them they established and held practically every target shooting record of their day, some of which still stand. The .32-44 and .38-44 were designed specially at the request of Ira Paine, who believed that a higher load with less recoil than the .44 Russian would improve his scores.

Cylinders were made 1 7/16″ and 1 9/16″ long. Both types were used on all models except the .44-40 and .38-40 which took long cylinders only.

	.44 Russian	*.450 Webley*	*.32-44*
Barrel Lengths:	4″, 5″, 6″, 6½″. 7½″, 8″	......	6½″
Land Diameter:	.417-.418	......	.310-.311
Groove Diameter:	.429-.431	......	.320-.321
Number of Lands:	5	......	5
Twist: One turn in	20″	......	18¾″
Direction of Twist:	Right	Right	Right
Diameter of Chamber:	.458-.459	......	.350-.351
Number of Chambers:	6	6	6

	.38-44	*.44-40*	*.38-40*
Barrel Lengths:	6½″	4″, 5″, 6½″	6½″
Land Diameter:	.350-.351	.417-.419	.388-.389

	.38-44	.44-40	.38-40
Groove Diameter:	.360-.361	.429-.431	.400-.401
Number of Lands:	5	5	5
Twist: One turn in	18¾"	20"	20"
Direction of Twist:	Right	Right	Right
Diameter of Chamber:	.388-.389	.442-.459-.473	.418-.456-.472
Number of Chambers:	6	6	6

SMITH AND WESSON
Double Action   .44 S&W Russian

This is the first S&W double-action revolver for this cartridge. The arm was made in other calibers also. For specifications and data see S&W under Caliber .44 W.C.F. (.44-40).

MISCELLANEOUS
Revolvers   .44 S&W Russian

Any Colt or Smith & Wesson revolver chambered for the .44 Special cartridge will handle the .44 Russian since it is in effect a short form of the .44 Special. The S&W New Century Model was made in limited quantity chambered specifically for the .44 Russian cartridge. (See S&W under Caliber .44 S&W Special).

.44 S&W Special

.44 S & W Special

246 Gr.

Muzzle Velocity in f.s.:	770
Vel. at 50 Feet:	760
Vel. at 150 Feet:	742

Calculated Energy

Muzzle Energy in ft. lbs.:	324
Energy at 50 Feet:	316
Energy at 150 Feet:	302

Calculated Drop

At 50 Feet:	.9 inch
At 150 Feet:	7.4 inches
At 300 Feet:	32.1 inches

Penetration at 15 Feet

⅞" soft pine boards	4

Length of Barrel in Which Tested

inches	6½

Shell Case

Weight:	77 grains
Max. Length:	1.160 inches
Outside Body Dia. at Head, Max.:	.457 inch
Outside Body Dia. at Neck, Max.:	.4565 inch
Inside Mouth Dia. Max.:	.429 inch
Volumetric Capacity to Base of Bullet in cubic inches:	.094

Bullet

Weight:	246 grains
Approx. Length:	.810 inch
Diameter Max.:	.432 inch
Area, Cross Sectional:	.146 square inch
Shape:	Round Nose

Powder

Amount and type varies with different lots manufactured.

Cartridge

Approx. Length, Loaded:	1.593 inches
Approx. Total Weight, Loaded:	333 grains

This is viewed in many quarters as the finest heavy-caliber target revolver cartridge ever developed. Except for length, dimensions are the same as the earlier 44 S&W Russian. It retains the superb accuracy of its ancestor.

Handloaders can duplicate the discontinued .44 S & W Russian cartridge by trimming .44 Special cases to a maximum length of .970". For identical ballistics with these modern solid head cases, the powder charge must be reduced slightly to compensate for the smaller case capacity and higher loading density.

COLT   .44 S&W Special
Revolvers

These cartridges may be used in the Colt S.A. Army Model and the New Service and Shooting Master (New Service Target) Double-Action models. (See Colt under Cal. .45 Colt for details.) The obsolete Colt Bisley (see under Cal. .44 W.C.F.) and Bisley Target (see under Cal. .44 S&W Russian) models were also chambered for this and other cartridges.

SMITH AND WESSON   .44 S&W Special
New Century

Official Model Name: Model .44 Hand Ejector (New Century)—Popularly known as The Triple Lock or Gold Seal Model.

Ammunition: .44 S & W Russian. .44 S & W Special. .450 Eley. .45 Colt. .44-40 Winchester. .455 Mark II.

Manufacturing Dates: Sept. 1907-May 10, 1915.

Number Manufactured: About 20,000.

Serial Numbers: From 1 through about 15,525 in .44 Hand Ejector Series. Originally these guns were numbered up to about 20,000. However, during World War I, 5,000 were converted to the English Service Revolver of .455 Mark II caliber. About 525 of these were left in the .44 Hand Ejector numbering series, while about 4,475 were transferred to a new numbering series known as the .455 Mark II Hand Ejector (English Service) series.

Finish: Blue or nickel.

Barrel Length: 4″, 5″, 6″½, 7″½.

Notes: This gun incorporated a special yoke lock operating between the barrel lug and a hardened insert in the face of the yoke. This feature was discontinued during World War I for quantity production and because many military authorities believe that the heavy barrel lug is not satisfactory on a weapon to be used under service conditions, on the theory that there is a chance of dirt collecting in its recess and jamming the action. After the war the third lock was not put back into the design due to its expense.

473

Cylinder swung out to show details of triple lock.

Quantities Produced in Each Caliber: .44 S & W Russian—uncertain. .44 S & W Special—about 13,700. .450 Eley—1,226. .45 Colt—21. .44-40 Winchester —uncertain. .455 Mark II—about 525 numbered in .44 H. E. Series; about 4,475 numbered in .455 Mark II numbering series.

	.44 Russian	.44 Special	.450 Eley	.45 Colt	.44-40
Land Diameter:	.417-.419	.417-.419	....	.447-.448	.417-.419
Groove Dia.:	.429-.431	.429-.431	....	.457-.458	.429-.431
No. of Lands:	5	5	6	5	5
Twist: One turn in	.20″	20″	....	20″	20″
Dir. of Twist:	Right in all models.				
Dia. of Chamber:	.458-.459	.458-.459	....	.482-.483	.442-.459-.473
No. of Chambers:	6	6	6	6	6

Note: In S & W revolvers the cylinders are normally locked at the rear of the cylinder when closed ready for firing, and are locked also at the front end of the ejector rod under the barrel. The yoke (or crane) lock, locking the arm which holds the cylinder to the frame, formed the third lock from which the popular name Triple Lock was derived. Pushing the thumb catch forward releases all the S & W locks.

The lesser-powered .44 S & W Russian cartridge may be used in the .44 S & W Special in emergency; the British .450 may be used in the .455 in emergency.

The S & W Model 1917 (.45 Hand Ejector Cal. 45 U. S. Service) was modified from this revolver.

SMITH AND WESSON
Hand Ejector Second Model

.44 S&W Special

Ammunition: .44 S & W Special.
.44-40 Winchester.
.45 Colt, 6½" only.
Manufacturing Dates: May 10, 1915-1937.
Serial Numbers: From about 15,525 in the .44 H. E. numbering series.
Finish: Blue or nickel.
Barrel Lengths: 4", 5", 6½", 7½".
Notes: Combined features of New Century and .455 Mark II English Service:
  a. Yoke lock of "Triple Lock" eliminated.
  b. Large barrel lug eliminated.
  c. Chambering as in the "Triple Lock".
  d. Distance from centerhole to charge holes as in the .455-.010 greater than in the Triple Lock. Cylinder cut in frame also as in the .455-.020 larger than the Triple Lock to take care of larger cylinder.
Cylinders heat-treated from about Dec. 1921—beginning with serial numbers around 16,600.

	.44 S & W Special	*.44-40 Winchester*	*.45 Colt*
Land Diameter:	.417-.419	.417-.419	.447-.448
Groove Diameter:	.429-.431	.429-.431	.457-.458
Number of Lands:	5	5	5
Twist: One turn in	20"	20"	20"
Direction of Twist:	Right	Right	Right
Diameter of Chamber:	.458-.459	.442-.459-.473	.482-.483
Number of Chambers:	6	6	6

475

.44 S&W Special

SMITH AND WESSON
Hand Ejector 1926 Third Model

Ammunition: .44 S & W Special, also a few made on special orders to chamber .44-40 Winchester.
Manufacturing Dates: From Dec. 27, 1926 to 1950.
Serial Numbers: From about 28,358 in the .44 Hand Ejector series.
Finish: Blue or Nickel.
Barrel Lengths Service guns—4", 5", 6½".
  Target guns—6½".
Notes: This model was made up on special request for Wolf & Klar of Ft. Worth, Tex., who took the first 3500 made and had exclusive sales rights at first.

Differed from the Second Model in many details including the installation of a hammer block and the re-introduction of the heavy barrel lug used on the Triple Lock.

Wolf and Klar discontinued their firearms department in 1956. They had been one of the largest distributors of Smith & Wesson revolvers in the southwest.

Land Diameter:	.417-.419	*Direction of Twist:*	Right
Groove Diameter:	.429-.431	*Diameter of Chamber:*	.458-.459
Number of Lands:	5	*Number of Chambers:*	6
Twist: One turn in	20"		

.44 S&W Special

MISCELLANEOUS
Revolvers

Belgian, German and Spanish imitations of Colt S.A. and swing-out cylinder revolvers, and of early S&W hinged-frame weapons have been made for Mexican and South American export. None can be recommended.

476

CARTRIDGE
Data

.44 WCF (.44-40)

.44 Winchester (.44-40)

200 Gr. S. P.

Muzzle Velocity in f.s.:	975
Vel. at 50 Feet:	956
Vel. at 150 Feet:	920

Calculated Energy

Muzzle Energy in ft. lbs.:	422
Energy at 50 Feet:	406
Energy at 150 Feet:	376

Calculated Drop

At 50 Feet:	.5 inch
At 150 Feet:	4.8 inches
At 300 Feet:	20.5 inches

Penetration at 15 Feet

7/8" soft pine boards	6

Length of Barrel in Which Tested

inches	7½

Shell Case

Weight:	87.5 grains
Max. Length:	1.305 inches
Outside Body Dia. at Head, Max.:	.465 inch
Outside Body Dia. at Neck, Max.:	.4415 inch
Inside Mouth Dia. Max.:	.4255 inch
Volumetric Capacity to Base of Bullet in cubic inches:	.121

Bullet

Weight:	200 grains
Approx. Length:	.595 inch
Diameter Max.:	.427 inch
Area, Cross Sectional:	.143 square inch
Shape:	Blunt Nose

Powder

Amount and type varies with different lots manufactured.

Cartridge

Approx. Length, Loaded:	1.593 inches
Approx. Total Weight, Loaded:	305 grains

Like the .38 WCF (.38-40) cartridge, this was developed by Winchester for use in their 1873 model repeating rifle. Colt produced a model of their Single Action Army revolver to handle it. The .44-40 has a slightly bottle-necked case and cannot be used in any revolvers except those specifically chambered for it. This cartridge is made in low velocity for use in revolvers or rifles, and in high-velocity loads suitable only for use in rifles. Cartridges of this caliber should be used only in revolvers when the label on the box indicates the loads are suitable for revolvers. Rifle-type ammunition may wreck the revolver.

.44 WCF (.44-40)   **COLT**
                                                        Revolvers

The Colt New Service Model and the S. A. Army Model are both manufactured with chambers to handle this cartridge. (See under Cal. .45 Colt.)
The obsolete Bisley Model was also issued in this caliber among others.

.44 WCF (.44-40)   **COLT**
                                                        Bisley

COLT BISLEY. Showing method of extraction in Bisley and S.A. Army models. Hammer is
half cocked, loading gate swung out, cylinder turned to line up a cartridge and ejector rod
pushed up into chamber. Spring returns the rod to position when released.

General Description: An adaptation of the Single Action Army differing
primarily in having a different hammer with a low, broad spur; a different
trigger wider at the sear point as well as at the fingerpiece; and a different
grip, the front and back straps being longer and of a new outline or curve.

Ammunition: See table below.

Manufacturing Dates: 1896 to 1912.

Serial Numbers: Concurrent with Single Action Army.

Finish: Casehardened frame, blued barrel and straps or full nickel plated.

Barrel Length: 4¾", 5½" and 7½" (in addition to these 3 standard lengths
3" and 4" were also available on order, but without the ejector).

Stocks: Rubber.

Bore Diameter: See table below.

Groove Diameter: See table below.

Rifling: (Left twist). 6 grooves, 1 turn in 16".

Number of Shots: 6.
Action: Single.
Approximate Weight: 38 ounces with 4¾" barrel.
Overall Length: 10¼" with 4¾" barrel.
Sights: Fixed.
Note: This arm was an improved Single Action Army, probably developed at the insistence of the early target shooter. At that time Slow Fire was the only formal competition and the longer grip, low hammer, and broad trigger offered definite advantage. With the growth of the 3-stage match (Slow, Timed and Rapid) ease of handling became a factor and another type of arm featuring shorter barrels, a quicker action, etc., came to the fore.

Ammunition:	*.32 L.C.*	*.32 Pol. Pos.* *(S & W)*	*.32/20*	*.38 L.C.*
Bore Diameter:	.305"—.001	.305"—.001	.305"—.001	*
Groove Diameter:	.312"—.001	.312"—.001	.312"—.001	

Ammunition:	*.38/40*	*.41 L.C.*	*.44 Russ.* *(&Spcl.)*	*.44/40*	*.45 Colt*
Bore Dia.:	.395"—.001	.395"—.001	.420"—.001	.420"—.001	.445"—.001
Groove Dia.:	.402"—.001	.402"—.001	.427"—.001	.427"—.001	.452"—.001

SMITH AND WESSON   .44 WCF (.44-40)
Double Action

S&W MODEL .44 CAL. DOUBLE ACTION (FRONTIER)

Official Model Names: Model .44 Caliber Double Action (First Model).
  Model .44 Caliber Double Action (Wesson Favorite).
  Model .44 Caliber Double Action (Frontier).
Ammunition: First Model—.44 S & W Russian, also made chambered for
  .38-40.
  Wesson Favorite—.44 S & W Russian.
  Frontier—.44-40 Winchester Rifle Cartridge.

---

* When this cartridge became obsolete the probable bore was .350 with a corresponding groove diameter of .357.

Manufacturing Dates: First Model—1881-1908.
                            Wesson Favorite—1882-1883.
                            Frontier—1886-1908.
Number Manufactured: First Model—55,000.
                            Wesson Favorite—Approximately 1,000.
                            Frontier—15,000.

Serial Numbers: The First Model and Wesson Favorite were numbered in the same series. The Frontier was numbered in a separate series.

Finish: Blue and nickel.

Barrel Lengths: First Model—.44 Russian, 4″, 5″, 6″, 6½″.
                  First Model—.38-40, 6½″.
                  Wesson Favorite—4″, 5″, 6″, 6½″.
                  Frontier—4″, 5″, 6″, 6½″.

	.44 Russian	*.38-40 Winchester*	*.44-40 Winchester*
Land Diameter:	.417-.419	.388-.389	.417-.419
Groove Diameter:	.429-.431	.400-.401	.428-.431
Number of Lands:	5	5	5
Twist: One turn in	20″	20″	20″
Direction of Twist:	Right	Right	Right
Diameter of Chamber:	.458-.459	.418-.456-.472	.442-.459-.473
Number of Chambers:	6	6	6

Notes: The Wesson Favorite differed from the First Model in that several extra cuts were taken and grooves milled externally to produce a lighter gun.

The Frontier was essentially the same as the First Model except for chambering.

.44 WCF (.44-40)   **SMITH AND WESSON**
                                                    Miscellaneous

See data under Cal. .44 S&W Special. The S&W .44 H.E. 1926 (3rd Model) and the .44 H.E. Second Model were made in this caliber also.

.44 WCF (.44-40)   **MISCELLANEOUS**
                                                     Revolvers

Spanish, German, and Belgian makers have made this caliber in hinged-frame type for export. These revolvers seldom have any identifying marks on them. The .44-40 is too powerful to be used safely in such revolvers.

Chapter 12
Caliber .45

CARTRIDGE   .45 S&W Center Fire
Data

While obsolete, this black-powder cartridge is still occasionally encountered. Originally designed for the hinged-frame S&W Army revolver of 1875 it was adapted to the Colt S.A. Army revolver. The government made this caliber for many years for army use, and it is often listed as the ".45 Colt Government." The cartridge measures 1.43 inches overall. Bullet diameter is .454 inch and the weight was, originally 230 grains. This cartridge is sometimes loaded with a 250-grain bullet. With the standard bullet and the 28-grain, black-powder charge the muzzle velocity is about 730 f.p.s. and the energy about 265 f.p. This cartridge must not be confused with the larger .45 Colt Revolver cartridge, though it may be loaded into the Colt chamber.

COLT   .45 S&W Center Fire
Single Action Army

This revolver in .45 Colt caliber will handle the old .45 S&W cartridge, which is shorter than the .45 Colt.

SMITH AND WESSON   .45 S&W Center Fire
SA Schofield

Manufacturing Date:	1875-77	*Groove Diameter:*	.447-.449
Number Manufactured:	Approx.	*Number of Lands:*	5
9,000.*		*Twist:* One turn in	24″
Finish: Blue or nickel.		*Direction of Twist:*	Right
Barrel Length:	7″	*Diameter of Chamber:*	.481-.482
Land Diameter:	.435-.437	*Number of Chambers:*	6

* About 3,000 of the first model were produced in 1875 and about 5,900 of the second model were produced from 1876-77.

Notes: This gun was specially designed for the U. S. Army Cavalry, using a heavy barrel catch developed by General Schofield.

Although the gun carried by General Custer at his famous Last Stand on the Little Big Horn has never been positively traced, reliable reports indicate that it was a S & W Schofield Model.

Gun No. 366 of this series was taken from Jesse James when he was shot by Robert Ford, on April 3, 1882. This gun has "Laura" scratched on the right side of the frame, the name of one of James' sweethearts.

.450 Webley (Adams)   CARTRIDGE
.450 Revolvers, Marks I, II and III   Data

This cartridge is obsolescent but is occasionally encountered. The actual bullet diameter is .450 inch—one of the few cases where the designation tells the true caliber. Cartridge length, 1.12 inches, weight of bullet 225 grains, muzzle velocity about 650 feet per second. Not adapted to modern revolvers. The old S&W Model No. 3 S.A. New Model (see under Cal. .44 S&W Russian) was chambered for this cartridge.

.45 Colt   CARTRIDGE
                                            Data

.45 Colt

255 Gr. Lub.

Muzzle Velocity in f.s.:	870
Vel. at 50 Feet:	856
Vel. at 150 Feet:	830

Calculated Energy

Muzzle Energy in ft. lbs.:	429
Energy at 50 Feet:	416
Energy at 150 Feet:	390

Calculated Drop

At 50 Feet:	.7 inch
At 150 Feet:	6.0 inches
At 300 Feet:	24.5 inches

Penetration at 15 Feet

⅞" soft pine boards	6

Length of Barrel in Which Tested

inches	5½

Shell Case

Weight:	80.5 grains
Max. Length:	1.285 inches
Outside Body Dia. at Head, Max.:	.480 inch
Outside Body Dia. at Neck, Max.:	.480 inch
Inside Mouth Dia. Max.:	.4545 inch
Volumetric Capacity to Base of Bullet in cubic inches:	.121

Bullet

Weight:	255 grains
Approx. Length:	.715 inch
Diameter Max.:	.455 inch
Area, Cross Sectional:	.162 square inch
Shape:	Blunt Nose

Powder

Amount and type varies with different lots manufactured.

Cartridge

Approx. Length, Loaded:	1.593 inches
Approx. Total Weight, Loaded:	347 grains

This is the famous revolver cartridge of the old west. The Single Action Army, popularly known as the Peacemaker, shot this cartridge. In its original black-powder loading it was an efficient heavy-duty cartridge. The large volume of the case made it less satisfactory in smokeless powder loads.

COLT .45 Colt

Single Action Army, Frontier, Peacemaker

General Description: Factory Model P. A heavy single-action revolver with rod ejection, cylinder turning on a removable base pin, loading gate in the general form of the ball-shaped rear of the frame, with the demountable straps and trigger guard of preceding powder and ball models.

Manufacturing Dates: From Government competition of 1873 to 1941, 1955 to date.

Serial Numbers: From Number 1.

Finish: Blue or Nickel (many arms of this model have been manufactured with frame and loading gate in a casehardened finish).

Barrel Lengths: 4¾", 5½" and 7½" have been the standard lengths of this model but many have been produced with 3", 3½" and 4" barrels (without ejectors). In the target grade a 7½" length only was available. This grade was also chambered for the .22 Short. In addition to calibers listed, approximately 2,000 were made in calibers .44 Rimfire. The U. S. Army cut a number of the 7½"-barrel pistols to 5½".

Stocks: Rubber, plain walnut on arms sold to U. S. Government. Hand-checked walnut with medallion on special orders.

Groove Diameter: See table below.

Rifling: (Left twist). 6 grooves. 1 turn in 16".

Number of Shots: 6.

Action: Single.

Approximate Weight: .45 caliber, 4¾" barrel: 36 ounces.

Over-all Length: 10¼" with 4¾" barrel.

Note: This arm has been manufactured since 1873 with no change in design except that the original base pin screw (requiring a screw driver for removal) was replaced by a base pin catch (an assembly of three parts) allowing the base pin to be withdrawn (and the cylinder removed) without the use of tools.

Ammunition:	*.32 L.C.*	*.32 Pol. Pos.*	*.32/20*
Land Diameter:	.305"—.001	.305"—.001	.305"—.001
Groove Diameter:	.312"—.001	.312"—.001	.312"—.001
Ammunition:	*.357*	*.38/40*	*.41 L.C.*	*.44 Spcl.*
Land Diameter:	.347"—.001	.395"—.001	.395"	.420"—.001

483

Ammunition:	.357	.38/40	.41 L.C.	.44 Spcl.
Groove Diameter:	.354″—.001	.402″—.001	.402″	.427″—.001
Ammunition:	.38 L.C.	.38 Pol. Pos.		.38 Spcl.
Land Diameter:	....	.347″—.001		.347″—.001
Groove Diameter:	*	.354″—.001		.354″—.001
Ammunition:	.44/40	.45 Colt		.45 A.C.P.
Land Diameter:	.420″—.001	.445″—.001		.444″—.001
Groove Diameter:	.427″—.001	.452″—.001		.451″—.001

With the advent of smokeless powder certain changes in materials together with the heat treatment thereof were made. Both changes date from approximately Number 165,000. It is interesting to note that it was possible to safely chamber this model without change for the modern high-velocity small-arms cartridges (including the .357) as they were developed. Probably no model has been so widely used by both amateur and custom gunsmiths as the basis for special arms to satisfy individual desire for research and experiment. Certainly no model has had a greater part in the settling of the West (and South-West), both in fact and in fiction.

Construction: The principal parts are the barrel, cylinder assembly, frame and lockwork.

The front sight is positioned on the barrel, while the rear sight is a slot machined into the top of the frame directly ahead of the hammer.

The cylinder is mounted on a removable axis pin in the solid frame. It is bored to provide six chambers for cartridges. A ratchet is machined into the center of the rear cylinder face to provide a piece against which the hand can exert pressure to revolve the cylinder as the hammer is cocked. As in all the later Colt swing-out cylinder revolvers, this hand has two points, one directly above the other. The upper point presses up against the ratchet as the hammer goes back and the revolution of the cylinder begins; the construction of the ratchet and hand are such that the hand moves in a perpendicular plane, while the ratchet moves in the arc of a circle. Because of this, the upper point on the hand loses its hold on the tooth of the ratchet before the cylinder has revolved a full one-sixth turn. The lower point on the hand picks up the next tooth of the ratchet at the proper instant to continue the cylinder rotation and bring a chamber in line with the axis of the bore.

The cylinder is also provided with a bushing projecting in front of it, which provides a third surface upon which the cylinder rotates. The design of the cylinder mounting in this revolver had much to do with its reputation for general reliability.

On the right side of the frame directly behind the cylinder a loading gate is provided which can be pushed out against spring tension to expose the chamber directly in front of it.

A sliding ejector rod, around which is a coil spring, is mounted below the barrel. The rod is offset so that whenever a chamber is in line with it, the rod may be pushed through to eject the empty cartridge.

The hammer is provided with three notches. Drawing the hammer back

---

* When this cartridge became obsolete probable bore diameter was .350 with a corresponding groove diameter of .357.

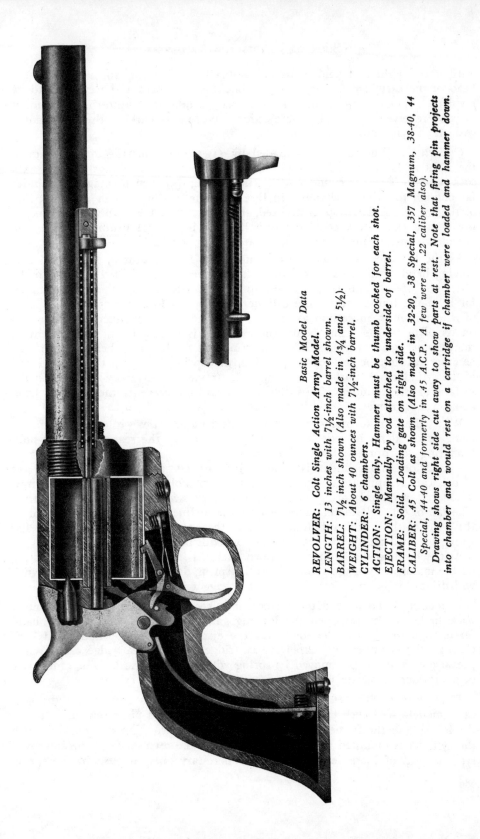

Basic Model Data

REVOLVER: Colt Single Action Army Model.
LENGTH: 13 inches with 7½-inch barrel shown.
BARREL: 7½ inch shown (Also made in 4¾ and 5½).
WEIGHT: About 40 ounces with 7½-inch barrel.
CYLINDER: 6 chambers.
ACTION: Single only. Hammer must be thumb cocked for each shot.
EJECTION: Manually by rod attached to underside of barrel.
FRAME: Solid. Loading gate on right side.
CALIBER: .45 Colt as shown (Also made in 32-20, 38 Special, 357 Magnum, 38-40, 44
   Special, 44-40 and formerly in .45 A.C.P. A few were in .22 caliber also).
   Drawing shows right side cut away to show parts at rest. Note that firing pin projects
   into chamber and would rest on a cartridge if chamber were loaded and hammer down.

until it is caught and held in its first notch lifts the firing pin away from the head of the cartridge in the chamber, but does *not* permit the cylinder to be revolved. When it is drawn back to the second or *half-cock* notch, the cylinder may be revolved for loading or ejection. Pulling it back to the third notch cocks it in firing position.

Operation: The revolver is loaded by (1) turning out the loading gate to the right as far as it will go; (2) then pulling the hammer back to the half-cock notch to free the cylinder so it will revolve; (3) then turning the cylinder far enough to bring a chamber in line with the loading slot in the right side of the frame. A cartridge is inserted, then the cylinder is revolved by hand to bring each chamber successively into line for individual loading. When the cylinder is fully loaded, the loading gate is snapped back into place.

As the hammer is drawn back to full cock by the thumb, the cylinder-revolving hand of the lockwork (which in this weapon is pivoted directly to the lower end of the hammer), is lifted up and pushed through the slot machined for it in the frame behind the cylinder. Its points force up against the teeth of the ratchet in succession as already described. The cylinder bolt mounted on its pivot in the frame below the cylinder, is forced out of engagement as the hammer reaches half-cock, compressing the small spring below it. As the hammer reaches the full-cocked position, this spring forces up the forward end of the cylinder bolt pushing it through the frame and engaging in a slot in the surface of the cylinder. This acts as a lock and prevents the cylinder from going past its correct line with the bore.

When the cam surface at the rear of the hammer rises while the hammer is being revolved on its axis for cocking, it presses up the rear end of the bolt, liberating its front end from the notch.

Just before the cylinder is completely revolved, the beveled lower surface of this cam is opposite its contact point on the bolt; the bolt is slit to permit it to carry a lateral spring while its head is pressed upwards by a flat spring. The tail of the bolt therefore slides over the inclined cammed surface, enabling the head of the cylinder bolt to catch in the notch in the cylinder. The flat spring is so slit and bent that it acts upon both bolt and trigger.

As the head of the hammer is drawn back, its inner surface, which is resting on the mainspring in the grip, presses the spring down to provide tension which will drive the hammer forward when the trigger is pressed.

Unloading: To unload the weapon it is necessary (1) to draw the hammer back to half-cock; (2) open the loading gate; (3) turn the cylinder by hand far enough to align a chamber with the ejector rod; (4) push the rod back through the chamber and expel the cartridge or empty cartridge case. When pressure on the rod is removed its spring will pull it forward. The same cycle of operations is necessary to unload each chamber in the cylinder.

Dismounting: To remove the cylinder. If the revolver is one of the very early models, half cock the hammer and loosen the axis pin screw mounted on the left side of the frame just forward of the cylinder. The axis pin on which the cylinder is mounted may be drawn out. If the revolver is of the improved type, instead of loosening a screw, it is necessary only to push in the spring catch on the left side of the frame far enough to free it from its notch in the axis pin which may then be pulled out.

Open the loading gate and the cylinder may be pushed out of the frame to the right.

If it is desired to strip the weapon further, the stocks may be removed by unscrewing the two screws just below the hammer and the one at the bottom of the butt strap. As the stocks cover part of the lockwork, they give access to the mainspring, hammer and trigger mechanism. Withdrawing the screw at the lower side of the frame on the right will permit removal of the loading gate. This screw is covered by the trigger guard and it is necessary to unscrew the trigger guard screw at the front end of the frame and remove the trigger guard and grip units. The loading gate has a spring and a catch and care should be taken in withdrawing them.

Unfastening the screw at the forward end of the ejector tube will permit the front end to be pushed off the barrel and pulled toward the muzzle.

The barrel may now be unscrewed, though if this is done it is a major gunsmith's job to reinsert and align it properly.

The cylinder bushing on which the cylinder rests and through which the axis pin passes, may be pushed out.

Reassemblying this weapon is merely a matter of reversing the stripping procedure.

COLT .45 Colt
Bisley Single Action

The obsolete Bisley Model (see under Cal. .44-40 W.C.F.) and Bisley Target Model (see under Cal. .44 S&W Russian) were also made for this cartridge.

COLT .45 Colt
Double Action Army

General Description: Colt's first heavy-frame (.45 caliber) double-action revolver, with limb work and general design similar to the .38/41 Double-Action, but having an assembly part with a circular closure on the left side and a lanyard loop as a standard item.

Ammunition: .32/20. .38/40. .41 L.C. .44/40. .45 Colt.

Manufacturing Dates: 1877 to 1909.

Serial Numbers: No record of initial series but probably from Number 1 to 51,169.

Finish: Blue or nickel.

Barrel Length: 4¾", 5½", 7½". All calibers.

Stocks: Rubber. Plain walnut.

	.32/20	.38/40	.41 L.C.	.44/40	.45 Colt
Bore Dia.:	.305"—.001	.305"—.001	.395"—.001	.420"—.001	.445"—.001
Groove Dia.:	.312"—.001	.402"—.001	.402"—.001	.427"—.001	.452"—.001

Rifling: (Left twist). 6 grooves.

Number of Shots: 6.

Action: Double.

Approximate Weight: 39 ounces with 7½" barrel.

Over-all Length: About 12½″ with 7½″ barrel.

Sights: Fixed. Front: integral with barrel. Rear: groove and notch in top of frame.

Note: Many of this model were made on Government order for cavalry use, differing from standard design in having a much larger trigger guard and longer trigger to permit use with a gloved hand. With these variations this arm has been known as the Alaskan Model and the Philippine Model.

.45 Colt

COLT
New Service

General Description: A large-caliber heavy-duty holster arm built on a .45 caliber frame designed especially for military and constabulary organizations.

Ammunition: See table below.
Manufacturing Dates: 1897 to 1943, when it was discontinued.
Serial Numbers: From Number 1.
Finish: Blue or Nickel.
Barrel Length: See table below.
Stocks: Rubber. Plain walnut. Checked walnut with medallion.
Bore Diameter: See table below.
Groove Diameter: See table below.
Rifling: (Left twist). 6 grooves. 1 turn in 16".
Number of Shots: 6.
Action: Double.
Approximate Weight: .45 caliber 4½", 39 ounces. .38 caliber 6", 43 ounces.
Over-all Length: 9¾" with 4½" barrel.
Sights: Fixed. Front: integral with barrel. Rear: groove and notch in top strap.

Note: With this model began the development of the modern Colt rebound lever which contributes much to both safety and simplicity. The first arms produced used a fly in place of the present solid cam. This change was in effect with the addition of the positive lock safety in the 1905.

During 1917-18 over 150,000 of this model were sold to the U. S. Government chambered for the .45 A.C.P. cartridge and with a head space of .090+ so that this cartridge (which is rimless) could be loaded (and ejected) using three-shot half-moon-shaped clips. On early production the cartridges seated so deeply in the chambers that the firing pin could not reach them unless they were inserted on the clips. Later this was remedied to permit the cylinder to be loaded with loose cartridges in emergency, but since the extractor had no hold on the rimless case, it was necessary to punch or pry the empties out of the chambers in the cylinder.

After World War I a .45 Auto-rim cartridge was brought out for commercial distribution obviating any need for clips. This model was also bought by the Government prior to World War I with a 5½" barrel and chambered for the .45 Colt cartridge. Standard specifications for these orders have included plain walnut stocks and a lanyard loop in the butt. Present refinements include rounded latch and matted top strap with a square cut notch of the Patridge type.

				.44 Russ. &
Ammunition: .38 Spcl.	.357	.38/40	.44/40	*S.&W. Spcl.*
Barrel Lengths: 4"	4"	4½"	4½"	4½"
5"	5"	5½"	5½"	5½"
6"	6"	7½"	7½"	7½"
Bore Dia.: .347"−.001	.347"−.001	.395"−.001	.420"−.001	.420"−.001
Groove Dia.: .354"−.001	.354"−.001	.402"−.001	.427"−.001	.427"−.001
Ammunition: .45 A.C.P.	.45 Colt	.450 Eley	.455 Eley	.476 Eley
Barrel Lengths: 4½"	*2 "	4½"	4½"	4½"
5½"	*3½"	5½"	5½"	5½"

———————
* With ramp-type front sight.

	.45 A.C.P.	.45 Colt	.450 Eley	.455 Eley	.476 Eley
	7½″	4½″	7½″	7½″	7½″
		5½″			
		7½″			
Bore Dia.:	.444″–.001	.445″–.001	No record	.445″–.001	No record
Groove Dia.:	.451″–.001	.452″–.001		.452″–.001	

.45 Colt

COLT

Target. New Service Shooting Master

General Description: Factory Model J. A heavy target revolver with checked straps, hand-finished action and all parts held to minimum tolerances. With the increased importance of the Timed and Rapid Fire stages in competition the 6″ barrel became standard, as well as a narrower curved butt, with the original butt available on special order only.

Ammunition: .38 Special. .357. .44 Special. .45 Colt. .45 A.C.P. .455 Eley.

Manufacturing Dates: From August 7, 1900 (first record of shipment) until discontinued in 1941.

Serial Numbers: Concurrent with New Service.

Finish: Blue.

	.38 Spcl.	.357	.44 Spcl.	.45 Colt	.45 A.C.P.	.455 Eley
Barrel Length:	6″	6″	6″	6″	6″	
			7½″	7½″	7½″	7½″

Stocks: Checked walnut with medallion.

	.38 Spcl.	.357	.44 Spcl.
Bore Diameter:	.347″–.001	.347″–.001	.420″–.001
Groove Diameter:	.354″–.001	.354″–.001	.427″–.001
	.45 Colt	.45 A.C.P.	.455 Eley
Bore Diameter:	.445″–.001	.444″–.001	.445″–.001

490

	45 Colt	.45 A.C.P.	.455 .Eley
Groove Diameter:	.452″—.001	.451″—.001	.452″—.001

Rifling: (Left twist). 6 grooves. 1 turn in 16″.
Number of Shots: 6.
Action: Double.
Approximate Weight: .38 caliber 6″, 44 ounces.
Over-all Length: 11¼″ with 6″ barrel.
Sights: Target type. Front: adjustable for elevation. Rear: for windage.
Note: Except for sights and finishing details noted, this model is the same as the New Service.

Current specifications for The Shooting Master give 6″ as the standard (and only) length.

SMITH AND WESSON   .45 Colt
Miscellaneous

The S&W New Century and the H.E. Model Second Model (see both under Cal. .44 S&W Special) were chambered also for this cartridge.

Same as under Caliber .44-40 W.C.F.

MISCELLANEOUS   .45 Colt
Revolvers

Inferior imitations of Colt and S&W patterns from Belgium, Germany and Spain have been widely circulated in Central and South America. Many have imitations of Colt or S&W insignia. They may be recognized by the fact that they either bear no name or have the American manufacturer's name or address deliberately misspelled. They range from fair to dangerous in quality.

.45 ACP

.45 Automatic

230 Gr. M.C.

Muzzle Velocity in f.s.:	860
Vel. at 50 Feet:	845
Vel. at 150 Feet:	817

Calculated Energy

Muzzle Energy in ft. lbs.:	378
Energy at 50 Feet:	365
Energy at 150 Feet:	341

Calculated Drop

At 50 Feet:	.7 inch
At 150 Feet:	6.3 inches
At 300 Feet:	26.4 inches

Penetration at 15 Feet

7/8" soft pine boards	6

Length of Barrel in Which Tested

inches	5

Shell Case

Weight:	86.5 grains
Max. Length:	.898 inch
Outside Body Dia. at Head, Max.:	.476 inch
Outside Body Dia. at Neck. Max.:	.472 inch
Inside Mouth Dia. Max.:	.450 inch
Volumetric Capacity to Base of Bullet in cubic inches:	.0622

Bullet

Weight:	230 grains
Approx. Length:	.680 inch
Diameter Max.:	.451 inch
Area, Cross Sectional:	.1597 square inch
Shape:	Round Nose

Powder

Amount and type varies with different lots manufactured.

Cartridge

Approx. Length, Loaded:	1.275 inches
Approx. Total Weight, Loaded:	327 grains

.45 Auto Super Match

230 Gr.

Muzzle Velocity in f.s.:	710
Vel. at 50 Feet:	700
Vel. at 150 Feet:	680

Calculated Energy

Muzzle Energy in ft. lbs.:	257
Energy at 50 Feet:	251
Energy at 150 Feet:	236

Calculated Drop

At 50 Feet:	.9 inch
At 150 Feet:	8.7 inches
At 300 Feet:	38.0 inches

Penetration at 15 Feet

7/8" soft pine boards	5

Length of Barrel in Which Tested

inches	5

Shell Case

Weight:	86.5 grains
Max. Length:	.898 inch
Outside Body Dia. at Head, Max.:	.476 inch
Outside Body Dia. at Neck. Max.:	.472 inch
Inside Mouth Dia. Max.:	.450 inch
Volumetric Capacity to Base of Bullet in cubic inches:	.062

Bullet

Weight:	230 grains
Approx. Length:	.680 inch
Diameter Max.:	.4505 inch
Area, Cross Sectional:	.1593 square inch
Shape:	Round Nose

Powder

Amount and type varies with different lots manufactured.

Cartridge

Approx. Length, Loaded:	1.275 inches
Approx. Total Weight, Loaded:	327 grains

.45 Auto Super-X

230 Gr. M.P.			*Shell Case*	
Muzzle Velocity in f.s.:	940		Weight:	86.5 grains
Vel. at 50 Feet:	922		Max. Length:	.898 inch
Vel. at 150 Feet:	887		Outside Body Dia. at Head, Max.:	.476 inch

230 Gr. M.P.

Muzzle Velocity in f.s.:	940
Vel. at 50 Feet:	922
Vel. at 150 Feet:	887

Calculated Energy

Muzzle Energy in ft. lbs.:	450
Energy at 50 Feet:	434
Energy at 150 Feet:	403

Calculated Drop

At 50 Feet:	.5 inch
At 150 Feet:	5.2 inches
At 300 Feet:	22.3 inches

Penetration at 15 Feet

7/8″ soft pine boards   11
    Length of Barrel in Which Tested
inches   5

Shell Case

Weight:	86.5 grains
Max. Length:	.898 inch
Outside Body Dia. at Head, Max.:	.476 inch
Outside Body Dia. at Neck, Max.:	.472 inch
Inside Mouth Dia. Max.:	.450 inch
Volumetric Capacity to Base of Bullet in cubic inches:	.058

Bullet

Weight:	230 grains
Approx. Length:	.675 inch
Diameter Max.:	.4505 inch
Area, Cross Sectional:	.1593 square inch
Shape:	Conical

Powder

Amount and type varies with different lots manufactured.

Cartridge

Approx. Length, Loaded:	1.275 inches
Approx. Total Weight, Loaded:	327 grains

This is a rimless cartridge. It is the official pistol cartridge of our armed forces and was extensively used by the British and Canadian troops in both World Wars. While it is very much shorter than the old .45 Colt Revolver cartridge, it is practically as powerful because its case was specifically designed for efficient combustion of smokeless powder, while the revolver cartridge was designed in black-powder days.

.45 ACP   **COLT**
Military (Old Model)

General Description: A holster arm of the military type with a slide stop, exposed hammer with spur but no safety device other than a floating firing pin. A small number of this type were made with a short-grip safety. Numerous experimental models of this type were developed for Government tests but were not generally marketed.

Ammunition: .45 A.C.P.
Manufacturing Dates: December 26, 1905 to 1911.
Serial Numbers: From Number 1.
Finish: Blue.
Barrel Length: 5" (approx.).
Stocks: Checked walnut, no medallion.
Bore Diameter: .444"−.001.
Groove Diameter: .451"−.001.
Rifling: (Left twist). 6 grooves. 1 turn in 16".
Number of Shots: 7.
Action: Semiautomatic, recoil operated. Locked breech.
Approximate Weight: 33½ ounces.
Overall Length: 8".
Sights: Fixed. Front: swaged in slide. Rear: driven in dovetail cut.
Note: The barrel was assembled to the receiver with two links with lugs on top fitting corresponding cuts in the slide. The slide was held on the receiver by a transverse slide lock which, when withdrawn, allowed the slide to be removed by drawing it to the rear.
Construction and Operation: See under Cal. .38 A.C.P. general description of the .38 Military Automatic Old Model.

.45 ACP   **COLT**
.45 Government (Model O-45)

General Description: A holster model designed strictly for military use yet achieving a wide acceptance with peace officers and sportsmen where a heavy arm with the convenience of the automatic is desirable.

Ammunition: .45 A.C.P. .455 Eley Automatic (British .455 S. L.).
Manufacturing Dates: Commercial from 1911 to date.
                     Government from 1911 to date.
Serial Numbers: Commercial from Number c1.
                     Government from Number 1.
Finish: Blue.
Barrel Length: 5".
Stocks: Checked walnut, no medallion. Plastic.

	.45 A.C.P.	.455 Eley Auto.
Bore Diameter:	.444"−.001.	.451"−.001.
Groove Diameter:	.451"−.001.	.458"−.001.

Rifling: (Left twist). 6 grooves. 1 turn in 16".
Number of Shots: 7.
Action: Semiautomatic, recoil operated. Locked breech.
Approximate Weight: 39 ounces.
Over-all Length: 8½".

COLT GOVERNMENT MODEL. *Insert shows external differences of original 1911 design from current 1911A1.*

Sights: Fixed. Front: swaged in slide. Rear: driven in dovetail cut.

Note: This model was developed from the older .45 Automatic (Old or Military Model) for the U. S. Government competition of 1911. The final design differed so radically from the older model that it was in fact an entirely new model. Among the requirements were simplicity and an arm that could be completely disassembled without tools, practical accuracy using a heavy bullet of maximum effectiveness, and reliability under unfavorable service conditions.

The original design, M1911, was followed until 1921 when certain changes were recommended by the Government. These included an arched and checked mainspring housing, a shorter checked trigger, recess cuts on both sides of the receiver to accommodate the trigger finger, a longer horn on the grip safety and a slightly shortened hammer spur. These redesigned parts are interchangeable with those of the original design. With these the arm took the governmental designation of M1911A1.

This arm is also produced commercially in two target-grade models, National Match (fixed sights) and National Match (adjustable sights). Both have hand finished actions, parts matched for maximum accuracy and minimum toler-

495

Colt Govt. Model 1911A1

All parts at rest except compressed magazine
spring. Note that barrel is locked into slide;
and rear of barrel is supported by the famous
Browning link. Details of the equally famous Browning safety firing pin,
slide construction and disconnector are also shown.

Note: Drawing on Page 501 is phantomed and cutaway to show operation
of unlocking, disconnecting and loading systems in full recoil position.

Basic Model Data
AUTOMATIC PIS-
TOL: Colt Govern-
ment Model.
LENGTH: 8½ inches.
BARREL: 5 inches.
WEIGHT: 39 ounces.
MAGAZINE: Detachable box. Thumb release on left
side of grip. Capacity 7 cartridges.
OPERATION: Short recoil, locked breech. Barrel
and slide start back locked together for short
travel. Slide continues to rear as it is unlocked.
LOCK: Ribs on top of barrel engage in recesses in ceiling of slide when barrel is up-
right on its supporting link. During recoil barrel swings down on link at chamber end to disengage from slide. On forward movement breechblock face of slide
strikes barrel and pushes it ahead and up on its link to lock. Link is locked to
receiver by traverse pin on slide stop. Barrel is supported at muzzle by bushing
in slide.
MAINSPRING: Coil in housing at bottom of grip. Serves hammer through a hammer strut.
DISCONNECTOR: Slide moving to rear rides over head of disconnector forcing it
down out of slide recess into receiver and breaking trigger contact with sear.
TRIGGER: Has stirrup across magazine well. Pressure pivots disconnector which is
mounted with sear causing sear to pivot to release hammer.
SAFETY: Manual. Thumb catch on left rear of receiver when pushed up positively
locks both hammer and sear and also prevents slide from being opened. Grip
safety. Squeeze grip is forced in by shooting hand to permit trigger contact to
be made. Automatic in operation.
RECOIL SPRING: Coil with guide housed below barrel. Housed in plug at muzzle
end. Plug retained by barrel bushing.
EXTRACTION EJECTION: Extractor is spring claw in right of slide. Ejector is solid upright piece pinned to receiver and rising into travel slot in underside of slide.
SLIDE STOP: Operated by magazine follower holds slide open. Release on left side of receiver.
CALIBER: .45 A.C.P. (Note: was also made for British .455 S.L.)

ances. The first has fixed sights, the latter a fixed front with a rear sight adjustable for both elevation and windage.

Construction: This pistol has three principal parts: the receiver, the barrel, and the slide.

The receiver has a hollow handle into which the magazine is inserted from below; and is machined to receive the magazine locking catch which is inserted through a hole in the receiver on the left side directly behind the trigger guard.

The receiver is also provided with guide to receive the slide which travels back and forth in it as well as a semitubular extension projecting forward from the front of the trigger guard and serving as an abutment for the slide to prevent it traveling too far to the rear.

Note that in this design the slide is inserted in the receiver from the front end. *It is therefore utterly impossible, as can happen in some automatic pistols, for the slide to be blown back off the weapon.*

The trigger is of the stirrup type. It is seated in the receiver, its front end projecting into the trigger guard. An arm on each side passes across the receiver and permits the magazine inserted in the handle below to pass up between its two arms without interfering with the trigger mechanism.

The firing mechanism is mounted in the rear of the receiver. It comprises the hammer, sear, automatic disconnector, grip safety, safety lock, sear spring, and mainspring housing assembly.

The hammer is fastened to the receiver on both sides by a hammer pin passing *through its axis.* It is provided with a full- and a half-cock notch. A strut is attached to the hammer in rear of its pivot. The end of this strut rests in a concave section of the mainspring cap.

The mainspring housing is a solid steel unit inserted in guides in the receiver from below. It is hollowed out to receive the coil mainspring and the concave cap which covers the mainspring, as well as a retainer pin which fastens the mainspring housing securely to the receiver at the bottom of the handle.

The sear spring is a flat spring with three leaves. A rib at its lower end fits into a slot in the rear wall of the receiver to keep the spring from moving vertically. The mainspring housing when inserted bears against the rear of the sear spring and locks it firmly into position and also gives it required spring tension.

A tube is mounted above the left grip on the receiver. In this tube are slide stop and safety lock plungers, with a spiral plunger spring seated between them. This spring acts to keep the slide stop plunger thrust firmly against the slide stop and the safety lock plunger firmly against the thumb safety lock. This spring is yielding enough to permit both the slide stop and the safety lock to be pushed down out of engagement without difficulty.

The ejector is secured to the top of the receiver near its rear end.

The semitubular extension at the forward end of the top of the receiver also serves to house the rear portion of the recoil spring as well as the recoil spring guide on which the spring is mounted.

The slide, which is also the breechblock in its rear section, is mounted on the receiver *from the front.* A tubular abutment below it strikes against the abutment on the forward extension of the receiver to positively prevent the slide being thrown to the rear off the receiver.

In this abutment at the front end of the slide the forward portion of the recoil spring rests, together with the sheet-metal plug which fits over its end. The rear end of the recoil spring and guide are firmly supported by a shoulder at the front end of the receiver.

A turning barrel bushing over the muzzle of the barrel locks into cuts in the inside of the slide when in position, and its arms below the muzzle retain the recoil spring plug and the recoil spring in position.

A slide stop is provided on the left side of the receiver. It has a checkered thumbpiece. When the last cartridge in the magazine has been fired, this stop is forced up by a step on the magazine follower and locks in a slot in the slide holding it back. Withdrawing the magazine and inserting a new one, permits quick loading by pushing down the thumbpiece which releases the lock from the slide and permits the slide to go forward to reload the weapon.

The barrel is fitted with two transverse ribs on its top which lock into corresponding slots on the inner surface of the slide.

There is a lug below the firing chamber at the rear of the barrel which is machined to receive a swinging link which is pivoted to the lug by a pin. When the slide stop pin is inserted as the weapon is assembled, the pin passes through the left side of the receiver, then through a lower hole in the swinging barrel link, and on through the receiver wall on the right-hand side of the pistol. This arrangement securely locks the barrel, slide, and receiver.

The thumb safety on the left side of the receiver can be pushed up into a recess in the slide when the hammer is cocked. As it is pushed up, a stud on its inner face positively locks the sear and the hammer to prevent the weapon from being fired.

A grip safety is provided in this weapon. Its upper part is pivoted by a pin to the receiver. Until it is pressed in when the pistol is gripped for firing, the weapon cannot be fired.

The automatic disconnector is pushed up by a leaf of the sear spring into a niche cut for it in the underside of the rear of the slide. *Unless the head of this disconnector can ride into this hole, it is impossible for the trigger to press against the sear* (which is locked into the full-cock notch in the hammer when the weapon is ready to be fired) and hence it is impossible to fire the weapon except when it is fully locked; and then only when the trigger is released *after each shot.*

The magazine is a tubular box with holes in its sides to permit counting the cartridges therein. It contains a spring which rests on the magazine bottom, whose top end exerts upward pressure against the magazine follower or platform on which the first cartridge rests. The cartridges are retained in the magazine by the lips at the rear at the top being bent over enough to hold them. The front end at the top is cut away enough to permit a cartridge to be placed on the follower and forced down and back under the lip.

The magazine also has a cut into which the magazine catch engages to hold it in the handle.

The front end of the magazine follower is split and its left half is bent down and shaped so that when the last cartridge has been fired, the bent section hooks under the slide stop and pushes the stop up to engage in the notch prepared for it in the left side of the slide. This holds the weapon open when the last shot has been fired to give notice that the pistol is empty.

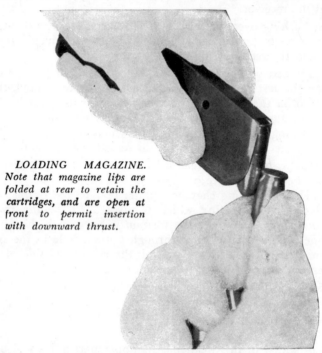

LOADING MAGAZINE.
Note that magazine lips are folded at rear to retain the cartridges, and are open at front to permit insertion with downward thrust.

Pushing down the slide stop will release the slide to go forward. If a loaded magazine has been inserted, and then the slide stop pressed, the chamber will be loaded automatically and the pistol ready for firing.

Operation: The magazine release button is pushed to withdraw the magazine. A cartridge is placed on the front end of the magazine follower and pushed down until it can be slid in under the lips of the magazine wall. Another cartridge is placed on top of the first one and forced down and slid in. This procedure is used until the magazine contains whatever cartridges are to be used. It will take any number from one to seven.

The magazine is now inserted in the handle and pushed in until the magazine catch engages in its slot in the magazine wall.

The pistol is now held firmly in the right hand with a finger outside the trigger guard and the slide is grasped firmly at its rear roughened section by the left hand and drawn to the rear as far as it will go. (If the hammer is thumbed back before the slide is withdrawn, the slide will come back much easier because it has less spring tension to overcome.)

As the slide being drawn to the rear passes over the top of the magazine, the

500

Inserting magazine.

Applying Thumb Safety.

magazine spring forces the top cartridge up into line. The recoil spring below the barrel is compressed around its guide. The hammer is cocked and the disconnector forced down to prevent the weapon from being fired.

When the slide is released, the recoil spring pulls it forward. The front breechblock face of the bolt strips the cartridge from between the magazine lips and chambers it. The extractor set in the face of the breechblock snaps into the extracting groove of the cartridge case. As the slide reaches its full forward position, the disconnector slot in it is in position to permit the spring below to force the disconnector up so that its top end fits into the slide and its lower end permits engagement between trigger, sear, and hammer for firing.

When the weapon is held securely, the grip safety is pushed in releasing the automatic disconnector. Pressure on the trigger will free the hammer from the sear to permit the mainspring pushing upward on the strut (which is attached to the hammer) to rock the hammer forward on its axis to strike the firing pin mounted in its slot in the slide. The pin will fly forward to strike and fire the cartridge in the chamber. The hammer blow also compresses the firing pin spring; which pulls the pin back into the breechblock. The firing pin is of the "flying" type. It is shorter than the length of its hole; thus as the hammer drives it forward and its point emerges from its hole to strike the primer and fire the cartridge, the spring around it is compressed; when its energy reacts, this spring draws the pin completely back into the block.

Discharge: When the powder in the cartridge case is exploded by the primer, it generates a huge volume of gas. This gas expands in all directions, but as the least resistance is offered by the bullet directly ahead of it, it starts the bullet down the barrel, the gas pressure following along after it during its travel. Meanwhile the outward thrust of the gases presses the brass cartridge case firmly against the walls of the firing chamber which prevents gas from leaking back past the walls. The backward thrust of the gases inside the cartridge case against the head of the case presses the head back against the breechblock which in this pistol is part of the slide.

The barrel and slide being locked together by the locking ribs on top of the barrel engaging in their slots in the underside of the slide, they remain securely locked together during the moment of high breech pressure. They go back for a short distance firmly locked together.

As the bullet leaves the barrel and the chamber pressure falls to safe limits, the resilient brass cartridge case contracts to its normal size moving away from the walls of the firing chamber. The barrel swinging backward on its link, which is firmly fixed to the receiver by the slide stop pin passing through it, is forced downward on the link by the continuing backward motion. The barrel strikes against its stop in the receiver and its rearward action is halted; while the slide continues on backwards in a straight line in its grooves in the receiver, the extractor mounted in the breechblock face carrying the empty cartridge case out of the firing chamber with it.

The barrel bushing around the muzzle of the barrel, which also locks and supports the recoil spring plug mounted in the slide abutment below the barrel, presses back against the plug to compress the recoil spring below the barrel over the recoil spring guide mounted in the abutment which forms the extension of the receiver above the trigger guard. This stores up energy for return movement of the action.

The momentum of the slide strikes the hammer a sharp blow driving it back to the full-cock position where the sear spring forces the point of the sear into the notch on the hammer to hold it at full cock.

At the first rearward motion of the slide, the beveled niche in the underside of the slide exerts pressure on the rounded head of the disconnector jutting up into the niche from the receiver below. This forces the disconnector down as the slide travels back over it and also rides over the hammer. This lowering of the disconnector, which is mounted on the same axis pin as the sear, removes the tail of the sear from engagement with the trigger stirrup.

As the hammer rocks back on its axis pin, it forces down the strut which is attached to it behind the axis pin, and the bottom of this strut, being mounted in the mainspring cap above the mainspring in the grip, thrusts downward to compress the mainspring to provide energy for the next forward motion of the hammer.

The trigger stirrup is pressing back against its leaf spring which returns it to firing position to permit engagement of sear and disconnector when the weapon next goes forward to fully closed position; and finger pressure is momentarily released.

When the breechblock end of the slide passes completely over the mouth of the magazine below, the ejection port in the right-hand side of the slide is fully exposed. At this point the cartridge case strikes against the ejector mounted in the receiver which frees it from the extractor and hurls it out the right top side of the pistol.

The magazine spring forcing the follower up to drive the cartridges up inside the magazine well, pushes the top cartridge up against the magazine retaining lips so that its head is in direct line with the breechblock which will strip it forward into the firing chamber when the slide again goes forward.

When the last shot has been fired from the magazine, the step at the left side of the magazine follower will push up the slide stop catch which will engage in the slot cut for it in the slide. This will hold the slide open to notify you that the pistol is empty. Pressing down the slide stop will depress the magazine follower and permit the slide to go forward. If a loaded magazine is inserted, before the slide stop is depressed, this forward motion of the slide will load the firing chamber leaving the weapon ready for immediate action.

Dismounting: 1. Press magazine release catch and withdraw magazine.

2. Push the plug below the barrel in far enough to permit the barrel bushing which locks it to be turned to the right until the plug can be eased out from the front. Remember this plug is under the tension of the recoil spring and must be eased out gradually.

3. Pull the slide back until the rear edge of the smaller of the two recesses near the center of the slide on the left-hand side lines up with the rear end of the slide stop.

4. Push the end of the slide stop pin which projects from the right-hand side of the receiver above the trigger guard. This will push the slide stop out on the left-hand side far enough to permit it to be withdrawn completely.

5. As this slide stop pin is the medium by which the barrel link and slide are locked to the receiver, withdrawing it releases the barrel and slide assembly. They may now be pulled directly forward off their guides in the receiver. The barrel bushing, recoil spring, and recoil spring guide will come off with them.

6. The recoil spring plug, recoil spring, and recoil spring guide may now be pulled out of the slide.

7. Turn the barrel bushing to the left as far as it will go. This will free it from its locking slots in the slide and it may now be withdrawn to the front.

8. The barrel may now be tilted to release its locking ribs from the slots in

the slide. Push the barrel link forward and the barrel may now be withdrawn through the front of the slide.

No further dismounting in this weapon is normally necessary. However in view of the widespread use and the importance of this weapon, complete dismounting instructions may be of value.

Dismounting the Receiver Assembly. (Note: These instructions also cover the .38 Super, .22 Ace, and .22 Service Ace receivers.)

1. Cock the hammer. Seize the thumbpiece of the safety lock, which projects on the upper left side of the receiver, firmly with the thumb and index finger and exert steady pressure to pull it outward at the same time that you twist it back and forth. This is necessary to overcome the tension of the spring directly ahead which normally serves to fasten it. The safety lock will thus come out of the receiver.

2. Lower the hammer by gripping the receiver as if for shooting to compress the grip safety and press the trigger; while holding onto the hammer to ease it down.

3. With the pin section of the safety lock, force the hammer pin out of the receiver. This will permit the hammer and the swinging hammer strut attached to it to be lifted out.

4. With the end of the hammer strut, push the mainspring housing pin out from the right side of the receiver. This pin is recessed. It passes through the receiver walls and through the bottom of the mainspring housing at the extreme lower rear of the handle.

5. Withdraw the mainspring housing assembly straight down out of its guides in the receiver.

6. The grip safety may now be removed rearward from its place in the receiver.

7. Again using the hammer strut, push the sear pin from right to left and remove it from the receiver. This will permit the sear and disconnector, which are both mounted on this pin, to be removed from the receiver.

8. The three-leafed sear spring may be removed.

9. The mainspring may be removed by forcing down with a punch on the mainspring cap and pushing out the small pin near the top of the housing which acts as a retainer. This will permit the mainspring cap and the mainspring to be withdrawn from the housing.

10. To remove the magazine catch lock (old type): Press in the checkered button on the left side of the receiver until it is even with the receiver itself. This will force the catch out on the right side of the receiver far enough to let it be turned from right to left about one-half turn. This releases the lock from its seat in the receiver permitting the catch, spring and catch lock to be removed as a unit. The magazine catch pin is *not* threaded. It is a *pin* removed by pushing and rotating.

11. To remove magazine catch lock (new type): Push the magazine catch in on the left side of the receiver until it is flush there. With a small screw driver, turn the catch lock a quarter turn from right to left. This locks it so that the magazine catch assembly may be removed as a unit.

The new-type catch lock may be instantly recognized by the fact that its head has a slot to permit insertion of a small screw driver.

12. The stirrup trigger may now be removed from the rear of the receiver.

13. The combination slide stop and safety lock plunger and the spring between them may be pushed out to the rear of the plunger tube.

14. Push the hammer strut against the head of the firing pin where it projects through its stop in the rear of the receiver. When the pin is forced in far enough against the tension of its spring to clear the hole in its stop, pushing downward with the stirrup will bring the stop down on its guides in the slide. When removing this stop, be careful the spring and pin do not fly out of the slide. Ease them out.

15. Removal of the firing pin units frees the extractor for removal. Push on its front end with the hammer strut outward against the slide and to the rear. It may then be withdrawn from the rear of the slide.

16. Drifting out the ejector pin will permit the ejector to be lifted out of its seat in the rear of the receiver.

Reassembling: While assembling the pistol is essentially merely reversing the instructions given for dismounting, the following special instructions will be found of assistance.

1. When the barrel and slide assembly are ready to be mounted on the receiver, hold both the slide and the receiver bottom side up. Make sure that the barrel link is tilted to the front as far as it will go and that the barrel link pin is flush in its seat. Then slide the receiver forward into the slide assembly.

2. The disconnector and sear are assembled together, and it is important that they be in proper position. To do this, first insert the rounded head of the disconnector in its hole in the receiver so that the flat face at the lower end of the disconnector rests against the yoke of the trigger. Mount the sear over the disconnector (curved section inward, lugs pointing to the bottom). Press the trigger easily and the free parts will line up. Holding them this way, insert the sear pin from the right side of the receiver and make sure that it passes through both the disconnector and the sear.

3. Next replace the sear spring. Make sure that its lower end is caught in the receiver slot prepared for it just a short distance from the bottom of the handle. The upper end of *the left-hand leaf* must rest against the sear. While retaining it in this position, slide the mainspring housing up in its grooves until its end is projecting only about one-eighth of an inch below the line of the bottom of the receiver.

4. Replace the hammer in the receiver together with its strut and insert the hammer pin.

5. Replace the grip safety.

6. Cock the hammer and replace the safety lock.

7. Lower the hammer. Then make sure that the hammer strut rests on the mainspring cap, and push the housing up into place below it. Insert the mainspring housing pin in place to lock the assembly.

8. If trouble is encountered when returning the safety lock to its place in

the receiver, the safety lock plunger may be forced back into its tube with the end of the magazine follower to make insertion of the safety lock easier. Remember the hammer must be cocked while this is done.

9. To replace the slide stop, make sure that its upper rear end stops on the receiver just below the small slide stop plunger. If the slide stop is pushed upward and inward at the same time, the round part of the stop will push the plunger back against the tension of its spring and permit the stop to snap into place in the receiver through its cut in the slide.

Differences Between the M1911 and the M1911A1: In the M1911A1 the following modifications of the original design have been made:

1. The top of the front sight has been widened.

2. The upper end of the grip safety extends further back to provide fuller protection for the pistol hand.

3. There is a clearance cut on the receiver directly behind the trigger and above the magazine release catch button to help afford a better grip.

4. The trigger face is cut back and scored to afford a surer finger grip.

5. The mainspring housing is shaped and curved to fit the palm of the hand. It is also scored to provide a more secure grip.

COLT .45 ACP
Revolver 1917

This is the New Service Model adapted in 1917 to take the .45 A.C.P. rimless cartridge. See photograph under Cal. .45 Colt.

Note: Except for comparatively minor manufacturing differences as generally indicated under individual models, the following applies to all Colt swing-out-cylinder revolvers.

Construction: The principal parts of this revolver are the barrel, cylinder, assembly, frame, and lockwork.

The front sight is machined onto the barrel. The rear sight is a slot machined into the top of the frame directly ahead of the hammer.

The cylinder may be swung out on a crane to the left side of the weapon. It is provided with six chambers to receive cartridges. In the model 1917, as distinguished from other Colt revolvers, the cartridges used are the automatic pistol cartridges, which are rimless. While these may be inserted directly into the chamber individually, since the extractor head cannot catch under them, they cannot be simultaneously extracted.

To provide for this, the cartridges are mounted in semicircular clips of three. Hence six cartridges may be loaded with only two motions, each motion inserting a clip of three cartridges in the cylinder. The head of the extractor can catch under these clips to provide simultaneous extraction. (Note: The first 50,000 of these manufactured will *not* discharge unless the cartridges are on clips. Later numbers have shoulders at the front end of the chambers to prevent cartridges going in too far for the firing pin to strike them when singly inserted.)

Operation: The thumb latch on the left side of the frame below the hammer is drawn back with the thumb. This withdraws the attached latch pin

Basic Model Data

REVOLVER: Colt Army Model 1917 (the New Service
  Model with chambers modified for rimless cartridges).
LENGTH: 10¾ inches.
BARREL: 5½ inches.
WEIGHT: 40 ounces.
CYLINDER: 6 chambers. First models can be fired only
  when cartridges are on clips. Later model chambers
  were modified to permit use of rimless cartridges, but
  empty cases must be individually pried out of chambers.
ACTION: Double. May be fired by thumb cocking and
  trigger pressure or by trigger pressure direct.
EJECTION: Hand ejection, simultaneous when clip loaded.
FRAME: Solid. Swing-out cylinder. Swings to the left.
CALIBER: .45 A.C.P. rimless with clip. Also .45 Auto rim.
SAFETY: Mechanical only. If cylinder is not fully closed
  safety bar blocks rear of recoil stud. Hammer rebounds
  under action of shoulder of mainspring lever against
  arm of hammer as trigger is released after firing.
  Drawing shows all parts in repose.

Hammer cocked to show mainspring compression. Cylinder swung out on crane and extractor rod part way back. Only one clip in cylinder to show extraction details.

Detail drawings show system of mounting rimless cartridges in S&W design spring half moon clips.

from the head of the extractor and pulls it back into the frame far enough to release the cylinder. The cylinder is now free to pivot out on its crane to the left.

The latch pin is under pressure of a spring located in a hole in the side plate just behind the latch slot. When the thumb pressure is released from the latch, the spring forces the pin forward through the frame into the recess in the head of the extractor rod, thereby locking the cylinder when it is in its place in the frame.

When the revolver is opened and the cylinder is swung back into the frame, the head of the extractor mounted in the face of the center of the cylinder pushes this latch pin back enough to permit the cylinder to seat properly. The latch pin spring then forces the pin back when it can slip into the recess in the head of the extractor. This latching takes place automatically as the cylinder is swung in.

Single-action firing: As the hammer is drawn back with the thumb, the upper edge of the trigger engages in the full-cock notch (or bent) in the front end of the lower part of the hammer. This backward movement of the trigger disengages the positive safety lock. It also causes the hand to move forward through its slot in the frame and engage against the ratchet of the extractor to revolve the cylinder the distance of one chamber. This hand has two points, the lower of which supports the ratchet as the revolver is fired.

When the trigger is pressed, it moves out of engagement with the hammer, permitting the mainspring to drive the hammer forward to fire the cartridge in the chamber in line with the barrel.

Double-action firing: Pressure of the finger directly upon the trigger pushes the upper edge of the trigger into engagement with the hammer strut. This raises the hammer almost to the full-cocked position and then the strut slips out from the trigger which allows the hammer to be driven forward by the mainspring to fire the cartridge.

As the trigger goes back the safety lever attached to it pulls the safety bar out of the path of the hammer.

Note that this is a positive safety. It is impossible to fire this weapon accidentally. The safety bar is in the path of the hammer preventing it from striking a cartridge at all times except when the hammer is traveling forward from the full-cocked position where it has been released by a rearward pull on the trigger. If the hammer slips while being cocked, this safety bar effectively prevents it from passing through the frame to strike the cartridge head.

While the trigger is cocking the hammer, the rear end of the cylinder bolt above the trigger in the underside of the frame below the cylinder contacts the lug on the rebound lever. This pulls the nose of the bolt down out of the slot in the cylinder thereby freeing the cylinder so it can be rotated.

The hand (the arm which turns the cylinder) is pivoted to the trigger. At this point it swings on its pin and is elevated. The upper end of the hand passing through the recess in the frame behind the cylinder, engages the ratchet on the extractor and as it rises causes the cylinder to revolve the distance of one firing chamber.

As the chamber nears the point where it will line up with the barrel, while the trigger continues its rearward movement, the lug on the rebound lever slips off the rear end of the bolt. The nose of the bolt drops into its recess in the cylinder directly above it. This securely locks the cylinder from below.

As the hammer falls, therefore, the cylinder is locked at the bottom by the bolt protruding through the frame seating in the recess in the face of the cylinder, at the top by the lower point on the hand engaging against the extractor head, and by the latch pin coming through the frame and seating in the recess in the head of the extractor.

When the trigger is pulled and the hammer dropped, easing the pressure on the trigger permits the lower arm of the mainspring (which is exerting pressure on the rebound lever) to force the hammer back to safety position with the firing pin in its nose withdrawn entirely into the frame. The trigger is now forced forward. Simultaneously, the safety lever moves the safety bar up in front of the hammer. The revolver is now safe and ready for the next trigger pull.

Ejection: When the thumb latch is drawn to the rear and the cylinder swung out to the left on its crane, pressure on the front end of the floating extractor rod will push it up inside the cylinder. Its head, which is engaged under the cartridge clips, will lift the clips and the empty cartridge cases completely out of their chambers and eject them from the cylinder. This pressure compresses the extractor spring, which is inside the center arbor of the crane wound around the extractor. When pressure of the hand is released, this spring will pull the extractor back into its position in the cylinder with the extractor head properly seated in the recesses machined for it in the cylinder head.

Dismounting: While dismounting revolvers is not recommended for any except gunsmiths or armorers, the following detailed instructions are given because of the widespread use of Colt revolvers.

1. The crane lock and its screw are mounted on the right side of the frame just above and ahead of the trigger. Unscrew the screw and remove the two units.

2. Draw the thumb latch to the rear and push the cylinder out to the left. The cylinder and crane assembly may now be drawn to the front off the frame.

3. Partly remove the stock screw until it is free enough to be tilted and pushed through to force off the right-hand stock. Then, reaching in from the right side, push off the left-hand stock. This will prevent marring the grip.

4. Remove the two side plate screws on the left side of the revolver and take off the side plate. Tap the frame just behind the plate with a block of wood or a screw driver handle until it is loose enough that it can be lifted off. Prying off will invariably result in scratching or marring it.

5. The thumb latch and its latch spring directly behind it may now be pushed forward out of the side plate.

6. Squeeze the mainspring together (a pair of pliers may be necessary for

this) until its rear end can be lifted from its seat in the handle. The long end is then disengaged from the hammer stirrup.

7. The hand may then be lifted off the rebound lever.

8. The rebound lever (the long bar below the hammer pin) may then be removed by drifting its pin out to the right.

9. Lift the trigger off its pin in the frame above the trigger guard.

10. Pull the hammer back as far as it will go and it may be lifted off the hammer pin.

11. Drift out the hammer stirrup pin and remove stirrup from hammer.

12. Drift out the strut pin and remove the strut and its spring.

13. The safety lever may now be lifted off its pivot.

14. The safety can now be lifted from its resting place in the frame.

15. The latch pin may now be removed from its place in the frame.

16. Remove the bolt screw and lift out the bolt and bolt spring.

17. Note that the hammer, trigger, swivel stud, and stock pins are riveted to the frame. If they are removed it will be necessary to rerivet them.

18. The forward end of the extractor rod must be firmly held (preferably in a protected vise) while downward pressure is exerted on the cylinder until the extractor and ratchet emerge from their recess in the cylinder, when the extractor may be unscrewed from its rod. The end of this rod is peened into the bore of the ratchet slightly as a precaution against its working loose. Unscrewing this member, therefore, calls for extreme care to prevent injury.

19. When the extractor or ejector is removed, the rod and spring and the cylinder may then be removed from the crane. Be careful not to lose the extractor rod guide bushing mounted directly under the ratchet if this assembly is dismounted.

20. The extractor (or ejector) rod head may be unscrewed and withdrawn from the front of the crane which permits removal of the ejector rod itself.

Barrel: The barrel in this revolver is not retained by a pin. However it is screwed solidly into the frame. As the barrel and frame threads are right hand, if the barrel is clamped in a properly protected vise, the frame is unscrewed from right to left when facing the butt of the revolver.

Proper reassembly and aligning of the barrel is a task only for the most expert workman.

The firing pin is attached to the hammer by a retaining pin. Drifting this out will permit its removal.

.45 ACP   SMITH AND WESSON
                                                              Army 1917

Official Model Names: Model .45 Caliber Hand Ejector (U. S. Service). Also known as the 1917 Army Model .45.

Ammunition: .45 A.C.P. when held in three-cartridge half-moon clips developed by Smith & Wesson. The rimless cartridge can also be shot without clips, but it is then difficult to extract. Also uses .45 Auto Rim Cartridge without clip.

This is the commercial model. The Government issue has plain walnut stocks.

Manufacturing Dates: Oct. 9, 1917—Jan. 1919 for U. S. Army. Manufactured commercially after war.

Serial Numbers: In separate series from one on.

Number Manufactured: 153,000 produced for the U. S. Army during World War I. 25,000 also manufactured on military contract in 1938 for the Government of Brazil.

Finish: Military: Brush polish blue—smooth stocks.

Commercial: Bright polish blue—checkered stocks.

Notes: All cylinders heat-treated. Hammer blocks installed in guns from about Serial Number 185,000.

In 1917, when the U. S. entered the First World War, our Army was desperately in need of sidearms. However, only guns firing the rimless .45 A.C.P. cartridge which was then standard in the U. S. Army could be used, and automatic pistol production could not be expanded to fill the requirements. On Oct. 9, 1917, Smith & Wesson produced its first 1917 Army Model .45 using an ingenious halfmoon clip which adapted the rimless .45 Auto cartridge for use in revolvers. This made it possible to double handgun production for the U. S. Army during the War—153,311 Smith & Wesson revolvers and 151,700 Colt revolvers being made in addition to the 438,000 pistols made principally by Colt & Remington Arms-Union Metallic Cartridge Co.

Land Diameter:	.444-.445	*Twist:* One turn in	14.650″
Groove Diameter:	.450-.451	*Direction of Twist:*	Right
Number of Lands:	6	*Diameter of Chamber:*	Front:
		.4735-.475; Back: .4795-.481	

When they are used with the three-shot clips, all the cartridges are simultaneously ejected in standard fashion when the cylinder is swung out and the ejector rod pushed back. The clips may be re-used.

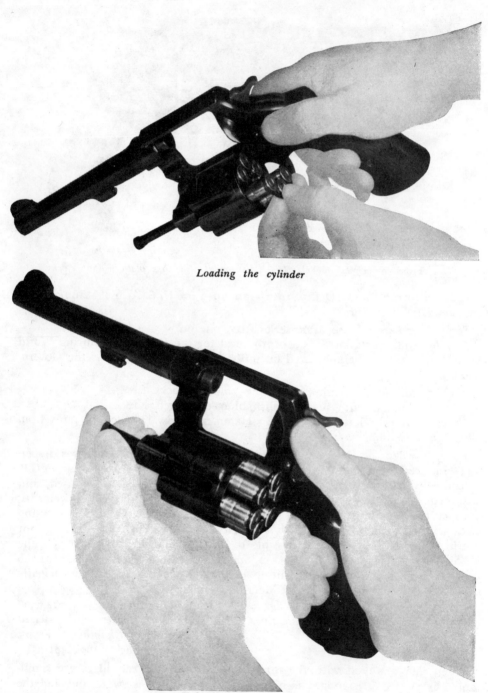

Loading the cylinder

Unloading the Cylinder

514

When the rimless .45 ACP cartridges are inserted in the chambers *without* the clips, the extractor head cannot lift them out of the chambers for ejection; hence, it is necessary to swing out the cylinder, then punch out or pry out the empties.

When the .45 Auto-Rim cartridges are used, the revolver functions for ejection in regular fashion, since the cartridge is substantially the .45 Auto Colt Pistol cartridge except that it has a rim to catch on the extractor head. It appears with a full-jacketed bullet weighing 230 grains whose ballistics are practically identical with those of the regular .45 auto pistol cartridge, and also with a lead bullet of 255 grains whose performance is about the same as the regular .45 Colt revolver cartridge.

STAR   **.45 ACP**
Automatic

SPANISH STAR with full auto device which is useless and dangerous. Insert shows external details of fire control bar unit. The French UNION (Cal. 7.63mm and 9mm Luger) and the Argentinian Ballester Molina (.45 A.C.P.) are very close modifications of the Star system.

This is a Spanish modification of the Colt Government Model. The modifications are all in the direction of cheaper manufacture and are entirely undesirable. One model is modified to make it a full-automatic pistol and is properly designated as a sub-machine gun or machine pistol. The Star outwardly resembles the Colt.

The pistol has dispensed with the Colt grip safety. A bar from the trigger operates on the right side of the pistol to force against a sear stud. There is a plate pivoted on the right side under the grip in line with the hammer axis pin, its upper end engaging with a bar on the right of the slide which moves vertically; while its lower end has a hole through which a stud on the trigger bar projects. The plate movement is spring controlled.

The breech locking system follows that of the Colt, only the firing mechanism being different. When the fire control bar on the slide is in its lower position the trigger bar stud is not affected by the plate through which it projects, since the hole is oval. As a result, the jar caused by the slide in closing jars the sear out of engagement and lets the hammer fall for full-automatic fire. Barrel and slide are locked at instant of firing.

When the fire control bar is in its upper position, the plate is moved by its spring to prevent the trigger bar stud from rising to engage the sear tail until the trigger is released, thereby giving single shot fire.

In actual practice it has proved impossible to fire fewer than six shots on a single pull when fired full auto. Under these conditions it is utterly impossible for the average shooter to control the pistol, even when used with a shoulder stock.

Measurements and weights are about the same as for the Colt.

.45 ACP

MISCELLANEOUS
Weapons

Several pistols are made in Spain on the general pattern of the Star. Most of them bear no brand name. Some are exact duplicates of the Colt in external appearance, even to carrying the Colt insignia; these have no name on them. The Llama pistol generally resembles the Colt in outline but can be recognized at a glance by the fact that the barrel protrudes well beyond the slide.

Excellent imitations of the Colt .45 Govt. Model with only minor modifications have been produced in Norway. Those classed by the Germans as "Norwegian Colts" are likely to be encountered in the United States. Stocks of these excellent weapons seized by the Germans were used by them as sidearms, and many were brought to this country as souvenirs by our troops who took them from the Germans.

Note: In 1907 the U. S. Chief of Ordnance referred to a special Board at Springfield Armory a group of pistols of .45 caliber for the tests which led to the official adoption of the Colt Govt. Model in 1911. Experimental models of the Bergmann, Knoble, Luger, Savage and White-Merril were submitted in competition with the Colt. Such of these pistols as are still in existence are collector's items. Only the Savage (200 delivered) and the Colt Military are likely to be encountered by shooters or police authorities. The Grant-Hammond experimental auto of 1917 also is a collection piece.

In passing it should be noted that pistols bearing the U. S. Govt. Property stamp were made by several factories from the Colt patents during both World Wars, and that copies of the Colt caliber .45 Automatic Model 1911A1 are made at Rosario in Argentina—the Model 1927—and at Itajuba in Brazil.

CARTRIDGE
Data

.45 Auto Rim

.45 Auto Rim

230 Gr. M.C.

Muzzle Velocity in f.s.:	820
Vel. at 50 Feet:	807
Vel. at 150 Feet:	781

Calculated Energy

Muzzle Energy in ft. lbs.:	343
Energy at 50 Feet:	333
Energy at 150 Feet:	312

Calculated Drop

At 50 Feet:	.7 inch
At 150 Feet:	6.8 inches
At 300 Feet:	29.0 inches

Penetration at 15 Feet

⅞" soft pine boards	6

Length of Barrel in Which Tested

inches	5½

Shell Case

Weight:	95 grains
Max. Length:	.898 inch
Outside Body Dia. at Head, Max.:	.472 inch
Outside Body Dia. at Neck, Max.:	.472 inch
Inside Mouth Dia. Max.:	.450 inch
Volumetric Capacity to Base of Bullet in cubic inches:	.062 inch

Bullet

Weight:	230 grains
Approx. Length:	.645 inch
Diameter Max.:	.4505 inch
Area, Cross Sectional:	.1593 square inch
Shape:	Round

Powder

Amount and type varies with different lots manufactured.

Cartridge

Approx. Length, Loaded:	1.275 inches
Approx. Total Weight, Loaded:	340 grains

This cartridge was developed after World War I to meet the demand for a rimmed cartridge which could be used in the Colt and S&W Model 1917 Army revolvers to eliminate the necessity for using clips while permitting simultaneous ejection of the type normal to modern revolvers. It is adapted only to these revolvers, and to their commercial successors.

Chapter 13
Caliber .455 to .577

.455 Webley Revolver

This was the heavy British service revolver cartridge at the beginning of World War II. The cartridge measures 1.23 inch loaded. The case has a head diameter of .528 inch, body diameter of .475 inch, and measures .77 inch. The bullet weighs 265 grains and is loaded with lead or metal-cased bullet. The bullet is conical in shape and has a base diameter of .457 inch. Muzzle velocity is about 600 feet per second, muzzle energy about 212 foot-pounds.

.455 Webley Revolver

COLT
Revolvers

The only current Colt revolver for this cartridge is the New Service Model. Earlier models of the Bisley, S.A. Army and New Service Target were chambered for it. (For photographs and specifications see under Cal. .45 Colt).

.455 Webley Revolver

SMITH AND WESSON
Mark II HE English Service

Manufacturing Dates: May 10, 1915—May 26, 1917.
Number Manufactured: 54,675 for the English Services; 14,500 for the Canadian Services; 1,105 commercially, total 70,280.
Serial Numbers: Numbered in separate series starting from 1.

Finish:	Blue	*Twist:* One turn in	20″
Barrel Length:	6½″	*Direction of Twist:*	Right
Land Diameter:	.447-.448	*Diameter of Chamber:*	.481-.482
Groove Diameter:	.457-.458	*Number of Chambers:*	6
Number of Lands:	5		

Notes: This model differed principally from the Triple Lock in that no yoke lock was used, the heavy barrel lug was eliminated, and the center distance was increased .010″ to allow for the larger .455 cartridge. Since 1869 Smith & Wessons have been made with interchangeable parts.
Note: The New Century Model was also chambered for the .455. See under Cal. .44 S&W Special.

.455 Webley Revolver

WEBLEY
Revolver No. 1, Mark VI

In the British service this revolver is listed as the Pistol, Revolver No. 1 Mark VI, .445 inch. It measures 11¼ inches overall with 6-inch barrel (a target model has a 7½-inch barrel), weighs 38 ounces and has a cylinder with 6 chambers. This is a hinged-frame revolver with a stirrup lock mounted on the standing breech and locking over the barrel strap.

Construction and Operation. The principal parts of this revolver are (1) the receiver or frame. This forms the handle and receives the lockwork, provides

518

the standing breech face which supports the cartridge heads, and is slotted out and forms a joint for the barrel. (2) The barrel which is retained in the frame by a screw at the joint extends back over the cylinder to form a barrel strap which closes down over the standing breech. (3) The cylinder which carries the extractor plate in its face. It fits on the cylinder axis. (4) The double-action lockwork.

As the hammer is pulled back in single-action firing the mainspring is compressed. The bent of the hammer bears against the nose of the trigger during this motion and rotates the trigger. At full cock the nose of the trigger is forced into the hammer bent by the mainspring lever.

Pressing the trigger releases the trigger nose from the hammer and the compressed mainspring drives the hammer ahead. The firing pin is part of the hammer nose. When the trigger is released the mainspring lever pushed by the mainspring forces the lower half of the hammer ahead and thus draws the upper half back into the frame. At the same time it pushes the trigger ahead.

Cylinder rotation is brought about as follows: When the trigger moves the lifting pawl or hand attached to it rises. It passes through the cut in the recoil plate to engage with the ratchet tooth on the extractor head. Thus the upward movement of the hand turns the cylinder. When the trigger is released the cylinder rises and engages a notch in the cylinder holding it in firing position. Further forward movement of the trigger draws down the hand ready for the next cycle.

Double-Action firing is the same except that the action takes place by direct trigger pull. The nose of the trigger bears behind the hammer catch and lifts the hammer until the nose of the trigger rises high enough to slip off the end of the hammer catch.

Basic Model Data

REVOLVER: *Webley .455 British Service.*
LENGTH: *11¼ inches.*
BARREL: *6 inches.*
WEIGHT: *38 ounces.*
CYLINDER: *6 chambers.*
ACTION: *Double.*
EJECTION: *Automatic. Extractor is forced up as barrel is swung down, extracting all cartridges simultaneously.*
    Extractor spring draws extractor back into cylinder at end of stroke.
FRAME: *Hinged. Stirrup lock on standing breech. Operated by pushing forward on stirrup lever on left side*
    of revolver.
CALIBER: *.455 Mark II.*
SAFETY: *Mechanical only. Has rebounding hammer.*
Drawing is cut away to show all parts in repose.

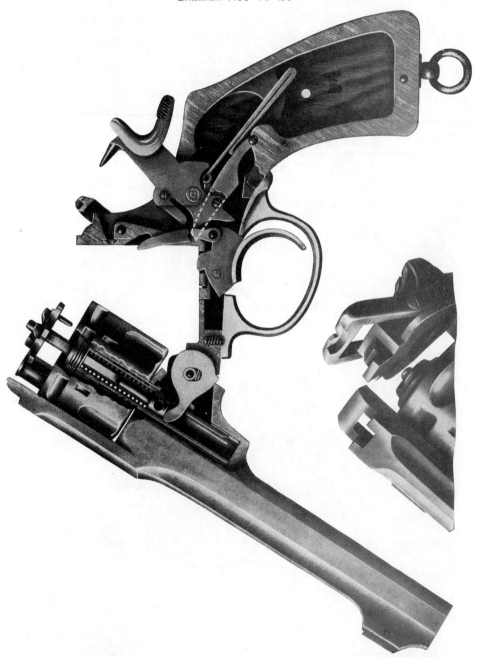

Hammer at full cock to show method of mainspring compression. Cylinder cut away to show operation of extractor. Note fixing pin on extractor head which seats in hole in cylinder to assure rigidity of extractor mounting.

Lower details show stirrup lock held back to disclose details of stirrup breech lock.

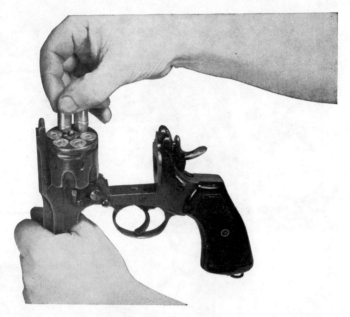

Barrel bent down on hinge for loading.

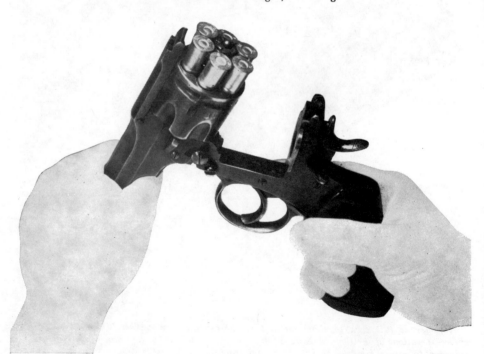

Extraction started as barrel is being bent down and extractor is forced up.

Loading and firing procedure is the same as that already described for the British Pistol, Revolver No. 2 described under Caliber .38 S&W.

Dismounting: After making sure that there are no cartridges in the chambers, proceed as follows:

1. Unscrew the stock screw and remove the stocks.

2. Unscrew the trigger guard screws (mounted from below through the trigger guard into the receiver) and withdraw the trigger guard.

3. Lift the mainspring out of its stud hole. To do this it will be necessary to press the arms close together with pliers while unhooking the claw of the spring from the hammer swivel. (This must be done with great care to prevent injuring the spring.)

4. Lift out the mainspring lever.

5. Unscrew trigger screw and lift out trigger and attached pawl (or hand).

6. Unscrew the hammer screw and take out the hammer.

7. Unscrew the cam lever fixing screw (at the forward left side of the frame just ahead of the cylinder). Now press the barrel catch and open the pistol as far as it will go.

8. Push the cam lever toward the cylinder and the cylinder with the extractor may be lifted up out of the cylinder axis.

9. Completely unscrew the cam lever screw and remove the cam lever.

10. Unscrew the joint pin screw (at the front end of the frame on the *right-hand* side). Push the joint pin out to the left and the barrel will be freed to be removed from the frame.

11. When the barrel is taken from the frame, the extractor lever mounted in it will drop out. Be careful this is not lost.

12. Unscrew the barrel-catch screw in the thumbpiece on the left-hand side of the frame and withdraw it. The barrel catch may now be worked off the frame and the catch spring on the right-hand side of the frame may be removed.

13. Unscrew the cam screws and remove the cam.

14. Unscrewing the extractor nut will permit the extractor and the spring to be withdrawn from the cylinder.

15. The recoil plate is removed by unscrewing the screw and driving the plate from left to right.

Note that in these revolvers the extractors are not interchangeable in cylinders. Particular care must be taken to keep the extractor with its cylinder if several revolvers are being dismounted. The cylinders also are individually fitted and should be kept with the original revolver whenever possible.

Assembling: Replace the extractor and spring in the cylinder and screw home the extractor nut on the bottom.

Replace the cam. Then replace the cylinder on its axis and spin it to be sure it moves freely.

Put the extractor lever in the joint and assemble the barrel to the frame.

Replace the joint pin from the left-hand side and make sure that the stud on the pin is opposite the recess in the frame. Then screw home the joint pin screw from the right.

Replace the cam lever and fasten in its screw. Then fasten the cam lever fixing screw.

Reverse the stripping procedure to complete the rest of the assembly.

WEBLEY AND SCOTT

.455 Webley Revolver
Solid Frame RIC

This weapon usually bears the stamp R.I.C., meaning Royal Irish Constabulary. Various models with minor modifications have been made, but the general functioning of all models is the same.

This is a double-action weapon. It has been made with 2¼″, 3¼″, 3½″, 4″ and 4½″ barrels and weighs one pound nine ounces with a 2¼″ barrel. The cylinder holds six cartridges. The weapon uses the standard British Service .455 revolver cartridge except the 1867, 1868 Models which use the .442 cartridge.

The frame is solid. To load it is necessary, first, to half cock the hammer. The loading gate on the right-hand side of the frame is then pushed out and a cartridge inserted in the chamber through the loading slot. The cylinder must be revolved by hand for the insertion of each cartridge.

To eject empty cartridges it is necessary to half cock the hammer, swing out the loading gate, pull forward the extractor rod below the barrel until it emerges from its seat, then swing it out to the right side of the revolver on its crane until it lines up with the chamber in line with the loading and unloading slot. Pushing the ejector rod straight back through the chamber forces out the empty case. The ejector must then be pulled forward and the cycle repeated to unload each chamber in the cylinder.

There is a dangerous feature about this revolver. When the hammer is cocked and the trigger goes back, a sharp section of the trigger is exposed inside the trigger guard. If the finger slips during rapid fire, it is possible to get it pinched between this sharp edge and the lower part of the frame. If the hammer then falls, it can produce serious injury to the trigger finger.

Dismounting. Pull the extractor rod forward and swing it out on its crane. Pry out the hollow cylinder axis pin. Open the loading gate. Remove the cylinder. Except for removal of the stocks to facilitate oiling and cleaning, no further dismounting should normally be attempted.

This weapon is of extremely sturdy construction, but it is held together essentially by pins and dismounting and reassembling is a job to be done only in a properly equipped shop.

This weapon was long an official arm of the Royal Irish Constabulary and has a grim record as a manstopper at close quarters. It may be found bearing the stamp of the jobber who marked it. This was formerly a common British and European practice.

This revolver has been widely and cheaply imitated on the Continent. Imitations are seldom reliable or of good workmanship.

WEBLEY-FOSBERY
Automatic Revolver

.455 Webley Revolver

This revolver is quite different in construction from any standard type. The barrel, receiver, and cylinder form a unit which slides back and forth in grooves in the frame of the weapon.

The frame, which does not recoil, comprises the grip or handle, the trigger and trigger guard, and the cocking unit. The receiver unit, to which is mounted the barrel and the cylinder, slides in a groove on top of the frame during recoil of the weapon. It is held forward normally (and is thrust forward after recoil) by a long lever pivoted at the lower front end of the grip. This lever is actuated by a recoil spring.

There is a projection inside the groove on top of the frame to which is attached a rotating stud.

Zigzag grooves are cut on the outside surface of the cylinder. The frame stud works in the zig-zag grooves.

The extractor and the barrel lock are the standard Webley type.

The hammer has a tail and a bent. The sear has a half-cocked bent, a full-cocked bent, and a projecting arm which engages with the trigger.

The trigger is pivoted on a screw at its forward end, and a small V-spring bears against it there to keep the trigger pressed down. The trigger catch is pivoted on this screw in a recess near the top surface of the trigger. The trigger catch can revolve slightly on the screw and is provided with a small tooth on its top which engages with the end of the sear. The tooth of the trigger catch is kept pressed to the rear by a small spiral spring and plunger in the trigger.

The mainspring resembles that of the standard Webley. Its short arm rests in a bent in the mainspring auxiliary, pressing it upward. This in turn bears against the sear, pressing it upwards.

A spring is screwed onto the barrel extension. There is a tooth on the

WEBLEY-FOSBERY AUTOMATIC REVOLVER. Insert shows barrel and cylinder assembly in full recoil. Cylinder has been revolved one half turn and hammer cocked. Recoil spring will thrust assembly home and revolve cylinder ready for next shot. Model shown is the .455. This revolver was also made in Cal. .38.

underside of the rear end of this spring and, when the revolver is open, this tooth engages in the grooves in the cylinder to assure the cylinder being in correct position to permit closing. When the revolver is fully closed, the rear end of this spring is raised and the cylinder is free to be rotated by the stud in the frame.

Operation: This weapon must be cocked by hand for the first shot. (The only other way of preparing it for the first shot is to hold the handle rigidly with the right hand and with the left push the barrel back sharply.) From there on, recoil will function it. In the event of a misfire, however, since there is no recoiling action, the hammer must again be drawn back manually.

After the hammer has been cocked, pressing the trigger will raise the tooth of the trigger catch to lift the end of the sear. The bent of the sear is thus released from the hammer bent, permitting the mainspring to drive the hammer forward on its axis to fire the cartridge in its line.

If the weapon is being gripped securely in the firing hand, the barrel, cylinder, and other recoiling units will be driven straight back, as the receiver slides in the groove in the top of the frame. (Note that it is necessary to hold this revolver *firmly* at the instant of firing to insure the functioning of the recoil mechanism.)

As the hammer goes back, turning on its pin, the hammer tail strikes a cocking stud in the frame and is brought to full cock and is retained there by the full-cock bent of the sear.

The rotating stud mounted in the receiver on the frame is engaged in one of the diagonal grooves in the front end of the cylinder. As the cylinder comes back, the stud, travelling in this groove, rotates the cylinder *one-half* the movement necessary to bring a new chamber into line.

During this movement, the recoil lever has pressed against its recoil spring to store up energy for the forward movement. The recoil lever is now forced forward by this spring and drives the recoiling parts to the front.

During this forward motion, the rotating stud passes down the next diagonal groove in the cylinder and gives the cylinder the *second* twist necessary to bring the loaded chamber into line with the hammer.

The end of the sear strikes the tooth of the trigger catch, pressing it upward as the recoiling parts complete their forward movement.

When the pressure of the trigger finger is released, the trigger rotates on its axis pin downward and forward, enabling the tooth of the trigger catch to come back under the thrust of its spring and plunger and seat itself below the end of the sear. This acts as a disconnector, preventing the discharge of more than one chamber on each trigger pull.

Pressing the trigger will again drop the hammer to fire the cartridge and repeat the recoiling operation.

When the last shot has been fired, pushing forward on the lock stirrup on the left side of the pistol will draw back its upper locking face as it rotates on its axis pin to unlatch the barrel extension, permitting the barrel and barrel extension to be hinged down. The extractor will function in standard Webley fashion to extract and eject the empty cartridges.

While this weapon is normally loaded in standard cartridge revolver fashion by inserting single cartridges, a special clip loader may also be used. This is a circular disc, usually of brass, with holes permitting the insertion of six cartridges. The six cartridges are inserted in the cylinder as a unit, a center hole fitting over the extractor rod.

There is no ratchet on the head of the extractor rod in this weapon. The cylinder is revolved, as the weapon recoils and goes forward, by the action of the rotating stud in the frame travelling in the diagonal grooves in the cylinder to compel rotation. No cylinder-rotating hand is necessary as in standard revolvers, hence no cylinder ratchet is required.

This revolver has a thumb safety on the left side of the grip. When this thumbpiece is pushed up, it forces the recoiling members to the rear. This action moves the sear away from the tooth of the trigger catch, so that pressure on the trigger will not operate the sear to permit the hammer to be dropped. This also locks the frame to the recoiling parts.

Note: This system of turning the cylinder by a stud operating in zigzag grooves was patented by Samuel Colt early in his career. It was later employed on a revolver invented in Germany by Paul Mauser.

Stud-actuated feeds are used today on U. S. Browning and on German Model 34 and 42 Machine Guns.

.455 Webley Self Loading   CARTRIDGE
                                                                    Data

This cartridge resembles the .45 A.C.P. to a considerable degree, but is recognizable by its peculiarly blunt pointed bullet and by the fact that it is semirimmed. The cartridge measures 1.23 inches overall. The case has a head diameter of .50, a body diameter of .474 and is .93 inch long. The jacketed bullet weighs 220 grains, is .59 inch long and has a base diameter of .455 inch. These dimensions make it the largest automatic pistol cartridge in commercial production. With a 7-grain cordite load it develops about 750 feet per second muzzle velocity and a muzzle energy of about 270 foot-pounds.

.455 Webley Self Loading   COLT
                                                               Government

The U. S. Colt Government Model was manufactured during World War I for this cartridge. See under Cal. .45 A.C.P.

.455 Webley Self Loading   WEBLEY AND SCOTT
                                                                    1904

This pistol is of interest only to collectors as few were manufactured and sold. It is not to be confused with the 1913 Model which was an official British Navy pistol.

.455 Webley Self Loading   WEBLEY AND SCOTT
                                                          Self Loading Pistol

This pistol was officially adopted by the Royal British Navy but is not standard today. Its action was not satisfactory under service conditions. It measures 8½ inches overall, has a 5-inch barrel, weighs about 39 ounces and has a magazine capacity of 7 cartridges.

Construction. The locking system of this pistol is unique. At the instant of discharge the barrel and slide are firmly locked together. A locking shoulder on top of the barrel is engaged with a corresponding shoulder inside the slide. As the two units move to the rear and the chamber pressure drops to safe limits, the barrel moves down diagonal grooves to unlock from the slide.

As the barrel strikes the stops in the receiver, halting its rearward motion, the slide continues to the rear. The slide in this weapon does not cover the entire length of the barrel as in most autoloading pistols. The extractor mounted in the top forward face of the slide draws the empty cartridge case out of the chamber and to the rear until it strikes against the ejector which hurls the empty case from the pistol.

On the right side of the action is a very powerful V-shaped spring to which is attached a bar that is connected with the slide. As the slide goes back this V-spring is compressed to store up energy for the forward movement of the action.

When the barrel moves down its diagonal grooves to unlock from the slide, it pushes down the disconnector which in turn forces the trigger lever away from the sear lever. It is impossible for the disconnector to rise until the barrel rises into locking position. Firing, except when the weapon is fully locked is, therefore, impossible.

During recoil the rear section of the slide forces back and rides over the hammer to bring it to full cock. In the grip below the hammer is a grip safety. The sear, sear lever, and hammer are mounted in the top section of this grip safety.

When the weapon is gripped for firing and the safety pressed in, the sear lever is brought into contact with the trigger lever. This cannot be done until the safety is pushed in. Pressure on the trigger moves a lever against the sear lever to rotate the sear, thereby releasing the hammer to strike the firing pin and fire the cartridge.

The magazine system on this weapon is somewhat unusual in that it provides for use of the weapon as a single-shot pistol while keeping the fully loaded magazine in reserve. The magazine is released by a pressure button on the rear of the grip near the lanyard loop. However, there are two engagement notches cut into the magazine wall for engagement by the catch of the thumbpiece.

If the magazine is inserted only until the catch locks in the first notch, the weapon will not feed from the magazine. The slide may be withdrawn by hand and will remain open so that a cartridge may be loaded directly into the firing chamber through the breech. Pressing the slide stop release will let the slide go forward and load the piece. If the weapon is fired, while the magazine is thus engaged in the first notch, the empty case will be ejected and the slide will stay open to permit another cartridge to be inserted through

Basic Model Data

AUTOMATIC PISTOL: Webley & Scott
    Self Loading.
LENGTH: 8½ inches.
BARREL: 5 inches.
WEIGHT: About 39 ounces.
MAGAZINE: Detachable box with butt release catch. Capacity 7 cartridges. Magazine has two catch notches. When magazine is held by catch in upper notch, pistol may be used as a single loader with magazine in reserve. Pushing it in until lower notch engages brings the magazine into position for standard feeding.
OPERATION: Short recoil, locked breech.
LOCK: A locking shoulder at top of barrel engages against a shoulder in the slide when the breech is closed. As barrel and slide recoil together the barrel is forced down diagonal grooves in the receiver to unlock.
RECOIL SPRING: V spring under the right stock. Pinned at bottom. Forward arm hooks up with a pivoted lever which is drawn back by the slide to compress the spring.
DISCONNECTOR: Barrel moving down in grooves to unlock forces disconnector down to push trigger lever away from sear lever. Disconnector cannot rise until barrel does.
TRIGGER: When trigger is pressed its lever contacts the sear lever, rotating the sear to free the hammer.
MAINSPRING: Coil. Hammer, mainspring sear and sear lever are mounted in the top section of the grip safety.
BARREL: Machined at top of breech end to pass under slide. Tongued on sides to travel in diagonal receiver grooves to impart up and down motion for locking and unlocking.
FIRING MECHANISM: External hammer system with flying firing pin in slide.
SAFETY: Automatic grip safety. When pressed brings sear lever into contact with trigger lever.
CALIBER: .455 Self Loading. (A modification was made in .38 caliber in limited quantity.)

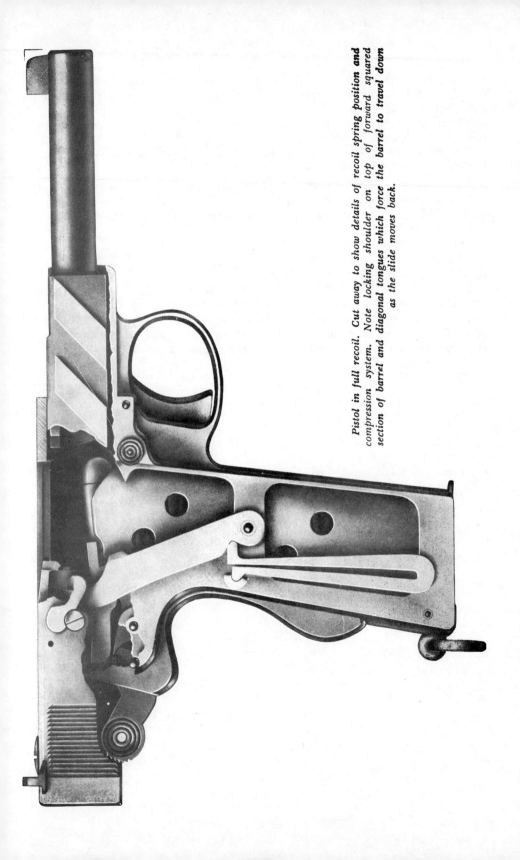

Pistol in full recoil. Cut away to show details of recoil spring position and compression system. Note locking shoulder on top of forward squared section of barrel and diagonal tongues which force the barrel to travel down as the slide moves back.

the breech. By this system a full magazine may be held constantly in reserve ready for instant use by merely pushing it into the handle a fraction of an inch further.

When the magazine engages the second notch the weapon functions in a normal autoloading manner.

The hammer, which resembles that of the Mauser military pistol, has a half-cock notch. No thumb safety is provided.

Dismounting. 1. Move the slide back about one-quarter of an inch and press in the small milled stud on the right side of the pistol just behind the trigger. This is the recoil lever stop. Pushing it in locks the recoil spring out of action.

2. Push the slide forward as far as it will go. This frees the slide stop as the recoil spring is locked out of action. This stop, which is on the right-hand side of the slide should now be pulled out as far as it will come.

3. The slide may now be drawn directly to the rear until it passes completely over the barrel. The barrel may now be lifted up out of its guide. Now push the slide forward off the receiver. Removing the stock screws and lifting off the stocks give access to the recoil spring and lever and to the pins locking the other operating units which may be removed if necessary.

CARTRIDGE
Data

11:75mm. Montenegrin Gasser

This is the largest cartridge ever to achieve a reasonably wide sale. It and the enormous (4 to 5 pound) revolvers to shoot it were manufactured in Belgium on a very wide scale for Balkan and South American trade. It was originally designed for the Montenegrin Government, although officers were expected to buy their own. The cartridge comes in two lengths. The long cartridge is far too long to chamber in the .45 Colt type of cylinder.

The standard revolver for these cartridges is a hinged-frame model with dual locking levers. Pressing the pivoted levers draws pins attached to their upper ends out of engaging holes in the standing breech and in the barrel strap to permit the barrel to be hinged down.

This is an obsolete black powder cartridge at one time used in the British service. It was used in the old British Pryse revolver and in the Enfield revolver of 1880. Colt records show that a few New Service revolvers were chambered for it. It was also used to some degree in early Webley & Scott hinge frame revolvers, notably the so-called "Chinese Navy Model" which had a weak barrel lock operating through a lever on each side of the frame.

This cartridge and revolvers for it are merely collector's items.

.577

Several varieties of cartridges were manufactured in the 1880's in England in this caliber. Tranter and Bland revolvers chambered them. These are curios today, though some German manufacturers were producing .577 Center Fire Pistol cartridges as late as 1914.

Note. The largest cartridges commercially manufactured for general distribution in recent years were the 15mm. Pin Fire types made in Belgium and Germany for export to Argentina where revolvers to fire them are still in use on the Pampas.

Appendix I
Identification of Miscellaneous Pistols

Name: Alkar
Model: Vest Pocket
Cal.: 25
O. A. Length: 4.53
Bl. Length: 2.09

Weight: 13.96
Mag. Cap.: 7
Lands 6
Rifling: 10.63
Twist: Right

Name: Alkartasuna
Model: Vest Pocket
Cal.: 25
O. A. Length: 4.329
Bl. Length: 2.028

Weight: 12.31
Mag. Cap.: 6
Lands: 6
Rifling: 12.03
Twist: Right

Name: Apache
Model: Vest Pocket
Cal.: 25
O. A. Length: 4.368
Bl. Length: 2.184

Weight: 13.58
Mag. Cap.: 7
Lands: 6
Rifling: 10.17
Twist: Right

Name: Astra
Model: 1911
Cal.: 25
O. A. Length: 4.33
Bl. Length: 2.40

Weight: 11.95
Mag. Cap.: 6
Lands: 6
Rifling: 9.06
Twist: Left

Name: Astra
Model: 1924
Cal.: 25
O. A. Length: 4.33
Bl. Length: 2.21

Weight: 12.20
Mag. Cap.: 6
Lands: 6
Rifling: 9.34
Twist: Left

Name: Atlas
Model: Vest Pocket
Cal.: 25
O. A. Length: 4.53
Bl. Length: 2.28

Weight: 13.15
Mag. Cap.: 6
Lands: 6
Rifling: 9.06
Twist: Right

Name:
   "Automatic" Pistol
Model: 1916
Cal.: 25
O. A. Length: 4.446
Bl. Length: 2.184

Weight: 13.96
Mag. Cap.: 6
Lands: 6
Rifling: 9.86
Twist: Right

Name:
   Automatic Pistol
   B. H.
Model: Vest Pocket
Cal.. 25
O. A. Length: 4.407

Bl. Length: 2.184
Weight: 12.59
Mag. Cap.: 6
Lands: 6
Rifling: 9.52
Twist: Left

Name:
   Automatic Pistol
   B. C. Eibar
Model: 1924
Cal.: 25
O. A. Length: 4.49

Bl. Length: 2.13
Weight: 13.47
Mag. Cap.: 6
Lands: 6
Rifling: 10.24
Twist: Right

Name:
   Automatic Pistol
Model: Vest Pocket
Cal.: 25
O. A. Length: 4.57
Bl. Length 2.17

Weight: 13.72
Mag. Cap.: 6
Lands: 6
Rifling: 9.30
Twist: Right

536

Name:
  Automatic Pistol
Model: Vest Pocket
Cal.: 25
O. A. Length: 4.485
Bl. Length: 2.184

Weight: 13.79
Mag. Cap.: 6
Lands: 6
Rifling: 11.58
Twist: Right

Name: Avion
Model: Vest Pocket
Cal.: 25
O. A. Length: 4.45
Bl. Length: 2.13

Weight 13.54
Mag. Cap.: 6
Lands: 6
Rifling: 11.42
Twist: Right

Name: Bayard
Model: 1908
Cal.: 25
O. A. Length: 4.96
Bl. Length: 2.25

Weight: 14.74
Mag. Cap.: 6
Lands: 6
Rifling: 9.84
Twist: Left

Name: Bayard
Model: 1923
Cal.: 25
O. A. Length: 4.329
Bl. Length: 2.145

Weight: 12.02
Mag. Cap.: 6
Lands: 6
Rifling: 9.72
Twist: Left

Name: Bayard
Model: 1930
Cal.: 25
O. A. Length: 4.37
Bl. Length: 2.09

Weight: 11.35
Mag. Cap.: 6
Lands 6
Rifling: 9.69
Twist: Right

Name: Beretta
Model: 1915
Cal: 25
O. A. Length: 4.49
Bl. Length: 2.36

Weight: 12.37
Mag. Cap.: 7
Lands: 6
Rifling: 10.48
Twist: Right

Name: Bronco
Model: Vest Pocket
Cal.: 25
O. A. Length: 4.329
Bl. Length: 2.106

Weight: 13.61
Mag. Cap.: 6
Lands: 6
Rifling: 11.6
Twist: Right

Name: Browning
Model: Vest Pocket
Cal.: 25
O. A. Length: 4.53
Bl. Length: 2.13

Weight: 13.22
Mag. Cap.: 6
Lands: 6
Rifling: 11.81
Twist: Right

Name: Bufalo
Model: Vest Pocket
Cal.: 25
O. A. Length: 4.485
Bl. Length: 2.067

Weight: 14.03
Mag. Cap.: 6
Lands: 6
Rifling: 10.69
Twist: Left

Name:
  Caucelegui-Hnos
Cal.: 25
O. A. Length: 4.368
Bl. Length: 2.145

Weight: 13.58
Mag. Cap.: 8
Lands: 6
Rifling: 9.91
Twist: Right

Name: Chylewski
Model: Vest Pocket
Cal.: 25
O. A. Length: 4.61
Bl. Length: 2.25

Weight: 13.22
Mag. Cap.: 6
Lands: 6
Rifling: 10.36
Twist: Right

Name: Clement
Model: 1912
Cal.: 25
O. A. Length: 4.64
Bl. Length: 2.25

Weight: 13.60
Mag. Cap.: 6
Lands: 6
Rifling: 8.66
Twist: Right

Name: Clement
Model: 1912
Cal.: 25
O. A. Length: 4.53
Bl. Length: 2.40

Weight: 11.6
Mag. Cap.: 6
Lands: 6
Rifling: 9.65
Twist: Right

Name:
  Clement
Model: 1908
Cal.: 25
O. A. Length: 4.64
Bl. Length: 1.81

Weight: 13.54
Mag. Cap.: 6
Lands: 6
Rifling: 9.26
Twist: Right

Name:
  Clement
Model: 1909
Cal.: 25
O. A. Length: 4.72
Bl. Length: 2.01

Weight: 12.90
Mag. Cap.: 6
Lands: 6
Rifling: 9.45
Twist: Right

Name: Colon B H
Model: (none listed)
Cal.: 25
O. A. Length: 4.407
Bl. Length: 2.145

Weight: 13.43
Mag. Cap.: 6
Lands: 6
Rifling: 10.66
Twist: Left

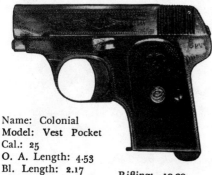

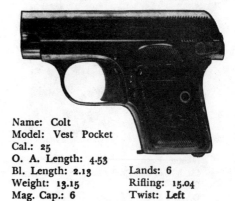

Name: Colonial
Model: Vest Pocket
Cal.: 25
O. A. Length: 4.53
Bl. Length: 2.17
Weight: 13.8
Mag. Cap.: 6
Lands: 6

Rifling: 10.00
Twist: Right

Name: Colt
Model: Vest Pocket
Cal.: 25
O. A. Length: 4.53
Bl. Length: 2.13
Weight: 13.15
Mag. Cap.: 6

Lands: 6
Rifling: 15.04
Twist: Left

Name: Continental   Weight: 15.09
Model: Vest Pocket   Mag. Cap.: 7
Cal.: 25   Lands: 6
O. A. Length: 4.57   Rifling: 7.68
Bl. Length: 2.09   Twist: Right

Name: Cow Boy   Weight: 14.24
Model: Vest Pocket   Mag. Cap.: 6
Cal.: 25   Lands: 6
O. A. Length: 4.49   Rifling: 20.08
Bl. Length: 2.17   Twist: Right

Name: Danton   Weight: 14.49
Model: Vest Pocket   Mag. Cap.: 6
Cal.: 25   Lands: 6
O. A. Length: 4.61   Rifling: 11.02
Bl. Length: 2.13   Twist: Left

Name: Destroyer   Weight: 11.49
Model: Vest Pocket   Mag. Cap.: 6
Colt: 25   Lands: 6
O. A. Length: 4.251   Rifling: 11.14
Bl. Length: 1.989   Twist: Right

Name: Delu   Weight: 11.67
Model: Vest Pocket   Mag. Cap.: 6
Cal.: 25   Lands: 7
O. A. Length: 4.25   Rifling: 9.45
Bl. Length: 2.17   Twist: Right

Name: Dreyse   Weight: 14.03
Model: Vest Pocket   Mag. Cap.: 6
Cal.: 25   Lands: 4
O. A. Length: 4.53   Rifling: 10.04
Bl. Length: 2.13   Twist: Right

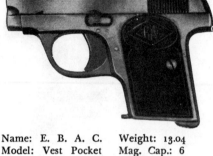

Name: Dictator   Weight: 14.21
Model: Vest Pocket   Mag. Cap.: 6
Cal.: 25   Lands: 6
O. A. Length: 4.72   Rifling: 9.45
Bl. Length: 2.28   Twist: Right

Name: E. B. A. C.   Weight: 13.04
Model: Vest Pocket   Mag. Cap.: 6
Cal.: 25   Lands: 6
O. A. Length: 4.53   Twist: Left
Bl. Length: 2.17

Name: Eley   Weight: 12.76
Model: Vest Pocket   Mag. Cap.: 7
Cal.: 25   Lands: 6
O. A. Length: 4.602   Rifling: 9.88
Bl. Length: 2.028   Twist: Right

Name: Etna   Weight: 13.75
Model: Vest Pocket   Mag. Cap.: 6
Cal.: 25   Lands: 6
O. A. Length: 4.57   Rifling: 9.84
Bl. Length: 2.17   Twist: Right

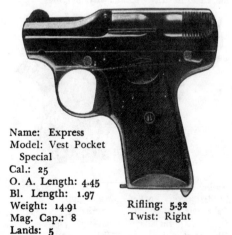

Name: Express
Model: Vest Pocket
Cal.: 25
O. A. Length: 4.25
Bl. Length: 1.97
Weight: 12.41   Rifling: 7.48
Mag. Cap.: 6   Twist: Right
Lands: 6

Name: Express
Model: Vest Pocket
   Special
Cal.: 25
O. A. Length: 4.45
Bl. Length: 1.97
Weight: 14.91   Rifling: 5.32
Mag. Cap.: 8   Twist: Right
Lands: 5

541

Name: Express
Model: Special
Caliber: 25
O. A. Length: 4.68
Bl. Length: 2.21

Weight: 14.91
Mag. Cap.: 8
Lands: 6
Rifling: 16.14
Twist: Right

Name:
   Fabrique d'Armes
Model: Vest Pocket
Cal.: 25
O. A. Length: 4.61
Bl. Length: 2.21

Weight: 12.23
Mag. Cap.: 6
Lands: 6
Rifling: 9.37
Twist: Left

Name: Fiel
Model: Vest Pocket
Cal.: 25
O. A. Length: 4.37
Bl. Length: 2.15

Weight: 11.18
Mag. Cap.: 6
Lands: 6
Rifling: 12.52
Twist: Right

Name: Fiel
Model: Special
Cal.: 25
O. A. Length: 4.563
Bl. Length: 1.599

Weight: 13.22
Mag. Cap.: 8
Lands: 6
Rifling: 11.22
Twist: Right

Name: Fortuna
Model: Vest Pocket
Cal.: 25
O. A. Length: 4.57
Bl. Length: 2.13

Weight: 13.68
Mag. Cap.: 7
Lands: 6
Rifling: 9.65
Twist: Right

Name: Le Francais
Model: Staff Officer
Cal.: 25
O. A. Length: 4.37
Bl. Length: 2.340

Weight: 11.25
Mag. Cap.: 7
Lands: 6
Rifling: 86-91
Twist: Right

Name: Le Francais
Model: Policeman
Cal.: 25
O. A. Length: 6.084
Bl. Length: 3.482

Weight: 12.34
Mag. Cap.: 7
Lands: 6
Rifling: 80-90
Twist: Right

Name:
    Frommer, Pat.
Model: Lilliput
Cal.: 25
O. A. Length: 4.37
Bl. Length: 2.95
Weight: 10.5
Mag. Cap.: 6

Lands: 4
Rifling: 10.44
Twist: Right

Name: Gallus
Model: Vest Pocket
Cal.: 25
O. A. Length: 4.368
Bl. Length: 2.106

Weight: 12.55
Mag. Cap.: 6
Lands: 6
Rifling: 10.66
Twist: Right

Name: Gloria
Model: 1913
Cal.: 25
O. A. Length: 4.41
Bl. Length: 2.17

Weight: 11.39
Mag. Cap.: 6
Lands: 5
Rifling: 10.62
Twist: Right

Name:
    Harrington and
        Richardson
Model. Vest Pocket
Caliber: 25
O. A. Length: 4.45

Bl. Length: 2.13
Weight: 12.27
Mag. Cap.: 7
Lands: 6
Rifling: 12.21
Twist: Right

Name: Heim, C. E.
Model: Vest Pocket
Cal.: 25
O. A. Length: 4.25
Bl. Length: 2.17

Weight: 10.93
Mag. Cap.: 6
Lands: 6
Rifling: 10.44
Twist: Right

543

Name: Helfricht   Weight: 11.39
Model: 3   Mag. Cap.: 6
Cal.: 25   Lands: 6
O. A. Length: 4.29 Rifling: 9.78
Bl. Length: 1.97   Twist: Right

Name: K. Helfricht Weight: 11.61
Model: 4   Mag. Cap.: 6
Cal.: 25   Lands: 6
O. A. Length: 4.22 Rifling: 9.84
Bl. Length: 1.93   Twist: Right

Name: Herman   Weight: 15.13
Model: Vest Pocket Mag. Cap.: 6
Cal.: 25   Lands: 6
O. A. Length: 4.875 Rifling: 10.06
Bl. Length: 2.535   Twist: Right

Name: Hudson   Weight: 13.19
Model: Vest Pocket Mag. Cap.: 6
Cal.: 25   Lands: 6
O. A. Length: 4.485 Rifling: 9.44
Bl. Length: 2.184   Twist: Left

Name: Jieffeco   Weight: 12.37
Model: Vest Pocket Mag. Cap.: 6
Cal.: 25   Lands: 6
O. A. Length: 4.57 Rifling: 9.62
Bl. Length: 2.17   Twist: Right

Name: Joha   Weight: 13.72
Model: Vest Pocket Mag. Cap.: 6
Cal.: 25   Lands: 6
O. A. Length: 4.57 Rifling: 10.24
Bl. Length: 2.13   Twist: Right

Name: Jubala
Model: Vest Pocket
Cal.: 25
O. A. Length: 4.329
Bl. Length: 2.067

Weight: 12.38
Mag. Cap.: 6
Lands: 6
Rifling: 9.06
Twist: Right

Name: Kaba Special
Model: Special
Cal.: 25
O. A. Length: 4.41
Bl. Length: 2.14

Weight: 12.16
Mag. Cap.: 6
Lands: 6
Rifling: 10.44
Twist: Right

Name: Kaba Special
Model: V. P.
Cal.: 25
O. A. Length: 4.53
Bl. Length: 2.17

Weight: 13.26
Mag. Cap.: 6
Lands: 6
Rifling: 15.35
Twist: Right

Name: Kobra
Model: Vest Pocket
Cal.: 25
O. A. Length: 4.524
Bl. Length: 2.301

Weight: 12.94
Mag. Cap.: 6
Lands: 4
Rifling: 2.06-2.15
Twist: Right

Name: Kommer
Model: 1
Cal.: 25
O. A. Length: 4.41
Bl. Length: 2.09

Weight: 12.69
Mag. Cap.: 8
Lands: 4
Rifling: 9.84
Twist: Right

Name: Kommer
Model: 2
Cal.: 25
O. A. Length: 4.33
Bl. Length: 2.05

Weight: 12.13
Mag. Cap.: 6
Lands: 6
Rifling: 9.45
Twist: Right

545

Name: Langenhan   Weight: 17.74
Model: II   Mag. Cap.: 7
Cal.: 25   Lands: 6
O. A. Length: 5.71 Rifling: 9.84
Bl. Length: 3.15   Twist: Right

Name: Langenhan   Weight: 15.48
Model: III   Mag. Cap.: 5
Cal.: 25   Lands: 4
O. A. Length: 4.84 Rifling: 9.84
Bl. Length: 2.32   Twist: Right

Name: Libia   Weight: 12.90
Model: Vest Pocket   Mag. Cap.: 6
Cal.: 25   Lands: 6
O. A. Length: 4.29   Rifling: 10.0
Bl. Length: 1.89   Twist: Right

Name: Lignose   Weight: 13.93
Model: 2   Mag. Cap.: 6
Cal.: 25   Lands: 6
O. A. Length: 4.72 Rifling: 9.65
Bl. Length: 2.13   Twist: Right

Name: Lignose   Weight: 14.35
Model: 2A   Mag. Cap.: 6
Cal.: 25   Lands: 6
O. A. Length: 4.72 Rifling: 9.84
Bl. Length: 2.13   Twist: Right

Name: Bl. Length: 2.05
   Lilliput, August   Weight: 9.41
   Menz   Mag. Cap.: 6
Model: 1925   Lands: 6
Cal.: 25   Rifling: 13.78
O. A. Length: 4.06   Twist: Right

APPENDIX I: MISCELLANEOUS PISTOLS

Name: Little Tom	Weight: 13.22
Model: D. A.	Mag. Cap.: 6
Cal.: 25	Lands: 6
O. A. Length: 4.53	Rifling: 14.17
Bl. Length: 2.36	Twist: Right

Name:	Weight: 14.53
Looking Glass	Mag. Cap.: 6
Model: V. P.	Lands: 6
Cal.: 25	Rifling: 10.24
O. A. Length: 4.1	Twist: Left
Bl. Length: 2.21	

Name:	Weight: 12.94
Looking Glass	Mag. Cap.: 6
Model: Special	Lands: 6
Cal.: 25	Rifling: 9.92
O. A. Length: 4.45	Twist: Left
Bl. Length: 2.05	

Name:	Bl. Length: 2.17
Looking Glass	Weight: 7.14
Model:	Mag. Cap.: 6
Target Special	Lands: 6
Cal.: 25	Rifling: 9.69
O. A. Length: 4.84	Twist: Left

Name: M.A.B.	
Model: A	
Cal.: 25	
O. A. Length: 4.57	
Bl. Length: 2.6	
Weight: 14.10	
Mag. Cap.: 6	Rifling: 12.88
Lands: 6	Twist: Right

Name: Mann	
Model: W. T.	
Cal.: 25	
O. A. Length: 4.02	
Bl. Length: 1.77	Lands: 6
Weight: 8.81	Rifling: 9.65
Mag. Cap.: 5	Twist: Right

547

Name: Marina
Model: V. P.
Cal.: 25
O. A. Length: 4.63
Bl. Length: 2:21

Weight: 13.36
Mag. Cap.: 6
Lands: 6
Rifling: 9.06
Twist: Left

Name: Marte
Model: V. P.
Cal.: 25
O. A. Length: 4.45
Bl. Length: 2.21

Weight: 14.14
Mag. Cap.: 6
Lands: 6
Rifling: 12.01
Twist: Left

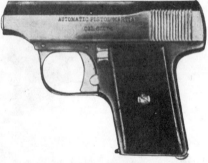

Name: Martian
Model: V. P.
Cal.: 25
O. A. Length: 4.41
Bl. Length: 1.97

Weight: 11.2
Mag. Cap.: 6
Lands: 6
Rifling: 12.41
Twist: Right

Name: Mauser
Model: WTP II
Cal.: 25
O. A. Length: 4.056
Bl. Length: 2.028

Weight: 10.22
Mag. Cap.: 6
Lands: 6
Rifling: 1.11-1.19
Twist: Right

Name: Mauser
Model: WTP I
Cal.: 25
O. A. Length: 4.08
Bl. Length: 2.40

Weight: 11.6
Mag. Cap.: 6
Lands: 6
Rifling: 7.09
Twist: Right

Name Mayor
Model: V. P.
Cal.: 25
O. A. Length: 4.641
Bl. Length: 2.145

Weight: 11.56
Mag. Cap.: 5
Lands: 6
Rifling: 9.76
Twist: Left

Name: Melior
Model: V. P.
Cal.: 25
O. A. Length: 4.49
Bl. Length: 2.17

Weight: 13.01
Mag. Cap.: 6
Lands: 6
Rifling: 9.84
Twist: Right

Name: Melior
Model: Pocket
Cal.: 25
O. A. Length: 4.80
Bl. Length: 2.32

Weight: 12.66
Mag. Cap.: 6
Lands: 6
Rifling: 10.63
Twist: Right

Name:
  Menta, August
  Menz
Model: V. P.
Cal.: 25
O. A. Length: 4.64

Bl. Length: 2.48
Weight: 13.54
Mag. Cap.: 6
Lands: 6
Rifling: 8.86
Twist: Right

Name:
  Menz, August
Model: V. P.
Cal.: 25
O. A. Length: 4.64
Bl. Length: 2.36

Weight: 14.77
Mag. Cap.: 6
Lands: 6
Rifling: 8.66
Twist: Right

Name: Mikros
Model: V. P.
Cal.: 25
O. A. Length: 4.017
Bl. Length: 1.950
Weight: 9.48
Mag. Cap.: 6
Lands: 6

Rifling: 9.43
Twist: Left

Name: Minerve
Model: V. P.
Cal.: 25
O. A. Length: 4.61
Bl. Length: 2.37
Weight: 12.87
Mag. Cap.: 7
Lands: 6

Rifling: 9.69
Twist: Right

Name: Mondial
Model: V. P.
Cal.: 25
O. A. Length: 4.72
Bl. Length: 2.44
Weight: 12.06
Mag. Cap.: 7
Lands: 6
Rifling: 10.36
Twist: Left

Name: Monobloc
Model: V. P.
Cal.: 25
O. A. Length: 4.57
Bl. Length: 2.09
Weight: 13.72
Mag. Cap.: 6
Lands: 6
Rifling: 9.45
Twist: Right

Name: Omega
Model: V. P.
Cal.: 25
O. A. Length: 4.49
Bl. Length: 2.13
Weight: 12.80
Mag. Cap.: 6
Lands: 6
Rifling: 11.42
Twist: Left

Name: Orbea
Model: V. P.
Cal.: 25
O. A. Length: 4.368
Bl. Length: 2.145
Weight: 12.94
Mag. Cap.: 7
Lands: 6
Rifling: 10.97
Twist: Left

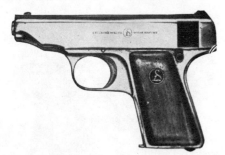

Name: Ortgies
Model: Pocket
Cal.: 25
O. A. Length: 5.20
Bl. Length: 2.71
Weight: 13.36
Mag. Cap.: 6
Lands: 6
Rifling: 7.29
Twist: Right

Name: Owa
Model: V. P.
Cal.: 25
O. A. Length: 4.72
Bl. Length: 1.97
Weight: 14.49
Mag. Cap.: 6
Lands: 6
Rifling: 10.24
Twist: Right

Name: Paramount   Weight: 14.35
Model: V. P.   Mag. Cap.: 6
Cal.: 25   Lands: 6
O. A. Length: 4.485 Rifling: 10.84
Bl. Length: 2.145   Twist: Right

Name: Patent   Weight: 14.21
Model: V. P.   Mag. Cap.: 6
Cal.: 25   Lands: 6
O. A. Length: 4.64   Rifling: 11.42
Bl. Length: 2.21   Twist: Left

Name: Phoenix   Weight: 11.56
Model: V. P.   Mag. Cap.: 6
Cal.: 25   Lands: 6
O. A. Length: 4.64   Rifling: 11.30
Bl. Length: 2.28   Twist: Right

Name: Pieper   Weight: 11.92
Model: C.   Mag. Cap.: 6
Cal.: 25   Lands: 6
O. A. Length: 4.96   Rifling: 9.26
Bl. Length: 2.44   Twist: Right

Name: Pinkerton   Weight: 11.60
Model: V. P.   Mag. Cap.: 6
Cal.: 25   Lands: 6
O. A. Length: 6.30   Rifling: 9.45
Bl. Length: 1.85   Twist: Left

Name: Praga   Weight: 12.23
Model: 1921   Mag. Cap.: 6
Cal.: 25   Lands: 4
O. A. Length: 4.18   Rifling: 10.59
Bl. Length: 2.01   Twist: Right

Name: Premier   Weight: 11.95
Model: 1913   Mag. Cap.: 7
Cal.: 25   Lands: 6
O. A. Length: 4.49   Rifling: 12.41
Bl. Length: 2.09   Twist: Right

Name: Princeps   Weight: 10.6
Model: V. P.   Mag. Cap.: 6
Cal.: 25   Lands: 5
O. A. Length: 4.14   Rifling: 8.66
Bl. Length: 1.93   Twist: Right

Name: Protector   Weight: 13.12
Model: V. P.   Mag. Cap.: 6
Cal.: 25   Lands: 6
O. A. Length: 4.407   Rifling: 1.12-1.21
Bl. Length: 2.106   Twist: Right

Name: Regent   Weight: 13.86
Model: V. P. Special   Mag. Cap.: 6
Cal.: 25   Lands: 6
O. A. Length: 4.68   Rifling: 10.63
Bl. Length: 2.21   Twist: Right

Name: Regent   Weight: 13.22
Model: V. P.   Mag. Cap.: 6
Cal.: 25   Lands: 6
O. A. Length: 4.485   Rifling: 10.87
Bl. Length: 2.223   Twist: Left

Name: Royal   Weight: 13.01
Model: V. P.   Mag. Cap.: 6
Cal.: 25   Lands: 6
O. A. Length: 4.76   Rifling: 12.21
Bl. Length: 2.09   Twist: Right

APPENDIX I: MISCELLANEOUS PISTOLS

Name: Ruby
Model: V. P.
Cal.: 25
O. A. Length: 4.095
Bl. Length: 1.872

Weight: 11.07
Mag. Cap.: 6
Lands: 6
Rifling: 0.90-0.95
Twist: Left

Name:
  Ruby Guernica
Model: V. P.
Cal.: 25
O. A. Length: 4.53
Bl. Length: 2.05

Weight: 13.64
Mag. Cap.: 6
Lands: 6
Rifling: 12.01
Twist: Right

Name: Sauer
Model: V. P.
Cal.: 25
O. A. Length: 4.8
Bl. Length: 3.45

Weight: 14.42
Mag. Cap.: 7
Lands: 6
Rifling: 14.17
Twist: Right

Name: Seam
Model: V. P.
Cal.: 25
O. A. Length: 4.53
Bl. Length: 2.13

Weight: 13.40
Mag. Cap.: 6
Lands: 6
Rifling: 12.01
Twist: Right

Name: Simson
Model: V. P.
Cal.: 25
O. A. Length: 4.49
Bl. Length: 2.19

Weight: 13.12
Mag. Cap.: 6
Lands: 6
Rifling: 9.84
Twist: Right

Name: Singer
Model: V. P.
Cal.: 25
O. A. Length: 4.49
Bl. Length: 2.17

Weight: 12.90
Mag. Cap.: 6
Lands: 6
Rifling: 14.57
Twist: Right

553

Name: S. M.
Model: V. P.
Cal.: 25
O. A. Length: 4.57
Bl. Length: 2.21

Weight: 13.50
Mag. Cap.: 6
Lands: 6
Rifling: 10.04
Twist: Right

Name:
  Societe d'Armes
Model: V. P.
Cal.: 25
O. A. Length: 4.53
Bl. Length: 2.13

Weight: 13.36
Mag. Cap.: 5
Lands: 6
Rifling: 10.63
Twist: Right

Name: Star
Model: Pocket
Cal.: 25
O. A. Length: 4.953
Bl. Length: 2.652

Weight: 15.62
Mag. Cap.: 8
Lands: 6
Rifling: 11.02
Twist: Left

Name: Star
Model: E.
Cal.: 25
O. A. Length: 3.94
Bl. Length: 1.989

Weight: 9.94
Mag. Cap.: 6
Lands: 6
Rifling: 10.04
Twist: Left

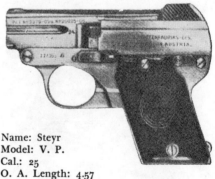

Name:
  Stern, Albin
    W. Z. M.
Model: B
Cal.: 25
O. A. Length: 4.96
Bl. Length: 2.40
Weight: 15.51
Mag. Cap.: 10

Lands: 6
Rifling: 9.84
Twist: Right

Name: Steyr
Model: V. P.
Cal.: 25
O. A. Length: 4.57
Bl. Length: 2.09
Weight: 12.37
Mag. Cap.: 6

Lands: 6
Rifling: 8.86
Twist: Right

554

APPENDIX I: MISCELLANEOUS PISTOLS

Name:
  Stock, Franz
Model: V. P.
Cal.: 25
O. A. Length: 4.72
Bl. Length: 2.48

Weight: 12.41
Mag. Cap.: 7
Lands: 4
Rifling: 9.65
Twist: Right

Name: Stosel
Model: V. P.
Cal.: 25
O. A. Length: 4.57
Bl. Length: 2.17

Weight: 13.40
Mag. Cap.: 6
Lands: 6
Rifling: 9.84
Twist: Right

Name: Thunder
Model: 1919
Cal.: 25
O. A. Length: 4.41
Bl. Length: 1.97

Weight: 13.22
Mag. Cap.: 6
Lands: 6
Rifling: 11.22
Twist: Right

Name: Titanic
Model: V. P.
Cal.: 25
O. A. Length: 4.57
Bl. Length: 2.28

Weight: 13.75
Mag. Cap.: 6
Lands: 6
Rifling: 10.63
Twist: Right

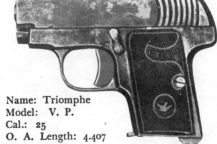

Name: Tiwa
Model: V. P.
Cal.: 25
O. A. Length: 7.33
Bl. Length: 4.92
Weight: 15.23
Mag. Cap.: 6
Lands: 6

Rifling: 10.18
Twist: Right

Name: Triomphe
Model: V. P.
Cal.: 25
O. A. Length: 4.407
Bl. Length: 2.145
Weight: 13.08
Mag. Cap.: 6
Lands: 6

Rifling: 1.04-1.08
Twist: Right

555

Name: Union	Weight: 13.57
Model: V. P. 1	Mag. Cap.: 6
Cal.: 25	Lands: 6
O. A. Length: 4.57	Rifling: 9.65
Bl. Length: 2.21	Twist: Right

Name:	Bl. Length: 2.13
Unique Eibar	Weight: 12.90
Model: 1910	Mag. Cap.: 6
Cal.: 25	Lands: 6
O. A. Length: 4.1	Rifling: 10.50
	Twist: Right

Name: Vencedor	Weight: 11.81
Model: V. P.	Mag. Cap.: 6
Cal.: 25	Lands: 6
O. A. Length: 4.368	Rifling: 10.87
Bl. Length: 2.145	Twist: Right

Name: Venus	Weight: 12.87
Model: V. P.	Mag. Cap.: 6
Cal.: 25	Lands: 5
O. A. Length: 4.37	Rifling: 6.69
Bl. Length: 2.09	Twist: Right

Name:	Weight: 14.10
Verney-Carron	Mag. Cap. 6
Model: V. P.	Lands: 6
Cal.: 25	Rifling: 11.62
O. A. Length: 4.72	Twist: Right
Bl. Length: 2.28	

Name: Vesta	Weight: 11.88
Model: V. P.	Mag. Cap.: 7
Cal.: 25	Lands: 6
O. A. Length: 4.49	Rifling: 11.02
Bl. Length: 2.09	Twist: Right

Name: Victoria   Weight: 11.53
Model: V. P.   Mag. Cap.: 6
Cal.: 25   Lands: 6
O. A. Length: 4.29 Rifling: 12.01
Bl. Length: 2.17   Twist: Right

Name: Vite   Weight: 13.58
Model: 1912   Mag. Cap.: 8
Cal.: 25   Lands: 6
O. A. Length: 4.446 Rifling: 9.86
Bl. Length: 2.145 Twist: Right

Name: Vite   Weight: 14.31
Model: 1913   Mag. Cap.: 6
Cal.: 25   Lands: 5
O. A. Length: 4.64 Rifling: 9.69
Bl. Length: 2.17   Twist: Right

Name: Waldman   Weight: 11.46
Model: V. P.   Mag. Cap.: 6
Cal.: 25   Lands: 5
O. A. Length: 4.37 Rifling: 10.44
Bl. Length: 2.13   Twist: Right

Name: Waldman   Weight: 11.92
Model: V. P.   Mag. Cap.: 6
Cal.: 25   Lands: 6
O. A. Length: 4.53 Rifling: 12.21
Bl. Length: 2.21   Twist: Right

Name: Walther   Weight: 9.76
Model: 2   Mag. Cap.: 6
Cal.: 25   Lands: 6
O. A. Length: 4.22 Rifling: 9.65
Bl. Length: 2.13   Twist: Right

Name: Walther
Model: 5
Cal.: 25
O. A. Length: 4.22
Bl. Length: 2.3

Weight: 9.62
Mag. Cap. 6
Lands: 4
Rifling: 9.45
Twist: Right

Name: Walther
Model: 7
Cal.: 25
O. A. Length: 5.32
Bl. Length: 3.04

Weight: 11.81
Mag. Cap.: 8
Lands: 4
Rifling: 9.84
Twist: Right

Name: Walther
Model: 8
Cal.: 25
O. A. Length: 5.12
Bl. Length: 2.92

Weight: 12.83
Mag. Cap.: 8
Lands: 6
Rifling: 9.84
Twist: Right

Name: Walther
Model: 9
Cal.: 25
O. A. Length: 3.94
Bl. Length: 2.01

Weight: 8.95
Mag. Cap.: 6
Lands: 6
Rifling: 9.06
Twist: Right

Name: Walther
Model: P. P.
Cal.: 25
O. A. Length: 6.54
Bl. Length: 3.35

Weight: 23
Mag. Cap.: 8
Lands: 6
Rifling: 7.48
Twist: Right

Name:
  Webley and Scott
Model:
  V. P. Hammerless
Cal.: 25
O. A. Length: 4.25

Bl. Length: 2.13
Weight: 10.75
Mag. Cap.: 6
Lands: 6
Rifling: 10.83
Twist: Right

Name:
  Webley and Scott
Model:
  V. P. Hammer
Cal.: 25
O. A. Length: 4.75

Bl. Length: 2.13
Weight: 11.75
Mag. Cap.: 6
Lands: 6
Rifling: 10.24
Twist: Right

Name: Ydeal
Model: V. P.
Cal.: 25
O. A. Length: 4.02
Bl. Length: 1.85

Weight: 10.51
Mag. Cap.: 6
Lands: 6
Rifling: 15.55
Twist: Right

Name: Ydeal
Model: V. P.
Cal.: 25
O. A. Length: 4.10
Bl. Length: 1.89

Weight: 10.05
Mag. Cap.: 6
Lands: 6
Rifling: 15.55
Twist: Right

Name: Zehna
Model: V. P.
Cal.: 25
O. A. Length: 4.68
Bl. Length: 2.40

Weight: 13.08
Mag. Cap.: 6
Lands: 4
Rifling: 7.09
Twist: Right

Name: Alkartasuna
Cal.: 32
O. A. Length: 5
Bl. Length: 3.94
Weight: 22.60

Mag. Cap.: 7
Lands: 6
Rifling: 10.04
Twist: Left

Name: Allies
Model: V. P.
Cal.: 32
O. A. Length: 5.07
Bl. Length: 2.574

Weight: 21.34
Mag. Cap.: 6
Lands: 6
Rifling: 9.97
Twist: Left

Name:
  Automatische
    Selbstlade
      Pistole
Model: V. P.
Cal.: 32
O. A. Length: 5.36

Bl. Length: 2.64
Weight: 21.40
Mag. Cap.: 7
Lands: 4
Rifling: 10.24
Twist: Right

Name: Azul
Model:
Cal.: 32
O. A. Length: 5.343
Bl. Length: 2.613

Weight: 21.90
Mag. Cap.: 7
Lands: 6
Rifling: 10.61
Twist: Right

Name: Bayard
Model: 1908
Cal.: 32
O. A. Length: 4.96
Bl. Length: 2.25

Weight: 16.57
Mag. Cap.: 6
Lands: 6
Rifling: 14.37
Twist: Left

Name: Bayard
Model: 1923
Cal.: 32
O. A. Length: 5.86
Bl. Length: 3.35

Weight: 18.62
Mag. Cap.: 6
Lands: 8
Rifling: 9.84
Twist: Left

Name: Beretta
Model: 1915
Cal.: 32
O. A. Length: 6
Bl. Length: 3.315

Weight: 19.82
Mag. Cap.: 7
Lands: 6
Rifling: 0.86-0.97
Twist: Right

Name: Beholla
Model: Pocket
Cal.: 32
O. A. Length: 5.51
Bl. Length: 2.92

Weight 22.14
Mag. Cap.: 7
Lands: 6
Rifling: 9.26
Twist: Right

Name: Broncho
Model: 1918
Cal.: 32
O. A. Length: 5.07
Bl. Length: 2.535

Weight: 20.49
Mag. Cap.: 6
Lands: 6
Rifling: 11.02
Twist: Left

Name: Browning
Model: 1900
Cal.: 32
O. A. Length: 6.75
Bl. Length: 4.02

Weight: 22.22
Mag. Cap.: 7
Lands: 6
Rifling: 9.06
Twist: Right

Name: Bufalo
Model: Pocket
Cal.: 32
O. A. Length: 6.045
Bl. Length: 3.354

Weight: 22.36
Mag. Cap.: 7
Lands: 6
Rifling: 9.94
Twist: Left

Name: Cobra
Model: Pocket
Cal.: 32
O. A. Length: 6.46
Bl. Length: 3.31

Weight: 30.19
Mag. Cap.: 9
Lands: 6
Rifling: 9.84
Twist: Left

Name: Clement
Model: 1909
Cal.: 32
O. A. Length: 5.91
Bl. Length: 2.96

Weight: 20.59
Mag. Cap.: 6
Lands: 6
Rifling: 12.99
Twist: Right

Name: Colt
Model: Pocket
Cal.: 32
O. A. Length: 6.73
Bl. Length: 3.78

Weight: 24.47
Mag. Cap.: 8
Lands: 6
Rifling: 14.25
Twist: Left

Name: Continental   Weight: 22.22
Model: Pocket   Mag. Cap.: 8
Cal.: 32   Lands: 6
O. A. Length: 6.58   Rifling 8.27
Bl. Length: 3.89   Twist: Right

Name: Danton   Weight: 24.05
Model: Pocket   Mag. Cap.: 9
Cal.: 32   Lands: 6
O. A. Length: 6.11   Rifling: 11.81
Bl. Length: 3.35   Twist: Right

Name: Destroyer   Weight: 22.32
Model: 1914   Mag. Cap.: 7
Cal.: 32   Lands: 6
O. A. Length: 5.733   Rifling: 11.09
Bl. Length: 3.237   Twist: Right

Name: Dreyse   Weight: 23.98
Model: 1907   Mag. Cap.: 8
Cal.: 32   Lands: 4
O. A. Length: 6.22   Rifling: 16.54
Bl. Length: 3.58   Twist: Right

Name: A. Errasti   Weight: 18.93
Model: V. P.   Mag. Cap.: 7
Cal.: 32   Lands: 6
O. A. Length: 5.12   Rifling: 12.60
Bl. Length: 2.64   Twist: Left

Name: Express   Weight: 23.80
Model: Pocket   Mag. Cap.: 8
Cal.: 32   Lands: 6
O. A. Length: 5.99   Rifling: 13.78
Bl. Length: 3.27   Twist: Right

562

Name:
  F. N. Browning
Model: 1899
Cal.: 32
O. A. Length: 7.176
Bl. Length: 4.758

Weight: 26.94
Mag. Cap.: 8
Lands: 5
Rifling: 4.5-5.9
Twist: Right

Name: F. N.
Model: 1922
Cal.: 32
O. A. Length: 7.04
Bl. Length: 4.45

Weight: 24.68
Mag. Cap.: 9
Lands: 6
Rifling: 10.63
Twist: Right

Name: Frommer
Model: Stop
Cal.: 32
O. A. Length: 6.50
Bl. Length: 3.82

Weight: 21.30
Lands: 4
Rifling: 9.45
Twist: Right

Name:
  Frommer Pat.
Model: Baby
Cal.: 32
O. A. Length: 4.84
Bl. Length: 2.13

Weight: 17.6
Mag. Cap.: 6
Lands: 4
Rifling: 17.32
Twist: Right

Name:
  Gregorio
    Bolumburn
Model: Pocket
Cal.: 32
O. A. Length: 6.201

Bl. Length: 3.471
Weight: 30.899
Mag. Cap.: 9
Lands: 6
Rifling: 11.82
Twist: Left

Name:
  G. V. Nordheim
Model: Pocket
Cal.: 32
O. A. Length: 6.15
Bl. Length: 3.66

Weight: 21.02
Mag. Cap.: 7
Lands: 4
Rifling: 11.93
Twist: Right

Name: H & R
Model: Pocket
Cal.: 32
O. A. Length: 6.50
Bl. Length: 3.50

Weight: 21.93
Mag. Cap.: 8
Lands: 6
Rifling: 12.05
Twist: Right

Name:
   The Infallible
Model: Pocket
Cal.: 32
O. A. Length: 6.552

Bl. Length: 3.198
Weight: 24.72
Mag. Cap.: 7
Lands: 6
Rifling: 8.4:
Twist: Right

Name: Jäger
Model: Pocket
Cal.: 32
O. A. Length: 6.5
Bl. Length: 3.9

Weight: 22.89
Mag. Cap.: 7
Lands: 4
Rifling: 9.65
Twist: Right

Name: Jieffeco
Model: Pocket
Cal.: 32
O. A. Length: 5
Bl. Length: 2.17

Weight: 15.94
Mag. Cap.: 7
Lands: 6
Rifling: 9.45
Twist: Right

Name: Kebler
Model: Pocket
Cal.: 32
O. A. Length: 6.46
Bl. Length: 3.74

Weight: 22.81
Mag. Cap.: 7
Lands: 4
Rifling: 8.47
Twist: Right

Name: Langenhan
Model: Army
Cal.: 32
O. A. Length: 6.61
Bl. Length: 4.14

Weight: 22.89
Mag. Cap.: 8
Lands: 4
Rifling: 9.65
Twist: Right

Name: Leonhardt Weight: 21.65
Model: Army Mag. Cap.: 7
Cal.: 32 Lands: 6
O. A. Length: 5.55 Rifling: 9.45
Bl. Length: 2.92 Twist: Right

Name: Little Tom Bl. Length: 3.11
Model: Weight: 20.56
 Double Action Mag. Cap.: 8
Cal.: 32 Lands: 6
O. A. Length: 5.47 Rifling: 14.77
 Twist: Right

Name: Weight: 27.01
 Looking Glass Mag. Cap.: 9
Model: Pocket Lands: 6
Cal.: 32 Rifling: 10.12
O. A. Length: 6.07 Twist: Left
Bl. Length: 3.35

Name: Mann Weight: 12.45
Model: Pocket Mag. Cap.: 5
Cal.: 32 Lands: 4
O. A. Length: 4.64 Rifling: 9.65
Bl. Length: 2.36 Twist: Right

Name:
 Manufacture
  d' Armes a Feu
Model: Pocket
Cal.: 32
O. A. Length: 5.71
Bl. Length: 3.23 Lands: 6
Weight: 20.13 Rifling 7.09
Mag. Cap.: 8 Twist: Right

Name: Martian
Model: Pocket
Cal.: 32
O. A. Length: 5.67
Bl. Length: 2.92
Weight: 21.26
Mag. Cap.: 7 Rifling: 10.87
Lands: 6 Twist: Right

Name: Mauser	Weight: 21.47
Model: 1910	Mag. Cap.: 8
Cal.: 32	Lands: 6
O. A. Length: 6.07	Rifling: 7.68
Bl. Length: 3.43	Twist: Right

Name: Mauser	Weight: 21.62
Model: 1934	Mag. Cap.: 8
Cal.: 32	Lands: 6
O. A. Length: 6.045	Rifling: 1.01-1.06
Bl. Length: 3.432	Twist: Right

Name: Melior	Weight: 20.80
Model: Pocket	Mag. Cap.: 7
Cal.: 32	Lands: 5
O. A. Length: 6.07	Rifling: 9.06
Bl. Length: 3.54	Twist: Right

Name: Menz (Special)	Weight: 24.69
Model: 111	Mag. Cap.: 8
Cal.: 32	Lands: 6
O. A. Length: 6.123	Rifling: 090-097
Bl. Length: 3.471	Twist: Right

Name: Oyez	Weight: 21.86
Model: Pocket	Mag. Cap.: 7
Cal.: 32	Lands: 6
O. A. Length: 5.733	Rifling: 1.26-1.38
Bl. Length: 2.847	Twist: Right

Name: Paramount	Weight: 28.95
Model: 1914	Mag. Cap.: 9
Cal.: 32	Lands: 6
O. A. Length: 5.928	Rifling: 1.16-1.26
Bl. Length: 3.237	Twist: Left

Name: Pieper
Model: 1908
Cal.: 32
O. A. Length: 6.03
Bl. Length: 3.04

Weight: 21.19
Mag. Cap.: 7
Lands: 6
Rifling: 9.06
Twist: Right

Name: Precision
Model: Pocket
Cal.: 32
O. A. Length: 5.031
Bl. Length: 2.535

Weight: 19.75
Mag. Cap.: 6
Lands: 6
Rifling: 1.45-1.61
Twist: Left

Name: Regina
Model: Pocket
Cal.: 32
O. A. Length: 5.616
Bl. Length: 3.159

Weight: 22.36
Mag. Cap.: 7
Lands: 6
Rifling: 0.64-0.83
Twist: Right

Name: Regina
Model: Pocket
Cal.: 32
O. A. Length: 4.836
Bl. Length: 2.418

Weight: 17.38
Mag. Cap.: 6
Lands: 6
Rifling: 1.30-1.60
Twist: Right

Name: Remington
Cal.: 32
O. A. Length: 6.42
Bl. Length: 3.50

Weight: 21.19
Mag. Cap.: 8
Lands: 7
Rifling: 16.34
Twist: Right

Name: Rheinmetall
Model: Pocket
Cal.: 32
O. A. Length: 6.46
Bl. Length: 3.63

Weight: 23.63
Mag. Cap.: 8
Lands: 4
Rifling: 16.54
Twist: Right

Name: Royal
Model: Pocket
Cal.: 32
O. A. Length: 6.07
Bl. Length: 2.96

Weight: 21.65
Mag. Cap.: 7
Lands: 6
Rifling: 16.14
Twist: Right

Name: Sauer
Model: Pocket, 1913
Cal.: 32
O. A. Length: 5.67
Bl. Length: 3.0

Weight: 19.32
Mag. Cap.: 7
Lands: 6
Rifling: 16.54
Twist: Right

Name: Sauer
Model: Behorden
Cal.: 32
O. A. Length: 5.79
Bl. Length: 3.0

Weight: 21.86
Mag. Cap.: 7
Lands: 6
Rifling: 13.59
Twist: Right

Name: Savage
Model: 1907
Cal.: 32
O. A. Length: 6.58
Bl. Length: 3.78

Weight: 19
Mag. Cap.: 10
Lands: 6
Rifling: 11.81
Twist: Right

Name: Savage
Model: 1917
Cal.: 32
O. A. Length: 6.58
Bl. Length: 3.78

Weight: 21.90
Mag. Cap.: 10
Lands: 6
Rifling: 11.42
Twist: Right

Name: Schwarzlose
Model: 1908
Cal.: 32
O. A. Length: 5.63
Bl. Length: 4.14

Weight: 18.79
Mag. Cap.: 7
Lands: 4
Rifling: 7.87
Twist: Right

Name: Singer   Weight: 22.89
Model: Pocket   Mag. Cap.: 7
Cal.: 32   Lands: 6
O. A. Length: 5.99   Rifling: 10.04
Bl. Length: 3.27   Twist: Right

Name:
  Sharp-shooter   Bl. Length: 3.75
Model: Pocket   Weight: 26.91
Cal.: 32   Mag. Cap.: 8
O. A. Length: 6.5   Lands: 6
    Rifling: 1.10-1.20
    Twist: Right

Name:
  Smith & Wesson   Weight: 25.71
Model: Pocket   Mag. Cap.: 7
Cal.: 32   Lands: 6
O. A. Length: 6.54   Rifling: 12.21
Bl. Length: 3.50   Twist: Right

Name: Star   Weight: 30
Model: Military   Mag. Cap.: 9
Cal.: 32   Lands: 6
O. A. Length: 7.5   Rifling: 12.0
Bl. Length: 4.8   Twist: Right

Name: Steyr
Model: Pocket 1909
Cal.: 32
O. A. Length: 6.45
Bl. Length: 3.54
Weight: 22.25
Mag. Cap.: 7   Rifling: 10.06
Lands: 6   Twist: Right

Name:
  Steyr-Solothurn
Model: Pocket
Cal.: 32
O. A. Length: 6.46
Bl. Length: 3.62
Weight: 22.78
Mag. Cap.: 7   Rifling: 10.04
Lands: 6   Twist: Right

Name: Stock | Weight: 23.17
Model: Pocket | Mag. Cap.: 8
Cal.: 32 | Lands: 4
O. A. Length: 6.75 | Rifling: 9.26
Bl. Length: 4 | Twist: Right

Name: Trust | Weight: 29.24
Model: Pocket | Mag. Cap.: 9
Cal.: 32 | Lands: 6
O. A. Length: 6.045 | Rifling: 115-145
Bl. Length: 3.315 | Twist: Left

Name: Venus | Weight: 20.31
Model: Pocket | Mag. Cap.: 6
Cal.: 32 | Lands: 6
O. A. Length: 4.914 | Rifling: 0.90-1.10
Bl. Length: 2.34 | Twist: Right

Name: Victoria | Weight: 21.30
Model: Pocket | Mag. Cap.: 7
Cal.: 32 | Lands: 6
O. A. Length: 5.79 | Rifling: 11.22
Bl. Length: 3.23 | Twist: Right

Name: Walther |
Model: 3 |
Cal.: 32 |
O. A. Length: 5.03 |
Bl. Length: 2.60 | Lands: 6
Weight: 16.64 | Rifling: 11.81
Mag. Cap.: 6 | Twist: Right

Name: Walther |
Model: 4 |
Cal.: 32 |
O. A. Length: 5.91 |
Bl. Length: 3.46 |
Weight: 18.58 |
Mag. Cap.: 8 | Rifling: 9.65
Lands: 4 | Twist: Right

Name: Walther	Weight: 23.94
Model: P. P.	Mag. Cap.: 8
Cal.: 32	Lands: 6
O. A. Length: 6.69	Rifling: 8.27
Bl. Length: 3.85	Twist: Right

Name: Walther	Weight: 18.83
Model: P. P. K.	Mag. Cap.: 7
Cal.: 32	Lands: 6
O. A. Length: 5.91	Rifling: 9.45
Bl. Length: 3.27	Twist: Right

Name:	Weight: 19.64
Webley & Scott	Mag. Cap.: 8
Model: M. P.	Lands: 6
Cal.: 32	Rifling: 10.04
O. A. Length: 6.15	Twist: Right
Bl. Length: 3.46	

Name: Bayard	Weight: 16.29
Model: 1911	Mag. Cap.: 6
Cal.: 380	Lands: 6
O. A. Length: 4.34	Rifling: 8.75
Bl. Length: 2.25	Twist: Left

Name: Bayard	Weight: 18.23
Model: 1923	Mag. Cap.: 6
Cal.: 380	Lands: 6
O. A. Length: 5.86	Rifling: 9.53
Bl. Length: 3.35	Twist: Left

Name: Colt
Model: Pocket
    Hammerless
Cal.: 380
O. A. Length: 6.73
Bl. Length: 3.73

Weight: 22.92
Mag. Cap.: 7
Lands: 6
Rifling: 16.74
Twist: Left

Name: F. N.
Model: 1910
Cal.: 380
O. A. Length: 6.03
Bl. Length: 3.43

Weight: 20.28
Mag. Cap.: 6
Lands: 6
Rifling: 9.61
Twist: Right

Name: F. N.
Model: 1922
Cal.: 380
O. A. Length: 7.18
Weight: 25

Mag. Cap.: 8
Lands: 6
Rifling: 9.61
Twist: Right

Name: Frommer
Model: Stop
Cal.: 380
O. A. Length: 6.50
Bl. Length: 3.8

Weight: 21
Mag. Cap.: 6
Lands: 4
Rifling: 9.39
Twist: Right

Name: Frommer
Model: Baby
Cal.: 380
O. A. Length: 4.34
Bl. Length: 2.17

Weight: 15.23
Mag. Cap.: 5
Lands: 4
Rifling: 10.0
Twist: Right

Name: Mann
Model: V. P.
Cal.: 380
O. A. Length: 4.76
Bl. Length: 2.36

Weight: 13.33
Mag. Cap.: 5
Lands: 4
Rifling: 11.81
Twist: Right

Name: Ortgies
Model: Pocket
Cal.: 380
O. A. Length: 6.5
Bl. Length: 3.25

Weight: 21.10
Mag. Cap.: 7
Lands: 6
Rifling: 9.41
Twist: Right

Name: Remington
Model: 51
Cal.: 380
O. A. Length: 6.38
Bl. Length: 3.58

Weight: 20.37
Mag. Cap.: 7
Lands: 7
Rifling: 16.62
Twist: Right

Name: Savage
Model: 1917
Cal.: 380
O. A. Length: 7.0
Bl. Length: 4.25
Weight: 24.15
Mag. Cap.: 9
Lands: 6

Rifling: 16.14
Twist: Right

Name: CZ
Model: 22
Cal.: .380
O. A. Length: 6
Bl. Length: 3.43
Weight: 21
Mag. Cap.: 8
Lands: 6
Rifling: 10.00

Twist: Right

High Standard G Series .22.

French Service Model 1935-A, Cal. 7.65mm. Special. Thumb safety on slide is hammer block. Browning type slide stop.

573

German Walther Armee Pistole. An enclosed hammer modification of the P. 38 design. Cal. 9 mm Luger. Walther. also made limited quantities of MP Models, blowback pistols on the PP system, as well as stamped designs for this cartridge.

Typical multi-barreled cartridge pistol. This is a .455 British Lancaster.

Swedish P. 40 (slightly modified Finnish Lahti), Cal. 9 mm Luger. Left closed. Takedown lever as in Luger. Bolt travels inside subreceiver. Lanyard loop and stock attachment. Bolt wings and head of recoil spring guide at rear. Locking block is raised and lowered inside subreceiver forward of bolt wings.

Right side open. Cut in top of bolt forward of wings is resting place for top of locking block when forced down by cam action as pistol closes. Bolt stop is released by drawing back and releasing bolt. Action is short recoil. Positive manual safety.

Appendix II
Identification of Typical Revolvers

Typical Iver Johnson hinged-frame pocket revolver with exposed hammer.

Typical European solid-frame revolver of the 'Bulldog' variety.

Typical Harrington & Richardson exposed hammer hinged-frame revolver of current manufacture.

Typical American hinged-frame 'hammerless' revolver. This is a Hopkins & Allen.

Typical British Webley hinged-frame revolver with birds-head grip.

Early rimfire revolver with typical sheath trigger. This specimen is a Merwin-Hulbert and was also made for center-fire cartridges.

Caliber .476 Revolver. This is the obsolete British Enfield.

Appendix III
Glossary of Pistol and Revolver Terms

A

ACTION. 1. The assembly of moving parts in a gun which (1) feed the cartridge into the chamber from the magazine (in a revolver, move a loaded chamber into position for firing), (2) seal and lock the chamber, (3) fire the cartridge, (4) unseal and unlock the chamber and extract the fired cartridge case, and (5) eject the empty case. The term is also loosely applied to the fixed housing; *i. e.*, the *Receiver* or *Frame* in which the action operates.

2. SINGLE ACTION. A weapon in which the hammer must be cocked before pressure on the trigger will fire the gun. Each act (cocking hammer and pressing trigger) is distinct from the other.

3. DOUBLE-ACTION. (1) A type of firing mechanism in a revolver by means of which a continuous pull on the trigger will (a) revolve the cylinder, placing a cartridge in position to fire, (b) cock the hammer, (c) release the hammer and fire the gun. The trigger must then be released and permitted to return fully forward; after which the cycle may be repeated. Most double-action revolvers having an outside hammer may be used also as single-action arms: *i. e.*, they may be cocked by drawing back the hammer (by pressing on the hammer itself, not on the trigger) to full-cock position, where it will remain until released by pressure on the trigger. (2) Some autoloading pistols are equipped with a type of double-action trigger which goes through the cycle of cocking and firing the first shot by continuous pressure on the trigger, but does not move a new cartridge from the magazine into the chamber.

4. DELAYED BLOWBACK—also called retarded or hesitation action. This type of action while not positively locked as is a recoil operated or gas operated action, incorporates a short delay usually by incorporating a mechanical disadvantage which must be overcome by the action to open. This delay gives the bullet time enough to leave the barrel thereby dropping the pressure in the barrel; the residual pressure assists in extracting the empty case. Although this type of action is more frequently found in submachine guns and rifles there are several pistols with delayed blowback actions. These usually have rotating barrels; knuckle joints are also frequently used in delayed blowback action.

5. RECOIL OPERATED. As pertains to automatic and semiautomatic arms, a weapon in which the barrel and breechblock are locked together at the instant of firing. As the bullet leaves the barrel, the rearward thrust of the powder gases starts the locked barrel and bolt to the rear. After a short travel, the barrel strikes an abutment, or is otherwise halted, and its locking device is withdrawn from the slide, breechblock, or bolt, which continues to the rear to eject the fired case and prepare for the reloading motion. (a) In *short-recoil* weapons the barrel travels to the rear, locked to the breech, a distance less than the length of the cartridge. (b) In *long-recoil* weapons the barrel remains locked to the breech for the full distance of the recoil stroke. The barrel is then unlocked and thrust forward, the bolt is held back, ejection is accomplished, and the chamber is reloaded. *Recoil-operated* actions are not to be confused with *blowback* actions, which are fired without the mechanical locking of the barrel and breechblock.

6. BLOWBACK. As pertains to automatic and semiautomatic arms, a weapon in which no mechanical locking system is employed. The breech is held closed at the moment of firing by the action of recoil springs and the weight of the slide, hammer, and other moving parts. The weight of these parts is so much greater than the weight of the bullet that the expanding powder gases drive the bullet out of the barrel before the inertia of the breech action has been overcome; then the breechblock action is blown backward by residual pressure.

7. BLOW FORWARD. An automatic or semiautomatic arm having a standing breech, in which the barrel is blown forward to open the action and eject the fired cartridge case. The barrel is then forced back against the standing breech by a powerful spring. The gun is cocked and reloaded as the barrel is forced to the rear.

Refer to the main headings for a fuller discussion of all the italicized words.

ADAPTER. 1. A device designed to alter the use or functioning of a weapon usually to permit practice with less expensive ammunition of smaller caliber. (See *Conversion Unit*.)

2. GRIP ADAPTER: A filler fitting back of the trigger guard of a revolver to provide a lower point of contact between the gun and the shooter's hand.

ANVIL. A firm, fixed point against which the explosive primer mixture is compressed by the action of the firing pin or striker in a gun. In the Berdan-type primer, the anvil is in the head of the cartridge case, forming a projection in the center of the primer pocket. In the American-type (Boxer) primer, the anvil is a small arbor of metal fastened rigidly across the primer cup over the explosive pellet. In rimfire cartridges there is no true anvil; the anvil is formed by the rear face of the barrel, which serves as the stop and resting place for the rim of the cartridge when it is inserted in the chamber. Thus, the anvil may be found (1) in the primer cup, (2) in the head of the cartridge case, or (3) in the gun.

ARSENAL. A manufacturing place for the production of arms or ammunition; as "Frankford Arsenal." Often used interchangeably with Armory.

ASSEMBLY. Any collection of parts operating together which are housed to form a single unit; as "magazine assembly," "bolt assembly," *etc.*

AUTOLOADING. 1. A weapon which, being manually loaded and fired for the first shot, will eject the fired cartridge case, load the next cartridge from the magazine, and cock the gun ready for refiring. Pressure on the trigger must be released after each shot and reapplied to fire the succeeding shot. The ejection and reloading operations are performed by utilizing the forces of gas expansion, recoil, and mechanical spring action. *Semiautomatic. Self-loading.*

2. Commonly but incorrectly called *Automatic.*

AUTOMATIC. As applied to small arms, a weapon which, being manually loaded and fired for the first shot, will eject the fired case, load the next cartridge from the magazine, fire and eject that cartridge, and repeat the process indefinitely so long as the initial pressure is maintained on the trigger, or until the cartridge supply in the magazine has been exhausted. The ejection, loading, and firing operations are performed by utilizing the forces of gas pressure, recoil, and mechanical spring action.

The term is generally, though incorrectly, applied to *semiautomatic* or *autoloading* arms. The classic example of the misapplication of the term is the designation of the Colt. caliber .45, Model 1911, as the "Automatic Colt Pistol" (".45 A.C.P.").

See *Autoloading.*

AUTOMATIC REVOLVER. See *Revolver 4.*

AUTOMATIC SAFETY. See *Safety 2.*

B

BACKLASH. 1. Excess motion in linked mechanical parts. Generally applied to the continued rearward travel of the trigger beyond the point where the firing pin, or hammer, has been released to fire the weapon.

2. Also commonly referred to in connection with the failure of sight-adjusting screws to move the sight positively the proper distance for each rotation of the adjusting screw.

BACKSTRAP. That portion of the frame which forms the rear of the grip.

BALLISTIC DRIFT. See *Drift 2.*

BALLISTICS. The study of bullets in flight and of the action of their propellants.

1. *Exterior* ballistics cover the flight of the bullet after it leaves the muzzle of the gun.

2. *Interior* ballistics have to do with the explosion of the primer, the ignition and burning of the propellant powder, internal pressures, and the stresses, strains, and torques resulting as the bullet is forced through the barrel .

BARREL. 1. The steel tube in a gun through which the bullet is driven by the explosion of the propellant charge.

2. SUBCALIBER BARREL. A barrel of smaller caliber generally inserted down the bore of a large-caliber gun, permitting it to be used for practice work with less powerful, cheaper ammunition, generally called a *Subcaliber Tube.*

BARREL EXTENSION. A frame to the rear of the barrel which houses the breechblock or similar working parts. This extension may be an integral part of the barrel forging (the Japanese Nambu), or it may be a separate member into which the barrel is screwed (the German Luger).

BENT. A notch (commonly in the hammer) in which the trigger or sear is held engaged, under the tension of the mainspring, until withdrawn by the action of the trigger.

BOLT. As applied to bolt-action weapons the bolt is the cylindrical or oblong block of steel which is so designed that it may be pushed forward and locked (or held in its closed position by spring action) so as to seal the breech for firing, then withdrawn so as to permit the ejection of the fired cartridge case and the loading of another cartridge. A type of breechblock which opens and closes the breech by moving forward and backward in the receiver. The rear section of a pistol slide.

BORE. The hole drilled in the gun barrel, through which the bullet is driven by the gases of the burning powder. *See Caliber 1.*

BORE DIAMETER. See *Groove Diameter.*

BREECH. 1. The outside rear of the barrel.

2. FACE OF BREECH. The extreme rear surface of the barrel or chamber where it meets the breechblock or bolt.

3. STANDING BREECH. (a) In a revolver, that section of the frame immediately behind the cylinder which supports the heads of the cartridges.

(b) That portion of the frame which supports the heads of the cartridges in a blow-forward or hinge-frame weapon.

BREECHBLOCK. 1. The movable part which seals the breech. In modern terminology breech-blocks are steel blocks mounted in the receiver so as to open and close the breech by swinging up, down, or to the side, or by sliding up and down in closely fitted slots in the receiver. The rear of the slide.

2. The more modern "bolt" is a type of breechblock but is practically always referred to as a bolt. Revolvers have a standing breech (see *Breech 2* and *Bolt*).

BREECHLOADER. A gun loaded from the rear, or breech, end. All modern weapons are breechloaders.

BUFFER. A part intended to absorb shock or check recoil.

BULLET. 1. A projectile fired from a gun.

2. ARMOR-PIERCING BULLET. A bullet having a hard metal core so supported by a soft metal envelope and by the bullet jacket that, when the bullet strikes armor, stopping the jacket and envelope, the armor-piercing core continues forward and penetrates the armor.

3. DUMDUM BULLET. "Dumdum" is an out-moded and generally misused term. It was an unofficial name first applied at Dumdum, an arsenal in India, where hollow point bullets were made. Gradually the term came to be applied to any expanding-point bullet. None of today's expanding-point bullets are properly called dumdum.

4. HOLLOW POINT. A bullet with a cavity in the nose designed to increase the expansion when it hits. Now mostly obsolete except in .22 rimfire cartridges.

5. INCENDIARY BULLET. A bullet which contains incendiary materials designed to start fires when they impact.

6. "Jacketed" bullets have a gilding metal, soft steel, cupro-nickel, or other tough metal envelope surrounding the lead core.

7. "Lead" bullets are actually a mixture of lead and one or more hardening ingredients.

8. METAL-CASED BULLET. Colloquially used to indicate either a metal-patched or full-metal-patched bullet.

9. METAL-PATCHED BULLET. Loosely, any metal-jacketed bullet. (a) Technically, a bullet having a metal cup over the base and extending forward over that portion of the bullet which bears against the rifling, the lead core being exposed at the nose of the bullet. The term "metal patched" originated when thin metal was substituted for the parchment-paper patches first used on lead bullets to protect the base from the heat of heavy charges of black powder or the early smokeless loads. There have been exceptions to the above rule in which the metal patch covered only the nose of the bullet and did not engage the rifling.

579

(b) A bullet on which the metal jacket covers the nose and is crimped over the core at the base is technically a full-metal-patched (F.M.P.) bullet.

10. MUSHROOM BULLET. Colloquially, any bullet designed to expand on impact. Technically, a metal-patched bullet with exposed rounded nose. Suitable only for use in weapons of comparatively low velocity.

11. STEEL JACKETED BULLET. Not common in America. Bullets having a soft steel jacket, often flash coated or plated with gilding metal to prevent rusting and reduce frictional resistance in the bore.

12. TRACER BULLET. A bullet containing a substance inside the jacket at the base of the bullet which is ignited when fired showing a brilliant "taillight" during its flight. Tracer bullets have an incendiary effect if they strike before the "taillight" has burned out.

13. "Wad-cutter" bullets are bullets with a square shoulder at or near the nose, to cut a clean round hole in paper targets.

C

CALIBER. 1. The distance across the bore of a weapon, measured from land to land. In the United States and Great Britain, usually measured in hundredths or thousandths of an inch; as "caliber .22," "caliber .455." In Europe and Asia, normally expressed in millimeters; as "8mm." The caliber used to designate the weapon commercially may be, and usually is, a somewhat arbitrary figure not necessarily within several thousandths of an inch of the real diameter.

2. BALLISTICALLY, the term caliber is also used as a convenient means of expressing comparative dimensions. A bullet may be said to have a length of "three calibers," meaning that its length is three times its diameter.

3. In connection with artillery pieces, the term caliber is also used to indicate the length of the barrel i. e., a 12″ 50 caliber gun is fifty times twelve inches or fifty feet in length.

CANNELURE. An indented ring or groove around a cartridge case or bullet.

CARTRIDGE. 1. In small-arms parlance, a complete round of fixed ammunition (see *Ammunition*) consisting of (1) the case, in which are inserted (2) the primer, (3) the powder, and (4) the bullet.

2. A BALL CARTRIDGE is any cartridge loaded with a single projectile.

3. A BLANK CARTRIDGE is a cartridge consisting of the case with its primer, a charge of powder, and a wad to retain the powder. No bullet is contained in this type of cartridge, but the wads will cause painful injuries at short range.

4. CENTER-FIRE CARTRIDGE. A cartridge in which the primer is contained in a small metal cup placed in a pocket in the center of the head of the cartridge case.

5. GUARD CARTRIDGE is one loaded with buckshot, or with a reduced charge.

6. RIMFIRE CARTRIDGE. A cartridge made of soft ductile metal, usually copper, in which the priming mixture is inserted inside the rim at the head of the case. The powder is then loaded into the case, abutting the primer. Thus, when the firing pin strikes the rim of the cartridge at any point on its circumference, the primer is exploded and the powder ignited.

7. SEMI-RIMMED CARTRIDGE. A cartridge having a shallow extractor groove and a rim projecting only slightly beyond the diameter of the body of the cartridge case. A compromise between rimmed and rimless cartridge cases.

8. RIMLESS CARTRIDGE. A cartridge having an extraction groove, or cannelure, around its circumference near the head, so that the head of the case is of the same diameter as the body, with no projecting rim, or flange. Rimless cartridges are all of the center-fire type.

9. RIMMED CARTRIDGE. A cartridge having a head larger than its body, forming a rim or flange around the circumference. This rim serves as a means of preventing the cartridge from entering too deeply into the chamber, and provides a surface which can be gripped by the extractor claw. Rimmed cartridges may be either of the rimfire or center-fire type.

10. A "Shot" cartridge is a metallic cartridge loaded with small shot.

11. A "Signal" cartridge is one containing vari-colored luminous balls of the "roman candle" variety.

CASE. 1. The main body of the cartridge; *i. e.,* the container in which the other elements of the cartridge are held. Cases may be of steel or aluminum, but are usually of copper in rimfire cartridges, of brass in center-fire cartridges. Often improperly called the "shell."

2. A BOTTLENECK CASE has a body larger in diameter than the caliber of the arm, the forward portion of the case being reduced in diameter (necked down) to hold the bullet. Shaped like a bottle.

3. RUPTURED CASE. (1) A cartridge case from which the head has been ripped during discharge. (2) Loosely, any cartridge case which has been split in firing so that gas has escaped. See *Crimp* and *Cartridge.*

CHAMBER. 1. That portion of the rear end of the barrel which receives and supports the cartridge when the breech has been closed. The chamber must align the bullet with the bore, and the primer with the firing pin.

2. In a revolver, the chambers are not a part of the barrel but are bored in the revolving cylinder behind the barrel.

CHAMFER. Angle of bevel between case chamber and bullet throat in pistols and revolvers. Some old revolvers, and some very cheap new ones, have straight-bored chambers with no chamfer, and no throat to support a bullet before it takes the rifling.

CONVERSION UNIT. 1. An assembly of gun parts replacing the corresponding parts of a standard weapon, thereby converting that weapon into a serviceable gun of smaller or larger caliber without appreciably changing its exterior appearance, balance, sight radius, or trigger pull.

2. An *Adapter.*

Examples: Colt, Luger, Webley conversions.

CORROSION. In the bore of a gun: rust. and the resultant pitting.

CRANE. In swing-out-cylinder revolvers, the part on which the cylinder is mounted and which is hinged to the forward end of the frame, below the barrel, so that the cylinder may be swung out for loading and unloading; the yoke.

CRANK. In an automatic pistol such as the Luger, this is a bent arm, in the form of a transverse pin, attached to an axle to serve as a lever in transmitting force from the recoiling breech mechanism to the recoil spring in the grip. It thus compresses the spring storing energy to drive the action forward and load and lock the pistol when the force of the explosion has been exhausted. Often called a bell crank.

CREEP. In the trigger mechanism, a dragging action which prevents the trigger from immediately releasing the hammer when the proper pressure is applied. See *Slack.*

CRIMP. 1. ROLLED CRIMP: one in which the mouth of the cartridge case is turned inward into a cannelure on the bullet all around its circumference, to retain the bullet at the proper seating depth.

2. STAB CRIMP, or INDENTCRIMP: a series of small indents at intervals around the cartridge case, engaging a cannelure in the bullet jacket. Both types of crimp are also used on high-pressure cartridges to hold the primer in the primer pocket.

CYLINDER. 1. That part of a revolver in which the chambers are bored.

2. A "swing-out" cylinder is mounted on a crane (or yoke) and swings out for loading but is firmly supported within the solid frame of the gun when ready for firing.

D

DERINGER. A short compact pistol with a small grip, usually of large caliber. Invented by a Philadelphia gunsmith, Henry Deringer. A muzzle-loading percussion type originally, it later reached its greatest popularity as a pocket pistol chambered for rimfire ammunition, notably in .41 caliber. Usually, but not always, single barreled.

DERRINGER. Imitations of the original Deringer often doubled the "r," perhaps in an effort to avoid trouble with the inventor or his heirs. Remington Derringers were made with two barrels, one over the other, which could be fired successively by a quick adjustment of the hammer. There were many other variations, some called Deringer, some Derringer. Four-barreled pistols of this general type, chambered for smaller cartridges, made use of a rotating firing pin to fire the barrels one after another.

DETENT. A pawl, stud, ball-check or some similar mechanical projection which serves to hold a removable part in place until turned or pulled into a particular position which disengages the stop or removes the spring tension which has held the stop in place.

DISCONNECTOR. A device built into an automatic pistol to prevent the weapon from being fired except when the action is fully closed, and to prevent the firing of more than one shot for each pull of the trigger.

DOUBLING. 1. The failure of the disconnector in a semiautomatic weapon to function properly, with the result that two or more shots are fired automatically with only one continuing pressure on the trigger.

    2. In double-barrel guns, the unintentional firing of both barrels simultaneously or in rapid succession due to accidental pressure on both triggers, or to the jarring off of the second hammer by the shock of recoil from the first shot.

DRIFT. The movement of a bullet to the left or right of the straight line from gun muzzle to target. There are two kinds of drift:

    1. WINDAGE, or drift due to the pressure of prevailing winds. See *Windage*.

    2. BALLISTIC DRIFT, which is due to the precessional rotation of the bullet's nose around the curve of the trajectory (a gyroscopic phenomenon), plus the tendency of the bullet to "roll" on the air.

E

EJECTOR. 1. A small cam or projection inside the receiver against which the cartridge case strikes and is thrown clear of the gun when it has been pulled out of the chamber by the extractor.

    2. On hinge-frame guns, a spring arrangement working in conjunction with the extractor which snaps the extractor violently to the rear after the barrels have been swung into a position which will allow the ejected cartridge to be thrown clear of the gun.

    3. On hand-ejector models, the extractor is manually pressed to the rear until the cartridge case is clear of the chamber.

EROSION. The washing away of the bore by the action of the hot powder gases. Should not be, but often is, confused with *Abrasion* and *Corrosion*. See also *Fouling* and *Leading*.

EXTRACTOR. 1. A spring-steel claw attached to the bolt or breechblock, which slips over the head of the cartridge case, engaging in the rim or extractor groove, as the breech is closed. When the breech is opened, the claw withdraws the cartridge case from the chamber.

    2. A movable part forming a segment of the rear face of the barrel. When the breech is closed, the cartridge rim is forced against the rear face of the barrel, including this extractor segment. When the breech is opened, a cam or spring forces the extractor smartly to the rear, withdrawing the cartridge case from the chamber.

    3. In a revolver, the extractors form a segment of the rear face of the cylinder, the rims of the cartridge cases fitting against the extractors when the cylinder is closed. The extractors for all chambers are attached to the extractor rod, which is manually operable only when the cylinder is open. (See *Ejector*.)

F

FEATHER. In Frommer and similar automatic pistols, a rotary motion of parts as they move within other parts, the effect being accomplished by a camming action. (As in feathering an oar; feathering the blades of an airplane propellor.)

FEED GUIDES. 1. Surfaces formed within the receiver at the top of the magazine well to guide the cartridges from the magazine into the chamber.

    2. Lips formed at the top of the magazine to guide the cartridges from the magazine into the chamber.

FIRING LINE. 1. National Rifle Association of America definition, for competitive purposes: "The firing line is that part of the range immediately in rear of an imaginary line drawn through the several firing points."

    2. In general, a line of shooters.

FIRING MECHANISM. Those parts of a gun which operate together to detonate the primer and so fire the weapon. Normally, the trigger, sear, hammer, firing pin, mainspring, and the necessary pins, bolts, screws, auxiliary springs, etc.

FIRING PIN. 1. That part of the firing mechanism which strikes the primer to discharge the gun. It may be (1) integral with the hammer or striker, (2) separably mounted within the forward face of the hammer, or separably attached to the forward end of the striker, (3) a separate unit mounted in the standing breech or in the breechblock or bolt, free to move forward when struck by the hammer or striker and to rebound when the primer fires.

2. FLYING FIRING PIN. A firing pin shorter than the length of its travel in the breechblock. A spiral spring coiled around the pin retains it in position in the breechblock. When the impact of the hammer drives the firing pin forward, compressing the spring and exploding the primer, the compressed spring immediately draws the firing pin back into the breechblock. This is a safety feature, since the firing pin is not in contact with the primer except when driven forward by the hammer at the instant of firing.

Examples: Colt Government Model .45; Tokarev 7.62mm.

3. INERTIA FIRING PIN. A firing pin assembled into the breechblock and free to move forward or backward. It is impelled forward by the blow of the hammer or striker, and backward by the explosion of the primer. See *Hammer* and *Striker*.

FOLLOWER. The small metal platform atop the magazine spring, on which the bottom cartridge of the stack rests. The follower transmits the thrust of the magazine spring to the stack of cartridges, so that they will feed at the proper angle into the feed guides for delivery into the chamber of the gun.

FOULING. Foreign matter in the bore.

1. Ordinarily refers to burned powder grains, gummy matter, and light rust.

2. Lumpy metal deposits from bullet jackets are usually designated as metal fouling, or *leading*.

3. Heavy rusting is usually called *Corrosion* rather than fouling. See also *Erosion*.

FRAME. 1. Applied to American revolvers, the heavy forging which usually consists of the grip, the section carrying the lockwork, and the support for the cylinder, together with the section for insertion of the barrel in swing-out cylinder and solid-frame revolvers. In hinge-frame revolvers (see 2), the frame consists of the grip section, the section carrying the lockwork, and a forward extension above the trigger at whose forward end the barrel with its extension and the cylinder are hinged. The frame in a revolver roughly corresponds to the receiver in an automatic pistol.

2. HINGE (D) FRAME. A weapon in which the barrel or barrels (including the cylinder, in the case of a revolver) are pivoted to the forward end of the frame. Closing the gun swings the barrel (s) into firing position, where the chambers are firmly locked against the standing breech. A manually operated latch unlocks the barrel (s), the muzzle (s) being swung downward, pivoting the chambers above the top of the standing breech for unloading and loading. (In a few instances, the barrel (s) pivots to the right or left.)

3. SOLID FRAME. (a) In a revolver, a swing-out-cylinder or rod-ejector type. There is no break, or hinge, in the frame. Popularly used to indicate a revolver in which cartridges must be ejected singly, or in which the cylinder must be removed from the frame by withdrawing the axis pin. (b) In a rifle, a gun in which the barrel and stock cannot be quickly "taken down," *i. e.*, separated for ease in packing.

G

GILDING METAL. An alloy of copper and zinc which gives excellent performance as a bullet jacket.

GRIP. 1. That portion of the gun which is gripped by the hand that fires the weapon. 2. On pistols and revolvers, the handle. Commonly but improperly called the butt. 3. On rifles and shotguns, that portion of the stock immediately behind the breech; "the small of the stock." (See *Stocks*.)

GROOVES. The spiral cuts in the bore which impart a spinning motion to the bullet as it travels through the barrel.

GROOVE DIAMETER. The bore diameter as measured from the bottom of one groove to the bottom of the opposite groove.

H

HAMMER. 1. A type of firing mechanism which pivots around an axis, (*i. e.,* swings through an arc, hammer-fashion), to deliver the impulse to its firing pin. Thus, the hammer-type firing mechanism differs from the striker type which moves straight forward in line with the firing pin. The hammer may be visible, or it may be entirely inside the gun, as it is in many so-called "hammerless" guns. The hammer may carry the firing pin into contact with the primer, or it may strike a blow against a separate firing pin which is thereby impelled forward to strike the primer.

2. Burr Hammer. An exposed hammer having a serrated projection at the top to provide a gripping surface for cocking.

3. Spur Hammer. A hammer having a cocking spur.

HAMMERLESS. Loosely applied to any weapon in which the hammer or striker is concealed within the metal frame. (Examples: Smith & Wesson .32 Hammerless; Colt .32 Automatic.) The only truly hammerless weapons are those in which a striker is used instead of a hammer. (Examples: Colt .25 Automatic; Luger.)

HAND. A long, thin, steel unit so mounted in the lockwork of a revolver that it engages a projection near the center of the cylinder face and revolves the cylinder the distance of one chamber as the hammer goes to full cock. In Great Britain, the "lifter." (Examples: Colt and Webley revolvers.)

HANDGUN. 1. A *pistol* or a *revolver.*

2. In the early stages of firearms development, handgun was used to mean small arms as distinct from cannon.

HANGFIRE. Delayed ignition of the powder charge. Unpredictable, usually unexplainable, often dangerous. A hangfire may last many seconds from the time the firing pin strikes the primer until the gun discharges. Not to be confused with *Misfire.*

HEAD SPACE. 1. The distance a cartridge is permitted to stretch in length after the breech-block has been closed and locked. On every cartridge, there is either a flange on the head of the case (rimmed cartridge) or a shoulder where the neck of the case joins the body (rimless cartridge) which by coming in contact with a stop in the chamber, prevents the cartridge from entering the chamber deeper than the correct distance.

a. Head space in the chamber of a gun using rimmed cartridges is the distance from the face of the breechblock to the surface at the rear of the chamber on which the forward surface of the rim of the cartridge case rests. Calibrated shims may be used to measure head-space in a chamber built for rimmed cases.

b. Head space in a chamber for a rimless cartridge is the distance from the front face of the breechblock or bolt to some predetermined point on the shoulder of the chamber, where it slopes down from the body of the case to the neck. Head space of this kind cannot be measured with ordinary measuring devices, so a standard head space gauge of hardened and seasoned steel is deposited in the gauge laboratory of the factory. The working gauges used in manufacture are controlled in size by comparison with this standard.

c. Head space in a chamber for rimless straight-bodied cartridges, such as the Caliber .45 Colt Auto cartridge and the Caliber .30 Army Carbine, is measured from the squared shoulder of the chamber just in rear of the throat to the face of the breechblock.

I

IGNITION. Setting fire to the powder charge in a gun.

J

JACKET. The tough metal envelope covering the outside of a bullet.

JUMP. The extent to which the axis of the bore rises while the bullet is traveling down the barrel. See *Recoil; Kick.*

584

APPENDIX III: GLOSSARY OF HANDGUN TERMS

K

KEYHOLING. The failure of a bullet to remain gyroscopically balanced, with the result that it gyrates and eventually tumbles end over end. A tumbling bullet leaves an elongated hole in a target; hence "keyhole."

KICK. Shooters' term for *recoil*. Actually, the "kick" felt by a shooter is vastly different from the recoil measured by the ballistician. "Kick" includes recoil plus muzzle blast, torque, and varying thrusts imposed by the shape of the stock. Thus, a gun which seems to one shooter to have a vicious "kick" may seem to another shooter a very comfortable gun to fire. See *Recoil; Jump.*

L

LANDS. The raised portion of the spiral rifling in the bore of a rifled firearm; the metal standing between the grooves.

LANYARD RING. A ring on some revolvers, usually at the bottom of the butt, to which a lanyard can be attached.

LATCH. 1. In Colt revolvers of swing-out-cylinder type, the thumbpiece on the left side of the frame which, when drawn back, pulls the locking bolt with it to unfasten the cylinder and permit the cylinder to be swung out on its crane for loading or unloading.
2. In Smith & Wesson revolvers, this piece is called "thumbpiece" and is pushed forward to release the cylinder.

LEADING. Small bits of the lead bullet which adhere to the barrel from the bullet as a result of heat, friction, etc. (See *Fouling* and *Erosion*.)

LIMB WORK. That part of a revolver action (the crane and its components) on which the cylinder swings.

LOAD. 1. To insert a cartridge (or loading components) into a gun.
2. To insert primer, powder, and bullet into a cartridge case so as to make a complete cartridge.
3. Colloquially, a cartridge; as, "that revolver holds six loads."

LOADING GATE 1. A hinged cover for breech or magazine. The gate is opened to load the gun and closed to keep foreign matter out of the chamber or magazine.
2. In revolvers, a hinged segment of the standing breech; found only on revolvers having a cylinder which does not swing away from the standing breech for loading.

LOCK. 1. Originally, on muzzle-loading weapons, the firing mechanism.
2. With the introduction of hinge-frame breech-loading weapons, the term was broadened to include the hinge and the mechanism which locks the barrels firmly in position against the standing breech.
3. Now colloquially applied to all parts of the breechblock (bolt) and firing mechanism assemblies, as well as to the hinge and barrel-locking device on hinge-frame guns.
4. Technically, in modern usage, lock applies specifically to designated locking surfaces, lugs, cams, latches, etc.

LOCK PLATES. Removable plates giving access to the firing mechanism. Usually on revolvers. Sometimes on automatic pistols and other weapons. *Side plates.*

LOCKING CAMS. Movable cams so positioned in the lock work that they will engage suitable locking surfaces to seal the breech.

LOCKING LUGS. 1. Finely fitted protrusions, integral with the bolt, which lock the bolt firmly to the barrel to seal the breech. 2. In some autoloading arms locking lugs are provided on the barrel and slide to lock the two together at the moment of discharge. (Example: .45 A.C.P.)

M

MAGAZINE. 1. As pertains to small arms, that operating assembly in which cartridges are stored and which feeds those cartridges one at a time into position so that the closing of the bolt or breechblock will force a new cartridge into the chamber ready for firing. The

585

magazine may be built into the gun or may be a separable part. Magazines are of many types; tubular, box, rotary-box, drum, *etc.* (The cylinder of a revolver is, in effect, a magazine, but is not so called.)

2. As pertains to general ordnance, a magazine is a structure specifically designed to provide proper storage for explosives and ammunition.

MAINSPRING. The spring in the lockwork of a gun which provides energy for the forward movement of the hammer or striker.

MISFIRE. Absolute failure of the cartridge to fire after the primer has been struck by the firing pin. Not to be confused with *Hangfire.*

MUSHROOMING. The round, fairly regular expansion caused by impact of a bullet outward from the nose and flowing back toward the base, the bullet remaining mostly in one piece and retaining most of its original weight. A bullet which breaks into numerous pieces on impact does not mushroom. A bullet of any type may mushroom. There is no necessary connection between a mushroom bullet and one which has mushroomed or which exhibits good mushrooming qualities. See *Bullet 10.*

MUZZLE. The forward end of the gun barrel from which the bullet emerges.

MUZZLE BLAST. Atmospheric disturbance at the muzzle following the emergence of the bullet, caused by the expansion of the powder gases in the air.

MUZZLE ENERGY. The computed energy of the bullet as it leaves the muzzle of the gun. Usually measured in foot pounds.

MUZZLE FLASH. The incandescent flash in the air at the muzzle of the gun following the departure of the bullet; caused by the expansion of powder gases, the ignition of oxygen in the air and the expulsion of burning powder grains.

MUZZLE-LOADER. A gun which can be loaded only from the muzzle.

N

NECK. Pertaining to bottleneck cartridge cases, that forward portion of the case which is reduced in diameter to hold the bullet. See *Case 2.*

O

OGIVE. In ballistics, the radius of the curve of the nose of the bullet.

P

PARABELLUM. "For war." The popular European name for the German Pistol '08, the Luger. Also applied to the 9mm. German service pistol cartridge, to distinguish it from the 9mm. Short.

PARKERIZE. A grey rust-preventive finish for metal.

PENETRATION. The distance a bullet will travel through a given substance. For testing purposes 7/8-inch pine boards at given distances are used.

PIECE. Any firearm under discussion. The origin of this term in its application to guns is unknown.

PISTOL. 1. A firearm designed to be fired using one hand only, and having a chamber integral with, or permanently aligned with, the bore. Pistols may be single shot or magazine type.

2. Popularly, but improperly, used to designate any weapon designed to be fired using one hand only; *i. e.,* both *pistols* and *revolvers.* See also *Autoloading* and *Automatic.*

PITCH. 1. As pertains to rifling, the angle at which the rifling spiral is cut in relation to the axis of the bore. For convenience, usually expressed as the number of inches of bore required for one complete spiral; as, "one turn in sixteen inches." Commonly referred to as the "twist" of the rifling. Usually, the spiral is maintained at a uniform rate throughout the length of the barrel. Sometimes, the pitch is increased steadily from chamber to muzzle. The spiral may start at one turn in twenty inches, and increase to one turn in ten inches at the muzzle. This is called *gain-twist* rifling.

2. As pertains to pistol and revolver grips, the angle at which the grip slants in relation to the axis of the bore.

Appendix III: Glossary of Handgun Terms

POWDER. 1. As pertains to small arms, any propellant explosive.

    2. BLACK POWDER. A mechanical mixture of charcoal, sulphur and saltpetre. Burns with considerable white smoke.

    3. SMOKELESS POWDER, a propellant explosive which ignites and burns with a minimum of ash and smoke. A chemical compound normally built around nitrated cellulose. Often surface-coated mechanically.

PRESSURE. 1. The thrust of the powder gases expanding in the gun. In the United States, recorded in pounds per square inch.

    2. CHAMBER PRESSURE, the pressure generated within the chamber, erroneously called breech pressure.

    3. RESIDUAL PRESSURE is the pressure remaining in the chamber after the bullet has left the barrel. Generally used with reference to automatic weapons.

PRIMER. 1. The small charge which is detonated by the firing pin or striker, and which ignites the propelling powder.

    2. A metal cap containing a priming charge.

PROJECTILE. A bullet. Ballistically, a bullet does not become a projectile until it is in flight.

R

RANGE. 1. A place where target shooting is practiced.

    2. ACCURACY RANGE. The maximum distance at which a particular gun and cartridge will consistently place all shots in the standard target for that distance. A comparative term only.

    3. EFFECTIVE RANGE. The maximum distance at which a bullet may reasonably be expected to travel accurately and kill a particular type of game. A comparative term only.

    4. EXTREME RANGE. The greatest distance the bullet will travel when the cartridge is fired.

    5. GALLERY RANGE. An indoor target range. National Rifle Association of America gallery rules require a distance from firing point to target of 50 feet or 75 feet for .22 rimfire rifles; 50 feet or 60 feet for .22 rimfire pistols. On properly constructed indoor ranges, firing may be conducted with center-fire pistols and revolvers at ranges of 25 yards and 50 yards. Such installations are generally referred to as "indoor ranges," the term "gallery" being applied usually only to short-range .22-caliber installations.

    6. POINT-BLANK RANGE. Popularly used to indicate the distance the bullet will travel before it drops enough to require sight adjustment. A shot fired so close to the target that no sighting is necessary for effective aiming.

RECEIVER. 1. That metal portion of a gun in which the breech action and firing mechanism are housed, and to which the barrel and stocks are assembled.

    2. In revolvers and hinge-frame shotguns, called the "frame."

    3. In some types of autoloading pistols, the terms "frame" and "receiver" are used synonymously.

RECOIL. The backward thrust of the gun caused by the expansion of the powder gases which act to thrust the bullet forward and react to thrust the gun rearward. Ballistically, recoil is computed or measured (in foot pounds) as the rearward thrust in the line of the axis of the bore. This line of thrust is usually above the point of resistance to the thrust, which is the point where the hand grips the stocks of a handgun or where the shoulder rests against the butt of a shotgun or rifle. Hence, the muzzle of the gun tends to swing upward in an arc around the point of resistance. Different methods of holding the gun change the point of resistance, therefore change the apparent recoil. Several other factors also affect the reaction of the gun; so that simple ballistic recoil is not necessarily a measure of the recoil as it is felt by the shooter. (See *Kick* and *Jump*.)

RECOIL SPRING. In automatic and autoloading weapons, the spring (normally a spiral) which is compressed by the rearward motion of the barrel and/or breechblock (bolt) and which then returns the barrel and/or breechblock to its firing position, pushing a cartridge from the magazine into the chamber as it moves forward.

RECOIL SHIELD. In revolvers, the flanges on the standing breech just behind the cylinder face. Recoil shields prevent cartridges from moving back far enough out of the chambers to interfere with the revolution of the cylinder.

REVOLVER. 1. A firearm designed to be fired using one hand only and having a series of chambers in a cylinder, mounted coaxially with the barrel. A mechanism revolves the cylinder so that the chambers are successively aligned with the bore. Only the cartridge in the particular chamber which is in alignment with the bore is fired. Colloquially, a "six gun."

2. DOUBLE-ACTION revolvers are those in which continuous pressure on the trigger (a) revolves the cylinder to align a chamber with the bore, (b) cocks and then releases the hammer, discharging the piece.

3. SINGLE-ACTION revolvers are those in which the hammer must be manually cocked; *i. e.,* it cannot be cocked by trigger pressure. Cocking the hammer revolves the cylinder, aligning a chamber ready for firing. Pressure is then applied to the trigger, which performs the single function (action) of releasing the hammer to discharge the piece.

4. SEMI-AUTOMATIC revolvers are those in which the recoil from one shot plus spring action revolves the cylinder, aligns a chamber, and cocks the hammer ready for firing the next shot. Pressure must then be applied to the trigger to discharge the piece. Not to be confused with a "Hammerless Revolver" or semi-automatic pistol. Example: Webley-Fosberry .455 Revolver.

RICOCHET. A bullet which has struck and glanced off; or the act of so doing. The very rapid spinning motion of a bullet causes it to ricochet very easily and without much loss of forward velocity.

RIFLING. The spiral cut into the bore to impart a spinning motion to the bullet, to establish gyroscopic stability. Normally, the rifling consists of "grooves" and "lands," the latter being the metal left standing between the grooves. Through the years of firearms development, every conceivable form of boring the barrel to impart a rotary motion to the projectile has been tried, but the land and groove has survived as the most practicable type. See *Pitch.*

S

SAFETY. Any mechanism which blocks the hammer, sear, or trigger (or any combination of the three) to prevent the accidental discharge of a weapon. Ordinarily of two types:

1. GRIP or AUTOMATIC SAFETIES. Flat levers or plungers, normally protruding from some portion of the grip in such position that, when the hand firing the piece is squeezed around the grip, the safety lever is pressed inward without conscious attention by the firer, automatically releasing the firing mechanism. In most cases, when pressure on the grip is relaxed the safety automatically resets itself. In a few instances, it must be manually reset. An important variation is the automatic safety in the Walther H. P.

2. THUMB SAFETIES. Small levers or sliding buttons situated within comfortable reach of the thumb of the hand firing the gun. They must be deliberately set in the "safe" or "ready" position.

SEAR. One or more levers operating between the trigger and the hammer or firing pin to provide additional controlled leverage to improve trigger action while transmitting that action to the hammer.

SEAR SPRING. A small spring operating in connection with the sear.

SELF-LOADING. *Autoloading. Semiautomatic.* Commonly but incorrectly called *automatic.*

SIDE ARMS. Small arms which are designed to be carried on the belt and used in one hand. Includes edged weapons as well as pistols and revolvers.

SIDE PLATES. See *Lock Plates.*

SLACK. As pertains to small arms, the free travel against spring tension only, of a trigger *before* it begins to disengage the hammer or firing pin. Slack is not provided in target weapons or in most sporting arms. It is a form of safety device used mostly in military weapons. Not to be confused with *Creep,* which occurs *while* the trigger is disengaging the hammer or striker.

Appendix III: Glossary of Handgun Terms

SLIDE. In semiautomatic pistols, a metal sleeve covering part or all of the barrel and/or the top of the action. It usually forms the breechblock. It is driven back by recoil and returned to its forward position by spring action.

SMALL ARMS. Weapons which may be carried on the person and fired from one or two hands. In military usage, also machine guns. (Apparently because the Navy is essentially big-gun minded, U. S. naval usage includes 20 mm. and 40 mm. automatic weapons in the category of "small arms.")

SNAPHANCE. The earliest form of flintlock. In British usage, "snaphaunce."

STIRRUP. 1. In some automatic pistols, a form of trigger having two arms passing back, on either side of the magazine, stirrup fashion, so that pressure on the trigger is transmitted through the arms to the sear to release the hammer. (Example: Colt Government Model .45 A.C.P.)

2. In some revolvers, the latch which secures a tip-up barrel in its firing position is called the stirrup. (Example: Webley .455.)

STOCKS. Those parts, attached to the receiver or frame of a weapon, which make it possible to hold, aim, and fire the gun. The stocks, normally made of wood, may also be made of metal, plastics, or other rigid materials. Pistol and revolver stocks are attached to the rear frame, or handle, to form the *grip*.

STRIKER. 1. A rod type of firing pin which travels inside the bolt or breechblock and is directly actuated by its own spiral spring when released by the action of the trigger. It is not actuated by being struck by a hammer. The actual firing pin may be integral with the striker or may be a separable piece fastened to the forward end of the striker rod.

2. Sometimes loosely and improperly used to indicate any firing pin.

STRIPPING. 1. As pertains to weapons, disassembling. (a) FIELD STRIPPING is disassembling as far as necessary for normal cleaning and care.

2. As pertains to bullets, failure of the bullet jacket to properly grip the rifling so that the bullet fails to acquire the proper spin and bits of bullet jacket are stripped off and left in the bore.

3. As pertains to loading a magazine weapon, pressing the cartridges out of the charger clip into the magazine.

STRUT. A unit used to connect a coiled or flat spring with some pivoted part of the action. (Examples: Colt Government Model .45 A.C.P., Webley .455 revolver.)

T

THROAT. 1. The forward section of the chamber where it tapers to meet the diameter of the barrel bore. 2. In a revolver the enlargement of the bore at the breech end to permit the centering of the bullet in the barrel when it jumps from the cylinder into the barrel.

TRAJECTORY. 1. The path of the bullet in flight.

2. FLAT TRAJECTORY. A comparative term used to indicate very little curvature in the flight of the bullet from muzzle to point of impact. When the velocity is high, comparatively flat trajectory is achieved. There is no such thing as perfectly flat trajectory.

TRIGGER. 1. The finger-actuated lever, usually projecting below the receiver, used to release the firing mechanism and so discharge the gun.

2. DOUBLE-SET TRIGGERS. A pair of triggers so arranged that pressure on one trigger engages the sears in such fashion that the slightest touch on the second trigger will then discharge the gun.

3. FOLDING TRIGGER. A trigger hinged so that it can be folded forward close to the under side of the frame. Example: Italian 10.35 mm. Bodego.

4. HAIR TRIGGER. A term loosely applied to any trigger which can be released by very light pressure.

5. SET TRIGGER. An adjustable trigger designed to operate reliably with a very light trigger pull. Colloquially a "hair trigger."

6. SHEATH TRIGGER. An obsolete form of trigger in which no trigger guard was used The trigger was mounted in and projected only slightly from the frame just forward of the grip.

TRIGGER BAR. In some semiautomatic pistols, a connecting bar transmitting the pressure from the trigger to the sear. Sometimes also used in connection with the double-action unit of a semiautomatic pistol.

V

VELOCITY. 1. INSTRUMENTAL VELOCITY. The velocity of a projectile measured by scientific instruments at a specified point on its trajectory. In America usually measured in feet per second. Instrumental velocity figures always indicate the range at which the readings were made. In attempting to compare instrumental velocity figures for different cartridges or loads it is essential that comparisons be made only of those figures which were taken at identical ranges.

    2. MUZZLE VELOCITY. The velocity at which a projectile leaves the muzzle. In America usually measured in feet per second (abbreviation f.s.) .

W-Y-Z

WINDAGE. 1. The lateral drift of a bullet in flight due to the effect of wind.

    2. Generally applied to all lateral drift, including *Ballistic Drift*.

    3. The movement of sights to compensate for the lateral drift. To "take left windage" means to move the rear sight to the left.

YOKE. See *Crane*.

ZERO. The point at which sights are set so that, with a given load, a given range, and no wind, the bullet will strike the center of a target. The marksman uses this "zero sight setting" as the base point from which to adjust his sights for different loads, different ranges, and different weather conditions. A gun may be "zeroed in" at any range and with any ammunition. Hence, the term is relative only.

PART II: Pistol and Revolver Trends, 1945-1968

By JOSEPH E. SMITH

There is no one overall statement that succinctly covers the trend in pistols and revolvers over the past twenty-three years, but one can remark that there are now an extraordinary number of different makes and models available on the American scene. A glance through a dealer's catalog, circa 1939, and a comparison with the catalogs of 1967 will confirm this.

To the arms student, or the old gun "pro," there presently exists a wonderful opportunity to obtain many fine pieces which either did not exist or which were not easily available in the United States in former days. To the novice, this variety presents somewhat of a dilemma. There are some extraordinarily good buys in handguns today, but there are also some extraordinarily poor buys. Some of the poor buys are poor in terms of quality or design while others may be poor practical choices for the kind of use intended.

An example of the latter came to the writer's attention some years ago when the wife of an Army officer interested in target shooting called to find out if a caliber .22 derringer would be a suitable Christmas gift for her husband. Quite obviously the derringer, whether spelled with one or two "r"s, is not exactly the target shooter's dream, nor are many other pistols and revolvers now on the market. The wide selection of guns now available requires a bit of purchaser research if one wishes to obtain the right type and quality of pistol or revolver for his purposes.

There are two basic reasons for the proliferation in handguns which apply as well to the rifles of today. Number One is probably the new attitude toward model changes and the introduction of new models by United States arms manufacturers. Prior to World War II, the introduction of a new model pistol or revolver was a somewhat rare event. Many models were manufactured for well over fifty years with little change except in metallurgy. A few good old standbys still are, but the arms manufacturers seem to have, on an increasing scale, adopted the code of the automobile manufacturers; i.e., keep introducing new models to keep consumers interest and sales high. Even Henry

Ford had to abandon the Model T "in any color you wanted as long as it was black," and VWs now have gas gages plus a number of other competitive new "bug" off-shoots.

The other factor is the appearance on the American market of the products of a large number of foreign arms manufacturers, guns rarely encountered in this country prior to World War II. Tariff changes and the importation of large numbers of surplus foreign military handguns probably contributed to this influx of arms and their acceptance by American shooters. It is in this area, however, where "caveat emptor" prevails. While some exquisite examples of the gunmaker's art are coming from abroad, the flow includes some pretty horrible junk as well.

In the revolver field there have been no really great new design concepts introduced. There has been some use of aluminum alloys in frames and even cylinders, and there are now also colored revolvers designed to appeal to the feminine trade. Also of interest is the re-emergence of the single-action revolver styled on the Colt Frontier model.

This revolver, also known as the Peacemaker or 1873 Army, was not put back in production by Colt in the 1946-47 period. Television, which went in heavily for old cowboy movies in its earlier days—with most of the cowboys in the movies carrying Colt Frontier revolvers—stimulated public interest in the Old West, an interest which grew with television, and this interest—which continues unabated—undoubtedly contributed to the increasing demand for the single-action Colt. When later models of the original single-action Colt Frontiers, which had sold for $37 brand-new in 1940, began selling at prices in the $100 range, copies of the Frontier began to appear. Some, like the Great Western, were close copies of internal design as well as the general appearance. Though the Ruger single-action models also resemble the Colt Frontier, their internal designs are considerably different.

Higher-powered cartridges for revolvers have also appeared within the last decade. The .41 and .44 Magnum cartridges have considerably more muzzle energy than any pistol cartridges previously produced in this country. A caliber .22 center-fire for use in revolvers, the .22 Remington Jet, has also appeared, as have a number of other handgun cartridges later covered in this book.

In the various lines of automatic, or self-loading pistols that have appeared since World War II, there has been considerable use of lightweight alloys in receivers and slides. The double-action feature, which became popular with the advent of the Walther PP, PPK, and P-38, has appeared in a number of automatics, some of which are copies or modifications of the Walther. With the adoption in 1951 of the Browning Hi-Power as the official military side arm of Great Britain, the automatic pistol became a universal standard of the major world powers.

Revolvers are now issued as special-purpose weapons, when used at all, by the military of most of the world. True, a number of countries, however, still carry stocks of revolvers as war-reserve weapons, and some of the smaller states do still use revolvers extensively, but they are gradually replacing them with automatics. Several automatics chambered for the .38 S&W Special wad-cutter cartridge, intended principally for target work, are now available.

Although Colt and S&W no longer make single-shot target pistols, a number of generally excellent single-shot Free pistols of European manufacture are available on the U.S. market in addition to some new American numbers. The domestically-produced numbers vary from the Thompson "Contender," which is basically a single-shot target type, to the Savage .22 caliber Model 101, which is basically a plinking type. Within the last twenty years several rather short-lived single-shot pistols also were developed and produced such as the caliber .22 S&M and the Sheridan "Knocabout."

We have also seen the emergence of a new type single-shot pistol exemplified by the Remington .221 XP-100 and the Ruger .256 Hawkeye Magnum. These pistols fire small-caliber center-fire cartridges at very high velocity. They can be fitted with a scope and are capable of extraordinarily good shooting in the hands of an expert. The writer has seen the XP-100 outshoot some excellent rifles at a range of 200 meters, *but* the gentleman shooting the XP-100 was a Remington demonstration-shooter; the average man can hardly expect to match this performance. Be that as it may, some hardy souls—I might say some extremely steady souls—do regularly knock off woodchucks with these handguns at ranges once considered respectable for only rifle cartridges of at least the .22 Hornet class. Although definitely not of universal utility, the XP-100 and Hawkeye Magnum are very remarkable handguns.

The Centennial of the Civil War, plus the previously-mentioned renewed interest in the Old West and American history, in general, also resulted in manufacture of a number of black-powder handgun replicas within the last ten years. These vary from copies of Tower flintlock pistols to copies of the Colt Patterson and 1860 Army. Many are of foreign manufacture and, in both the domestic and foreign products, evince both very good and very poor manufacture.

As with most other products, price will give a relatively good indication of quality. Some of the replicas are made of much higher-quality materials than were available at the time the original pistols were produced. In addition to a rash of replicas, a rekindled interest in black-powder shooting has resulted in the production of at least one pistol which is not a replica but a modern design, produced as a target-type, muzzle-loading, single-shot, black-powder pistol. None of the other black-powder pistols, however, can be truly considered as target arms.

Although the period 1945-68 has seen the emergence of nuclear weapons, jet aircraft, and ICBMs as well as the advent, improvement, and widespread distribution of products and materials which were either unknown or purely laboratory curiosities prior to World War II, the handgun has not basically changed. There has been no "quantum" jump in handgun effectiveness during this period; only small changes characteristic of slow evolution are to be clearly seen. The same applies generally to all small arms since although many new concepts have been advanced, none has caught on to the extent of widespread adoption for either military or civilian uses.

Two examples of different handgun design concepts appear in the Dardick pistols, which used the plastic "Tround," and the MBA Gyro-Jet, which used a self-contained rocket cartridge. The latter therefore has no cartridge case to extract and eject. It allows a pistol of very light weight and construction since its propellent pressure, although of longer duration, remains at a considerably lower level than that common to conventional pistol cartridges. It should be borne in mind, however, that although there has been no "quantum" advance in small arm design since World War II, the necessity of small arms from a military point of view has not diminished, nor has the practicality of pistols and revolvers as arms of defense for the individual citizen been lessened by the appearance of any new product.

Meanwhile, as always, the thrill to all shooters of getting five in the X-ring lives on, as it always will!

Section One
Handguns of Various Countries

ARGENTINA

The Argentine Army uses the caliber .45 Model 1916 automatic pistol and the caliber .45 Model 1927 automatic pistol which are copies of the Colt caliber .45 Model 1911 and 1911A1, respectively. Some of these pistols were produced by Colt, but the majority were produced by the Argentines at the Fabrica Militar de Armas Portatiles "Domingo Mathieu," a government arsenal at Rosario. Province of Santa Fe. Argentina previously used the 7.65mm Model 1905 Mannlicher pistol; these weapons were sold off, mainly to United States arms dealers, within the last ten years. There is some reason to believe that Argentina may adopt the 9mm Browning Hi-Power and manufacture it under license from F.N. at Rosario.

COMMERCIAL PRODUCTION

There are a number of producers of commercial handguns in Argentina. The caliber .45 Ballester Molina which was manufactured by HAFDASA is no longer made; HAFDASA is now out of business. Among the pistols currently manufactured in Argentina are the .22 caliber Rubi Extra, and the Dos Leones which is made in caliber .22 and .32. Both models are patterned on the Smith & Wesson.

BERSA

The firm of Baraldo S.A.C.I. handles a line of .22 caliber automatic pistols which bear the name BERSA. There are two basic models, the Model 62 and the Model 64 and a number of variants of these two models distinguished mainly by barrel length. The Bersas are blowback-operated and are fed by a detachable box magazine. The following Bersa models exist: Model 62 (400) with 3.99-inch barrel; Model 64 (399) which has a ventilated rib on the slide; and the Model 62 (395) with 6.1-inch target-type barrel. All have eight-round magazines and duraluminum receivers.

Bersa Model 62 (400/2)

Caliber: .22 Long Rifle.
System of Operation: Blowback, semi-automatic.
Length Overall: 8.9".
Barrel Length: 6.1".
Feed Device: 8-round in-line detachable box magazine.
Weight: 1.12 pounds.

595

BERSA .22 Model 62 400/2.

The Bersa is of conventional design. The barrels which have dovetailed lugs under the chamber are held in place by the slide stop pin. Removal of the slide stop permits removal of the slide with barrel and recoil spring.

A.L.P.A.
A.L.P.A. .22 Single-shot Pistol

A.L.P.A. .22 pistol with aluminum-alloy frame.

On firing, the slide is forced to the rear and the empty case is blown out by residual pressure in the barrel. This aluminum-alloy frame pistol is no longer in production.

596

Another single-shot A.L.P.A. pistol is illustrated; this pistol is mainly of stamped construction and has a rounded bolt and receiver. The barrel is approximately 4.1-inches long and the arm is about 8.2-inches long overall. This pistol, too, is reportedly now out of production.

A.L.P.A. .22 pistol.

AUSTRIA

The Austrian Army uses the 9mm Parabellum Walther P-38. Only one commercial pistol is currently being made in Austria; this pistol, the 7.65mm Model SP, is made by Steyr-Daimler-Puch A.G.

7.65mm (.32 ACP) Model SP

The Model SP is rather streamlined in form, but its design philosophy is similar to the M1907 Roth Steyr. The trigger mechanism is of the double-action type; the trigger must be pulled through to raise and drop the hammer on every shot; i.e., the hammer is not cocked by rearward movement of the slide.

STEYR 7.65 Model SP.

The pistol has a push-button safety on the trigger; when pushed to the right it locks the trigger in place. The weapon is loaded in the normal manner for automatic pistols. The magazine catch is at the bottom rear of the grip. When it is pushed to the rear the magazine can be removed. When the loaded magazine is reinserted and the slide pulled to the rear and released, the weapon is loaded. Steady pressure on the trigger will then cause the pistol to fire.

To field-strip the Steyr SP, remove magazine, press in on knurled section of barrel bushing and rotate it to the left until the red point on the bushing lines up with the red point on the slide; the bushing and recoil spring can then be pulled forward over the fixed barrel. To assemble, reverse the above procedure.

The Model SP is considerably different from the earlier Steyr pocket pistols which broke open for disassembly and used a typical single-action concealed hammer and striker firing mechanism. The double-action feature of the current Steyr, while undoubtedly of value from a safety point of view, makes for a long and rather heavy trigger pull for each shot. However, in a pistol of this type which is designed basically for self-defense at very short ranges, the trigger pull is not particularly of great importance.

BELGIUM

The Belgian Army is equipped with the 9mm Parabellum FN Browning Hi-Power automatic pistol. This pistol is one of the most widely-distributed military self-loading pistols in the world and has been made in Canada, Indonesia and South Vietnam and is reportedly to be made in Argentina. Since the conclusion of WW II, this pistol as well as the other pistols made by FN are now commercially available in the U.S.A. where they are distributed by the Browning Arms Co. of St. Louis, Mo. In Canada, they are distributed by the Browning Arms Co. of Montreal.

COMMERCIAL PRODUCTION

The commercial model Browning Hi-Power is of considerably better finish than models manufactured for military use—especially better than those made during the German occupation of Belgium. While the Hi-Power as made for the Germans, easily recognizable by the Waffen Amt eagle and swastika stamps on slide and receiver, is of interest to collectors, it should be avoided by those who wish a well-made specimen. The Hi-Power as well as other Browning pistols may be obtained in the "Renaissance" engraved model.

FN has dropped the 1922 Model automatic from its post-war line and the pistols currently produced, not including .22 caliber types, are the 9mm Parabellum Hi-Power, the Model 1910—which is no longer referred to by that model designation in the Browning Arms Co. or FN catalogs—in .380 ACP (9mm Browning Short), and the .25 ACP (6.35mm) Baby Browning in regular and lightweight models.

9mm Parabellum BROWNING HI-POWER as made for sale in the U.S.

The FN Browning pistols, as manufactured for sale in the United States and Canada, are marked Browning Arms Co. St. Louis, and may have the additional address "Montreal, P.Q." They do not usually bear the initials "FN" or the marking "Fabrique Nationale D'Armes De Guerre Herstal-Bēlgique" as is found on the pistols made for sale in Europe. They are, however, the same pistols regardless of markings. The .25 caliber automatic has the additional marking "Baby" at the bottom of the grips as made for the European market, but Baby Brownings may be found with both FN markings and Browning Arms Co. markings.

.380 BROWNING automatic as made for sale in the U.S. and Canada.

.25 BABY BROWNING with FN marking.

FN introduced a new series of .22 caliber automatic pistols in 1961/62. They are all of standard blowback design similar to the Colt Woodsman. All have the rear sight separated from the slide so that it does not recoil. This is an advantage in timed-fire target events. There are interchangeable barrels of 4.75 and 6.75 inches available for each model; barrels may be changed by loosening a coin-slotted screw in the frame beneath the barrel. There are three different models produced.

FN BROWNING
Browning Medalist

This is the match-grade pistol. It is fitted with a wooden forend which can be replaced with a 2.41-oz. counterweight support. Counterweights of .94-oz., 1.79-oz. and 2.52-oz. are available. The Medalist has a barrel with ventilated rib; the rear sight has micrometer-click adjustments for windage and elevation. The trigger can be adjusted for backlash and weight of pull. The trigger-pull

FN BROWNING MEDALIST .22 automatic pistol.

FN BROWNING .22 MEDALIST field-stripped.

adjusting screw, the screw at the rear of the frame, is turned counterclockwise; it stops at the minimum-pull setting and should not be turned beyond this point. The backlash adjustment screw is on the top surface of the trigger; to get to it one must remove the barrel with the slide locked to the rear. Turn the screw clockwise to decrease backlash; it should not be turned too far or it will stiffen the trigger pull and can cause trigger malfunctions.

601

The Medalist has a dry-firing mode of operation which utilizes the safety. When the thumb safety is placed in the rear position it works only as a safety, but in the forward position it prevents the hammer from striking the firing pin yet permits a partial hammer fall with normal trigger pull for dry firing. A slight pressure on the safety allows the weapon to be fully cocked and it will fire if the trigger is pulled. Since the Medalist does not have a magazine safety, i.e., the weapon can be fired with the magazine removed, it is *mandatory* that the chamber be carefully checked before dry firing since return of the safety to the firing position will allow discharge of the weapon.

Disassembly for the Medalist and the other FN Browning caliber .22 automatic pistols is as follows: on all models first remove the magazine and check chamber before starting disassembly; on the Medalist remove the forearm; on the Medalist, Nomad and Challenger, loosen barrel-mounting screw, pull slide rearward and lock open. Tap the muzzle on a padded surface to loosen the barrel and remove the barrel back and up. Release slide and allow it to move forward slowly, taking care not to allow the recoil spring to push the slide violently off the frame. Additional disassembly is not recommended.

FN Browning Challenger

The Challenger is a sport model of the Medalist and is similar in construction except that it does not have the ventilated rib, the rear sight is adjustable for windage and elevation by means of a coin-slotted screw, but it does not have the dry-fire feature, forend, or provision for weights. It is a quality pistol comparable to similar Colt and Hi-Standard types.

Prototype of BROWNING CHALLENGER. 22 pistol, shows non-recoiling rear sight. Rear view shows the adjustable rear sight on the barrel extension. Lower arrow points to the trigger-pull adjusting screw.

FN Browning Nomad

The Nomad is a lower-priced version of the Challenger. It has a light alloy frame and plastic stock. It does not have an adjustable trigger pull or a slide stop. The rear sight is adjustable for windage and elevation via coin-slotted screws.

(See also FN Browning Characteristics listing, next page.)

FN BROWNING .22 NOMAD pistol.

CHARACTERISTICS OF POST-WW II FN BROWNING PISTOLS

	Medalist	Challenger	Nomad	Standard .25	Lightweight .25
Caliber:	.22 L.R.	.22 L.R.	.22 L.R.	.25 ACP.	.25 ACP.
Length Overall:	11.12"	8.87"*	8.87"*	4"	4"
Barrel Length:	6.75"	4.5" or 6.75"	4.5" or 6.75"	2.75"	2.75"
Feed Device:	(Cal. .22 models have 10-round removable box magazine.)			(Cal. .25 models have 6-round removable box magazine.)	
Sights:	Blade front and click-adjustable rear.	Blade front and screw adjustable rear.	Blade front and screw adjustable rear.	Blade and notch.	Blade and notch.
Weight:	2.87 lb.	2.18 lb.*	1.62 lb.*	Approx. .62 lb.	Approx. .5 lb.

Note: All models are blowback pistols. Characteristics of the 9mm Parabellum Hi-power and the .380 appear in chapters 9 and 10, respectively.
* With 4.5"-barrel.

BRAZIL

There are several makes of Brazilian revolvers which are now on the United States market, those of Amadeo Rossi and Co. and of Taurus. In addition, pistols are made by the Industria Nacional De Armas at Sao Paulo. The Rossi and Taurus revolvers are imported by Firearms International.

ROSSI

Rossi Caliber .22 L.R. Revolvers

Rossi .22 L.R. revolvers are similar in appearance to the old S&W Lady Smith pattern—Model M. Their frames are made of non-ferrous metal; all other parts are steel. There are two models: one with a 2-inch barrel and one with a 3-inch barrel. Overall length of the 2-inch barrel model is 6 inches; both models are chambered for 7 rounds. Note that the cylinder release is at the end of the ejector rod housing. The weights of the 2-inch and 3-inch barrel models are 11.25 and 11.5 ounces respectively.

ROSSI .22 revolver with 3-inch barrel.

ROSSI 32 Long revolver.

605

Rossi .32 Long Revolvers

Rossi also makes a revolver chambered for the .32 S&W Long cartridge. This revolver is patterned on the standard S&W M1905 design and has a cylinder chambered for six rounds. The barrel is 3 inches long and the revolver is 7 inches long overall; weight is 1.18 pounds.

ROSSI .38 Special revolver with 2-inch barrel.

Rossi .38 Caliber Revolvers

Rossi also makes .38 S&W Special revolvers also modeled on the standard S&W pattern. The model with a 2-inch barrel is most common but there is also a model with a 4-inch barrel. These weapons have 6-shot cylinders. All the Rossi revolvers have plastic stocks. Rossi also makes a double-barrel derringer type pistol chambered for the .22 Long Rifle cartridge.

TAURUS .38 Special revolver with 2-inch barrel.

TAURUS

Forjas Taurus S.A. produces a line of revolvers which are distributed in the United States by Firearms International Corp. The Taurus line is also modeled on the S&W and includes .22 caliber revolvers with 3 and 4-inch barrels, .32 caliber revolvers with 3, 4, and 5-inch barrels, and .38 Special with 2, 4 and 6-inch barrels. All have six-shot cylinders.

INA

The Industria Nacional De Armas in Sao Paulo also makes a copy of the S&W type which is being sold in this country as the "INA" or "Tiger." These revolvers come in .32 S&W Long and .38 Special with 2.25 and 3.25-in. barrel lengths available in each caliber. Blue or chrome finish may be obtained in any of the various models.

GREAT BRITAIN

The current standard handgun of the British Army is the Browning FN 9mm Parabellum Hi-Power as made in Canada by John Inglis of Toronto during World War II. This pistol, which was issued to British paratroops and Commandos during WW II, was standardized in the early Fifties at which time the Enfield revolvers were dropped as standard weapons. In the early Fifties the British Army ran service pistol tests of outstanding military automatic pistols. Unofficial stories indicate that the S&W 9mm Parabellum Model 39 automatic was the preferred choice of the British Army, but economy made it imperative that the Browning Hi-Power pistols already on hand be used. Be that as it may, the FN Browning Hi-Power is a fine pistol and a much better military weapon than the Enfield .38 revolvers it has replaced. Recently the British have purchased additional quantities of Hi-Power pistols from FN to replace those worn out, lost, strayed, or stolen.

COMMERCIAL PRODUCTION

Match Invader

The only new commercial pistol to appear in Great Britain since WW II is the single-shot Target Pistol Mark III. This pistol, called the "Match Invader" in the U.S.A., may be obtained in .22 L.R., .32 S&W Long, .38 S&W, or .38 S&W Special. It is a 1956 improvement on a pistol which originally appeared in 1908-09, improved in 1938, and again in 1952. It has a tipping barrel and plastic stocks with either right or left thumb rests. Barrels are 9.87-inches long in all calibers. Weight varies from 2.37 pounds for the .22 L.R. to 2.18 pounds for the .38 model. The trigger is adjustable for weight, and the rear sight is adjustable for windage and elevation.

WEBLEY .22 L.R. MARK III target pistol.

WEBLEY

The Mark IV series revolvers which originally appeared around 1929 are still carried in current British catalogs.

Mark IV .22 L.R. Revolver

This revolver weighs two pounds and has a 6-inch barrel fitted with a rear sight adjustable for windage and elevation.

Mark IV .38 S&W Revolver

This revolver, chambered for the .38 S&W cartridge, has a rear sight adjustable for windage and elevation. It has a 6-inch barrel and weighs two pounds. Except for sights and barrel it is quite similar to the Mark IV Military and Police Revolver.

WEBLEY .38 MARK IV MILITARY AND POLICE revolver.

.38 S&W Mark IV Military and Police Revolver

This revolver, which has a four-inch barrel, is made in .32 S&W Long as well as .38 S&W. In .38 S&W, it was a substitute standard British military revolver during WW II. Large quantities of these revolvers, sold by the British government as surplus, have appeared on the U.S. market. They are much more roughly finished than the commercial Webley revolver and bear British government ownership marks—the Broad Arrow—and the marking "War Finish." This revolver has a notch-type rear sight and weighs 1.8 pounds in .32 caliber and 1.56 pounds in .38 caliber.

Mark IV Pocket Model Revolver

This revolver is chambered for the .32 S&W Long or the .38 S&W. It has a three-inch barrel, a small grip and weighs 1.4 pounds in caliber .32 and 1.3 pounds in caliber .38.

Mark IV Pocket Model Revolver (O.P.)

This revolver is basically the same as the Pocket Model but has larger stocks.

Webley pistols made for commercial use are all finely finished, quality products.

609

CAMBODIA

Cambodia has produced a modified copy of the French 9mm Parabellum Model 1950 pistol. This pistol resembles the U.S. Colt .45 M1911 in that, unlike the French M1950, it has a barrel bushing and recoil-spring plug. The safety is mounted on the left rear of the slide as on the French pistol and the receiver and slide follow the general design lines of the M1950.

CAMBODIAN 9mm Parabellum, a modified copy of the French M1950 pistol.

CANADA

The standard pistol of the Canadian Armed Forces is the 9mm FN Browning Hi-Power as made by the John Inglis firm in Toronto during WW II. Parts are still made for these pistols at the Canadian Arsenal at Long Branch, Ontario. This pistol is also the standard side arm of Great Britain. Some variations among these pistols are explained below.

INGLIS

Pistol, Browning FN 9mm HP No 1 Mark 1

The butt is machined for a shoulder-stock holster and a tangent leaf rear sight graduated from 50 to 500 meters is used. The wooden shoulder-stock holster is no longer used by the Canadian forces.

Pistol, Browning FN 9mm HP No 1 Mark 1*

Also machined for a shoulder-stock holster, but the height of the ejector has been increased and a clearance cut has been made in the sight to accommodate this increased height. The extractor is also different and is not interchangeable with the Mark I extractor.

Pistol, Browning FN 9mm HP No 2 Mark 1

Not machined for shoulder-stock holster, has the smaller ejector and the Mark 1 extractor. It has a fixed notched rear sight.

PISTOL, BROWNING FN 9mm HP NO 2 MARK 1*.

Pistol, Browning FN 9mm HP No 2 Mark 1*

Same as No 2 Mark 1 except for ejector and extractor. Uses extractor Mark 2 and ejector Mark 2 for which slide clearance is machined. There are two models—Mark 1 and 2—of hammer and link in these pistols, but these are interchangeable. The models with fixed rear sight are the most common.

Inglis started producing these pistols for the Chinese Nationalist during WW II. After the war, Inglis came out with a lightweight version of the Hi-Power which was entered in post-war U.S. Army pistol tests.

611

The Inglis lightweight weighs 1.88 pounds fully loaded. The receiver is made of aluminum alloy and the slide has two weight reducing cuts on each side. This pistol performed very well in the U.S. pistol tests.

INGLIS lightweight version of the 9mm Browning FN Hi-Power.

NORTH AMERICAN ARMS COMPANY

NAACO Brigadier

The North American Arms Co. of Toronto, Canada came out with a prototype caliber .45 pistol called the Brigadier. The Brigadier is essentially a modified FN Hi-Power Browning designed around a new .45 caliber cartridge with an advertised 1600 f.p.s. muzzle velocity using a 230-grain bullet. The Brigadier

NAACO .45 BRIGADIER pistol.

has an aluminum-alloy receiver and the trigger, hammer, sear and disconnector assembly is removable as one unit. This takes the packaged sear and hammer assembly as found in the Soviet Tokarev TT M1933 and the French M1935 pistols one step forward in that the trigger and trigger spring are included in the packaged unit. The safety is mounted on the slide of the Brigadier rather than on the receiver as with the Browning FN Hi-Power. The trigger/hammer assembly is of the double-action type.

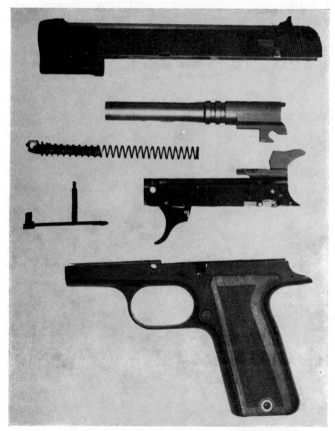

NAACO BRIGADIER field-stripped.

The Brigadier was made by Bob Herman at NAACO. There was a design utilizing the basic Brigadier pistol which converted it into a submachine gun called the Borealis. This consisted of a stock, barrel jacket, receiver-type assembly into which the longer barreled Brigadier was slipped. A 20-round magazine was to be used with this rig and apparently a selective-fire trigger mechanism.

CHARACTERISTICS OF THE BRIGADIER

Caliber:	.45 NAACO cartridge.
System of Operation:	Recoil.
Length Overall:	9.62"
Barrel Length:	5.5"
Weight, Loaded:	4.18 lb.
Feed Device:	8-round, in-line removable box magazine.
Muzzle Velocity:	1600 f.p.s.
Sights:	Blade and notch.

It is believed that only one specimen of this pistol was ever made. The Brigadier had several points in its favor, but the new caliber .45 cartridge required a heavy weapon even if with an aluminum-alloy frame, and at the time of its introduction the Canadian Army was firmly wedded to the 9mm Parabellum cartridge which had proved itself over many years as quite adequate for military purposes.

COMMUNIST CHINA

Communist China has not produced a Service handgun of native design. Copies of the Soviet 7.62mm TT M1933 Tokarev pistol are made in China where they are called the Type 51. There is no difference between the Soviet Tokarev and the Chinese Communist copy. A description of this pistol will be found in chapter 5 on 7.62mm handguns.

CHINESE COMMUNIST 7.62mm TYPE 51.

Within the past several years, the Communist Chinese have been referring to the Tokarev as the Type 54 though there is no apparent difference between the Type 51 and the Type 54.

CZECHOSLOVAKIA

The Czechs, who were very active in pistol design and manufacture prior to WW II, have continued this activity in the post-war period. In the initial days after WW II, the Czech Army was equipped mainly with German P-38s, Lugers, and some Czech Model 27 7.65mm (.32 ACP) pistols. Manufacture

7.65mm Model 27 pistol made after Communist takeover of Czechoslovakia.

of the Model 27 was continued for a while after WW II, apparently mainly for commercial sale. The marking "Narodni Podnik"—"Workers Enterprise"— "Peoples Factory," etc., found on some of these pistols indicate they were made after the Communists took over Czechoslovakia in 1948. The characteristics of this pistol are given in chapter 7 on 7.65mm handguns.

CZECH 7.65mm Model 50 pistol.

OFFICIAL ARMS
7.65mm Model 1950

A double-action automatic similar in general appearance to the Walther PP was introduced in 1950. The Model 1950 was produced for both local use—it apparently was used by Police and Border Guards, and may still be—and for export. A limited quantity were sold in America. Pistols made for export are usually marked "Made in Czechoslovakia." Model 50 pistols made for export may also bear the marking "Vzor 50" which means "Model 50." The Model 50 is loaded, fired and field stripped in the same manner as the Walther PP and PPK.

7.62mm Model 52

The Czechs adopted a new military pistol in 1952. The Model 52 is chambered for the Soviet 7.62mm pistol cartridge Type P which is called the Model 48 cartridge in Czechoslovakia. This cartridge is dimensionally interchangeable with the 7.63mm Mauser, but military loadings of the 7.62mm are considerably heavier than most 7.63mm Mauser loads. The Czech Model 48 cartridge averages about 20% more energy than the Soviet Type P cartridge. This makes for unpleasant recoil and blast in a pistol and the Czech 7.62mm military cartridges should not be used in older 7.63mm pistols.

The Model 52 is a native design which uses the same type locking mechanism as the German Model 42 (MG 42) machine gun. This is a rather complicated locking system for a semi-automatic pistol and makes the pistol very difficult to field-strip.

CZECH 7.62mm Model 52 pistol.

Loading and Firing the Model 52: The magazine catch is located at the bottom rear of the grip and will release the magazine when pushed to the rear. The magazine is conventionally loaded with eight cartridges and is then pushed back into its well in the grip. Draw the slide to the rear and release; a cartridge will now be chambered and the weapon is ready to fire if the

617

safety is in the *Fire* position. Pressure on the trigger will fire the pistol, and after the trigger is released it may be squeezed again and so on until the last cartridge is fired at which time the slide will remain open. The slide must then be drawn to the rear in order to release it for forward return. The safety is mounted on the left rear of the receiver and has three positions. The lowest position is *Fire* and the two top positions are *Safe*. The Model 52 is a single-action pistol; if there is a cartridge in the chamber with the hammer down the hammer must be cocked before the pistol can be fired. Pushing the safety into its top position causes the hammer to fall, but the gun will not fire.

Field-Stripping the Model 52: At the front of the triggerguard are the slide dismounting catches. These are pulled down and the slide assembly is pushed forward until it can be drawn straight up, to the rear and off the receiver. Removal of the barrel from the slide is difficult and parts can be injured if not done with care. A punch or small screwdriver should be inserted in the hole in the locking roller cam and the barrel must be pushed

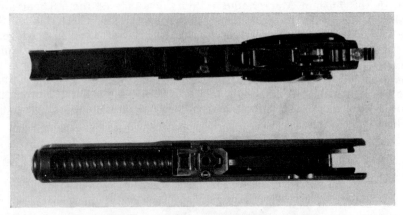

Top view of receiver and bottom view of slide, CZECH Model 52 pistol, barrel locked.

forward against the pressure of the recoil spring until the locking lugs clear their recesses in the receiver. The barrel and recoil spring can then be lifted out of the receiver and withdrawn to the rear, but with care, because the barrel is under the tension of the recoil spring.

Functioning: The only unusual feature in the functioning of the Model 52 is the locking mechanism. Barrel and slide are locked together by roller bearings for three-sixteenths of an inch of recoil. During this recoil period the roller bearings are locked in their recesses in the slide and in the barrel lug (located under the barrel) by the thick center section of the roller cam. The roller cam is a sleeve-like piece which encircles the barrel ahead of the barrel lug. It has a tongue-shaped section which extends through a longitudinal groove cut in the underside of the barrel lug. The roller cam is pressured from moving rearwards by a lug in the receiver just forward of the bullet ramp. When the narrowed section of the roller cam tongue lines up with the roller bearings and their locking slot in the barrel lug, the roller bearings are cammed completely into the cut-out portion of the barrel lug by the edges of the roller bearing recesses in the slide. The pistol is now unlocked. On return of the slide and barrel into the battery position, the roller bearings are cammed out of their position in the cut-out of the barrel and into the locking recesses of the slide. They are held in the locked position i.e., half in the slide and half in the cut-out of the barrel lug, by the wide central portion of the roller cam.

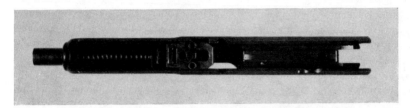

Bottom view of slide of Model 52 showing the barrel unlocked.

The Model 52 has a firing-pin lock which is mounted on the feed rib of the slide. A portion of this lock is seated in a semicircular notch cut in and near the head of the inertia-type firing pin. This both locks the firing pin and cams it back from the primer when the slide and barrel start to move to the rear. The forcing of the firing-pin lock upward by the sear arm allows the firing pin to move forward when struck by the hammer. Rearward movement of the slide disengages the firing-pin lock from the sear arm, allowing the firing-pin lock to come down under the pressure of its spring thus camming the firing pin rearward out of engagement with the cartridge primer.

The Model 52 is an unpleasant pistol to shoot with Czech Service ammunition. Recoil is heavy and the blast is sharp; the grip has sharp edges which bite into the hand. The weapon's finish is rather rough and it does not have the appearance expected in Czech-made arms.

CZECH .22 L.R. DRULOV target pistol.

CZECH SPORTING PISTOLS

The Czechs have produced a respectable number of sporting pistol designs in calibers from .22 through .38 Special. These arms are well made and, for the most part, intended for target shooting.

Caliber .22 L.R. Drulov Target Pistol

The Drulov, which has adjustable front and rear sights, is a single-shot pistol with a manually-operated turn-bolt breech mechanism. It has a push-through safety and does not appear to have any unusual or outstanding design features.

CZECH .22 L.R. PAV target pistol.

Caliber .22 L.R. PAV Target Pistol

The PAV is also a single-shot pistol. It was designed by Paulicek and tips up to load.

Champion Target Pistol

The Champion is a single-shot target pistol with a tipping barrel type action. The Champion may also be called the ZKP-493-S and may be found chambered for the 4mm, .22 Short or .22 L.R. cartridge. Sights are adjustable.

CZECH .22 L.R. ZKP 501-II target automatic.

ZKP 501-II .22 L.R. Target Automatic

This self-loading model has target adjustable sights, a very heavy barrel and is blowback operated. The slide, or more properly breechblock in this case, recoils internally within the massive barrel. There is a barrel extension piece on which both front and rear sights are mounted. The outer portion of the breechblock is serrated for cocking and can be seen just above the grip. To dismount for cleaning, the barrel swings open, pivoting on the mounting pin at the forward underside of the receiver. A thumb safety is mounted on the left rear of the receiver just forward of the tang.

ZKP-524 .22 Short Super Rapid Target Model Automatic

This .22 Short self-loading pistol is designed for use in the Olympic .22 Short rapid-fire matches. It has an internally mounted breechblock and a target adjustable rear sight which is mounted on a non-moving barrel/barrel extension. It has a rounded single-baffle compensator/recoil brake on which the front sight is mounted. This model is sometimes called the ZKP-54.

CZECH .22 Short ZKP-524 automatic.

ZKP-54 .22 Short Universal Model Target Automatic

This target pistol is similar to the ZKP-524, differing from it mainly in the shape of the barrel and with its muzzle-brake/compensator slab-sided rather than rounded as on the ZKP-524.

CZ Caliber .25 (6.35mm) Model 1945 Automatic

This blowback-operated pistol is a modification of the CZ Model 1936. On the Model 1936 there is a combination safety lock/slide-dismounting lock on the left side of the receiver. This part is not on the M1945; the lack of a safety is not too important since these pistols can only be fired double-action, but the disassembly of the pistol is more difficult because of the lack of a device to hold back the slide. Although it does not show on side views, this pistol has an externally-mounted hammer.

621

CZ .25 M1945 automatic.

ZKP 524 7.62mm Automatic

This self-loading, recoil-operated pistol, its design credited to Francis and Joseph Koucky, is a modified Browning design and has the tilting barrel of the Browning recoil-operated designs. It also has the typical Colt/Browning slide stop and safety. The arm is chambered for the 7.62mm Czech pistol cartridge which is basically the same as the Soviet 7.62mm pistol cartridge, dimensionally the same as the 7.63mm Mauser cartridge. Although this pistol is basically a military design, it has not appeared on the military market and may never have been made in quantity. The ZKP 524 is approximately 8 inches in overall length and weighs about 2 pounds.

CZECH ZKR 551. 38 Special target revolver.

ZKR 551 Caliber .38 Special Target Revolver

The ZKR 551 is a single-action revolver designed specifically for target work. The weapon has a side-loading cylinder which is loaded through a pull-back type loading gate on the right side. Cases are ejected by a spring-loaded ejector rod generally similar to those used on the Colt Peacemaker and the Ruger Single Action revolvers. The ZKR 551 has an adjustable rear sight and a screw type trigger stop. It was introduced in 1957.

Grand Caliber .38 Special Revolver

The Grand, which may be found chambered for .22 L.R. and .357 Magnum as well as the .38 Special, resembles the Colt externally, but is quite different internally. Two coil springs mounted on a rod within the grip function as both hammer spring and trigger spring, through the rod bearing against the hammer and a sear lever which extends across the top of the coil spring to the trigger. The cylinder locking bolt is mounted in the side plate and is operated by a lever also mounted in the side plate.

CZECH .38 Special GRAND revolver.

REPRESENTATIVE POST-WW II CZECH PISTOLS

	M1950	M52	Drulov	Champion
Caliber:	7.65mm (.32 ACP).	7.62mm.	.22 L.R.	.22 L.R.*
System of Operation:	Blowback, semi-automatic.	Recoil, semi-automatic.	Single-shot turn-bolt.	Single-shot top break.
Length Overall:	6.8"	8.25"	14.2"	11.5"
Barrel Length:	3.8"	4.71"	9.3"	7.5"
Feed Device:	8-round in-line removable box magazine.	8-round in-line removable box magazine.	(N/A)	(N/A)
Sights:	Blade and round notch.	Blade and square notch.	Adj. blade and adj. notched bar.	Blade and adjustable notched bar.
Weight:	1.5 lb.	2.31 lb.	2.8 lb.	2 lb.

*Can be found chambered for other cartridges as noted in the text.

REPRESENTATIVE POST-WW II CZECH PISTOLS (Continued)

	M1945	ZKR 551	Grand
Caliber:	6.35mm (.25 ACP).	.38 S&W Spec.	.38 S&W Spec.*
System of Operation:	Blowback, semi-automatic.	Single-action revolver.	Double-action revolver.
Length Overall:	5"	11.7"	9"
Barrel Length:	2.5"	6"	4"
Feed Device:	8-round in-line removable magazine.	6-round revolving cylinder.	6-round revolving cylinder.
Sights:	Machine-notched longitudinally down top of slide.	Blade and adj. notched bar.	Blade and notched frame.
Weight:	.93 lb.	2.2 lb.	—

*Can be found chambered for other cartridges as noted in the text.

DENMARK

The Danish Army is currently equipped with the 9mm Parabellum FN Hi-Power Browning automatic, which they call the 9mm PM/46 and the 9mm Parabellum SIG (P210) automatic which they call the 9mm PM/49.

SCHULTZ AND LARSEN

The firm of Schultz and Larsen at Otterup manufactures quality arms including a high-quality Olympic type Free pistol.

Schultz & Larsen .22 L.R. Model 51

This single-shot Free pistol has a bolt action, adjustable hair trigger with "feeling screw," rear sight adjustable for windage and elevation with spare rear-sight bars and front-sight blades having varying size notches and widths respectively. The barrel is 11 inches long with a 14-inch sight radius; overall length is 15 inches and weight runs from 2.75 to 3 pounds. The stock is grooved for all five fingers and has an adjustable hand rest. This pistol is distributed in the United States by Norma-Precision of South Lansing, New York. It was put in production in 1950.

SCHULTZ & LARSEN Model 51 Free pistol.

FRANCE

The standard French Service pistols during WW II were the 7.65mm Long Model 1935A and 1935S. These weapons continued in limited French military use until the mid-Fifties. A 9mm Parabellum pistol, the SE-MAS M1948, was produced in very limited quantity and the current French Service pistol, a further development of the M1948, is the 9mm Parabellum M1950. The French were supplied with quantities of U.S. cal. .45 M1911A1 pistols during WW II.

OFFICIAL ARMS

The 7.65mm M1935A and M1935S Pistols

These recoil-operated, automatic (self-loading pistols) are of modified Browning design and are based on the patents of C. Petter of SACM. They are chambered for a .32 Long cartridge which is similar to the cal. .30 pistol cartridge developed for the Pedersen device of 1918. This cartridge was made only in France and, except for occasional lots of surplus ammunition, is difficult to obtain in the United States.

FRENCH 7.65mm M1935A pistol.

The M1935A and S have "packaged" hammer, sear and disconnector assemblies similar to that used on the Soviet Tokarev TT M1933 pistol. The principal internal difference between the M1935A and S are that the M1935A has two lugs on the upper surface of the barrel which lock into mating grooves in the slide—as with the U.S. M1911A1 Colt automatic—while the 1935S has only one locking lug. Externally, the two pistols vary only in shape of grip and slide. These pistols are frequently found with a stovepipe enamel finish. Considerable numbers of them have been imported into the United States in recent years. Although the pistols are of reliable design and are safe enough when used with the proper cartridge, they are frequently found with a rather rough finish.

FRENCH 7.65mm M1935S automatic pistol.

The 9mm Model 1950

This is the most powerful and by far the best military pistol that has been adopted by the French thus far. It is a recoil-operated weapon which is similar in some respects to the U.S. Colt .45 Automatic and is chambered for the 9mm Parabellum cartridge. The safety is mounted on the slide as with the M1935A and 1935S and the recoil spring is internally mounted as with the Browning Hi-Power and the Polish Radom. The M1950 has the link and dual locking lugs of the Colt. It is loaded and fired as is the Colt, but cannot be fired with the magazine removed. There is a loaded-chamber indicator mounted in the slide.

FRENCH 9mm M1950 pistol.

627

Field-stripping of the M1950 is the same as the Colt Model 1911A1 except that since there is no recoil spring plug and barrel bushing, the pressure on the recoil spring cannot be relieved prior to dismounting the slide. The M1950 has a packaged hammer/sear assembly which can be removed as one piece as with the M1935 pistols.

CHARACTERISTICS OF FRENCH SERVICE PISTOLS

	M1935A	M1935S	M1950
Caliber:	7.65mm Long.	7.65mm Long.	9mm Parabellum.
System of Operation:	Recoil, semi-automatic.	Recoil, semi-automatic.	Recoil, semi-automatic.
Length Overall:	7.6"	7.4"	7.6"
Barrel Length:	4.3"	4.1"	4.4"
Feed Device:	8-round, in-line detachable, box magazine.	8-round, in-line detachable, box magazine.	9-round, in-line detachable, box magazine.
Sights:	Blade and U-notch.	Blade and U-notch.	Blade and U-notch.
Weight:	1.62 lb.	1.75 lb.	1.8 lb.

FRENCH COMMERCIAL HANDGUNS

There are three principal manufacturers of handguns for sport and personal defense in France. These are Manufacture D'Armes Automatiques of Bayonne commonly called MAB, Manufacture D'Armes Des Pyrenees Francaises, manufacturer of the Unique line of pistols, and Manufrance of St. Etienne, manufacturers of the Le Francais pistols. All these pistols are of good quality and the MAB line was sold in the United States for a number of years as the WAC by the Winfield Arms Co., a California arms distributor.

MAB .22 Long Rifle automatic Model F with WAC trade-mark.

MAB

MAB Caliber .22 L.R. Model F

This hammerless, blowback-operated automatic, i.e., self-loading pistol, was marketed in the United States under the WAC trademark. It has a manual and magazine safety and was introduced in early 1951. This pistol could be had in any of three barrel lengths: 4.1 in., 6 in., and 6.8 in. The pistol has non-adjustable sights and is purely a plinker. It is out of production.

MAB Caliber .22 L.R. Model R

This pistol is basically the same as the Model F except that it has an external hammer and is a bit more streamlined in design. This pistol, too, is out of production.

MAB .22 L.R. Model G.

MAB Caliber .22 L.R. Model G

This blowback-operated automatic is double-action. The Model G is also made in 7.65mm (.32 ACP) and may be found with either a steel or lightweight alloy receiver.

MAB Caliber .25 ACP Model A

This pistol, illustrated in Appendix I, is no longer in production.

MAB .25 ACP Model E

The Model E was first produced in 1949, but is no longer carried in the company's catalog. It is somewhat larger than the average .25 pistol and has a 10-round magazine. Its construction is similar to that of the 7.65mm Model C.

MAB .25 ACP Model E pistol.

MAB .32 ACP Model C

This arm originally appeared in 1933 and is still carried in current MAB catalogs. The construction of the Model C is much like that of the 1922 Browning and the Colt Pocket automatic. The recoil spring is held in its place around the barrel by a recoil spring retaining bushing which is mounted on the barrel and locks into the slide by a bayonet type catch. The slide and barrel are removed by rotating the barrel so that the lugs on its bottom disengage their mating grooves in the receiver.

MAB .32 ACP Model C pistol, current production.

The Model C has a grip safety and a manual safety which is mounted on the left side of the receiver at the top rear of the trigger guard. The Model C was made during the German occupation of France and may be found

630

with German acceptance marks. It was distributed by Winfield Arms Co. with the WAC trademark on the slide. The Model C is also made in .380 ACP (9mm Browning Short).

MAB .32 ACP Model D pistol of current manufacture.

MAB .32 ACP Model D

The Model D is basically an enlarged Model C. It was also made for the Germans during their occupation of France. It was also made for the French military. The Model D is also made in .380 ACP.

MAB 9mm Parabellum Model R.
(See next page.)

MAB Model R Court and Longue

The Model R was made in the .32 ACP (7.65mm Court) and the French .32 Long cartridge. It was also made in the .380 ACP. These pistols are no longer carried in the company's brochure.

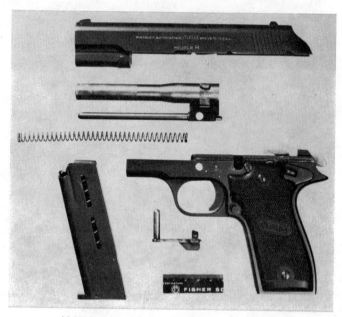

MAB 9mm Parabellum Model R field-stripped.

MAB 9mm Parabellum Model R

The Model R was made for the high powered 9mm Parabellum cartridge in a delayed blowback version which had a rotating barrel. The barrel is rotated by a lug on the top of the barrel which rides in a notch cut through the top of the slide. This model, which was introduced about 1958, has its rotating barrel mounted on the same piece as the recoil spring rod. This piece is held in place by the slide stop. This arm was made in two styles: an 8-shot model and a 15-shot model. It is not carried in the current company catalogs. This design, however, led to the current 9mm Parabellum MAB pistol.

MAB 9mm Parabellum Model P 15

The P 15 has the largest magazine capacity of any handgun in the 9mm Parabellum power category. Only the Soviet 9mm Stechkin (APS), which is really a machine pistol and uses a considerably smaller cartridge than the 9mm Parabellum, has a larger magazine capacity. The P 15 is also called the PA-15. The delay locking mechanism of the Model R has been modified in the Model P so that it is a positive lock. The barrel has lugs mounted on the top and bottom of the barrel over the chamber section. The bottom lug rides in a cam surface cut in a piece to which the recoil spring guide rod is

MAB 9mm Parabellum Model PA-15.

mounted. This piece also has the hole through which the slide stop pin is mounted. The top lug locks into a groove cut in the top inside of the slide. Rearward movement of the slide cams the bottom lug causing the top locking lug to cam out of its recess in the slide, allowing the slide to move to the rear by itself. The barrel of the PA-15, unlike the barrel of the 9mm Parabellum Model R, is not attached to any other piece; it rests in the camming piece.

MAB 9mm Parabellum Model PA-15 field-stripped.

It will be remembered that the lug of the 9mm Parabellum Model R barrel rides in an angular cut which goes completely through the top of the slide and the barrel rotates on a piece to which it is attached. Although it is a debatable point, the writer believes that the Model R is a delayed-blowback operating system while the Model P is a recoil-operated fully-locked system.

MAB 9mm Parabellum Model P 15 Competition
This is a target version of the P 15 and varies from it in having a longer barrel, 6 inches versus 4.6 inches; being heavier, having adjustable sights, and is available with walnut grips.

MAB 9mm Parabellum Model P 8
This is an 8-round version of the P 15 and a bit over an ounce lighter. It is thinner through the grip section than the P 15 and measures a bit less in height.

MAB 9mm Parabellum Model P 8.

UNIQUE
Unique Caliber .22 L.R., Models D 2, D 3, D 6
These blowback-operated pistols all utilize the same basic parts. Differences are in length of barrel. The D 2 was sold by Sears Roebuck as the J. C. Higgins Model 85 and by Montgomery Ward as the Western Field Model 50. On these pistols the barrel is permanently fixed to the receiver. Field stripping is simple: the slide is drawn to the rear and locked in place by the manual safety catch, then rotate take-down button on the right side 90° and dismount the slide. D 2 and D 6 are sold in the United States by Firearms International, Inc. as the "Corsair." Barrel lengths are as follows: D 2—4.25 inches, D 3—8.25 inches, and D 6—6 inches.

.22 L.R. UNIQUE MODEL D 6 with Corsair trade-mark.

Unique Caliber .22 L.R. Model D 4

The D 4 is a blowback-operated target pistol. It has an adjustable rear sight and can be fitted with barrel weights. Take-down is the same as the other Unique .22 automatic pistols.

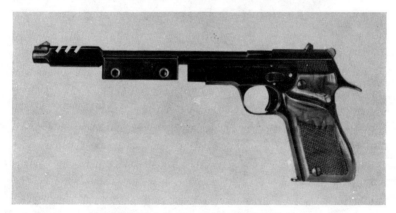

UNIQUE .22 L.R. Target Pistol MODEL D 4.

Unique Caliber .22 Short Model E 2 and E 6

These pistols are the same as the Unique Models D 3 and D 6 except that they are chambered for the .22 Short and have lightweight alloy slides.

Unique Caliber .22 Short Model E 4

This pistol is basically the same as the Model D 4 except that it is chambered for the .22 Short and has a lightweight alloy slide.

635

Unique Combo Pistol-Rifle

The Combo is made up of a Unique .22 L.R. Model L automatic pistol which is, after removal of the barrel, inserted into a stock and barrel assembly which uses the slide and receiver of the pistol to make up a semi-automatic rifle. The rifle barrel is 18 inches long; sights are mounted on the barrel and an operating rod mounted under the barrel is used to cock the slide. It can be obtained with open and peep rear sights. The Model L pistol can be obtained with either a steel or light alloy frame.

UNIQUE .22 L.R. MODEL L Pistol.

UNIQUE COMBO pistol rifle.

Unique Caliber .22 L.R. Model 52

The Model 52, a blowback-operated semi-automatic, has a fixed barrel like the D and E series pistols and disassembly is similar to these pistols. The Model 52 has a differently shaped grip, however, and is more obviously produced basically as a personal defense arm. The Model 52 has an external hammer.

636

UNIQUE .22 L.R. Model 52 pistol.

Unique Model D 1 and E 1

The caliber .22 L.R. D 1 and the caliber .22 Short E 1 are short-barreled versions of the D series pistols. They have barrels about 3.1 inches long and are apparently no longer in production since they are no longer carried in the manufacturer's catalogs.

UNIQUE .25 ACP MIKROS pistol.

Unique Caliber .25 ACP Mikros

This blowback-operated pistol is a post-war version of the original Mikros that was introduced in 1934 and illustrated in Appendix I. The current Mikros was introduced in 1958. Unlike the earlier pistol, it has an external hammer. It is also produced in .22 Short, in which caliber it may be had with either 2.25 inch or 4-inch barrels. In .25 caliber it is produced with 2.25-inch barrel only. The Mikros is also called Model K. The Mikros comes with either steel or lightweight alloy receivers.

Unique Models Rr-51 and Fr-51

These blowback-operated pistols are of conventional design. The Rr-51 is chambered for the .32 ACP cartridge and the Fr-51 is chambered for the .380 ACP. These pistols have external hammers with a half-cock notch, a manual safety, and a magazine safety. They are disassembled in a manner similar to that used with the Colt Pocket Automatic.

UNIQUE .32 ACP Model Rr-51 pistol.

UNIQUE .32 ACP Model Bcf-66 pistol.

Unique Model Bcf-66

The Bcf-66, a blowback-operated pistol which resembles the Unique D series, may be chambered for the .32 ACP. (Factory Model 540) or the .380 ACP (Factory Model 550). The principal structural difference between the

D-series pistols and the Bcf-66 is in the barrel and slide. The D series has a slide which is open at the top front end; that of the Bcf-66 has a top strap with front sight similar to those of the Berettas. The barrels of the D series are held in place by three pins while the barrels of the Bcf-66 pistols are joined to the receiver by a tongued lug which fits into mating grooves on the receiver. To field-strip the Bcf-66, the slide is locked to the rear by the safety catch on the left side of the receiver, then remove the magazine, push the barrel straight back and rotate it 180°. The barrel and slide may then be drawn forwards off the receiver.

MANURHIN COPIES OF WALTHER

Manufacture de Machines du Haut Rhin manufactured licensed copies of the Walther PP and PPK in 7.65mm (.32 ACP) and 9mm Short (.380 ACP) for a number of years after WW II. Manufacture was discontinued when Walther began making these pistols in West Germany. The Walther .22 L.R. PP Sport model was also made by Manurhin.

MANUFRANCE PISTOLS

Manufrance (Manufacture Francaise D'Armes et Cycles of St. Etienne) is still manufacturing the Le Francais series pistols. Three models are made: the 6.35mm (.25 ACP) Pocket model with a 2.3-inch barrel, the 6.35mm Policeman model with a 3.25-inch barrel and the standard Le Francais 7.65mm (.32 ACP) which has a 3.25-inch barrel. The method of operation of these pistols is explained in detail in chapter 4.

CHARACTERISTICS OF FRENCH SEMI-AUTOMATIC PISTOLS

	MAB Model F	Unique CORSAIR Model D 6	Unique Model D 4	Unique Model E 4
Caliber:	.22 L.R.	.22 L.R.	.22 L.R.	.22 Short.
Length Overall:	8.67"	9"	11.75"	11.75"
Barrel Length:	4.53" [1]	6"	8.5"	8.5"
Feed Device:	9-round, in-line detachable box magazine.	10-round, in-line detachable box magazine.	10-round, in-line detachable box magazine.	6-round, in-line detachable box magazine.
Sights:	Blade and notch.	Blade and notch.	Blade front; rear adjustable notched bar.	Blade front; rear adjustable notched bar.
Weight:	1.6 lb.	1.56 lb.	1.75 lb.[2]	1.62 lb.[2]

Note: All are blowback pistols.
[1] Also comes with 6.1" and 6.8"-barrels.
[2] A .93-lb. counterweight may be used with this pistol.

CHARACTERISTICS OF FRENCH SEMI-AUTOMATIC PISTOLS (Continued)

	Unique Model L	MAB Model R	Unique MIKROS	MAB Model E
Caliber:	.22 L.R.	.22 L.R.	.25 ACP.	.25 ACP.
Length Overall:	5.75"	10.52"	4.43"	6.9"
Barrel Length:	3.06"	7.4" [3]	2.25"	4"
Feed Device:	10-round, in-line detachable box magazine.	10-round, in-line detachable box magazine.	6-round, in-line detachable box magazine.	10-round, in-line detachable box magazine.
Sights:	Blade and notch.	Blade and notch.	Blade and notch.	Blade and notch.
Weight:	1.37 lb. w/steel frame; 1 lb. w/alloy frame.	1.43 lb.	.77 lb. w/steel frame; .58 lb. w/alloy frame.	1.56 lb.

Note: All are blowback pistols.
[3] Also comes with a 4.4"-barrel.

CHARACTERISTICS OF FRENCH SEMI-AUTOMATIC PISTOLS (Continued)

	MAB Model C	MAB Model D	MAB Model R	Unique Model Rv 51
Caliber:	.32 ACP.[4]	.32 ACP.[5]	.32 ACP.[6]	.32 ACP.
Length Overall:	6.2"	7.04"	6.80"	5.7"
Barrel Length:	3.3"	4"	3.94"	Approx. 3.5"
Feed Device:	7-round, in-line detachable box magazine.	9-round, in-line detachable box magazine.	9-round, in-line detachable box magazine.	9-round, in-line detachable box magazine.
Sights:	Blade and notch.	Blade and notch.	Blade and notch.	Blade and notch.
Weight:	1.43 lb.	1.56 lb.	1.67 lb.	1.62 lb.

Note: All are blowback pistols.

[4] Also made in .380 ACP.
[5] Also made in .380 ACP.
[6] Also made in 7.65mm Long.

CHARACTERISTICS OF FRENCH SEMI-AUTOMATIC PISTOLS (Continued)

	Unique Model Fr-51	Unique Model Bcf-66	MAB Model P-15	MAB Model P-15 COMPETITION
Caliber:	.380 ACP.	.380 ACP.[7]	9mm Parabellum.	9mm Parabellum.
System of Operation:	Blowback.	Blowback.	Recoil operated.	Recoil operated.
Length Overall:	5.7"	6.62"	8.08"	9.64"
Barrel Length:	Approx. 3.5"	3.95"	4.6"	6"
Feed Device:	8-round, in-line detachable box magazine.	8-round, in-line detachable box magazine.	15-round, staggered row, detachable box magazine.	15-round, staggered row, detachable box magazine.
Sights:	Blade and notch.	Blade and notch.	Blade and notch.	Blade front; adjustable-notch rear.
Weight:	1.62 lb.	1.5 lb.	2.18 lb.	2.43 lb.

[7] Also made in .32 ACP.

EAST GERMANY

Little in the line of handgun development has come out of East Germany since WW II. A copy of the Soviet 9mm Makarov (PM) is made in East Germany and is used by the East German Forces. This weapon is covered in detail in the section on the U.S.S.R. The East Germans call the Makarov the Pistol M.

E. GERMAN COPY of Soviet 9mm MAKAROV pistol.

EAST GERMANY .22 TARGET PISTOLS

"Buhag"—Buchsenmacher—Handwerksgenossenschaft m.b.h. of Suhl—makes two caliber .22 target pistols. The Centrum 11 is a Free pistol chambered for the .22 L.R. cartridge. The Olympia is a .22 Short automatic target pistol. It has a five-shot magazine and is about 11.8 inches long.

E. GERMAN BUHAG .22 Short OLYMPIA Model automatic.

WEST GERMANY

The West German Army has adopted the Walther 9mm Parabellum P-38 as the standard side arm of the West German Army; it is called the P1 in that Army.

The commercial arms industry in West Germany has been quite active and is now producing some fine handguns; unfortunately, they are also producing some of rather poor quality which will not be covered herein.

The firms which are currently producing pistols of good to fine quality in W. Germany are Carl Walther of Ulm A/D, Hermann Weihrauch of Bavaria, Heckler and Koch of Oberndorf A/N and Erma Werke of Erfurt. The Weihrauch firm manufactures the "Arminius" brand revolvers.

ARMINIUS
Arminius .22 L.R. Model HW3
This swing-out cylinder type revolver is of good quality, as is the entire Arminius line. It is a short-barreled revolver designed for personal defense. This revolver may also be found chambered for the .32 S&W cartridge.

ARMINIUS .22 L.R. Model HW3.

Arminius .22 L.R. Model HW5
The HW5 is a slightly larger gun than the HW3 and is more suitable for plinking because of its fuller grip and longer barrel. It is also made in .32 S&W.

643

ARMINIUS .22 L.R. Model HW5.

Arminius .22 L.R. Model HW7S

The HW7S has shaped grips, an adjustable rear sight, and a heavier barrel than the HW3 and HW5. The HW7 is similar, but does not have shaped grips, adjustable rear sight or a heavy barrel. The HW7 and HW7S can also be obtained chambered for the .32 S&W cartridge. Like the HW3, and 5, the HW7 series chambered for the .22 L.R. has an 8-round capacity, while those chambered for the .32 S&W have a 7-round capacity. There is also a Model HW7J which is similar to the HW7S but has a shorter barrel—5 inches as opposed to 6 inches.

ARMINIUS .22 L.R. Model HW7S.

Arminius .22 L.R. Model HW9

The HW9, which is made in .22 L.R. only, is the best revolver in the Arminius line. It has a heavier barrel with ventilated rib, a micrometer-adjustable rear sight, and can be fitted with several models of front sight and shaped grips. It also has a heavier cylinder than the other models since it is chambered for 6 rounds rather than 8. The Arminius line of revolvers is comparable to mid-priced U. S. handguns. They are not comparable to the products of the leading United States manufacturers of revolvers.

ARMINIUS .22 L.R. Model HW9.

ERMA

Erma .22 L.R. Model EP-22

This is the Erma Werke .22 Luger. Although this pistol resembles the Luger in appearance and general handling it differs in one major respect. The

ERMA .22 L.R. Model EP 22.

standard 9mm Parabellum Luger is recoil-operated, the Erma, using the much lower-powered .22, is blowback-operated.

HECKLER AND KOCH

Heckler and Koch Model HK4

The HK4 is a semi-automatic which can be obtained in .22 L.R., .25 ACP, .32 ACP or .380 ACP, or in all four. The basic receiver and slide can be used with barrels and magazines for any of these cartridges. HK4, which bears

HECKLER AND KOCH Model HK4.

Section view of the HK4.

some resemblance to the Mauser HSc, is double-action and has a light alloy receiver. There are two firing-pin channels in the slide and the position of the firing pin must be changed from the central position when using .22

caliber. The HK4 is a well-made, well-designed double-action automatic. It incorporates most of the desired features in a pistol of this type. Insertion of a loaded magazine into the receiver automatically causes the slide to run home, therefore the safety should always be set on before loading. The hammer can, as with most double-action automatics, be dropped safely by pulling the trigger *if the weapon is on Safe,* i.e., in the down position with white mark showing. The safety moves the firing pin out of the hammer's path.

REGENT

Regent Caliber .22

This inexpensive .22 revolver is manufactured by Karl Burgsmuller, Sr. of Kreiensen, Germany. Barrel length is 2 in., 4 in. or 6 in. The 8-shot cylinder handles .22 Short, Long or Long Rifle ammunition. The cylinder swings to the left after the ejector rod is pulled forward. The rebounding ejector provides simultaneous ejection. The firing pin is a floating type in a zinc frame. Sights are a square-notch rear and serrated-front, both fixed. Single or double-action. Checkered one-piece composition stocks. Production started early in 1960. Distribution is handled in the United States by Firearms International.

REGENT .22 revolver.

WALTHER

Walther .22 L.R. PP Sport Model

This model was made by Manurhin in France under Walther license for a while after WW II. It is currently listed in the Carl Walther catalogs and is presumably being made at Ulm A/D. The Sport Model is normally furnished in single-action but can be furnished in double-action if desired. It can also be furnished chambered for the .22 Short cartridge with 8.1-inch barrel, if desired. The Sport Model has an adjustable rear sight and may be obtained in .22 L.R. with a 6.1-inch barrel or an 8.25-inch barrel. The front sight is held on by a threaded ring and can be changed easily from barrel to barrel, however, the barrel is not of the quick-dismountable type as it is held to the receiver by a pin.

WALTHER .22 L.R. PP SPORT Model manufactured by Manurhin.

Walther .22 Short Model OSP

The OSP (Olympic Schnellfever Pistole) is Walther's .22 Short Olympic automatic. It is a very finely made pistol and has all the features one would expect in a quality target pistol: non-recoiling micro-adjustable rear sight,

WALTHER .22 Short Model OSP.

adjustable trigger pull, detachable barrel, thumb rest and adjustable shelf stocks. Late production models have four slots milled in the forward end of the barrel and a reinforced frame. The barrel is easily dismounted by pushing forward the barrel-dismounting latch.

Walther .25 ACP Model TP

This is the post-war Walther "Vest Pocket" pistol. Design differs from earlier Walther .25 automatics in the use of an external hammer.

WALTHER .25 ACP Model TP.

Walther PP and PPK

The PP and PPK are made in .22 L.R., .32 ACP and .380 ACP. They are essentially the same as they were prior to WW II. The PPK can be obtained with a light-alloy receiver in caliber .22 L.R. and .32 ACP.

649

CHARACTERISTICS OF WEST GERMAN .22 L.R. REVOLVERS

	Arminius HW3	Arminius HW5	Arminius HW7S	Arminius HW9
Overall Length:	7"	8.6"	11"	11.5"
Barrel Length:	2.75"	4"	6"	6"
Cylinder Capacity:	8 rounds.	8 rounds.	8 rounds.	6 rounds.
Sights:	Blade and notch.	Blade and notch.	Blade front; adjustable rear notched bar.	Blade front; rear bar adjustable for elevation and windage.
Weight:	1.5 lb.	1.56 lb.	2 lb.	2.3 lb.

CHARACTERISTICS OF WEST GERMAN .22 SEMI-AUTOMATIC PISTOLS

	Erma EP 22	Heckler & Koch HK 4	Walther PP Sport	Walther OSP
Caliber:	.22 L.R.	.22 L.R.[1]	.22 L.R.	.22 Short.
Overall Length:	9"	6.2"	11"	11.87"
Barrel Length:	3.25"	3.3"	8.25" or 6"	4.5"
Feed Device:	8-round, in-line detachable box magazine.	13-round, in-line detachable box magazine.[2]	8-round, in-line detachable box magazine.	5-round, in-line detachable box magazine.
Sights:	Blade and notch.	Blade and notch.	Blade front; rear notched blade adjustable for windage and elevation.	Square-blade front; rear micrometer-adjustable for windage and elevation.
Weight:	2.25 lb.	1.1 lb.	1.56 lb.	2.5 lb. w/barrel weights.

Note: All models listed are of blowback operation.
[1] Also comes in .25 ACP, .32 ACP and .380 ACP.
[2] Magazine capacity in calibers .25 ACP, .32 ACP and .380 ACP is 11, 9, and 8 rounds, respectively.

HUNGARY

The Hungarian Army adopted the Soviet 7.62mm TT M1933 (Tokarev) pistol as standard in 1948. They manufactured a copy of this pistol which they called the 48M—Model 48. During the same time frame, they produced a slightly modified copy of the Walther PP for paramilitary forces.

OFFICIAL ARMS

Hungarian 7.65mm (.32 ACP) Model 48

This pistol differs from the Walther PP mainly in the placement of its loaded-chamber indicator. The loaded-chamber indicator is a pin which projects from the left top of the slide rather than from the rear of the slide as in the Walther PP. Functioning and field-stripping are the same as that of the Walther.

Hungarian 9mm Browning Short (.380 ACP) Walam 48

The Walam 48 is a .380 ACP version of the Model 48 and is therefore also a modified copy of the Walther PP. It was apparently made for sale to Egypt, but has appeared on the commercial market elsewhere.

HUNGARIAN 9mm Browning Short Walam 48 pistol.

Hungarian 7.65mm (.32 ACP) Attila

The Attila is another Hungarian copy of the Walther PP. It differs from the Model 48 and the Walam in the following: It has thumb-rest plastic grips, the loaded-chamber indicator is not on top of the slide, and the receiver is made of lightweight alloy. This pistol is intended for commercial sale.

651

HUNGARIAN 7.65mm ATTILA pistol.

Hungarian 9mm Parabellum Tokagypt 58

This pistol, which was developed from the Soviet 7.62mm M1933 Tokarev, was reportedly produced at the request of the UAR (Egypt). Indications are that it was not a popular arm in that country and therefore Hungary sold these arms on the commercial market. The pistol differs from the Tokarev in caliber, in the mounting of a safety catch on the left rear of the receiver, the use of a plastic wrap around grip stock, and in the fingerpiece type floorplate on the magazine. The basic characteristics, i.e., length, weight, etc., are basically the same as those of the Tokarev.

HUNGARIAN 9mm Parabellum TOKAGYPT 58 pistol.

CHARACTERISTICS OF HUNGARIAN SEMI-AUTOMATIC PISTOLS

	Model 48	Walam 48	Attila
Caliber:	.32 ACP.	.380 ACP.	.32 ACP.
Length Overall:	7″	7″	7″
Barrel Length:	3.9″	3.9″	3.9″
Feed Device:	8-round, in-line detachable box magazine.	7-round, in-line detachable box magazine.	8-round, in-line detachable box magazine.
Sights:	Blade and U-notch.	Blade and U-notch.	Blade and U-notch.
Weight:	1.92 lb.	1.53 lb.	1.3 lb.

Note: Listed models are of blowback operation.

653

INDONESIA

The Indonesian Republic has had a hodgepodge of handguns ranging from Dutch 9.4mm M1873 revolvers to the 7.62mm Tokarev M1933 and the Walther PP. Indonesia has adopted the 9mm Browning Hi-Power as a standard pistol and manufactures a copy of the pistol at Pindad.

INDONESIAN 9mm BROWNING HI-POWER.

ISRAEL

The current standard handgun of the Israeli Forces is the 9mm Parabellum Model 1951 Beretta which is covered in detail under Italy (next text). Israel has, however, produced one revolver which has had police and possibly military use.

Israel manufactured a slightly modified copy of the S&W Military and Police revolver chambered for the 9mm Parabellum cartridge. This arm, manufactured by the Workers Industry for Arms uses two three-round clips similar to those used with the M1917 Colt and S&W revolvers chambered for the .45 ACP cartridge. This revolver is 11-inches long with a 6-1-inch barrel and weighs 1.9 pounds. The cylinder has six chambers.

ISRAELI 9mm Parabellum revolver.

ITALY

The current Italian Service pistol is the 9mm Beretta M1951 pistol. The 9mm Corto (.380 ACP) M1934 Beretta is still encountered among paramilitary and police units. The 9mm Parabellum M1951, which is sold commercially as the Brigadier, is by far the best high-powered self-loading pistol to come out of Italy. In addition to being the standard Service arm of Italy, it is also used by Israel and the UAR (Egypt). The receiver may be made of an aluminum alloy called Ergal by Beretta, or it may be steel. Pistols produced for Egypt bear the Egyptian coat of arms on the left side of the slide and have serial numbers preceded by an "E."

BERETTA 9mm Parabellum M1951.

ITALIAN SERVICE PISTOL

Beretta 9mm Parabellum Model 1951

This is a recoil-operated weapon that has a wedge-type locking device under the barrel which operates in the same manner as that of the Walther P-38. A plunger, mounted in a lug under the barrel, abuts against the receiver when the barrel is in the locked position and forces the locking lug down so that it engages the locking recesses in the slide. This locking system is explained in detail under the Walther P-38 pistol (see chapter 9).

Field-Stripping: The Beretta Model 1951, or M951 as it is frequently called, is field-stripped as follows: Remove magazine by depressing magazine catch on the left bottom of grip. Draw slide to the rear and align the dismounting latch on the right side of the slide with the dismounting notch on the slide. Push the dismounting latch upward toward the muzzle-end of the arm. Pull the slide group forward and off the receiver. Pull the recoil spring and guide assembly slightly to the rear and upward, removing it from the slide. Push barrel backward and withdraw it from the slide. No further disassembly is recommended.

BERETTA 9mm Parabellum Model 1951 as made for Egypt.

Safety: The safety on the M1951 is a push-through button positioned at the top rear of the grip; to put the weapon on *Safe,* the button is pushed through from right to left. The Beretta firm made a target version of the Model 1951 for Egypt. It has a longer barrel, micrometer-adjustable rear sight, and a ramp-mounted blade front sight. Wooden fitted grips with thumb rest are also used on this arm.

BERETTA 9mm Parabellum M1951 target pistol as made for Egypt.

ITALIAN COMMERCIAL AND SPORTING HANDGUNS

Italy manufactures a wide variety of sporting handguns. The leading manufacturers are Pietro Beretta of Gardone Val Trompia Brescia, an ancient and

657

widely-known firm which has an enviable reputation for quality arms, Vincenzo Bernardelli of Gardone Val Trompia, also a firm of high repute, and Industria Armi Galesi of Collebeato, Brescia, a somewhat smaller firm which was founded in 1910.

BERETTA

Beretta .22 Short Model 950B

This pistol is sold in the United States as the Minx M2. It is a blowback-operated arm with duraluminum receiver. The barrel tips up when the latch on the left side of the receiver is moved forward. The slide may then be pushed forward and removed. The tipping barrel allows the pistol to be used as a single-shot when the magazine is removed by tipping the barrel and loading the cartridge directly into the chamber. This pistol has no extractor; the case is blown out of the chamber by the residual pressure of the propellent gases. This pistol went into production in 1960. There is no safety catch, but the hammer has a half-cock notch.

BERETTA .22 Short Model 950B (Minx M2).

Beretta Caliber .22 Short Model 950cc Special

This pistol is sold in the United States as the Minx M4. It is the same as the Model 950, but has a longer—3.7-inch barrel as opposed to 2.37 inches.

Beretta Caliber .22 L.R. Model 71

This blowback-operated pistol has an aluminum alloy receiver. The Model 71 and other 70-series models replace the Beretta Model 1935 and Model 948. The first of the 70 series was introduced in 1958. The barrel mounting surface on the receiver, in which the barrel is dovetailed, is longer than on the 1935 series pistols. The 70 series use a cross-bolt safety which blocks the hammer and sear with the pistol fully cocked. The trigger linkage has been improved and a push-button type magazine release is used. The 70 series are field-stripped in the same manner as the M1951 Beretta. This pistol is sold in the United States as the Jaguar Plinker.

BERETTA .22 L.R. Model 71.

Beretta .22 L.R. Model 72

The Model 72 is the same as the Model 71, but is supplied with two barrels; a short 3.5 inch, and a long 5.9 inch. The Model 72 is also sold in the United States as the Jaguar Plinker.

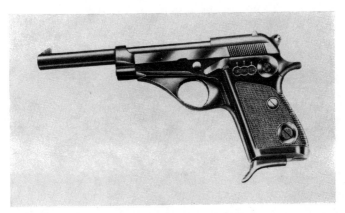

BERETTA .22 L.R. Model 72.

Beretta .22 L.R. Model 73

The Model 73 is basically the same as the Model 72 with a 5.9-inch barrel, but its rear sight is mounted on the barrel rather than on the slide.

Beretta .22 L.R. Model 74

The Model 74, although built on the same lines as the other Model 70 series pistols, is designed for target work. The rear sight is mounted on the 5.9-inch barrel and is adjustable for elevation and windage. The trigger pull

659

BERETTA .22 L.R. Model 73.

also can be adjusted. Adjustment is by a screw which is mounted near the disconnector; the right grip must be removed to gain access to the screw.

Beretta .22 L.R. Model 75

The Model 75 is the same as the Model 71, but has a longer 5.9-inch barrel.

BERETTA .22 L.R. Model 948.

Beretta .22 L.R. Model 948

The Model 948 (1948) which was in production until October, 1958, is of the Model 1934/35 series of Beretta pistols. Dismounting is the same as the 9mm Corto (.380 ACP) Model 1934 which is covered in detail in chapter 10. The Model 1948 came in two different barrel lengths.

Beretta .22 Short Model 949 Olympic

This pistol, which is also called the Model 949C, was designed for use in Olympic rapid-fire matches. The front sight is adjustable for elevation and the rear sight is adjustable for windage. The pistol has a removable barrel weight and a compensator/muzzle-brake. Design is in general the same as the Model 1934/35 series pistols. The shaped grips with thumb rest are of walnut. This is a high-quality target pistol. A .22 L.R. version, Model 949 L.R., was also made.

BERETTA .22 Short Model 949 OLYMPIC.

Beretta .22 Short Model 80 Olympic

The Model 80 is Beretta's latest model Olympic target pistol. The rear sight is adjustable for elevation and windage and does not recoil. There is no recoiling slide on the Model 80; the pistol has a bolt which recoils within its frame/receiver as in the Hungarian Frommer Stop and the Mauser military model. The stocks have a thumb rest.

BERETTA .22 Short Model 80 OLYMPIC.

661

Beretta .25 ACP Model 418

This blowback-operated pistol, which replaced the .25. Model 318, was in production until 1951. It was initially placed in production about 1946. The Model 418 has a modified grip safety; the manual safety is mounted on the

BERETTA .25 ACP Model 418.

left side of the receiver. A pin protrudes from the slide when the weapon is cocked. Dismounting of the Model 418 is the same as that of the Model 1934/35 series pistols. The Model 420 is the same as the Model 418, but is chromed and engraved, and the Model 421 is presentation-grade—completely engraved—gold-plated with turtle-shell grips.

The Model 418 was replaced by the Model 950, which in turn was replaced by the Model 950B, introduced in April 1960.

BERETTA .25 ACP Model 950B.

Beretta .25 ACP Model 950B

This pistol is sold in the United States as the Jetfire. It is basically the same pistol as the .22 Short Model 950B Minx M2 and the remarks covering that pistol apply to this model as well.

Beretta .32 ACP Model 70

This blowback-operated pistol is sold in the United States as the **Puma**. It is, except for caliber, the same as the .22 L.R. Model 71 which has been covered in detail. It can be obtained with either a steel or lightweight Aermetal receiver. The Model 70 replaced the .32 ACP Model 935 when introduced in 1958.

BERETTA .32 ACP Model 70.

BERETTA .32 ACP Model 935.

Beretta .32 ACP Model 935

The Model 935 is a modification of the Model 1931 and differs principally from that pistol in the shape of its grip which is patterned on that of the .380 ACP Model 1934. It was discontinued in 1958.

Beretta .380 ACP Cougar

This is the Model 934 (1934) pistol which is covered in detail in chapter 10. It is still in production and is sold in the United States as the Cougar. It is a fine pistol and was by far the best Italian pistol in use during WW II.

BERNARDELLI

Bernardelli .22 L.R. Baby

This is a conventional Browning-type blowback-operated pistol. It is also made in .22 Short. It is one of the smallest, if not the smallest, automatic pistol currently on the market. It was introduced in 1949.

BERNARDELLI .22 L.R. BABY.

Bernardelli .22 L.R. Model 60

The Model 60 is a blowback-operated pistol which may be obtained in .32 ACP or .380 ACP as well as .22. It has an outside hammer with half-cock notch, fixed barrel, magazine disconnector and twin recoil springs. The standard Model 60 in all calibers has a fixed-notch rear sight and blade front sight which are an integral part of the slide. In caliber .22 L.R. a model is made with 7.9-inch barrel that has an adjustable rear sight and a ramp-type front sight that is held on by a sleeve. The sleeve arrangement on the sight is necessary to dismount the slide from the barrel. The Model 60 pistols are field-stripped by pushing down on the dismounting latch mounted on left rear of receiver, and drawing the slide to the rear against the tension of the twin recoil springs, and lifting the rear of the slide clear of the frame. The slide may then be pushed forward off the barrel. The Model 60 in caliber .32 and .380 replace the Bernardelli pistols in those calibers which were introduced in 1947 and discontinued in 1966.

BERNARDELLI .22 L.R. Model 60 with long barrel.

Bernardelli .22 L.R. V.B. Revolvers

Bernardelli makes a series of caliber .22 and .32 S&W revolvers which are generally patterned on the Smith & Wesson. They have spring-loaded firing pins mounted in the frame and come in four different barrel lengths with the ordinary type revolver sight, i.e., notch in frame and blade on barrel. The models with 3.1 inch, 4.3 inch and 5.9-inch barrels have a squared butt. A Pocket Model is also made in .22 L.R. and .32 S&W. It has a rounded butt and a barrel of 2 or 2.5 inches, and an overall length of about 5.9 inches. Bernardelli also makes a .22 L.R. target revolver with adjustable rear sight, ramp-mounted front sight and a 5.9-inch barrel.

BERNARDELLI .22 L.R. VB POCKET Model revolver.

Bernardelli .25 ACP Pistol

This blowback-operated pistol is similar to the Bernardelli caliber .22 Baby in many respects, but has some major differences. Like the Baby, the end of the striker/firing-pin assembly protrudes from the slide when the pistol is cocked. The slide of the .25 Bernardelli covers the complete top of the barrel, i.e., it has no slots or open surfaces excepting the ejection port. The slide of the Bernardelli Baby is cut away at the top for about half of its length. In addition to the 8-round magazine which protrudes below the receiver, there is a 5-round magazine which is flush with the receiver when inserted in the pistol.

BERNARDELLI .25 ACP automatic with 8-round magazine.

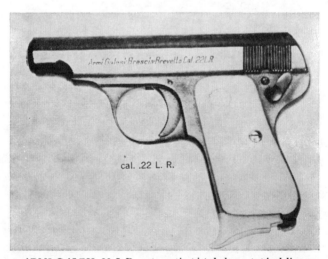

ARMI GALESI .22 L.R. automatic pistol shows typical lines.

GALESI

Galesi .22 L.R. Model 9

The Model 9 is, with slight modification, the same as the Galesi Model 1930. The designation Model 9 was given to the pistol in 1950. The Galesi is a simple blowback-operated pistol of attractive appearance and sells for a very reasonable price. The barrels are of stainless steel and should wear well. The Model 9 is also made in .22 Short, .25 ACP and .32 ACP.

667

REPRESENTATIVE POST-WW II ITALIAN PISTOLS AND REVOLVERS

	Beretta M1951	Beretta M950B	Beretta M950 cc Special	Beretta M721[2]	Beretta M948
Caliber:	9mm Parabellum.	.22 Short or .25 ACP.	.22 Short.	.22 L.R.[2]	.22 L.R.
System of Operation:	Recoil, semi-automatic.	Blowback, semi-automatic.	Blowback, semi-automatic.	Blowback, semi-automatic.	Blowback, semi-automatic.
Length Overall:	8″	4.5″	5.9″	6.49″	5.8″ w/3.3″-barrel.
Barrel Length:	4.51″	2.37″	3.7″	3.5″	3.3″ or 5.9″.
Feed Device:	8-round, in-line detachable box magazine.	6-round, in-line detachable box magazine.	6-round, in-line detachable box magazine.	8-round, in-line detachable box magazine.	8-round, in-line detachable box magazine.
Sights:	Blade and V-notch.	Blade and notch.	Blade and notch.	Blade and notch.	Blade and notch.
Weight:	1.93 lb. w/steel receiver.[1]	.62 lb.	.75 lb.	1 lb.	1 lb.

[1] 1.57 lb. w/aluminum receiver.
[2] M72 the same but also has 5.9″-barrel; weight is 1.1 lb. with 5.9″-barrel.

REPRESENTATIVE POST-WW II ITALIAN PISTOLS AND REVOLVERS (Continued)

	Beretta Olympic M949	Beretta Model 70	Bernardelli Baby	Bernardelli M60	Bernardelli VB Revolver
Caliber:	.22 Short or .22 L.R.	.32 ACP.	.22 Short or .22 L.R.	.22 L.R., .32 ACP or .380 ACP.	.22 L.R. or .32 S&W.
System of Operation:	Blowback, semi-automatic.	Blowback- semi-automatic.	Blowback, semi-automatic.	Blowback, semi-automatic.	Revolver.
Length Overall:	12.5"	6.49"	4.1"	6.5"	7.6", 8.6", 10.3"
Barrel Length:	8.75"	3.5"	2"	3.4"[3]	3.1", 4.3", 5.9"
Feed Device:	6-round, in-line detachable box magazine.	8-round, in-line detachable box magazine.	5-round, in-line detachable box magazine.	8-round, in-line detachable box magazine in .22 & .32; 7-round in .380	6-round revolving cylinder.
Sights:	Blade front adjustable for elevation; rear notch adjustable for windage.	Blade and notch.	Notch down top of slide.	Blade and notch.[4]	Blade and notch.
Weight:	2.37 lb.	1.37 lb.	.56 lb.	1.5 lb.	.22: 1.25, 1.31, 1.37 lb. .32: 1.06, 1.18, 1.19 lb.

[3] .22 L.R. also available with 7.9"-barrel.
[4] Long-barreled .22 has adjustable rear sight.

669

JAPAN

The Japanese Self Defense Forces were initially equipped with U.S. caliber .45 M1911A1 pistols and probably still have a number of these pistols on hand. The Japanese developed the 9mm Parabellum Type 57A New Nambu pistol produced by Shin Chuo Kogyo, K.K. Ltd.

None of the former Japanese Service pistols are used. Of interest is the 8mm Type 11 pistol which was in limited manufacture at the end of WW II. It was the result of work started in 1942 on development of a simplified 8mm pistol, and by 1945, Nagoya Arsenal had produced approximately 500 Type 11 pistols. The Type 11 is a simple blowback having a heavy slide and a heavy recoil spring.

NEW NAMBU

New Nambu 9mm Parabellum Model 57A

This recoil-operated pistol, which is similar in construction to the U.S. Colt M1911A1, was originally called the Type 57. The Model 57A has a hard chromed bore and plastic stocks. The principal difference between this pistol and the Colt .45 automatic is that the New Nambu does not have a grip safety. Loading, firing and field stripping the Model 57A is done in the same manner as with the Colt .45 Automatic, excepting unloading of the magazine from the pistol. The magazine catch is located at the bottom rear of the grip on the New Nambu.

NEW NAMBU 9mm Parabellum Model 57A.

New Nambu .22 L.R. Model 62 Target Pistol

This blowback-operated pistol is also produced by Shin Chuo Kogyo K.K. It has plastic stocks with thumb rest, nonrecoiling adjustable rear sight, a blade ramp-mounted front sight and a light metal receiver. The barrel is screwed into the receiver and the breech block (bolt) is mounted in the receiver from the rear. The weapon is cocked by grasping the knurled section of the bolt which protrudes beyond the receiver. The safety catch is mounted on the left rear of the frame. This model pistol is also furnished in .22 Short with 8.1-inch barrel and an overall length of 12 inches.

New Nambu .32 ACP Model 57B

This blowback-operated pistol is built along typical Browning lines. It has plastic grips, an outside hammer and a pin-type loaded-chamber indicator. The New Nambu is field-stripped in a manner similar to the Browning Model 1910.

NEW NAMBU .32 ACP Model 57B.

MIROKU .32 ACP pistol.

671

New Nambu .38 Special Revolver

Shin Chuo Kogyo manufacture a .38 Special revolver which is patterned on the Smith & Wesson.

MIROKU

Miroku .32 ACP Pistol

Miroku Firearms Manufacturing Co. Ltd. of Inari Cho Kochi, Japan, manufacture a blowback-operated automatic. It has a grip safety, external hammer and a manually operated safety catch which is mounted on the left top rear of the receiver.

Miroku .38 Special Model VI Revolver

The Miroku revolvers are patterned on the Colt in general configuration. The Model VI is a short-barreled "belly gun" with walnut grips. The Model VI weighs 1.1 lb. and has an adjustable trigger pull.

Early Model MIROKU .38 Special revolver.

Miroku Model XXI and Model VII Revolvers

These revolvers are made in .38 Special and .22 L.R. and can be obtained with either 4 or 2.5-inch barrels. Both are fitted with checkered walnut stocks. The Model XXI has a rear sight adjustable for windage and elevation; the Model VII has a groove cut down the top of the frame. There is an early version of the Miroku which has plastic stocks and a 2.5-inch barrel. Although the Miroku resembles the Colt, it is quite different internally.

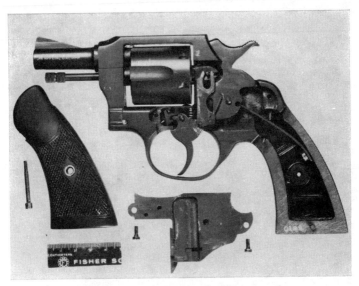

MIROKU revolver with sideplate removed.

673

REPRESENTATIVE JAPANESE POST-WW II PISTOLS

	New Nambu M57A	New Nambu Model 62	New Nambu M57B	Miroku
Caliber:	9mm Parabellum.	.22 L.R.	.32 ACP.	.38 Special.
System of Operation:	Recoil, semi-automatic.	Blowback, semi-automatic.	Blowback, semi-automatic.	Revolver, double-action.
Length Overall:	7.8"	10.25"	6.3"	7.5"
Barrel Length:	4.6"	6.5"	3.45"	2.5"
Feed Device:	8-round, in-line detachable box magazine.	10-round, in-line detachable box magazine.	8-round, in-line detachable box magazine.	6 chambers in cylinder.
Sights:	Blade and notch.	Blade and rear notch adjustable for windage and elevation.	Notch machined in top of slide.	Blade and rear notch machined on top of frame.
Weight:	2.12 lb.	1.75 lb.	1.3 lb.	1.9 lb.

MEXICO

The Mexican Army is equipped with the Colt .45 Model 1911A1 pistol and the Obregon caliber .45 automatic. The Obregon has been reported as out of production for a considerable time.

OBREGON

Obregon .45 Automatic

This recoil-operated pistol is chambered for the .45 ACP cartridge. Outwardly it is quite similar in appearance to the U.S. .45 M1911A1 automatic except for the rounded contour of the forward half of the sides of the slide. Internally the Obregon is quite different from the Colt. The Colt, as with all the Browning recoil-operated designs, has a barrel which tips to unlock; the barrel of the Obregon rotates as does that of the Steyr Model 12. The safety and slide stop are both mounted on one bar, the pin of which holds in the receiver the piece which cams the barrel into and out of the locked position.

MEXICAN OBREGON pistol.

The barrel has locking lugs which lock into recesses in the slide and a camming lug which operates in the barrel cam piece set in the receiver. Loading and firing of the Obregon are the same as that for the U.S. caliber .45 M1911A1 and field-stripping is essentially the same. Care must be exercised when re-assembling the pistol that the barrel camming piece is inserted with the camming surface up.

675

MEXICAN .45 OBREGON field-stripped.

CORLA

Zaragoza .22 L.R. Model Corla

This blowback-operated pistol is externally patterned on the lines of the Colt Model 1911. It is manufactured by Fabrica De Armas Zaragoza, Puebla, Mexico. It appears to be of good quality manufacture. The specimen shown is serial number 12 and few of these pistols are encountered. Production is probably quite limited.

ZARAGOZA .22 L.R. Model CORLA.

MENDOZA

Mendoza .22 L.R. Model K62

This is a single-shot pistol manufactured principally from stampings and plastic. It is patterned on the general lines of the single-action Colt Frontier model. The notched rear sight is adjustable for windage. The breechblock is a modification of the old Flobert action and is of stamped construction. On a specimen examined by Kent Bellah, the breechblock was loosely fitted, having excessive headspace. However, he, pointed out that he fired 50 rounds of Mexican-made CCI High Speed .22 L.R. without any trouble and the specimen that he examined may not have been typical. It is recommended that the breechblock be examined carefully before using this pistol. The pistol has a caddy for three spare rounds on each side of the frame.

MENDOZA .22 L.R. Model K62 single-shot pistol.

This pistol is manufactured by the Productos Mendoza S.A. Bartilache 1914, Mexico City 12, D.F. Mexico. This firm was founded by the outstanding arms designer, Rafael Mendoza, who died in 1967. This highly-talented designer produced a number of successful rifle, machine gun and submachine gun designs. This firm also produced the Model Mx .22 L.R. Survival Pistol. This weapon has a 16-inch barrel and a wire, folding stock. Since its barrel is 16 inches, it is classified in this country—by ATU definition—as a rifle.

TREJO

Trejo .22 L.R. Model 1

This pistol, which is one of a series made by Armas Trejo S.A. De C.V. of Zacatlan, Pue, Mexico, is a selective-fire pistol, i.e., it is capable of full and semi-automatic fire. As such, its registration has been required with the Firearms Branch, Alcohol Tax Unit of the Internal Revenue Service. A selector is mounted on the left top side of the receiver. When the selector is set on

677

"R" and the trigger is pulled, the weapon will fire automatically until the magazine is empty or pressure is released on the trigger. Operation is straight blowback.

TREJO .22 L.R. Model 1 selective-fire pistol.

Trejo .22 L.R. Model 2 Special

The blowback-operated Model 2 Special is similar to the Model 1 Trejo, a selective-fire pistol. The Model 2 has a Williams-type floating chamber similar to that used on the Colt Ace automatic and the Colt .22/45 conversion kit. It is somewhat larger than the Model 1 and has a ventilated ramp on the slide with an adjustable rear sight. Like all Models of the Trejo, the safety catch is on the right rear top side of the receiver. The Trejos all have a magazine release button on the left side of the receiver by the triggerguard.

TREJO .22 L.R. Model 2 Special.

Selector switch and fire selector mechanism on TREJO selective-fire pistols.

Trejo .380 ACP Model 3

This blowback operated model is semi-automatic only. In general configuration it is similar to that of the Colt .45 M1911A1. The plastic grips do not have thumb rests as do the other Trejo models. The barrel is held to the receiver by the pin of the slide stop which goes through a hole in the lug on the rear underside of the barrel.

TREJO .380 ACP Model 3.

CHARACTERISTICS OF MEXICAN PISTOLS

	Obregon	Zaragoza CORLA	Mendoza K62
Caliber:	.45 ACP.	.22 L.R.	.22 L.R.
System of Operation:	Recoil, semi-automatic.	Blowback, semi-automatic.	Manually-operated block.
Length Overall:	Approx. 8.5".	6.6"	8" w/4.5"-barrel.
Barrel Length:	Approx. 5".	3.45"	4.5", 5.5", 6.6"
Feed Device:	7-round, in-line detachable box magazine.	8-round, in-line detachable box magazine.	Single-shot.
Sights:	Blade and dove-tailed bar with notch.	Blade and notched bar.	Blade and notched bar adjustable for windage.
Weight:	Approx. 2.5 lb.	1.44 lb.	.93 lb. w/4.5"-barrel.

	Trejo Model 1	Trejo Model 2 Special	Trejo Model 3
Caliber:	.22 L.R.	.22 L.R.	.380 ACP.
System of Operation:	Blowback, semi- and full automatic.	Blowback, semi- and full automatic.	Blowback, semi-automatic.
Length Overall:	6.3"	7.87"	6.7"
Barrel Length:	3.2"	4.1"	3.45"
Feed Device:	8-round, in-line detachable box magazine.	10-round, in-line detachable box magazine.	7-round, in-line detachable box magazine.
Sights:	Blade and notched bar.	Blade and notched rear bar adjustable for windage and elevation.	Blade and notched bar.
Weight:	1.37 lb.	1.75 lb.	1.48 lb.

SOUTH VIETNAM

The South Vietnamese forces are currently equipped with U.S. .45 caliber M1911A1 pistols. At the time South Vietnam was founded as one of the four independent states formed out of French Indo-China, the South Vietnamese Army was equipped with French 7.65mm M1935A, 1935S and 9mm M1950 pistols. During the period prior to the time that the Diem regime gained the greater control of South Vietnam, there were numerous groups including the Cao Dai whose workshops made copies of the Colt Model 1911A1 and the FN Browning Hi-Power, both chambered for the 9mm Parabellum cartridge. These pistols were made at a small jungle-workshop-type factory near Tay Ninh and were of remarkably good finish considering their somewhat questionable background.

SOUTH VIETNAMESE copy of 9mm Parabellum FN Hi-Power Browning.

SOUTH VIETNAMESE copy of 9mm Parabellum, U.S. Model 1911A1.

Numerous other hand-made pistols were used by the Viet Cong; some of these are of a modified-Mauser design chambered for the 7.62mm ChiCom or Soviet pistol cartridge and are similar to hand-made pistols from China.
(See also Cambodia.)

VIET CONG 7.62mm hand-made pistol.

Communist 7.65mm Silenced Pistol

This is a Chinese Communist blowback-operated semi-automatic pistol which is chambered for a special rimless rather than semi-rimmed 7.65mm cartridge. This pistol is unusual in several respects; it was designed to be used specifically as a silenced weapon—it is not an improvisation of an existing conventional pistol with an added silencer. It also can be used either as a semi-automatic, i.e., self-loading pistol, or as a single-shot pistol which does not eject fired cases. The slide contains a separate bolt which is held in a fixed position when the pistol is used as a self-loader and which otherwise locks into receiver recesses when the pistol is used as a non-ejecting single-shot. The trigger mechanism is double-action and an outside hammer is used.

CHINESE COMMUNIST SILENCED PISTOL and special 7.65mm cartridge. Sometimes referred to as an assassin's pistol used by the Viet Cong.

SPAIN

The current standard Spanish Service pistol is the 9mm Largo Super Star. The 9mm Largo cartridge is also called the 9mm Bergman Bayard and is quite similar to the .38 Super Automatic cartridge.

9mm Parabellum Super Star

This is a recoil-operated pistol which is similar in design and operation to the U.S. Colt .45 M1911A1 with the following major exceptions: The trigger is pinned in place and pivots rather than slides. The slide stop is of two piece construction, there is no grip safety, and the locking and disassembly procedures are different.

SPANISH 9mm SUPER STAR.

This pistol is sold commercially as the Super A in 9mm Largo or Super .38 Auto, Super B in 9mm Parabellum, Super M in 9mm Largo or Super .38 Auto. and the Super S in .380. Details of the locking mechanism and field-stripping instructions for the Super Star series pistols will be found later in text relevant the Star .380 Super S.

SPANISH COMMERCIAL PISTOLS AND REVOLVERS

Spain produces a large number of handguns with a good variety of models available. Spanish arms gained a somewhat unsavory reputation in the United States in the period between the two World Wars. This was due to the import of significant quantities of poorly-made pistols and revolvers which were "job shop"-made, usually of poor materials. During WW II, Spain made respectable quantities of small arms for Germany and the United Kingdom and changed her proof standards, or more stringently enforced them, so the age of the Spanish "booby-trap pistol" is over. The principal Spanish makers: Star Bonifacio Echeverria S.A. of Eibar, Astra Unceta y Compania S.A. of Guernica, and Llama-Gabilondo Y Cia S.A. of Vitoria always made, as they make today, quality arms.

ASTRA

Astra .22 Short Cub

The Cub is a blowback-operated weapon which is made in .25 ACP as well as .22 Short. The Cub is sold in the U.S. by Colt as the Junior Colt. A manual safety catch is located on the left side of the hammer. The Cub also has a magazine safety, i.e., the pistol will not fire when the magazine is removed. The magazine catch is on the lower left side of the grip.

ASTRA .22 Short CUB.

Astra .22 Short Camper

The Camper, which was discontinued in 1966, is identical to the Cub but has a longer barrel.

ASTRA .22 Short CAMPER.

Astra .22 Experimental Target Pistol

Astra produced an experimental .22 match pistol complete with muzzle-brake compensator, weights, adjustable rear sight, and checkered grips with thumb rest. The pistol appears to be built on the basic frame of the Model 4000 Falcon.

ASTRA .22 experimental target pistol.

Astra .22 Caliber Cadix Model 224

The Astra Cadix revolvers are made in .22 (200 series), .32 (300 series) and .38 (.38 Special). Barrels come in 2, 4 and 6-inch lengths in each caliber. Revolvers with 4 and 6-inch barrels have adjustable rear sights. The .22 Cadix revolvers have nine-chambered cylinders which swing out to the left side for loading and ejecting. The Cadix has a shrouded ejector rod somewhat similar to that of the Smith & Wesson. Stocks may be of wood or plastic.

ASTRA .22 CADIX Model 224 revolver.

Astra .25 ACP Model 200 Firecat

The Model 200 is a straight blowback vest-pocket pistol. It has a grip safety and a safety catch. The magazine catch is at the bottom rear of the grip. This model was discontinued by Astra in 1966.

ASTRA .25 ACP Model 200 FIRECAT.

Astra .32 ACP Model 5000 Constable

The Constable is of entirely different design than earlier Astra automatics, most of which continued along the line of the earlier Campo Giro. The Constable is a double-action automatic built along the general lines of the Walther PP, PPK series and the many other streamlined double-action automatics. Astra built a number of prototypes before settling on the final design for the Constable.

The Constable has a fixed barrel; the safety catch is mounted on the slide and works basically the same as that of the Walther double-action automatics. Dismounting is different than the Walther types; a slide-dismounting catch is located just to the rear of the front of the triggerguard. A slide stop, which holds the slide open after the last round is fired, is located on the left top of the receiver behind the trigger. The button-type magazine catch is below it on the grip. The Constable will be made by Astra in .22 L.R. and .380 ACP (9mm Short) as well as .32 ACP.

Astra .32 ACP Model 4000 Falcon

The Falcon is a blowback-operated pistol built along classic Campo Giro-Astra lines. It is basically the same as the earlier 400 and 3000 series with one exception. The Model 400 has its magazine catch at the bottom rear of the grip,

ASTRA .32 ACP Model 5000 CONSTABLE.

the Model 3000 has its magazine catch behind the trigger on the left of the receiver while the Falcon has a button-type magazine catch on the bottom rear of the left grip. Like all of this series, a heavy spring encircling the barrel provides the inertia necessary to hold the slide closed until the chamber pressure drops to a safe level. The Falcon has been made in .22 L.R. and .380 ACP as well as .32 ACP. The earlier Model 300 was made in .32 ACP and .380 ACP.

ASTRA .32 ACP Model 4000 FALCON.

Astra .38 Special Cadix Pocket Model Revolver

This revolver with a 2-inch barrel is basically the same as the Cadix revolvers covered earlier but has a smaller, rounded butt. There are Cadix .38 Special revolvers with 4 and 6-inch barrels which have a larger squared butt and adjustable rear sight. The cylinder of all the .38 Special Cadix revolvers is chambered for 5 rounds.

ASTRA .38 Special CADIX POCKET REVOLVER.

Astra .380 ACP Model 4000 Experimental

Astra made up a limited number of the Model 4000 Falcon with a differently shaped slide and receiver. The slide on this pistol has a squared side and top as compared to the round slide of the standard Model 4000. There is also a

ASTRA .380 ACP Model 4000 EXPERIMENTAL.

pronounced hump at the top rear of the slide. The receiver also has a flattened side. Like the standard model Falcon, this pistol has a loaded-chamber indicator pin mounted at the top rear of the slide.

Astra 9mm Parabellum Model 800 Condor

The Condor is the post-war version of the Model 600 Astra. It differs from the earlier Astra models principally in having an external hammer. The Condor is a straight blowback-operated weapon. The heavy recoil spring, which is wrapped around the barrel, keeps the breech closed until the chamber pressure has dropped to safe limits.

The Condor has a pin-type loaded-chamber indicator which protrudes from the rear of the slide when the chamber is loaded. This pistol has a magazine safety; it will not fire when the magazine is removed.

ASTRA 9mm Parabellum Model 800 CONDOR.

DICKSON 32 ACP SPECIAL AGENT.

689

DICKSON

Dickson .32 ACP Special Agent

This is a Spanish-made blowback-operated automatic which is currently being sold in the United States. It has a light alloy receiver and is double-action. Some pistols of this model were made with nickel-plated slides and were marked "Dickson Cal. .32." The receiver or frame breaks into two assemblies when field-stripped: the top frame, which contains the fixed barrel, recoil spring, disconnector, hammer, ejector and slide stop assemblies, and the bottom frame or grip assembly, which contains the trigger, and magazine catch assemblies. The Dickson Special Agent is also made in .22 L.R. and .25 ACP. It is imported by American Imports.

LLAMA

Llama .22 Short Model XVII

This is a blowback-operated pistol with ventilated rib, which is essentially of the vest-pocket type. It does have sights, however, and the grip is better shaped for close shooting than are those of most other vest pocket-types. Like all the Llama automatic pistols and Ruby revolvers, it is a product of Llama-Gabilondo and Co. It is sold in the United States as the Llama Executive.

LLAMA .22 Short MODEL XVII.

Llama .22 L.R. Model XV

The Model XV outwardly resembles the Colt .45 Model 1911A1 as do most of the Llama automatic pistols. It is blowback-operated and has a fixed barrel. In addition to the safety catch mounted on the left top rear of the receiver, as with the Colt, it has a grip safety. The Model XV has a ventilated rib along the top of the slide; the rib is not continuous, however, as there is a gap at the top of the ejection port. The Model XV has plastic grips with thumb rest.

LLAMA .22 L.R. MODEL XV.

Llama .22 L.R. Model XVI

The Model XVI is the same as the Model XV Llama in all features except the material from which the receivers are made. The Model XV receiver is made of steel, and the Model XVI receiver is made of lightweight alloy—Airlite.

Llama .25 ACP Model XVIII Executive

The Model XVIII is exactly the same as the .22 Llama Model XVII, but is chambered for the .25 ACP (6.35mm) cartridge.

Llama .32 ACP Model X-A

The Model X-A is a blowback-operated pistol which is the same as the XV except for the caliber.

Llama .32 ACP Model XX

The Model XX is the same as the Model XVI except for caliber, i.e., it is a lightweight version of the Model X-A, as the Model XVI is a lightweight version of the Model XV.

Llama .380 ACP Model III-A

The Model III-A externally resembles Model XV and Model X-A, but unlike these is a locked breech, recoil-operated pistol. The locking mechanism is the same as the Colt .45 Automatic.

Llama .380 ACP Model XIX

The Model XIX is the lightweight version of the Model III-A. It has a receiver made of Airlite.

Llama .45 ACP Model IX-A

The Model IX-A is very difficult to distinguish externally from the Colt .45 M1911A1. There is little difference internally. Operation and field-stripping

691

are the same as with the Colt. The IX-A has a matted rib which is divided into two sections by the ejection port, on top of the slide. The Model VII is the same as the Model IX-A, but is chambered for the Super .38 Auto cartridge.

LLAMA .45 ACP MODEL IX-A.

Other Llama Pistols

Llama .45 ACP and Super .38 Match Pistols are also available. They have rear sights adjustable for windage and elevation and are more finely made than the standard models. Characteristics are the same as for the Model IX-A and Model VIII excepting sights. These are handsome pistols at a quite reasonable price.

RUBY EXTRA .22 L.R. MODEL XIV.

RUBY

Ruby Extra .22 L.R. Revolver Model XIV

The Model XIV is, like all current Ruby revolvers, patterned on the Smith & Wesson. Kent Bellah reported that many of the Ruby and Smith & Wesson parts are interchangeable. The top of the frame and barrel are matted as is the rear surface of the front sight. The Model XIV can be obtained in 2, 3.25 and 6-inch barrels.

Ruby Extra .22 L.R. Revolver Model XXIV

The Model XXIV somewhat resembles the Smith & Wesson K-22, but has a ventilated rib. It is a target revolver with micro-adjustable rear sight, molded checkered-nylon oversize grips and a 6-inch barrel.

Ruby Extra .32 S&W Long Model XIII

The Model XIII is of Smith & Wesson pattern and comes with 2 inch, 3.25 inch and 6-inch barrels. The top of the frame, barrel, and rear of the front sight are matted. The grips are checkered walnut.

RUBY EXTRA .32 S&W Long revolver.

Ruby Extra .38 Special Model XII Revolver

The Model XII is basically the same as the .32 caliber Model XIII. It can be obtained with 2, 4 or 6-inch barrels.

Ruby Extra .38 Special Model XXIII Olympic

This target revolver is a new addition to the Llama Gabilondo line. It has a ventilated rib, micro-adjutable rear sight, muzzle-brake and oversized walnut grips with thumb rest. The barrel is 6-inches long with a sight radius of 8 inches.

RUBY EXTRA .38 Special MODEL XXIII OLYMPIC.

STAR

Star .22 L.R. Model H.K. Lancer

The Lancer is a blowback-operated pistol with fixed barrel. It has a lightweight alloy receiver and a manual safety catch on the top rear of the left side of the receiver in addition to a half-cock notch on the hammer. The Lancer may be obtained with a chromed slide and black, gray, gold, blue or green receiver.

STAR .22 L.R. Model H.K. LANCER.

Star .22 L.R. Model FR

The Model F originally appeared prior to WW II, and the FR is a post-war improvement of that model. It is a blowback-operated pistol. The barrel is screwed to the frame and the slide is cut away for more than one-half its length at the top. The current Model FR is more streamlined than the pre-war model and has better shaped plastic grips with thumb rest. The Model FR also comes in deluxe models which are either chromed with mother-of-pearl grips, or chromed and engraved with mother-of-pearl grips. These grips do not have a thumb rest. The change of model designation from F to FR for this series pistol, is a recent move on the part of the manufacturer.

STAR .22 L.R. Model FR.

STAR .22 L.R. Model FR Target Pistol.

Star Model FR Sport

This pistol is the same as the Model FR, but has a 6-inch barrel as opposed to the 4.25-inch barrel of the basic Model FR. The rear sight may be fixed or adjustable for windage and elevation.

Star Model FR Target

The Model FR Target has a seven-inch barrel and a rear sight adjustable for windage and elevation.

Field-Stripping (FR Series): (1) Remove magazine, (2) cock the hammer, (3) push disassembly button, located forward of the safety catch on the left side of the receiver, pull slide a quarter-inch to the rear and lift up. This disengages the slide from the receiver and allows it to be drawn off the barrel. The recoil spring, which is under the barrel, may then be removed.

Star .22 Short Model FR Olympic

This is the .22 Short target model of the FR series. It has a 6-inch barrel and a detachable barrel weight. The rear sight is adjustable for windage and elevation.

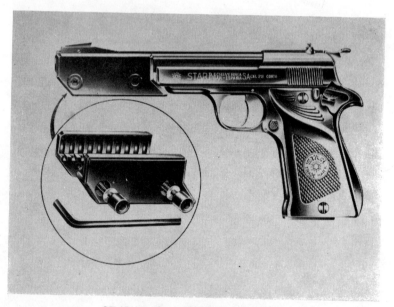

STAR .22 Short Model FR OLYMPIC.

Star .25 ACP Model C.U. Starlet

The Starlet is basically the same as the .22 L.R. Model HK Lancer; it has a light-alloy frame. In addition to black, the slide may be obtained in chrome and the receiver may be obtained in Antique Gold, Caribbean Blue and Steel Gray.

696

Star .32 ACP Model IR

The Model IR is the same as the .22 L.R. Model FR and, like the Model FR covered earlier in this chapter, has been modernized since WW II.

Star .32 ACP Model SI

The SI is somewhat unusual in that it is a recoil-operated locked-breech pistol. The locking mechanism is similar to that of the Colt .45 Automatic M1911 and field-stripping is the same. The Model S Star is the same as the Model SI but is chambered for the .380 ACP cartridge. These pistols have a safety catch mounted in the same position as that of the Colt .45 automatic.

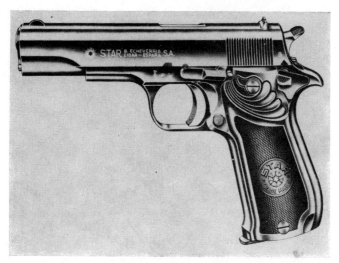

STAR .32 ACP Model SI.

Star 7.63mm Model MM

This recoil-operated pistol comes with a shoulder-stock holster and may be obtained either in semi-automatic only or semi and full automatic. In either the semi-automatic or selective-fire versions, this pistol must be registered with the Firearms Branch of the Alcohol Tax Unit, Internal Revenue Service

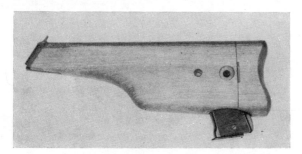

STAR 7.63mm Model MM in shoulder-stock holster.

697

if the shoulder stock is also held. The MM is internally quite similar to the Colt .45 Automatic except for the full-automatic switch and its assembly on the selective-fire version.

This pistol has been made in 9mm Parabellum and is called Model MB in that caliber. The Star company reports that there are few requests for this pistol in Super .38 and .45.

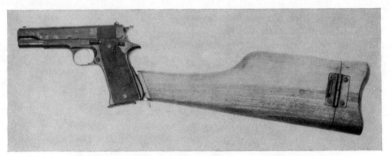

STAR 7.63mm Model MM w/shoulder-stock holster.

Star .380 ACP Model Super S

This recoil-operated pistol is similar to the Star .380 Model S, but differs from it in the locking details. As previously mentioned, the Model S locks as does the Colt .45 Automatic. The Super S also has locking lugs on the barrel which lock in mating recesses in the slide. The barrel, however, is cammed up into and down out of its locked position by a camway cut into a lug on the bottom rear of the barrel, moving on the slide-stop pin. This locking system is similar to that of the FN Browning Hi-Power. The Super S is field-stripped in a manner somewhat different than the Model S or the Colt .45 Automatic.

STAR .380 ACP Model SUPER S.

The Super S has a dismounting lever on the right side of the receiver which is pushed down and forward allowing withdrawal of the slide from the front. The recoil spring, recoil spring guide, and recoil spring plug are removed from the slide after the slide is removed from the receiver, as is the barrel and barrel bushing.

Star .380 ACP Model D.K. Starfire

The Starfire is a recoil-operated pistol. It locks in a manner similar to the Colt .45 Automatic and the Star Model S. The Starfire has a safety catch mounted on the left top rear of the receiver. The magazine catch is behind the trigger on the receiver. The receiver is made of lightweight alloy. The Starfire may be obtained with different colored receivers like the Model CU Starlet.

STAR .380 ACP Model D.K. STARFIRE.

Star 9mm Bergmann Bayard Model A

This is a recoil-operated pistol which is similar to the Colt .45 Automatic in most respects. In common with all the Star automatics, it does not have a grip safety. The Model A will also chamber and fire the Super .38 cartridge. The Star Model B, which is the same size, is chambered for the 9mm Parabellum cartridge. The Model M and Model P, which are slightly larger, are chambered for the Super .38 or 9mm Bergmann Bayard and .45 ACP, respectively.

STAR 9mm Bergmann Bayard Model A.

SPANISH SEMI-AUTOMATIC .22 PISTOLS

	Star H.K. LANCER	Star FR	Star FR SPORT	Star FR TARGET	Star FR OLYMPIC
Caliber:	.22 L.R.	.22 L.R.	.22 L.R.	.22 L.R.	.22 Short.
Length Overall:	5.52"	7.25"	9"	10"	9"
Barrel Length:	2.95"	4.25"	5.9"	7"	5.9"
Magazine Capacity:	8 rounds.	10 rounds.	10 rounds.	10 rounds.	6 rounds.
Sights:	Blade and notch.	Blade and notch.	Blade front; rear adjustable or fixed notch.	Blade front; notched bar rear adjustable for windage and elevation.	Blade front; notched rear bar adjustable for windage and elevation.
Weight:	.88 lb.	1.56 lb.	1.81 lb.	1.93 lb.	1.75 lb.

Note: These models are all of blowback operation; all use in-line detachable box magazines in load capacities listed.

SPANISH .22 PISTOLS AND REVOLVERS

	Astra FALCON	Astra CUB	Astra CAMPER	Astra CADIX 226 [1]
Caliber:	.22 L.R.	.22 Short.	.22 Short.	.22 L.R.
System of Operation:	Blowback, semi-automatic.	Blowback, semi-automatic.	Blowback, semi-automatic.	Double-action revolver.
Length Overall:	6.5"	4.43"	6.18"	10.93"
Barrel Length:	3.7"	2.25"	4"	6"
Feed Device:	10-round magazine.	6-round magazine.	6-round magazine.	9-round cylinder.
Sights:	Blade and notch.	Blade and notch.	Blade front; rear notch adjustable for windage.	Blade front; notched rear bar adjustable for windage and elevation.
Weight:	1.25 lb.	.68 lb.	.75 lb.	1.81 lb.

Note: The pistols listed use in-line detachable box magazines in load capacities indicated.
[1] Model 222 Cadix revolver has a 2"-barrel, overall length of 6.43", does not have adjustable rear sight. Model 224 Cadix has 4"-barrel, overall length of 8.93", has adjustable rear sight.

SPANISH .22 PISTOLS AND REVOLVERS

	Llama XVII EXECUTIVE	Llama XV & XVI	Ruby XIV	Ruby XXIV
Caliber:	.22 Short,	.22 L.R.	.22 L.R.	.22 L.R.
System of Operation:	Blowback, semi-automatic.	Blowback, semi-automatic.	Double-action revolver.	Double-action revolver.
Length Overall:	4.75"	6.75"	Approx. 6".	Approx. 11".
Barrel Length:	2.37"	4.25"	2", 3.25", 6"	6"
Feed Device:	6-round magazine.	9-round magazine.	6-round cylinder.	6-round cylinder.
Sights:	Blade and square notch.	Blade and notch.	Blade and notch.	Blade front; notched rear bar adjustable for windage and elevation.
Weight:	.81 lb.	1.31 lb. w/steel receiver, 1.06 lb. w/airlite receiver.	1.1 lb. w/2"-barrel.	1.6 lb.

Note: Both pistols listed employ in-line detachable box magazines.

SPANISH .25 ACP SEMI-AUTOMATIC PISTOLS

	Star Model CU STARLET	Astra CUB	Astra FIRECAT Model 200	Llama XVIII EXECUTIVE
Length Overall:	4.75"	4.43"	4.3"	4.75"
Barrel Length:	2.37"	2.25"	2.2"	2.37"
Feed Device:	8-round magazine.	6-round magazine.	6-round magazine.	6-round magazine.
Sights:	Blade and notch.	Blade and notch.	Notch cut in top of slide.	Blade and notch.
Weight:	.68 lb.	.68 lb.	.75 lb.	.87 lb.

Note: All are blowback pistols. Magazines are in-line detachable-box design.

SPANISH .32 ACP (7.65mm) SEMI-AUTOMATIC PISTOLS

	Star IR	Star SI	Astra FALCON	Llama X-A & XX	Astra Model 5000[1] CONSTABLE
Length Overall:	7.25"	6.5"	6.5"	6.25"	6.6"
Barrel Length:	4.25"	4.75"	4.3"	4.37"	3.5"
Feed Device:	9-round magazine.	9-round magazine.	8-round magazine.	8-round magazine.	8-round magazine.
Sights:	Blade and notch.	Blade and notch.	Blade and notch.	Blade and notch.	Blade and notch.
Weight:	1.75 lb.	1.37 lb.	1.5 lb.	1.3 lb. w/steel receiver; 1 lb. w/Airlite receiver.	1.54 lb.

Note: The Star SI is a recoil-operated pistol; the other models are blowback. All employ in-line, detachable box magazines.
[1] The CONSTABLE is also supplied in .22 L.R. w/10-round magazine and in .380 ACP w/7-round magazine.

SPANISH .38 SPECIAL DOUBLE-ACTION REVOLVERS

	Astra CADIX 386[1]	Ruby Model XII[2]
Length Overall:	10.9"	(Depending on barrel.)
Barrel Length:	6"	2", 4", 6"
Cylinder Capacity:	5 rounds.	5 rounds.
Sights:	Blade front; notched rear bar adjustable for windage and elevation.	Blade and notch.
Weight:	1.5 lb.	1.8 lb.

[1] Model 382 has a 2"-barrel, overall length of 6.4", does not have adjustable rear sight. Model 384 has 4"-barrel, overall length of 8.9", does have adjustable rear sight.
[2] Ruby Model XIII Olympic is target version of this revolver with 6"-barrel, adjustable sights, weight—2.3 lb.

SPANISH .32 S&W DOUBLE-ACTION REVOLVERS

	Ruby XIII	Astra CADIX 326[1]
Length Overall:	(Depending on barrel.)	10.9"
Barrel Length:	2", 3.25", 6"	6"
Cylinder Capacity:	6 rounds.	6 rounds.
Sights:	Blade and notch.	Blade front; notched rear bar adjustable for windage and elevation.
Weight:	1.12 lb. w/3.25"-barrel.	1.54 lb.

[1] Model 322 has a 2"-barrel, overall length of 6.4", does not have adjustable rear sight. Model 324 has 4"-barrel, overall length of 8.9", does have adjustable rear sight.

SPANISH .380 ACP (9mm Short) SEMI-AUTOMATIC PISTOLS

	Star Model DK STARFIRE	Star Model S	Star Super S	Astra FALCON
System of Operation:	Recoil-operated.	Recoil-operated.	Recoil-operated.	Blowback.
Length Overall:	5.5"	6.5"	6.5"	6.5"
Barrel Length:	3.1"	4.75"	4.75"	4.3"
Magazine Capacity:	6 rounds.	8 rounds.	8 rounds.	7 rounds.
Sights:	Blade and notch.	Blade and notch.	Blade and notch.	Blade and notch.
Weight:	.93 lb.	1.37 lb.	1.37 lb.	1.5 lb.

Note: All models employ in-line, detachable box magazines.

SPANISH HIGH-POWERED AUTOMATIC PISTOLS

	Star Model MM	Star Model A [1]	Star Model P [3]
Caliber:	7.63mm Mauser.	.38 Super.[2]	.45 ACP.
System of Operation:	Recoil-operated, semi-automatic only, or selective-fire version available.	Recoil-operated, semi-automatic.	Recoil-operated, semi-automatic.
Length Overall:	8.5"	8.5"	8.5"
Barrel Length:	5"	5"	5"
Magazine Capacity: [4]	9 rounds.	8 rounds.	7 rounds.
Sights:	Blade and notch.	Blade and notch.	Blade and notch.
Weight:	2.4 lb.	2.2 lb.	2.4 lb.

[1] Model B chambered for 9mm Parabellum has same characteristics, but weighs 2 oz. more.
[2] Also made for 9mm Bergmann Bayard (9mm Largo in Spain).
[3] Model M made for .38 Super has same characteristics, but has 9-round magazine.
[4] All models employ an in-line, detachable box magazine.

SPANISH HIGH-POWERED SEMI-AUTOMATIC PISTOLS

	Star Super A [1]	Astra CONDOR	Llama Model IX-A [3]
Caliber:	.38 Super.[2]	9mm Parabellum.	.45 ACP.
System of Operation:	Recoil-operated.	Blowback.	Recoil-operated.
Length Overall:	8.75"	8.25"	8.5"
Barrel Length:	5.2"	5.25"	5"
Magazine Capacity: [4]	9 rounds.	8 rounds.	7 rounds.
Sights:	Blade and notch.	Blade and notch.	Blade and notch.
Weight:	2.2 lb.	2 lb.	2.37 lb.

[1] Super B chambered for 9mm Parabellum has same characteristics; Super M chambered for .38 Super is .1" longer.
[2] Also made for 9mm Bergmann Bayard (9mm Largo in Spain).
[3] Model VIII chambered for .38 has same characteristics, but has 9-round magazine. Match versions of Llama Super .38 have micro-adjustable rear sights and weight 2.5 lbs.
[4] Magazines are of the in-line, detachable box design.

SWITZERLAND

Switzerland was the first country to adopt the Luger pistol—1900—which pistol was chambered for the 7.65mm (.30 cal.) Luger cartridge. The Swiss kept the 7.65mm Luger in its various models—1906, 1906/29—until 1948 when they adopted the SIG-developed 9mm Parabellum SP47/8, which is called the Model 49. Switzerland also used a 7.5mm revolver, the Model 1882, modified in 1929 and called the 1882/29 until after WW II.

The SIG SP47/8, now commercially called the P210 by SIG, traces its ancestry back to the 1937 patents of Charles L. Petter, an employee of Societe Alsacienne de Construction Mechaniques (SACM) of France. These patents were basically on an improvement on the Colt/Browning system. Prior to WW II, Schweiz Industrie Gesellschaft—Swiss Industrial Company—commonly called SIG, purchased the patent rights from SACM. SIG produced some prototypes in 7.65mm Luger and 9mm Parabellum, circa 1937-39. Around 1942, SIG began modifying the Petter design and in 1944 produced the 9mm Parabellum Model 44/16 which has a 16-round magazine and the Model 44/8 which has an 8-round magazine. SP47/8 is a direct outgrowth of the Model 44/8.

SIG

SIG 9mm Parabellum P210 (SP47/8) Swiss Service Model 49

This pistol is very similar to the Colt/Browning locked-breech recoil-operated pistol in that it has a tipping barrel with locking lugs, on its top rear, which are cammed up into locking recesses in the top of the slide to lock, and cammed down out of the locking recesses when unlocking. Unlike the Colt, however, no link is used to pull the barrel down out of the locked position. The pin section of the slide-stop operates in an enclosed cam track cut out of the barrel lug on the rear underside of the barrel. This system is similar to that

SIG 9mm P210 (M49).

used on the Browning Hi-Power, the Spanish Super Star, the Polish Radom, etc., except that the camway in the P210 is completely enclosed. Disassembly is basically the same as that of the Browning Hi-Power with one notable difference; like the French M1935A and M1935S and the Soviet M1933 Tokarev, the P210 has a packaged hammer, sear, and ejector assembly.

The SIG P210 is loaded and fired in a manner similar to that of the Colt .45 Automatic except that the magazine catch is at the bottom rear of the butt and the safety is forward of the grip on the P210.

P210-1—9mm Parabellum

Conversion kits are available for 7.65mm Luger and .22 L.R. calibers. The conversion kit for the 7.65mm Luger consists of a barrel and recoil spring with guide; that for the .22 L.R. consists of a slide, barrel, recoil spring with guide, and magazine. The barrel lug of the .22 L.R. has a hole for the pin of the slide-stop rather than a cam slot and there are no locking lugs on the barrel. Therefore, with the .22 L.R. conversion kit installed, the pistol operates as a straight-blowback. The P210-1 has wooden grips and a highly-polished finish.

P210-2

Same as the P210-1 with lanyard loop, sandblasted finish, plastic grips; can also be obtained in 7.65mm Luger or used with 7.65mm and .22 L.R. conversion kit.

P210-5

9mm Parabellum or 7.65mm Luger target pistol with 6-inch barrel, micro-adjustable rear sight and finer front sight.

SIG 9mm Parabellum P210-5 target pistol.

P210-6

9mm Parabellum or 7.65mm Luger target pistol with 4.75-inch barrel, micro-adjustable rear sight and finer front sight.

9mm Parabellum SIG P210-6 target pistol—front sight on this specimen varies from current production.

HAMMERLI

Hammerli of Lenzburg has a world-wide reputation as a manufacturer of precision target pistols, rifles, and air guns. Hammerli match pistols have won far more than their fair share of events at the outstanding matches of the world for quite a number of years. Hammerli does not produce a full line of handguns as do the outstanding U.S. and Western European manufacturers. They manufacture no personal defense or military pistols; manufacture is limited to target-type arms.

Hammerli .22 L.R. Model 101 Free Pistol

The 101 is a Free pistol with micrometer-adjustable rear sights, shaped walnut grips with vertically-adjustable hand rest, set trigger, heavy barrel, interchangeable post front sights, and a dull blue finish. The action is of the drop-block type with an operating lever on the left side of the frame.

HAMMERLI Model 101.

Hammerli .22 L.R. Model 102

The same as the Model 101, but has a polished blue finish.

Hammerli .22 L.R. Model 103

Has an octagonal barrel as opposed to the round barrel of the Model 101 and 102, and a polished blue finish. The Model 103 was the only pistol exhibited in the Museum of Modern Art of New York in the Design for Sport display, circa 1962-66.

Hammerli .22 L.R. Model 104 Free Pistol

This pistol has the same general characteristics as the earlier Model 100 series pistols, but the center of gravity has been changed and it has a new grip design with adjustable palm shelf and trigger-finger rests.

Hammerli .22 L.R. Model 105 Free Pistol

Same as the Model 104, but with deluxe finish and octagonal barrel.

Hammerli .22 L.R. 106 Free Pistol

The 106 was introduced about June, 1966 with an improved trigger mechanism. A finer trigger-pull adjustment—.18 to 3.5 ounces—has been provided, and the trigger itself can be adjusted sideways, vertically or in length. Action as in earlier models.

Hammerli .22 L.R. Model 107

The 107 is a deluxe variation of the 106 with octagonal barrel. The Hammerli 107 was displayed at Expo 67 in Montreal in the Tools of Man exhibits.

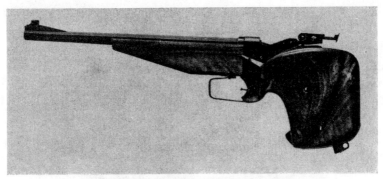

HAMMERLI .22 L.R. Model 107 Free pistol.

Hammerli-Walther .22 L.R. Model 200

This blowback-operated match pistol is of Walther design and was manufactured by Hammerli from 1945 until the introduction of the Model 207. It was the basic model of match automatic made by Hammerli. It is basically the same as the pre-war Walther Olympia model, described in chapter 3. The Model 200 was made in .22 Short as well as .22 L.R. The Model 203 is the same as the Model 200, but has adjustable grips with hand rest.

HAMMERLI-WALTHER OLYMPIA Model 200 pistol.

HAMMERLI-WALTHER .22 L.R. Model 203 match pistol.

Hammerli-Walther .22 L.R. Model 205 American Model

This is a modification of the standard Model 200 which has a slide stop to hold the slide open after the last round is fired, larger and heavier barrel weights

HAMMERLI AMERICAN Model 205.

than are available with the Model 200, rear sight micro-adjustable for elevation and windage and, as with the Model 203, adjustable grips with hand rests. The Model 204 is the same as the Model 205 but has standard non-adjustable grips.

Hammerli .22 L.R. Model 206 Olympia

This is a Hammerli deviation from the Walther design. While it follows the Walther design in general, many of the details have been changed. The top of the barrel is flattened and grooved, and the sights and their method of mounting have been changed. The rear sight is mounted on a block which is dovetailed to the receiver. This block is cut out and slotted to allow for the movement of the slide; the rear sight therefore does not recoil with the slide as it does on the earlier model Hammerli automatics. There is a barrel weight fitted under the forward half of the barrel. The Model 206 is made chambered for the .22 Short cartridge as well as the .22 L.R.

Hammerli .22 L.R. Model 207 Olympia International

This pistol is the same as the Model 206, but has adjustable grips with hand rest; also made in .22 Short.

HAMMERLI .22 L.R. Model 207 INTERNATIONAL.

Hammerli .22 Short Model 209 Olympia

The 209 is similar to the Model 206, but has some outstanding differences. This pistol is designed specifically for the Olympic rapid-fire event; this match requires a pistol with a minimum of recoil, jump or rise, so that relaying of the sights on the target requires minimal time and movement. The Model 209 has a new design of muzzle-brake and a rather unique feature—6 gas port holes drilled in the top of the barrel, 3 of these holes are threaded, and plugs can be screwed into them to seal them off. These gas-escape holes are positioned from a point just forward of the chamber to a point about halfway down the length

711

of the barrel. By using the gas port screw plugs to make up for ballistic differences in various brands and/or lots of ammunition, barrel rise can be kept to a minimum due to the downward thrust produced by the exit of high-pressure gas from the ports. Trigger pull is adjustable from 12½ to 27 ounces. The muzzle-brake can be adjusted by the individual shooter to correct any slight lateral muzzle movement.

Hammerli .22 Short Model 210 Olympia International

The Model 210 is the same as the Model 209 excepting that it has adjustable grips with hand rest.

HAMMERLI .22 Short Model 210 OLYMPIA INTERNATIONAL.

CHARACTERISTICS OF POST-WW II SWISS PISTOLS

	SIG P210-2 (Model 49)[1]	SIG P210-5[3]	Hammerli Model 101[4]	Hammerli Model 105
Caliber:	9mm Parabellum.[2]	9mm Parabellum or 7.65mm Luger.	.22 L.R.	.22 L.R.
System of Operation:	Recoil; semi-automatic.	Recoil; semi-automatic.	Drop-block single-shot.	Drop-block single-shot.
Length Overall:	8.5″	9.6″	Approx. 17″.	Approx. 17″.
Barrel Length:	4.75″	6″	11.5″	11.3″
Magazine Capacity:[5]	8 rounds.	8 rounds.	Single-shot.	Single-shot.
Sights:	Blade and notched-bar.	Blade front; notched-bar rear adjustable for windage and elevation.	Post front; notched-bar rear fully micro-adjustable.	Post front; notched-bar rear fully micro-adjustable.
Weight:	2.18 lb.	2.31 lb.	3.1 lb.[6]	2.8 lb.

[1] 210-1 has better finish and walnut grips, but is otherwise the same.
[2] Conversion kit for .22 L.R. and 7.65mm Luger available.
[3] P210-6 same but has 4.7″-barrel.
[4] Model 102 characteristics the same.
[5] In-line, detachable box magazines used in the semi-automatic pistols listed.
[6] Model 103 characteristics the same, but weighs 2.8 lb.

CHARACTERISTICS OF POST-WW II SWISS PISTOLS (Continued)

	Hammerli American Model 205	Hammerli Model 207	Hammerli Model 210
Caliber:	.22 L.R.	.22 L.R. or .22 Short.	.22 Short.
Length Overall:	11.75"	12.5"	11.8"
Barrel Length:	7.5"	7.1"	4.75"
Magazine Capacity:	8 rounds.	L.R.—8 rounds. Short—6 rounds.	5 rounds.
Sights:	Blade front; notched-bar fully micro-adjustable rear.	Blade front; notched-bar fully micro-adjustable rear.	Blade front; notched-bar fully micro-adjustable rear.
Weight:	2.2 lb.	W/weights: .22 L.R.—3.1 lb. .22 Short—2.7 lb.	2.5 lb. w/weight.

Note: These models are all blowback semi-automatics in which in-line, detachable box magazines are used.

TURKEY

The Turkish Army has used a great many different types of handguns. German, Spanish and British types have been used and, since the United States has given military assistance to Turkey, also the U.S. Colt .45 Model 1911A1.

The Turkish government arms plant at Kirikkale has made copies of the Walther PP in both .380 ACP (9mm Short) and .32 ACP (7.65mm). This pistol is identical to the Walther except for minor variations in machining and the addition of a finger rest to the magazine. It is loaded, fired, and field-stripped in the same manner as the Walther PP.

TURKISH COPY of .380 ACP Walther.

UNITED STATES

The standard U.S. Service pistol is the Colt caliber .45 Model 1911A1 automatic pistol. Other pistols and revolvers are issued for special purposes such as air crew personal armament, weapons for counter intelligence personnel, training, etc. Among these are the .32 and .380 Colt automatic pistols, the .38 Colt Detective Special, the .38 Colt Police Positive, the .38 Colt Special Official Police, the .38 Smith & Wesson Military and Police, and the Smith & Wesson .38 Chiefs Special Airweight.

All of the above are chambered for the .38 Special cartridge. Smith & Wesson Military and Police revolvers chambered for the .38 S&W cartridge have also been used. Caliber .22 revolvers and pistols are used for training.

POST-WW II EXPERIMENTAL ARMY PISTOLS

At the conclusion of WW II, the U.S. Army drew up a number of requirements for new weapons to include a new pistol. The new pistol was to be light (25-ounce maximum) and to be chambered for a cartridge of not more than .35 or less than .30 caliber with certain penetration capabilities. Length of the new pistol was not to exceed 7 inches and a double-action trigger mechanism was considered desirable.

A series of tests were held at Aberdeen Proving Ground and at Fort Benning, Georgia. The .45 ACP and 9mm Parabellum Colt Commander, the 9mm Parabellum S&W Model 39, the Inglis lightweight version of the 9mm Parabellum FN Browning Hi-Power, and the 9mm Parabellum T3, a pistol developed by High Standard under contract with the U.S. Army, were tested. All of the above pistols, with the exception of the T3, are described elsewhere in this book.

T3

The T3 differed from all the other pistols in that it used the blowback system of operation as opposed to the recoil system used by the other pistols.

The T3 has a heavy spring around the barrel which helps retard rearward movement of the barrel and returns the slide to battery position. The cocking of the external hammer also offers some resistance to the rearward movement of the slide. An unusual feature which was designed to retard opening of the slide is a circumferential cut near the end of the chamber. The case expands into this cut on firing and the effort required to extract the cases helps to retard rearward movement of the slide.

The receiver is of lightweight alloy. The T3 has a pivoting trigger which operates the sear through a connector located on the left side; the connector also serves as a disconnector. A projection on the rear of the connector engages a cut on the bottom of the hammer to accomplish double-action trigger operation. The safety, located on the left top rear of the slide, locks the sear in a rearward poistion when moved upward. There is no device to hold the slide to the rear, i.e., no slide stop. To field-strip, the slide is pulled slightly to the rear and the barrel lock, located on the left side of the receiver above the trigger, is rotated 180°. The slide group may then be pushed forward off the receiver. The magazine catch is located at the bottom rear of the grip section of the receiver.

716

The T3 triggerguard may be pushed to the left, disengaged at the rear, and rotated to the front where it locks into a lug on the front underside of the slide, thus completely exposing the trigger for use with heavily-gloved hands. The movement of the triggerguard to the forward position depresses a retainer which compresses springs that operate on a plunger, thereby causing the weight of the trigger pull to be increased. This decreases the possibility of accidental discharge when the trigger is exposed. The barrel of the T3 is dovetailed to the receiver and is easily removable. A later version of the T3 has a slide stop and button-type magazine catch.

The T3 did not make out very well in the tests primarily because of its blowback system of operation. The 9mm Parabellum is a high-pressure cartridge and, although it has been used successfully in blowback-operated pistols such as the Astra Model 400 and Model 600, it requires a great deal of weight and/or an extremely heavy recoil spring to prevent early opening of the slide. The ringed chamber resulted in many case splits, but this could be a matter of brass characteristics as well as the characteristics of the weapon. It should be borne in mind, however, that any military pistol must be able to use marginal ammunition.

The T3 had the following characteristics: overall length, 7.5 in.; barrel length, 4.12 in.; fed by 7-round, in-line detachable box magazine; weight loaded, 1.94 lb.

Late version of 9mm Parabellum Model T3.

None of the pistols tested met the requirements exactly, but several were very close in most respects and gave very creditable performances. About 1955, a decision was made at the top levels of the Defense establishment to retain the .45 caliber Model 1911A1 because of logistical considerations. Thus ended the pistol tests; the net benefit to the American shooter was the proving and/or possible improvement of the Colt Commander and the Smith & Wesson Model 39.

Although these pistols were not developed specifically for these tests or on government contract, they were both thoroughly tested and were considered leading contenders.

SPECIAL PURPOSE HANDGUNS

During WW II, several special-purpose handguns were developed and one was manufactured in quantity.

The .45 Caliber Flare Projector

This is a single-shot, smoothbore pistol that was designed to be dropped into enemy-occupied Allied countries. The idea for the development originated with the Joint Psychological Committee. The Ordnance Department made up some rough sketches of a weapon which would be made of stampings with a smooth-bore barrel made of seamless steel tubing. Inland Manufacturing Div. of General Motors prepared the manufacturing drawings and Guide Lamp Division of General Motors manufactured one million of these pistols by 21 August, 1942 at a cost of slightly over $1.71 each.

FLARE PROJECTOR, caliber .45

The Flare Projector is chambered for the .45 Model 1911 automatic pistol cartridge. It has a simple breechblock which rides in slots at the end of the barrel. This breechblock is manually lifted after the cocking piece/firing-pin assembly are drawn to the rear and turned to the right side. After firing, the empty case is extracted with a wooden rod, one of which was packed with each pistol together with ten cartridges and an instruction sheet. The entire kit, including waterproof packaging, cost the U.S. $2.10.

A two-shot version of the Flare Projector was designed, but never produced in quantity. This pistol had a rectangular block with two chambers bored through it mounted between the barrel and the breechblock. The pistol worked on the system of the harmonica gun which has been with us for centuries. The firing-pin guide rod which projects forward from the top front of the cocking piece/firing pin locks the chambers in place for firing; when the cocking piece/firing-pin is drawn to the rear and rotated, the chambers may be moved laterally.

The Stamped .45

A .45 automatic pistol was made principally of stampings with the exception of the link, a few pins, the barrel and a piece of bar stock at the back of the slide to hold the firing-pin and serve as the breech face. The rear sight, when rotated on its retaining rivet, acted as a safety by preventing the hammer from striking the firing-pin. The barrel was a piece of seamless tubing around which was wrapped and welded a sleeve which served to reinforce the chamber and act as a barrel-locking shoulder mating with a pierced groove in the top of the slide. The lower part of this sleeve was elongated at the rear and drilled to form a mounting place for the link and link pin.

Prototype .45 automatic pistol made of stampings.

The standard Colt Model 1911 magazine was used with this pistol. Barrel length is 5 inches, overall length 8.6 inches, and weight 2.3 pounds. Only a few of these pistols were made possibly because of the large British and Canadian production of 9mm Sten submachine guns which became the most common weapon in air drops to resistance movements in occupied Europe.

POST-WW II COMMERCIAL HANDGUNS

The production of commercial pistols and revolvers was relatively slow after WW II and it was a seller's market for the first 3 or 4 years after the war. In general, it might be said that the first guns to appear on the market were, for the most part, pre-war models for which tooling was already in existence. Unhappily, some models which were manufactured before the war were not reinstated, notably the single-action Colt Frontier, which rose like the Phoenix a bit later, and the Colt .25, .32 and .380 automatics. The writer particularly bemoans the demise of the latter two. Their death was undoubtedly due to economic factors, but in finish, reliability, and flatness, they can hardly be matched today. Ultra-sophisticated they were not, nor did they look like this year's Mustang, but they were grand pistols. Their desirability has been proved by the escalating prices on the relatively few that have been bought from surplus British arms stocks in the last decade.

CHARTER ARMS CORP.

The Charter Arms Corp. of 265 Asylum St., Bridgeport, Conn., is a newcomer in the United States handgun business, having started business in 1964. They have entered the highly-competitive personal defense revolver businss with a highly-competitive product at a very reasonable price.

Charter Undercover .38 Special

This is a swing-out cylinder, double-action revolver of all-steel construction. The cylinder is chambered for 5 rounds and the revolver is available with 2 or 3-inch barrels. Overall length is 6.25 inches with 2-inch barrel and 7.3 inches with 3-inch barrel. The Undercover may be obtained with smooth walnut grips or larger checkered grips. The hammer has a relatively short fall as its arc from the cocked to fire position is 55°, a fall approximately 5° less than that in most other revolvers.

CHARTER ARMS UNDERCOVER .38 Special revolver.

The firing pin of the Undercover, which is mounted in the frame, is made of berylium copper, a very tough material. The cylinder, which swings out to the left, locks both front and rear and may be released either by pulling forward on the ejector rod or by pressing the cylinder release catch on the top left rear of the frame. A steel bar hammer block linked to the trigger prevents accidental discharge by dropping, release of trigger before firing, etc. All springs used in the arm are coil springs. The front sight is a square blade and the rear sight is a square notch. The Undercover weighs 1 pound with 3-inch barrel.

COLT

Colts Patent Firearms Manufacturing Co. is now the Colt Firearms Division of Colt Industries. Colt has changed hands a number of times since WW II. As with most other U.S. arms manufacturers, it is a division of a larger diversified corporation. Happily, the current Colt management is quite interested in gun development. As pointed out in the previous editions of this book, Colt handguns have a well-deserved international reputation for ruggedness, dependability, and finish. Imitation is often regarded as the highest form of flattery and Colt pistols and revolvers have had more than their share of imitators throughout the world for many years.

Many of the pre-war models are still in production with little or no change, but many new models have been added as well.

Colt .22 L.R. Huntsman (Model S-5)

The Huntsman is descended from the Challenger which was introduced in 1950 as an economy version of the Woodsman. The Challenger and Huntsman do not have ramp-mounted front sights or an adjustable rear sight and the walnut grips do not have a thumb rest. The Huntsman, which came out in 1955, has a non-slip trigger and an improved short action.

COLT .22 L.R. HUNTSMAN.

Colt .22 L.R. Targetsman (Model S-4)

The Targetsman is basically the same as the Huntsman, but has an adjustable rear sight and thumb rest on the left grip. It is essentially an economy version of the Woodsman target pistol. The Targetsman was introduced in 1959.

721

COLT .22 L.R. TARGETSMAN.

Colt .22 L.R. Woodsman

The postwar version comes in two models, the Sport (Model S-1), 4.5-inch barrel, and the Target (Model S-2), with 6-inch barrel. They differ from the pre-war Woodsman in having shaped grips with thumb rest, ramp-mounted front sights and Accro adjustable rear sights. Triggers are grooved and straighter, and the slide serrations are slanted to the rear.

Colt .22 L.R. Woodsman Match Target (Model S-3)

The Match Target is Colt's best .22 caliber automatic. As compared to the pre-war Match Target, the grips are differently shaped, the fixed weight built into the underside of the barrel has been extended to the muzzle thus adding four ounces to the pistol's weight, the front and rear sights are different, and the post-war model has a slide stop and a magazine safety, i.e., the weapon will not fire if the magazine is removed.

COLT .22 L.R. WOODSMAN MATCH TARGET.

Colt .22 Frontier Scout (Model Q-1)

The Frontier Scout is a scaled-down version of the Single Action Army and was introduced in January 1958. As originally, made, it had a bright aluminum-alloy frame and blued-steel barrel, cylinder and ejector assembly. An all-blue model was introduced, also with aluminum-alloy frame, in September 1958. The Frontier Scout is currently available in blue (Model Q-1) and nickel (model K-3).

COLT FRONTIER SCOUT, two-tone.

The Frontier Scout 62 (Model K-1) has stag grips and a Midnight Blue finish. All models of the Frontier Scout can be supplied chambered for the .22 Short, Long and Long Rifle or for the .22 Winchester Magnum Rimfire. They may also be obtained with fitted spare cylinders so that one may have one revolver and be able to use all the .22 rimfire cartridges.

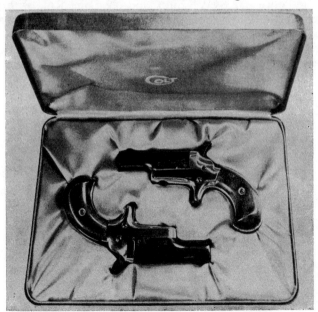

A pair of COLT DERRINGERS, caliber .22.

723

Colt .22 Buntline Scout (Model Q-2)

This long-barreled—9.5-inch barrel—version of the Frontier Scout was introduced in January 1959. It differs from the basic single-action Frontier in having a floating firing pin in the frame, a base pin held by a screw instead of a spring catch, a loop on the bottom of the mainspring, and in having a one-piece grip frame and triggerguard with provision to hold the mainspring loop without a screw. The finish of the Buntline Scout is blue. The Buntline Scout 62 (Model K-2—blue finish and K-4—nickel finish) was introduced in 1962 and has stag grips. The Buntline Scouts are chambered for the .22 Short, Long and Long Rifle or the .22 Winchester Magnum.

Colt .22 Short Derringer No. 4

This revival of an old Colt single-shot began in 1959. It is no longer in production. It is an almost exact reproduction of the .41 Rim Fire Derringer. They were sold in matched pairs or as single pistols, and have gold-plated and blued frames. Value—sentimental only!

Colt .25 ACP Junior Colt (Model O-6)

This blowback-operated pocket pistol is made for Colt by Astra in Spain. It is sold by Astra as the Cub and may be obtained in .22 Short as well as .25 ACP. A .22 Short conversion-kit can also be obtained for the .25 ACP. The pistol is described under Spain. This Colt differs from the Astra in its markings and the presence of the Colt escutcheon on the grip.

Colt .32 Courier

This revolver was introduced in 1954 and discontinued in 1955. It was made for the .32 New Police (.32 S&W Long), and .22 Long Rifle with a frame and cylinder of lightweight alloy. The finish is Dual Tone Blue and the barrel length is 3 inches. This revolver has a blade front sight and notched rear sight. The Courier weighed .87 pounds in .32, and 1.25 pounds in caliber .22. Since its production was extremely limited, this revolver may be a collector's item some day.

COLT 357, target stocks, target hammer.

Colt .357 Three Fifty Seven

This heavy revolver was introduced in October 1953 and discontinued in 1961 when it was replaced by the Trooper model. It was supplied with plain checkered and target-type grips as well as a standard width hammer or a wide-spur target-type hammer. Rear sight adjustable for elevation and windage and a ramp front sight were fitted. A floating firing pin, fitted on the frame, is used in the Three Fifty Seven.

Colt .357 Python (Model I-3)

The introduction of the Python in 1955 marked a new series of revolvers for Colt. The Python is quite different in appearance from previous Colt revolvers. A ventilated rib is mounted on the top of the barrel and the ejector rod is shrouded, with the shroud extending to the end of the barrel. The Python has a floating firing pin in the frame, target hammer, and target sights. This is one of Colt's finest revolvers, if not the finest. Colt now calls this revolver the New Police Python.

COLT .357 NEW POLICE PYTHON.

Colt .38 Special Diamondback

The Diamondback is Colt's newest revolver and is similar to, but somewhat lighter and smaller than the Python. The Diamondback can be obtained in .22 WMR and .22 Short, Long and Long Rifle, as well as .38 Special.

Colt .38 Special Trooper (Model I-4)

The Trooper was put into production in April 1953 in .38 Special and .22 L.R. It is no longer carried by Colt in .22 L.R., but the .357 Magnum version was introduced in January 1962. The Trooper is a target-grade heavy-duty revolver.

COLT .38 Special DIAMONDBACK.

It is available with either standard grips and standard hammer, or target-type fully-checkered walnut grips with target hammer. The Trooper is of the conventional Colt design.

COLT .38 Special TROOPER.

Colt .38 Special Cobra (Model D-3)

The Cobra was put into production in May 1950. The frame and sideplate are made of Coltalloy—a lightweight aluminum alloy; barrel and cylinder are of steel. Essentially the Cobra is an improved lightweight version of the Detective Special. A hammer shroud may be attached to this pistol, if desired. The Cobra is made in .38 New Police (.38 S&W) and .32 New Police (.32 S&W Short and Long) in addition to .38 Special. The Cobra was originally made with 2 and 4-inch barrels and is now made with 3 and 5-inch barrels, as well.

COLT .38 Special COBRA.

Colt .38 Special Agent

The Agent, introduced in 1955, is a lightweight revolver similar to the Cobra, but with a shorter grip. It is available with a 2-inch barrel.

COLT .38 Special AGENT.

Colt .38 Special Border Patrol

Approximately 400 of this model revolver were sold to the Treasury Department in 1952. This revolver was made on the Detective Special frame with square butt and a heavy untapered 4-inch barrel. It has a ramp-type front sight and is marked "Colt Border Patrol"—".38 Spec—Heavy Duty" on the left side of the barrel. This revolver weighs 2.2 pounds.

Colt .38 Special Official Police (Model E-1)

The Official Police is little changed from the pre-WW II model. It is now made with 4, 5, and 6-inch barrels in .38 Special and .22.

Colt .38 Special Police Positive Special (Model D-2)

The Police Positive is, for the most part, the same as it was before WW II. It is made in .32 Police Positive (.32 S&W Long) as well as .38 Special. In .32, it is made with 4-inch barrel, and in .38 Special, with 4 and 5-inch barrel.

Colt .38 Special Detective Special (Model D-1)

The Detective Special is also made in .32 Police Positive. It has changed but little from its pre-WW II form. It has a 2-inch barrel in .32, and a 2 or 3-inch barrel in .38 Special, and still is one of the best "belly guns" available.

Colt .38 Special Officers Model Match (Model I-1)

The Officers Model is made in .22 L.R. as well as .38 Special. This is still a target-grade handgun as it was before WW II and is currently made with 6-inch barrel and improved adjustable rear sights.

Colt .38 Super Automatic (Model O-2)

This model is still in production with no significant alteration.

Colt .38 Special Gold Cup National Match (Model O-5)

The Gold Cup National Match .38 Special is chambered for wad cutter or mid-range cartridges. It is a target arm designed to take advantage of the fine degree of accuracy obtainable from the .38 Special mid-range load. The fact that the .38 Special, especially with mid-range loads, is the most accurate pistol cartridge in the heavy calibers available today, is borne out by Czech production of target revolvers for this cartridge. These revolvers are used by shooters from Communist countries in international shooting events.

COLT GOLD CUP NATIONAL MATCH .38 Special Mid-Range automatic pistol.

728

The .38 Special Gold Cup externally resembles the .45 Government Model, but is normally fitted with the flat type—M1911—mainspring housing; the arched mainspring housing—M1911A1—can be obtained on special order. Internally it is quite different from the .45 Government Model or the .45 Gold Cup. The slide is milled out on the inside and the barrel diameter has been reduced. The barrel is of the floating type and is not mounted on a link attached to the slide-stop pin. An internal lug is slotted for the slide-stop pin and the barrel recoils straight back .14 inch. In other words, this pistol is not a locked-breech design as is the .45 Government Model and the .45 Gold Cup. Because of the relatively low power of the .38 Special Mid-range cartridge, the blowback system increases the power of recoil and aids feeding. The straightline barrel movement, as opposed to the tipping barrel of the Government Model, should improve accuracy. A special bushing maintains the position of the barrel. The barrel has a long feed ramp which is sloped at a gentle angle.

The spring-loaded trigger stop is fitted with an adjustable screw. With empty pistol and magazine, weigh the trigger pull with the magazine catch removed, and then with magazine catch in place. The magazine catch is removed as described under the .45 Government Model (M1911A1). It is not recommended that the adjustment be turned too fine. The 5-round magazine has a follower-button like that found on many .22 caliber magazines and on the Luger. The rear sight is adjustable for elevation and windage. In 1963, this pistol was modified by the introduction of a new barrel system, barrel bushing, hand-fitted slide, and a new sear. In 1965, the Gold Cup series and the .22 Match pistol were fitted with the improved Colt-Elliason rear sight.

Colt .45 ACP Gold Cup National Match (Model O-5)

This recoil-operated pistol is the current match version of the Government model. Externally it resembles the .38 Special Gold Cup and internally resembles the Government model excepting the extractor, barrel, barrel bushing, and fitting of the parts. Although not specifically a Colt product, this is an appropriate place to say a few words about the U.S. Army .45 ACP M1911A1 National Match. For a number of years, the Army has had issue .45 automatics accurized for use in the National Matches. These pistols were originally accurized at Springfield Armory, but in the last several years private contractors have also performed this job. Selected pistols are refinished and fitted with special barrels, barrel bushings, aluminum tipped triggers, trigger stops, adjustable rear sights and enlarged rear sights. These components were all stamped "NM." On occasion these pistols can be purchased by National Rifle Association members from the Director of Civilian Marksmanship.

Colt .45 ACP Commander (Model O-4)

The Commander, which is also made in .38 Super and 9mm Parabellum, is a lightweight shortened version of the Government model. The hammer-spur is rounded. Receiver and the mainspring housing are made of Coltalloy, an aluminum alloy. The Commander, which has a dual-tone blue finish, was introduced in 1949.

COLT .45 ACP COMMANDER.

Colt .45 Single Action Army (Model P-1)

After being out of production since 1941, the Single Action Army (Peacemaker) was re-introduced in 1955. It is currently made with 4.5, 5.5 and 7.5-inch barrels in calibers .45 Colt and .357 Magnum, and with 5.5 and 7.5-inch barrels in .44 Special.

Colt .45 New Frontier Single Action Army (Model P-4)

This is a target version of the Single Action Army. It has a ramp-mounted front sight and a target type rear sight adjustable for windage and elevation. The New Frontier can be obtained in .357 Magnum and .44 Special as well as .45 Colt.

COLT NEW FRONTIER Target Grade Revolver.

Colt .45 New Frontier Buntline Special (Model P-5)

This model is the same as the New Frontier, but is made only for the .45 Colt cartridge with 12-inch barrel.

COLT .45 NEW FRONTIER BUNTLINE SPECIAL.

Colt .45 Buntline Special (Model P-2)

Same as New Frontier Buntline, but does not have adjustable sights.

Colt has produced a large number of Commemorative pistol models in the last ten years. These are essentially presentation-type arms and are usually the Frontier Scout or Single Action Army with special engraving. Numbers produced are limited and include matched pairs as well as single specimens. An interesting commemorative piece was a single-shot .22 Short, a 7/8ths replica of the 1860 Army. In 1967, Colt brought out a Commemorative version of the .45 Model 1911 which is nicely finished and beautifully engraved. Several more commemorative versions of this pistol will be brought out in 1968 as they commemorate the 50th anniversary of WW I battles in which the United States participated. Colt has also made, in special limited orders, the .45 Sheriffs Model Single Action which does not have an ejector rod. About 500 of these were made in 1960.

CENTENNIAL ARMS COLT SHERIFF'S Model .45.

731

POST-WW II COLT PISTOLS AND REVOLVERS

	Frontier Scout	Buntline Scout	Huntsman [3]	Woodsman Match Target	Courier
Caliber:	.22 L.R. or .22 WMR.	.22 L.R. or .22 WMR.	.22 L.R.	.22 L.R.	.32 New Police and .22 L.R.
System of Operation:	Single-action revolver.	Double-action revolver.	Blowback; semi-automatic.	Blowback; semi-automatic.	Double-action revolver.
Length Overall:	9.3″	14.75″	9″, 10.25″	9″, 10.25″	7.25″
Barrel Length:	4.75″	9.5″	4.25″, 6″	4.25″, 6″	3″
Feed Device:	6-round cylinder.	6-round cylinder.	10-round magazine.	10-round magazine.	6-round cylinder.
Sights:	Blade and notched top strap.	Blade and notched top strap.	Blade and notch.	Ramp-mounted blade; notched-bar rear adjustable for windage and elevation.	Blade and notch.
Weight:	1.5 lb.[1]	1.8 lb.[2]	1.8 lb. w/4.25″-barrel; 1.9 lb. w/6″-barrel.	2.25 lb. w/4.25″-barrel. 2.5 lb. w/6″-barrel.	.87 lb. in .32 cal. 1.25 lb. in .22 cal.

[1] Frontier Scout w/nickel finish and Frontier Scout 62 have same characteristics, but weight is 1.8 lb.
[2] Buntline Scout 62 has same characteristics, but weighs 2.1 lb.
[3] Targetsman has same characteristics as Huntsman with 6″-barrel, but has rear sight adjustable for windage and elevation. These semi-automatics use conventional in-line, detachable box magazines.

POST-WW II COLT DOUBLE-ACTION REVOLVERS

	Three Fifty Seven	Trooper	Python	Cobra	Agent
Caliber:	.357 Magnum.	.357 Magnum or .38 Special.[1]	.357 Magnum.	.38 Spec., .32 New Police or .22 L.R.	.38 Special.
Length Overall:	9.25", 11.25"	9.25", 11.25"	7.75", 9.25", 11.25"	6.5", 7.75", 8.75", 9.75"	6.75"
Barrel Length:	4", 6"	4", 6"	2.5", 4", 6"	.22 L.R. 3"; .32 2"; 3"; .38 2", 3", 4", 5"	2"
Cylinder Capacity:	6 rounds.	6 rounds.	6 rounds.	6 rounds.	6 rounds.
Sights:	Ramp-mounted blade; notched-bar rear adjustable for W & E.	Ramp-mounted blade; notched-bar rear adjustable for W & E.	Blade on rib; notched-bar rear adjustable for W & E.	Blade and notched top strap.	Blade and notched top strap.
Weight:	2.25 lb. or 2.4 lb. depending on barrel.	2.25 lb. or 2.4 lb. depending on barrel.	Approx. 2.4 lb., 2.6 lb. or 2.75 lb. depending cn barrel.	.93 lb.	.87 lb.

[1] Trooper model was also made in .22 L.R. with 4"-barrel.

733

POST-WW II COLT REVOLVERS AND PISTOLS

	Diamondback	New Frontier	Buntline Special [1]	Gold Cup National Match	Commander
Caliber:	.38 Special, 22 L.R. or .22 WMR.	45 Colt, .44 Special, and .357 Magnum.	.45 Colt.	.45 ACP and .38 Special.	.45 ACP, 9mm Parabellum, .38 Super.
Method of Operation:	Double-action revolver.	Single-action revolver.	Single-action revolver.	.45 ACP–recoil. .38–blowback semi-automatic.	Recoil, semi-automatic.
Length Overall:	7.25″, 9″	11.5″, 13.5″	18″	8.5″	8″
Barrel Length:	2.25″, 4″	5.5″, 7.5″	12″	5″	4.25″
Feed Device:	6-round cylinder.	6-round cylinder.	6-round cylinder.	5-round, in-line, detachable box magazine.	.45 ACP–7 round, 9mm Parabellum and .38 Super–9-round in-line detachable box magazine.
Sights:	Blade on rib; notched bar rear adjustable for W and E.	Blade on ramp; notched bar rear adjustable for W and E.	Blade and notched top strap.	Blade front; notched bar rear adjustable for W and E.	Blade and notch.
Weight:	1.5 lb. or 1.8 lb. in .38; approx. .18 lb. more in .22 cal.	3.5 lb. or 4 lb. in .45; 3.75 lb. or 4.5 lb. in .357 Mag.	2.7 lb.	2.4 lb.	1.6 lb.

[1] New Frontier Buntline Special has same characteristics, but has ramp-mounted front sight and adjustable rear.

DARDICK

David Dardick developed a handgun around a new type of small arms cartridge called the "tround." The tround, reportedly was originally developed for use in aircraft guns to help speed up rates of fire and cut down on space requirements for ammunition. Because of its triangular shape, three trounds occupy the same space as do two conventional-round cartridges. The Dardick pistol, which is not an automatic and not truly a revolver but rather basically a magazine pistol, is built around the "tround" and the open-chamber concept. The Dardick does not have reciprocating parts; a three-legged piece similar to a star-wheel serves the following purposes: (1) It indexes the cartridges as they are fed upwards by the spring-loaded magazine follower. (2) It forms two walls of the triangular-sided chamber; the receiver serves as the third—top—wall of the chamber. (3) It serves to eject the fired case from the right rear of the receiver.

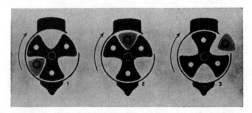

DARDICK—DIAGRAM SHOWING LOADING AND EJECTION.

This diagram illustrates how the three open chambers of the Dardick cylinder function as they revolve 120° clockwise with each pull of the trigger. Figure 1 shows a chamber picking up a cartridge (tround), where it moves to Figure 2 in alignment with the bore and is fired, and the empty hull being ejected in Figure 3. The double-action mechanism with gas assist uses the gas force of the fired cartridge to reduce the trigger pull.

The tround has a triangular case which was originally made of extruded aluminum and, as of 1958, was changed to Fortiflex, a polyethylene plastic. The bullet, primer and propellent are conventional. The .38 Special bullet was the one principally used, but 9mm Parabellum (also .357 in. in diameter), .380 ACP and .22 (with adaptors and .22 barrel) bullets were also used. The trounds could be used in 10-round stripper clips.

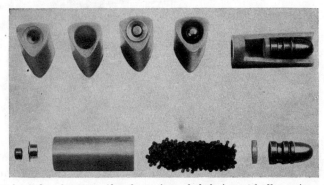

TROUNDS, loaded and empty. Also shown is exploded view of bullet casing and contents.

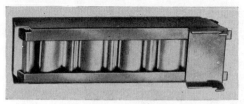

STRIP CLIP is used to package ammunition and for fast loading of magazine.

The pilot models of the Dardick were handmade in 1956 and used parts of the Smith & Wesson revolver frame, trigger and hammer mechanism. Kent Bellah reported that three of these specimens were made. Production was started on finalized models in 1959 in Hamden, Conn. Production ceased in 1960 and all facilities plus weapons and parts finished were auctioned to Numrich Arms in 1960. Kent Bellah reported that only about 40 arms were produced. Although there are many good features about the Dardick design, it did not catch on with the military or sporting shooters.

Dardick .38 1500 Series

This model comes with two 6-inch interchangeable barrels, one for .38, the other for .22. The .22 has to be used with adaptors and the position of the firing pin is manually changed by turning the screw at the top left of the frame to strike the .22 rim. The adaptors are simply plastic trounds into which the .22 Short, Long or Long Rifle cartridges are placed. The cartridges can be loaded singly or by stripper-clips. Overall length is 9 inches, weight is 2.1 pounds.

DARDICK .38 Series 1500.

Dardick .38 Series 1100

The 1100 holds 11 trounds and was supplied with a .38 and a .22 caliber barrel, both 3-inches long. The overall length of this arm is 6 inches and it weighs 1.56 pounds.

Dardick .38 Series 2000

This is a 20-shot version.

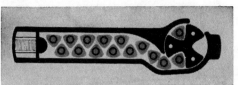

Diagram of SERIES 1500 cylinder and magazine full-loaded with 15 trounds, showing nesting and feed-through. These are polyethylene plastic triangular cases with conventional .38 cal. lead-alloy bullets, primers and powder.

Dardick Rifle Conversion

All models of the Dardick could be converted to a rifle by removing the barrel and fitting the frame into a stocked rifle fitted with an aperture-type rear sight. The whole rig is similar to the Unique Combo.

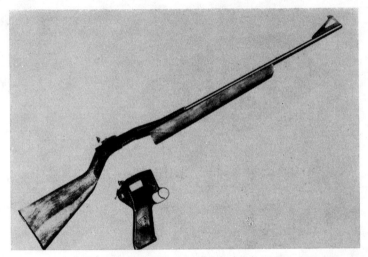

DARDICK rifle conversion unit.

In the Dardick, all the work of feeding, indexing, firing and ejecting is done by a pull of the trigger. The star-wheel type "cylinder/indexer" is rotated when the trigger is pulled. It rotates 120° clockwise with each pull of the trigger, picking up the round from the magazine, aligning it with the barrel and ejecting the empty case out the right side. Each of these actions, except the first, requires a separate pull of the trigger. It is therefore quite difficult to have a light pull with this arm.

HARRINGTON AND RICHARDSON

Harrington & Richardson (H&R) of Worcester, Mass., has been producing good quality, relatively low-priced revolvers since 1871. They also produce rifles and shotguns and have since the time of the Korean War, produced considerable quantities of M1s and M14s.

737

H&R .22 Model 949 Forty Niner

The Model 949 is a double-action revolver of Western-style with encased spring-loaded ejector rod under the barrel and loading gate on the left side. It was introduced in 1960. The hammer spur is wide and the grip is of hog-leg style with walnut grips. The Model 949 can use the .22 Short, Long and Long Rifle, and has a cylinder chambered for 9 rounds.

H&R .22 L.R. Model 999 Sportsman

The Model 999 is a double-action revolver that was originally introduced in 1932. A number of modifications of this arm have been produced since WW II. The most recent is the Model 999 Deluxe which has a ventilated rib and hand-checkered walnut grips. The 999 is a top-break revolver with a 9-round cylinder and rear sight adjustable for windage and elevation. It is H&R's best .22 revolver. A chromed version, the Silver Sportsman, was introduced in 1964.

H&R Model 999.

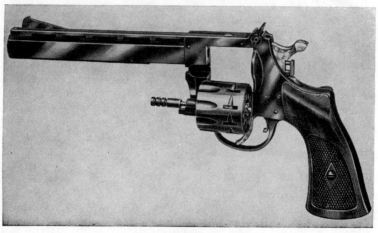

H&R Model 939.

H&R .22 L.R. Model 939 Ultra Sidekick

This swing-out cylinder, double-action revolver was introduced in 1956. It has an adjustable rear sight and the cylinder is chambered for 9 cartridges. The cylinder is released by pulling a catch on the back of the hammer. The Ultra Sidekick has an H&R locking feature; a lock mounted in the grip and turned by a removable key locks the action shut. The Ultra Sidekick has a ventilated rib over the barrel.

H&R .22 Model 929 Sidekick

The Model 929 has a swing-out cylinder which is chambered for 9 rounds. It will use the .22 Short, Long and Long Rifle. Plastic grips are used on this model. The Model 930 is similar but is chromed. The Model 732 is the .32 S&W Long version of this revolver; the Model 733 is the chromed .32. Both the Model 722 and the Model 723 have 6-chambered cylinders.

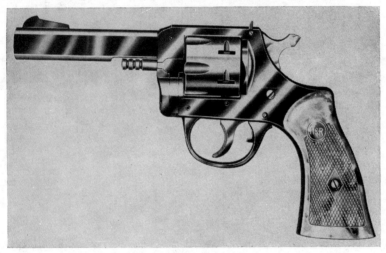

H&R Model 732.

The Model 732 and 733 have the H&R patented lock in the butt and Model 732 has a rear sight adjustable for windage. The Model 929 and 930 were introduced in 1956 and the Models 732 and 733 were introduced in 1958. The Model 732 and 733 are called the "Guardsman."

H&R .22 Models 622 and 623

These are double-action revolvers in which the cylinders are removed completely to extract the fired cases. The cylinder rod is removed by pushing in on the catch on the lower front of the frame. The cylinder pin is then pushed into the front of the cylinder and it pushes the extractor out to eject all cases simultaneously. The cylinder is chambered for six rounds and the grips are plastic. The Model 623 is a chrome version of the 622. These revolvers use the .22 Short, Long or Long Rifle cartridge. They replace the H&R 922 Series revolvers.

CHARACTERISTICS OF HARRINGTON AND RICHARDSON .22 DOUBLE-ACTION REVOLVERS

	Model 999 DELUXE	Model 949	Model 939	Model 929
Barrel Length:	6"	5.5"	6"	2.5", 4", 6"
Cylinder Capacity:	9 rounds.	9 rounds.	9 rounds.	9 rounds.
Sights:	Blade on front ramp, adjustable for elevation; notched-bar rear adjustable for windage.	Blade front; notched-bar rear adjustable for windage.	Blade front; notched-bar rear adjustable for windage and elevation.	Blade front; rear notch on 2.5"-barrel; notched bar adjustable for windage on 4" and 6"-barrels.
Weights:	1.8 lb.	1.9 lb.	2.1 lb.	From 1.3 lb. to 1.75 lb. depending on barrel.

Note: All models listed accept Short, Long or L.R. cartridges.

CHARACTERISTICS OF HARRINGTON AND RICHARDSON DOUBLE-ACTION REVOLVERS

	Model 622	Model 900	Model 732	Model 925
Caliber:	.22 L.R.	.22 L.R.	.32 S&W & .32 S&W Long.	.38 S&W
Barrel Length:	2.5", 4", 6"	2.5", 4", 6"	2.5" and 4"	2.5" and 4" [1]
Cylinder Capacity:	6 rounds.	9 rounds.	6 rounds.	5 rounds.
Sights:	Blade and notch.	Blade and notch.	Blade front; 2.5"-barrel, notch rear; 4"-barrel, notched bar rear adjustable for windage.	Blade front adjustable for elevation on 4"-barrel; notched-bar rear adjustable for windage.
Weight—				
W/2.5"-barrel:	1.3 lb.	1.2 lb.	1.5 lb.	1.3 lb.
W/4"-barrel:	1.6 lb.	1.5 lb.	1.6 lb.	1.5 lb.
W/6"-barrel:	1.75 lb.	1.6 lb.	(N/A)	(N/A)

[1] Overall length w/2.5"-barrel, 7.5"; w/4"-barrel, 9".

H&R Model 622.

H&R .22 Model 900 and Model 901

These are double-action revolvers which have a snap-out cylinder-pin method of loading and unloading. The cylinder pin is pushed through to extract all cases simultaneously. The Model 901, which is no longer listed in H&R catalogs, is chromed. The cylinders are chambered for 9 rounds and the grips are plastic. These models have a rebounding-hammer safety.

H&R SNAP-OUT Model 900.

H&R .38 S&W Model 925 Defender

The Model 925 is a top-break revolver with a cylinder chambered for 5 rounds. The rear sight is adjustable for windage. When first introduced in 1950, it was chambered for .22 as well as .38 S&W; the .22 version was dropped from the line in 1965.

H&R DEFENDER Model 925.

HIGH STANDARD

The High Standard Manufacturing Corp. produced .22 automatics exclusively prior to WW II. They also manufactured tools and drills, but arms manufacture was limited to the manufacture of improvements on the .22 "Hartford" pistol whose rights and properties they bought in 1932. They have considerably expanded their operations in the firearms field and now manufacture .22 revolvers, rifles, and shotguns. They are currently probably the largest manufacturer of .22 pistols and revolvers in the world.

High Standard has brought out a large number of models since WW II; some of these were in production during WW II. The Model H-DM was developed during WW II for military training; it continued in production until 1951 and was the last of the D-series High Standard pistols. In 1947 the G-series commercial pistols were put into production.

The G-series actually originated with the G-.380, a blowback design with outside hammer developed by High Standard for the Army Special Services during WW II. Mr. William J. Donovan of High Standard stated that 4,000 G-.380s were delivered to the Army during the last few years of the war as well as the .22 H-DM with silencer. Mr. Donovan also stated that High Standard, in the late 40s, developed an exposed-hammer pistol similar to the G-series for the .38 Special cartridge.

Samples of the gun were produced and it was even advertised, but was withdrawn before production started. High Standard discovered that, although the pistol worked perfectly with factory-loaded ammunition, overloads such as might be experienced with handloaded ammunition would fracture stop lugs during endurance tests. He further stated that High Standard might produce this pistol at a later date, but it will be several years hence. Improved metallurgy would make the difference between the pistol of the late 40s and the pistol of the 70s.

The G-.380 went out of production in 1946; other G-series were dropped in 1952 and were replaced by the Olympic series, which appeared in 1950, 1951, and 1954, and by the King series, i.e., Sport King, Field King, Flite King. The

Supermatic, which is similar to the Olympic model of 1951, is chambered for the .22 L.R. rather than the .22 Short as are the Olympic series. Supermatic Trophy and Supermatic Citation were improved Supermatics introduced in 1959. The Duramatic, a lower-priced arm produced to compete with the Ruger, was introduced in 1954.

In 1965, High Standard introduced the Trophy Military and Citation Military. The Sentinel, the first of High Standard's revolvers, first appeared in 1955, and was followed by two other series of revolvers, all with a Western flavor, which appeared in 1958 and 1960. High Standard makes the line of pistols marketed by Sears Roebuck as the J. C. Higgins. They are the same as the standard High Standard pistols, but do not bear the High Standard name.

Hi-Standard .22 L.R. Free Pistol

This pistol was developed by High Standard in conjunction with the Army Advanced Marksmanship Unit (AAMU) in 1960. It is a single-shot pistol with an electrically-operated firing mechanism. Two 6.5-volt batteries in the grip power a magnet which operates the rotary sear. These are custom-built pistols,

HI-STANDARD FREE PISTOL (a pilot model).

which weigh up to 3.1 pounds and have 8, 9 or 10-inch barrels. The trigger can be set as light as 1/10th oz. without danger of premature discharge, if the muzzle is elevated. This is a pistol for the advanced expert match shooter. In the hands of a tyro, it could be extremely dangerous.

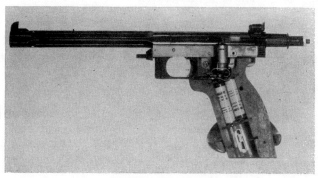

Note electric let-off.

743

Hi-Standard .380 Model G-.380

As previously noted, the G-.380 was developed for the O.S.S. and was really the first of the G-series to appear. It is a blowback-operated design which was made only with 5-inch barrel. The barrel is locked to the receiver by a spring-loaded latch which engages a cut-out in the rear underside of the barrel. The lower part of this latch protrudes from the front bottom of the receiver and is pushed up to release the barrel. The barrel can then be drawn forward off the receiver; the slide is also dismounted by drawing it forward off the receiver. This dismounting system is basically the same as that used on the Webley .32 automatic, in which the front part of the triggerguard serves as the barrel-locking lug.

HI-STANDARD G-.380.

This takedown system was used with all the G-series automatics and all the other Hi-Standard automatics until 1954.

Hi-Standard .22 Long Rifle Model G-D

The G-D has a target-type rear sight and blade front sight. It was normally equipped with flat checkered grips, but could be supplied with thumb rest grips. The hammer is mounted internally.

Hi-Standard .22 Long Rifle Model G-E

The G-E is also a target-type pistol and was regularly supplied with walnut grips with thumb rest; the rear sight is adjustable for elevation and windage. The hammer is mounted internally.

Hi-Standard .22 L.R. Model G-B

This is the cheapest of the G-series automatics and is fitted with fixed rear sight and diamond-checkered plastic grips. The safety on all the G-series automatics is a latch-type at the top left rear of the receiver. The hammer is mounted internally. All .22 models could be supplied with interchangeable 6.75 or 4.5-inch barrels.

Hi-Standard .22 Short Olympic (1st Model)

This pistol is essentially the same as the G-E, except for the cartridge utilized and its light alloy slide.

Hi-Standard .22 Short Olympic (2nd Model)

This model has the same takedown system as the G-series, but differs in a number of other ways. The safety is mounted at the top of the left grip and the slide stop is mounted at the top of the right grip. The barrel is ribbed and the front and rear backstraps are grooved. On the underside of the barrel is a dovetailed rib which is used to mount barrel weights. The slide is made of light alloy and its top is matted as is that of the barrel rib. The rear sight is click-adjustable for windage and elevation. The plastic stocks are checked and have a thumb rest.

This pistol is one of High Standard's early ventures in the .22 Short Olympic-type automatics and, while not really comparable with today's pistols of that type, is quite a nice piece. The author has one and has only one complaint; the steel slide stop has a tendency to batter the alloy slide when it engages it and holds it to the rear after the last round is fired.

The Olympic, as with all the G-series except G-.380, could be supplied with a pair of interchangeable 4.5 and 6.75-inch barrels. The Olympic could also be supplied with hand-carved walnut thumb rest grips.

The third model Olympic (Model 9121 and 9122) was introduced in 1954. It has slots cut through the barrel on each side of the front sight to act as a compensator. Dismounting system is the same as the earlier models, but the latch has a different external appearance.

HI-STANDARD OLYMPIC .22 Short (3rd Model).

Hi-Standard .22 L.R. Supermatic (1st Model)

Basically the same as the second model Olympic, but has a steel slide and uses the Long Rifle cartridge.

Hi-Standard .22 L.R. Supermatic (2nd Model)

This model (9118 and 9119) is basically the same as the third Model Olympic but has a steel slide.

Hi-Standard .22 L.R. Supermatic Citation (Models 9261 and 9262)

Introduced about 1958, there were a number of changes in this model from earlier models. The takedown system, which is used on all current models, consists of a spring-loaded button which protrudes from the top front of the receiver. The back end of this button engages a grooved stud which is pinned to the rear of the barrel. The barrel is light as compared to the early Supermatics, but has a heavy detachable muzzle-brake/stabilizer, or barrel stabilizer, as High Standard calls it. The trigger pull is adjustable with anti-backlash feature and the safety has been modified. The rear sight is mounted on the fixed barrel and therefore does not recoil. The undercut front sight is ramp-mounted. As with the G-series, barrels are of different length. There is also a Supermatic Citation (Model 9260) with 6.75-inch barrel and rear sight mounted on the slide, same in all other respects to Models 9261 and 9262.

The Supermatic Tournament (Model 9270, 9271) is a cheaper model of this pistol. It does not have the barrel stabilizer, barrel weight and the rear sight is mounted on the slide rather than the barrel. The Supermatic Citation was also made in a bull-barrel model (Model 9263) with heavy barrel; this model, excepting barrel, is basically the same as the Supermatic Tournament.

Hi-Standard .22 L.R. Supermatic Trophy (Models 9251-9252)

The Supermatic Trophy was High Standard's best grade of .22 Long Rifle target automatic. It is basically the same as the Supermatic Citation but has a gold-plated trigger, gold safety button, and gold-inlaid lettering and diamond checkered walnut grips. Model 9250 Supermatic Trophy is the same as above, but has a 6.75-inch barrel and its rear sight is mounted on the slide.

HI-STANDARD SUPERMATIC TROPHY .22 L.R.

Hi-Standard .22 Short Olympic (Model 9281)

Introduced about 1959, this pistol is identical to the Supermatic Citation but is made for the .22 Short and has an 8-inch barrel.

746

Hi-Standard .22 Short ISU Olympic

This pistol is furnished in a Citation grade (Model 9299) and Trophy grade (Model 9289). Both models comply with the International Shooting Union regulations. Both grades are made with 6.75-inch barrel having the integral stabilizer feature muzzle-brake compensator and accommodation for weights. The pistols are finished as are the Citation and Trophy grades respectively. Rear sight is mounted on the slide on both pistols.

Hi-Standard .22 L.R. Supermatic Trophy Military

In 1965, High Standard introduced new military versions of their .22 automatics. Internally these pistols are almost identical to their predecessors, but there have been two principal external changes. The angle and shape of the grip have been changed so that they practically match the Colt .45 Model 1911A1 Service pistol; the rear sights are mounted on a bridge which is attached to the receiver in a fashion somewhat similar to that of the Soviet Margolin. The sights therefore, do not recoil, and the sight radius is longer than earlier Hi-Standards with the rear sight on the barrel. These pistols also have a wedge roller which, under spring pressure, presses the magazine upward. The magazine follower is made of Detrin, a self-lubricating material. The Trophy Military can be obtained with heavy 5.5-inch bull barrel or with a fluted 7.25-inch barrel. Both barrels have cuts near the muzzle which help stabilize the barrel in fire. The grips may be had with or without thumb rest.

HI-STANDARD TROPHY MILITARY with bull barrel, grip that duplicates GI .45, and non-recoiling rear sight that leaves wide-open breech for better functioning. One of the world's finest .22 match pistols.

Hi-Standard .22 L.R. Supermatic Citation Military

This pistol differs from the Trophy Military in the same way that the Citation differs from the Trophy.

HI-STANDARD CITATION MILITARY with 7¼" fluted barrel, grip that duplicates GI .45, and non-recoiling rear sight. One of the world's finest .22 match pistols.

Hi-Standard .22 L.R. Supermatic Tournament Military

The Tournament grade pistols are cheaper versions of the Citation Military. They differ in having their rear sights mounted on the slide and the trigger travel and pull cannot be adjusted. The Tournament may be obtained with 5-inch bull barrel with barrel-stabilizing slots or 6.75-inch straight barrel.

Hi-Standard .22 Short ISU Olympic Military

This pistol is the military version of the ISU Olympic, with non-recoiling rear sight. This pistol has a thumb rest on its checkered walnut stocks.

Hi-Standard .22 L.R. Field King

The first model Field King was almost identical to the first model Supermatic excepting the barrel and front sight. The barrel of the Field King does not have a matted rib on the top or a dove-tailed rib on the bottom for barrel weights. The front sight is a fixed blade as opposed to the adjustable ramp-mounted front sight of the Supermatic. The Field King was discontinued before 1958.

HI-STANDARD SPORT KING .22 L.R.

Hi-Standard .22 L.R. Sport King

The first model Sport King which was introduced in 1950 had a lighter weight barrel than the Field King and a fixed rear sight. Like all of the series which appeared at that time, it could be obtained with interchangeable 6.75 inch and 4-inch barrels. By 1954, the later type safety had been fitted to this pistol and it could be had with light alloy or steel slide (Models 9156, 9157 or 9100 and 9101 respectively). The Sport King all-steel model was redesigned for the new takedown system, circa 1959, and is still advertised in High Standard catalogs.

Hi-Standard .22 Short Flite King

The Flite King, which was introduced in 1953, resembles the Sport King. It has a light alloy slide and has been dropped from the High Standard line.

Hi-Standard .22 L.R. Duramatic

The Duramatic was introduced in 1954 to compete with less expensive .22 automatics. The Duramatic has a cross-bolt safety mounted at the top left middle of the receiver. Sights are fixed and the barrel is removed by loosening the screw located on the underside of the receiver ahead of the triggerguard. The Duramatic does not have a conventional receiver or frame. The receiver does not extend down to form the grip frame; the grip is entirely of plastic. This pistol is made for Sears Roebuck as the J. C. Higgins Model 80. It is still in production.

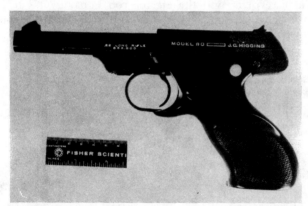

HI-STANDARD .22 L.R. DURAMATIC as J.C. HIGGINS Model 80.

Hi-Standard .22 Sentinel

The Sentinel is a side-swinging revolver which uses the .22 Short, Long, and Long Rifle cartridge. It was introduced in 1955 with blue and nickel finish. In 1957 it was introduced in pink, turquoise and gold in the Sentinel Snub, a 2.3-inch barreled revolver. The Sentinel Snub can still be obtained with blue or nickel finish; it is no longer carried in exotic colors. Exotic colors have also been tried in marketing rifles and shotguns without any outstanding success. The Sentinels have an aluminum frame. The Sentinel Imperial, introduced in

1961, has a squared butt with walnut stocks and comes with 4 or 6-inch barrel as does the standard Sentinel. The Sentinel Deluxe, introduced in 1965, is currently carried in the catalogs as is the Sentinel Snub. The Sentinels use coil mainsprings.

HI-STANDARD SENTINEL.

Hi-Standard .22 Double 9

This model was introduced in 1958 and is built on Western lines. It is a swing-out cylinder revolver and the ejector rod housing under the barrel is a dummy. Like the Sentinel, the Double 9 cylinder is released by pulling forward on the ejector rod. The Double 9 is still in production.

HI-STANDARD DOUBLE 9 .22.

Hi-Standard .22 Longhorn

The Longhorn is similar to the Double 9 but comes with 4.5-inch barrel and pearl-style grips, with 5.5-inch barrel and stag-style grips, and with 9.5-inch barrel and walnut grips. They all have a blue finish.

Hi-Standard .22 Posse

The Posse also resembles the Double 9 but has a 3.5-inch barrel, walnut grips and a brass-finished backstrap and guard. It does not have a dummy ejector rod housing.

Hi-Standard .22 Natchez

The Natchez resembles the other High Standard Western-style revolvers. It has a 4.5-inch barrel and "bird's-head" ivory-colored grips. All of the High Standard revolvers have 9-round cylinders and can use .22 Short, Long or Long Rifle cartridges.

HI-STANDARD REVOLVERS. Numbers 2, 4, 5, 6, 7, and 8 are the LONGHORN series. No. 1 is the NATCHEZ; No. 3 the POSSE.

CHARACTERISTICS OF HIGH STANDARD SEMI-AUTOMATIC PISTOLS

	G-380	G-E [1]	G-D	G-B	OLYMPIC (2d Model) [2]
Caliber:	.380 ACP.	.22 L.R.	.22 L.R.	.22 L.R.	.22 Short.
Barrel Length:	5"	4.5", 6.75"	4.5", 6.75"	4.5", 6.75"	4.5", 6.75"
Magazine Capacity:	6 rounds.	10 rounds.	10 rounds.	10 rounds.	10 rounds.
Sights:	Blade front; notched-bar rear.	Blade front; notched-bar rear adjustable for W and E.	Blade front; notched-bar rear adjustable for W and E.	Blade and notched bar.	Adjustable front blade on rib; notched-bar rear adjustable for W and E.
Weight:	2.5 lb.	2.4 lb. w/4.5"-barrel.	2.6 lb. w/4.5"-barrel.	2.1 lb. and 2.2 lb.	2.1 lb. and 2.4 lb.

Note: All models are of blowback operation and employing in-line detachable box magazines.
[1] First Model Olympic the same, but uses .22 Short and is 3-oz. lighter. Third Model Olympic the same, but slightly lighter.
[2] First Model Supermatic the same, but uses 22 L.R. and is 3 oz. heavier w/6.75"-barrel and 4 oz. heavier w/4.5" barrel. Second Model Supermatic same, but slightly lighter.

CHARACTERISTICS OF HIGH STANDARD .22 L.R. SEMI-AUTOMATIC PISTOLS

	Field King (1st Model)[1]	Sport King (1st Model)[2]	Duramatic	Supermatic Citation	Supermatic Trophy
Barrel Length:	4.5", 6.75"	4.5", 6.75"	4.5", 6.75"	8", 10"[3]	8", 10"[4]
Sights:	Blade front; notched-bar rear adjustable for W and E.	Blade and notched bar.	Blade and notched bar.	Ramp-mounted blade front; notched-bar rear adjustable for W and E.	Ramp-mounted blade front; notched-bar rear adjustable for W and E.
Weight:	2.3 lb. and 2.6 lb.	2.2 lb. and 2.4 lb.	2 lb. and 2.1 lb.	W/8" barrel, 2 lb. W/10" barrel, 3.3 lb. W/barrel weight.	W/8" barrel, 3.2 lb. W/10" barrel, 3.3 lb. W/barrel weight.

Note: These are all blowback models equipped with 10-round in-line detachable box magazines.

[1] Second Model Field King same, but slightly lighter.

[2] Second Model Sport King same, but slightly lighter in steel, also available w/lightweight alloy slide. Third Model Sport King (all-steel) essentially the same. First Model Flite King same as lightweight Second Model Sport King but uses .22 Short. Second Model Flite King same as Third Model Sport King, but chambered for .22 Short.

[3] Also comes w/6.75"-barrel, rear sight mounted on slide, weight 3.1 lb. w/barrel weight, or 5.5"-bull barrel, rear sight mounted on slide, weight 2.6 lb.

[4] Also comes with 6.75"-barrel, rear sight mounted on slide, weight 3.1 lb. w/barrel weight.

CHARACTERISTICS OF HIGH STANDARD .22 SEMI-AUTOMATIC PISTOLS

	Supermatic Tournament	Olympic (4th Model)	Olympic ISU[1]	Supermatic Trophy Military[2]	Supermatic Tournament Military
Caliber:	.22 L.R.	.22 Short.	.22 Short.	.22 L.R.	.22 L.R.
Barrel Length:	4.5", 6.75"	8"	6.75"	5.5", 7.25"	5.5", 6.75"
Sights:	These models all have ramp-mounted blade front and notched-bar rear adjustable for windage and elevation.				
Weight:	2.5 lb. and 2.75 lb.	3 lb.	2.5 lb.	2.76 lb. for both barrel lengths.	2.8 lb. for both barrel lengths.

Note: These are all blowback pistols equipped with 10-round in-line detachable box magazines.
[1] Olympic ISU Military is the same but weighs .5 oz. more.
[2] Supermatic Citation Military has same characteristics.

CHARACTERISTICS OF HIGH STANDARD DOUBLE-ACTION .22 REVOLVERS

	Sentinel	Sentinel Imperial	Sentinel Snub	Double 9
Barrel Length:	4", 6"	4", 6"	2.3"	5.5"
Weight:	1.4 lb. and 1.5 lb.	1.3 lb. and 1.6 lb.	1.2 lb.	1.75 lb.

	Posse	Natchez	Longhorn
Barrel Length:	3.5"	4.5"	4.5", 5.5", 9.5"
Weight:	1.4 lb.	1.6 lb.	1.6 lb., 1.75 lb., and 2 lb.

Note: These models all have 9-round cylinders in which Short, Long or Long Rifle cartridges may be used and all are equipped with blade and notch sights.

Hi-Standard .22 Derringer Model D-100

This weapon was introduced in .22 L.R. in 1962 and in .22 Winchester Magnum Rimfire in May 1963 (the Model DM 101). These are both 2-shot weapons with aluminum-alloy frame, steel barrels, dual extraction, and chambers recessed to protect the cartridge heads. The front of the triggerguard is cut away; a built-in hammer-block-safety prevents accidental discharge even if the arm is dropped. Of little utility except for defense, or as a sentimental type collector's item.

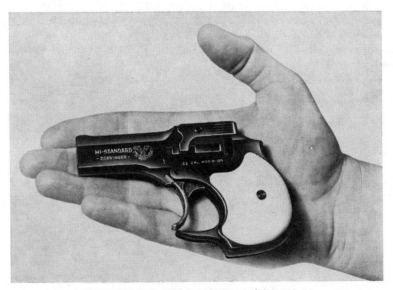

HI-STANDARD DERRINGER, Model D-100 .22.

IVER JOHNSON

Iver Johnson Arms and Cycle Works of Fitchburg, Mass. was established in 1871. They make inexpensive revolvers of good quality and have introduced several features such as their "Hammer the Hammer" safety design and the "Flash Control" cylinder. The cylinder has a rim on its front end which helps deflect flash, or lead splatter that might escape between the cylinder and the breech face of the barrel. This feature was introduced in 1954. The "Hammer the Hammer" design has the firing pin in the frame and the hammer does not engage the firing pin unless the trigger is being pulled. The hammer rests on the frame above the firing pin if there is no pressure on the trigger. Some Iver Johnson revolvers have a rebounding-type hammer.

Iver Johnson .22 Model 855 Armsworth

This single-action revolver was in production for a short time in the Fifties. It is a break-open design with automatic extractor and has a finger rest behind the trigger guard. The Armsworth has a rebounding type hammer and a one-piece checkered walnut grip. The rear sight is adjustable. This is the best

755

target-grade revolver Iver Johnson has made since WW II. It can be used with .22 Short, Long or Long Rifle cartridges.

Iver Johnson .22 Model 844 Supershot

The Supershot is a double-action version of the Armsworth, but differs from it somewhat internally as it has the "Hammer the Hammer" safety device.

Iver Johnson .22 Model 55 Target

This is a solid-frame revolver with rebounding hammer. The tenite grips have a thumb rest. The Model 55 had a ramp-type front sight; the current production model, the 55A, has a plain blade. The Model 55 does not have a fluted cylinder as does the Model 55A. Like all IJ .22 revolvers, it uses .22 Short, Long and Long Rifle cartridges.

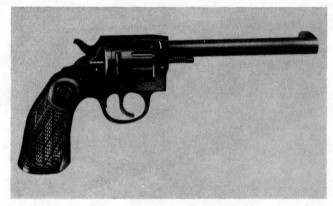

IVER JOHNSON .22 Model 55A.

IVER JOHNSON .22 Model 57A.

CHARACTERISTICS OF IVER JOHNSON .22 REVOLVERS

	Model 855 [1]	Model 844	Model 55A	Model 57A
Length Overall:	10.75"	9.25", 10.75"	9.25", 10.75"	9.25", 10.75"
Barrel Length:	6"	4.5", 6"	4.5", 6"	4.5", 6"
Sights:	Front blade adjustable for E; notched-bar rear adjustable for W.	Front blade adjustable for E; notched-bar rear adjustable for W.	Blade and notch.	Front blade adjustable for E; notched-bar rear adjustable for W.
Weight:	1.8 lb.	1.6 lb. and 1.8 lb.	Approx. 1.8 lb. in 6" barrel.	1.8 lb. w/6" barrel.

Note: Except for Model 855, these are double-action revolvers with cylinders chambered for 8 rounds in which Short, Long or Long Rifle cartridges may be used.
[1] Single-action.

CHARACTERISTICS OF IVER JOHNSON DOUBLE-ACTION REVOLVERS

	Model 55S-A	Model 50	Model 67 Viking [1]	Model 67S
Caliber:	.22 L.R., .32 S&W, .38 S&W.	.22 L.R.	.22 L.R.	.22 L.R., .32 S&W, .38 S&W.
Length Overall:	7"	11.25"	9.25", 11"	7"
Barrel Length:	2.5"	6"	4.5", 6"	2.75"
Sights:	Blade and notch.	Blade and notch.	Front blade adjustable for E; notched-bar rear adjustable for W.	Front blade adjustable for E; notched-bar rear adjustable for W.
Weight:	1.5 lb.	1.9 lb.	1.9 lb. and 2.1 lb.	1.6 lb.

Note: Cylinders of the .22 models listed accept 8 cartridges—Short, Long or Long Rifle; these revolvers in other than .22 caliber have cylinders chambered for 5 rounds.
[1] Model 66 Trailsman with 6"-barrel has the same characteristics as the 6"-barrel Viking model.

Iver Johnson .22 Model 57 Target

The Model 57 is basically the same as the Model 55, but has a front sight adjustable for elevation and rear sight adjustable for windage. It was made with 2.5, 4.5 and 6-inch barrels, but the current model—the 57A—has only 4.5 or 6-inch barrels. The Model 57 has a half-cock notch on the hammer; it does not have a fluted cylinder as does the Model 57A.

Iver Johnson .22 Model 55-S Cadet

The 55-S is a solid-frame revolver with 2.5 inch barrel. It does not have the "Hammer the Hammer" safety device; the front sight is of the ramp type. The cylinder of the 55-S is not fluted. The current model 55S-A, has a plain blade front sight, fluted cylinder, and may be obtained in the .32 S&W Short and Long and .38 S&W. The 55-S has walnut grips.

Iver Johnson .22 Model 50 Sidewinder

The Model 50 is a double-action Western-style revolver with spring-loaded ejector rod mounted under the barrel. It has a wide-spur hammer, half-cock notch and walnut grips.

IVER JOHNSON .22 Model 50.

IVER JOHNSON VIKING .22 cal. revolver, showng 6"-barrel.

Iver Johnson .22 Model 67 Viking

The Model 67 is a top-break revolver with the "Hammer the Hammer" safety feature. The front sight is adjustable for elevation and the rear sight is adjustable for windage. The bore is chromed and the plastic grips have a thumb rest. Ejection on the 60 series is manual; the ejector rod which is mounted under the barrel must be pushed to the rear to clear the chambers.

The Model 67S Snub is the short-barreled version of the Viking. It may be obtained chambered for the .32 S&W in addition to the .22.

Iver Johnson .22 Model 66 Trailsman

The Model 66 is the same as the Model 67 except that it has a rebounding-type hammer rather than the "Hammer the Hammer"-type safety used on the Model 67. The Model 66 is now made only with 6-inch barrel, but has been made with 2.75-inch barrel as well.

IVER JOHNSON .22 Model 66.

J. KIMBALL ARMS CO.

This firm, which opened in 1958 and went out of business in a relatively short time, produced a semi-automatic pistol chambered for the U.S. Caliber .30 Carbine cartridge. The Kimball pistol was a delayed-blowback design. It has

KIMBALL COMBAT Model with 3"-barrel, fixed sights.

Courtesy GUNS Magazine.

759

a grooved chamber reminiscent of the High Standard T3, and a barrel which recoils about 3/16-inch against a spring to delay opening until residual pressure has dropped. The Kimball was made in two models: a Target model with a 5-inch barrel and micro-adjustable rear sights and a Combat model with 3-inch barrel and fixed sights. Both models had 7-round magazines and weight was about 2 lb.

The Kimball failed because of design weaknesses—the rear slide lugs had a tendency to fracture—one failed in a test run by W. B. Edwards of *Guns Magazine* after 192 rounds had been fired. The carbine cartridge is much too hot to handle in a delayed-blowback mechanism of the type used in the Kimball. As a matter of interest, Smith & Wesson developed a revolver to fire the carbine cartridge during WW II. It was submitted for test in January, 1944, and 1,232 rounds were fired from it with no malfunctions. The average instrumental velocity, measured at 53 feet, was 1,277 feet per second and an extreme spread of 4.18 inches with a mean radius of 1.39 inches was obtained at 25 yards, using both hands while shooting from a sandbag rest. The blast was very sharp and caused much discomfort to the shooter. All in all, the caliber .30 carbine cartridge is really not very suitable for pistols.

KIMBALL TARGET Model with 5"-barrel, micro-sight.

Courtesy GUNS Magazine.

MBA ASSOCIATES

This firm, located at San Ramon, California, developed the Gyrojet, a rocket cartridge. The Gyrojet is a self-contained rocket-propelled bullet which has the rocket motor contained in the base of the bullet. The base plate is drilled to provide angled venturis, or nozzles, and a cartridge primer is located in the center of the base plate. The angled nozzles spin the bullet in flight, giving it stability. As illustrated in the diagram, action of the hammer is the reverse of what usually occurs in small arms. The hammer swings rearward engaging the nose of the projectile driving it backward so that the primer engages the fixed firing pin, which is mounted at the rear of the barrel launcher, igniting the rocket motor and causing the rocket/bullet to move forward. In moving forward, the rocket/bullet cams the hammer down so that the hammer engages the sear and another rocket/bullet is fed into firing position by the magazine follower. If the trigger is pressed again, the process will be repeated. Gyrojet ammunition has been made in 7.62mm, 13mm and 20mm. The 13mm is the size used in handguns.

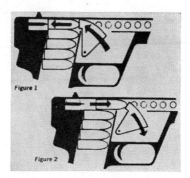

Fig. 1 arrows show how forward hammer drives Gyrojet back against fixed firing pin. Fig. 2 arrows show how ignited Gyrojet recocks hammer by moving it forward and down to clear vented launcher tube.

MBA Mark I Gyrojet Handgun

This 13mm arm has a magazine which holds 5 rocket/bullets. The barrel/-launcher tube has a series of ports along both sides—18 on each side on the 5-inch barrel model, 12 on each side on the 2-inch barrel model. These ports prevent pressure from building up in the barrel/launcher which is an aluminum-alloy casting made in two sections with a ported steel liner tube. A safety, which blocks the firing pin, is fitted on the left rear of the arm. The Mark I with 2-inch barrel weighs .81 pounds and the Mark I with a 5-inch barrel weighs one pound. The 5-inch barrel version could be obtained with black finish and antique nickel finish. The Mark I Presentation Model is specially engraved and mounted in a fitted walnut case with 10 dummy rockets and a bronze medallion of Robert H. Goddard. It also has a 5-inch barrel. The first 1000 Gyrojets, available in June 1965, were "Presentation" models.

MBA MARK I (Collectors' Model) Gyrojet 13mm Rocket Pistol, cased with rockets.

761

The standard 13mm Gyrojet weighs 185 grains. It has a maximum, all-burned velocity, of 1250 feet per second at 0.12-second after launch. The bullet/rocket is made of heat-resisting steel. Maximum energy of this round is 700 foot pounds. A 110-grain high velocity load was also made with an all-burned velocity of 2300 feet per second which equals an energy of 1250 foot pounds. Other loads developed were a 275-grain Gyrojet at 1500 feet per second, a 310-grain Gyrojet at 400 feet per second, and a 110 Target Gyrojet at 400 f.p.s.

.45 ACP cartridge beside 13mm Gyrojet rocket, and recovered Gyrojet that penetrated sheet steel.

The Gyrojet has the advantage of light weight of gun/launcher and light weight of ammunition, but there is a drawback to everything. The main problem with free-flight rockets is accuracy; larger free-flight rockets have CEP (circular error probable) of from 10-15 mils. A mil equals one meter at 1000 meters, or one yard at a thousand yards. This is relatively poor accuracy by gun standards. MBA, in 1965, claimed that they could guarantee 5-mil accuracy, but this is still high for a gun. Continual improvements in the rocket field, development of more even burning propellents, better nozzle control, etc., are improving accuracy standards of the larger rockets and the results of these technological advances should be applicable to smaller rockets at a later date.

REMINGTON

Remington's re-entry into the pistol field for the first time in over thirty years is essentially a modified Model 600 carbine action mounted on a plastic pistol-type stock.

Remington .221 Model XP-100

The single-shot bolt-action with 10.5-inch barrel is mounted on a stock of Zytel plastic. Introduced in 1962, this arm brought with it the Remington .221

REMINGTON Model XP-100, cal. .221.

Fireball cartridge. The XP-100 has an open notch rear sight adjustable for windage and elevation and a fixed front sight mounted on a ventilated rib. The receiver is grooved for a scope.

The XP-100 is 16.5-inches long and weighs 3.75 pounds. The grip is shaped to fit either the left or right hand and is belled out at the bottom to produce a palm rest.

RUGER

Sturm, Ruger and Co. is rather an unusual firm in that it was established, expanded and has done a highly successful business in sporting arms—originally only handguns—during a period in which most of the major arms producers that were not already divisions of larger and more diversified corporations, were becoming so. Starting in 1949 with the Standard Model automatic, the company has moved steadily forward. Most of this success is attributed to the design skill of Bill Ruger.

Ruger .22 L.R. Standard Model

Introduced in 1949, the Standard Model caught on immediately because of its design and its low price. The Standard Model's grip frame section, which contains the firing mechanism, is made of two heavy gauge steel stampings which are welded together. The barrel is screwed into the circular receiver, which is held to the grip frame by heavy steel lugs and a cross-bolt and the bolt reciprocates within the receiver. The trigger is made from an aluminum die casting. The button-type safety, located on the top left rear of the grip frame, locks both the sear and the bolt. The firing pin is of rectangular section with chisel point. The magazine catch is mounted at the bottom rear of the grip frame. The "Standard" model may be had with 4.75 inch or 6-inch barrel. Since the fixed rear sight is mounted on the receiver, it does not recoil. The only screws in the arm are those used to mount the plastic grips; coil springs are used throughout the pistol.

RUGER STANDARD Model .22 L.R. pistol.

Ruger .22 L.R. Mark I Target Model

The Mark I Target Model is similar to the Standard Model, but has an adjustable rear sight, an undercut front sight, a 6.8-inch barrel and a specially finished trigger. The sight radius of the Mark I Target is 9.3 inches. This pistol was introduced in 1950.

RUGER MARK I Target pistol.

Ruger .22 L.R. Mark I Bull Barrel

This pistol is the same as the Mark I Target, but is equipped with a 5.5-inch heavy, untapered barrel. The undercut front sight is mounted on a ramp. The sight radius is 8 inches. This model was introduced in 1963.

RUGER .22 L.R. MARK I BULL BARREL.

Ruger .22 Single Six

The Single Six, which is patterned on the Colt Single-Action Army, was introduced in 1953 at which time the Colt was out of production. The Rugers have always been among the best, if not the best, of the post-WW II single-actions modeled on the old Colt. As first made, the loading gate on the Single Six was flat, but in 1957 it was changed to fit the contour of the receiver like that of the Colt. The Single Six is not as large as the Colt Single Action Army and the grip frame is of aluminum alloy. The frame itself is made of chrome

RUGER SINGLE-SIX .22 L.R. revolver.

molybdenum steel. The grips are of walnut, and Nylok screws are used at all points where trouble has been experienced in the past with single action screws loosening up. Internal components have been redesigned as compared to the old Colt Single Action Army and coil springs are used throughout. In 1959 the Single Six, which originally was made for .22 Short, Long and Long Rifle, was brought out in .22 Winchester Magnum Rimfire as well.

Ruger .22 Convertible Single Six

Introduced in 1961, this version of the Single Six is furnished with two cylinders; one chambered for .22 Short, Long, and Long Rifle and the other for the .22 Winchester Magnum Rimfire.

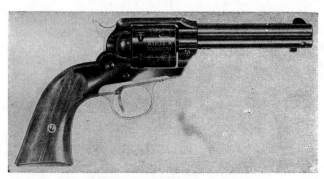

RUGER BEARCAT .22 revolver.

Ruger .22 Super Single Six Convertible

This is a deluxe version of the Single Six Convertible which has a ramp-mounted front sight and an adjustable rear sight which is protected by ribs or "ears" of the top strap. Introduced in 1964.

Ruger .22 Bearcat

The Bearcat is a lightweight single-action with aluminum-alloy frame. The cylinder is not fluted and it has a notched top strap rear sight. The Bearcat uses .22 Short, Long or Long Rifle and was introduced in March 1958.

Ruger .357 Magnum Blackhawk

The Blackhawk, which appeared in 1955, is one of the best-made single-action revolvers available. The Blackhawk is a very strong arm, well-made of good materials. The Blackhawk has a rebounding-type firing pin mounted in the frame. The rear sight is adjustable for elevation and windage. In 1961, the design was slightly modified by the addition of protective back strap ribs to the sight and slight changes in the grip. As with all other Ruger pistols, only

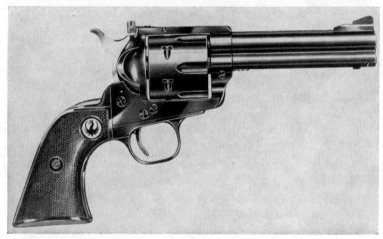

RUGER BLACKHAWK .357 revolver.

coil springs are used. Recently, Ruger introduced two new Blackhawks; one is chambered for the .30 caliber carbine cartridge which is furnished only with 7.5-inch barrel, and the other is a .357 Magnum—9mm Parabellum Convertible. The Convertible is supplied with both .357 Magnum and 9mm Parabellum cylinders. Its characteristics are the same as the .357 Blackhawk.

Ruger .44 Magnum Super Blackhawk

After experimenting with the standard Blackhawk chambered for the .44 Magnum in 1956, Ruger brought out a new revolver for this powerful cartridge in the same year. The Super Blackhawk has a larger frame than the Blackhawk and the cylinder is not fluted. The rear of the triggerguard is flattened

CHARACTERISTICS OF RUGER PISTOLS AND REVOLVERS

	Standard	Mark I Target	Mark I Bull Barrel	Single Six	Single Six Convertible[1]
Caliber:	.22 L.R.	.22 L.R.	.22 L.R.	.22 S, L, and L.R.	.22 S, L, and L.R.; .22 WMR.
System of Operation:	Blowback, semi-automatic.	Blowback, semi-automatic.	Blowback, semi-automatic.	Single-action revolver.	Single-action revolver.
Length Overall:	8.75″, 10″	10.8″	9.5″	11.8″	11.8″, 12.8″, 15.8″
Barrel Length:	4.75″, 6″	6.8″	5.5″	5.5″	5.5″, 6.5″, 9.5″
Feed Device:	9-round, in-line detachable box magazine.	9-round, in-line detachable box magazine.	9-round, in-line detachable box magazine.	6-round cylinder.	6-round cylinder.
Sights:	Blade and notched bar.	Undercut blade front; notched-bar rear fully adjustable.	Undercut blade front; notched-bar rear fully adjustable.	Blade and notched bar.	Blade and notched bar.
Weight:	2.2 lb. and 2.3 lb.	2.6 lb.	2.6 lb.	2.1 lb.	2.1 lb, 2.2 lb., 2.3 lb.

[1] Super Single Six Convertible same, but has adjustable rear sight and does not come with 9.5″-barrel.

CHARACTERISTICS OF RUGER REVOLVERS

	Blackhawk	.41 Magnum Blackhawk	Super Blackhawk	Hawkeye
Caliber:	.357 Magnum; .30 Carbine; 9mm Parabellum.	.41 Magnum.	.44 Magnum.	.256 Win. Magnum.
System of Operation:	Single-action revolver.	Single-action revolver.	Single-action revolver.	Swinging block single-shot.
Length Overall:	10.1"; 12", 13.1"	10.25", 12.1"	13.1"	14.1"
Barrel Length:	4.6"; 6.5", 7.5" (.30 Carbine)	4.6", 6.5"	7.5"	8.5"
Feed Device:	6-round cylinder.	6-round cylinder.	6-round cylinder.	Single-shot.
Weight:	2.3 lb., 2.5 lb., 2.7 lb.	2.3 lb., 2.5 lb.	3 lb.	2.8 lb.

Note: A blade front sight and a notched-bar rear adjustable for windage and elevation are standard with each of these models.

in a fashion reminiscent of the Col. Dragoon. This is a massive revolver and is one of the few from which the .44 Magnum cartridge can be fired without discomfort. The target-type trigger is wide and grooved and the hammer-spur is wide and of low contour.

RUGER SUPER BLACKHAWK .44 revolver.

Ruger .41 Magnum Blackhawk

Ruger uses the .44 Magnum Super Blackhawk frame for the .41 Magnum; other than that it is the same as the standard Blackhawk.

RUGER HAWKEYE .256 Win. Magnum.

Ruger .256 Win. Magnum Hawkeye

After an unsuccessful attempt to chamber the Blackhawk for the .256 Win. Magnum, Ruger introduced the Hawkeye, a single-shot which uses the Blackhawk frame, in 1963. The chamber is in the barrel and the cylinder has been replaced with a breechblock. The firing pin is mounted in the breechblock and the ejector rod has an extractor which engages the case at the rim. The Hawkeye has been dropped from the Ruger catalog.

SAVAGE

The Savage Arms Corp. of Westfield, Mass., now a division of American Hardware, is producing a pistol for the first time since 1928.

Savage .22 Model 101

The Model 101 is a single-action, single-shot pistol built to look like a single-action Western revolver. The 101, which will fire .22 Short, Long or Long Rifle cartridges, has a one-piece die-cast frame. The barrel, which is of alloy steel, is integral with the false cylinder and swings out away from the frame to load and eject. The spring-loaded ejector rod is mounted below the barrel and is attached to a rim-type extractor.

SAVAGE Model 101 .22 pistol.

The Model 101 is 9.5 inches long with a 5.5-inch barrel and weighs 1.25 pounds. It has a blade front sight and notched-bar type rear sight. The hammer is of the rebounding type and the grips are of compressed impregnated wood.

SHERIDAN

Sheridan Products Inc., of Racine, Wisc. introduced a low-cost single-shot pistol in 1953. About 20,000 were made before production was discontinued in 1962. The firm still makes airguns.

Sheridan .22 Knocabout

This inexpensive single-shot may be used with the .22 Short, Long or Long Rifle cartridge. It has a tipping-barrel type action which is operated by pressing the release button located ahead of the trigger. The barrel is forced up by spring pressure and forces the extractor to the rear extracting the fired case.

SHERIDAN KNOCABOUT Single-shot .22 pistol.

The safety, located on the left rear top of the frame, blocks the hammer. The mainspring is a coil type, and the firing pin is a floating design. The "Knocabout" weighs 1.5 pounds and is 6.75 inches long with a 5-inch barrel.

SMITH AND WESSON

Smith & Wesson, Inc., (S&W) of Springfield, Mass. is now well into its second century of quality handgun manufacturing. A number of new revolvers have been introduced since WW II and some of the older models have been continued. Smith & Wesson reentered the automatic pistol field in 1955, and now manufactures .22 and higher-powered guns. Kent Bellah reported that S&W had trouble with the "U" and "W"-type springs that they introduced on the "N"-frame guns around 1955. The trouble was faulty ignition with some ammunition types and brands due to light hammer blow. Bellah, who had very extensive shooting experience and close contacts with many shooters and police officials, stated that he had received many reports of this problem. It must be kept in mind, however, that every major U.S. manufacturer of automobiles has had to call in cars within the last several years for modification of defects, some being in critical components such as the steering gear. Smith & Wesson is a reliable manufacturer and will remedy defects found in their arms as readily, or possibly even more readily, than the automobile manufacturers.

S&W .22 L.R. K-22 Masterpiece (Model 17)

This double-action revolver was introduced in 1931, but has been modified considerably since that time. In 1940, a micrometer-adjustable rear sight, an anti-backlash trigger and speed-lock action were incorporated. The third model, which went into production in 1946, introduced the barrel rib and the magna-type grips.

S&W .22 MRF K-22 Masterpiece (Model 48)

This revolver is identical to the Model 17, but is chambered for the .22 Winchester Magnum Rimfire cartridge.

S&W .22 L.R. 1953—.22/32 Target (Model 35)

This revolver was introduced in 1935 and modified in 1953 by the fitting of a new sight, flat-top cylinder release, Magna-type grips, and 6-inch barrel.

S&W .22 1953 Model 22/32 TARGET.

S&W .22 L.R. 1953—.22/32 Kit Gun (Model 34)

Differs from the original in sights and grips. Made with 2 inch and 4-inch barrels. Round or square butt.

S&W .22 1953 Model 22/32 KIT GUN.

772

S&W .22 MRF 1955 .22/32 Kit Gun Airweight (Model 43)

Same as Kit Gun, but has 3.5-inch barrel and is lighter.

S&W .22 1955 Model 22/32 KIT GUN AIRWEIGHT.

S&W .22 MRF 1960 .22/32 Kit Gun (Model 51)

Same as other Kit Gun models, but chambered for the .22 WMR and supplied with 3.5-inch barrel and round or square butt.

S&W .22 Combat Masterpiece (Model 18)

The .22 Combat Masterpiece is like the K-22, but has a 4-inch barrel and a Baughman quick-draw sight.

S&W .22 COMBAT MASTERPIECE.

S&W .22 Jet Magnum (Model 53)

The .22 Magnum was introduced in 1961 and is an interesting and different revolver. It is built on the small K-frame and the cylinder is chambered for the .22 Remington Jet center-fire cartridge. This cartridge has a listed muzzle-

773

velocity of 2190 f.p.s. with a 40-grain bullet. In addition to the Jet center-fire cartridge, the Model 53 can, by the use of chamber inserts, use .22 Short, Long or Long Rifle ammunition. There are two floating firing pins mounted in the frame, one for the center-fire .22 Jet and one for the .22 rimfire. Flipping a button on the top of the hammer to the rear causes the hammer to strike the uppr (rimfire) firing pin; pushing the button forward causes the hammer to strike the center-fire firing pin. The Model 53 has target stocks, target sights, and comes with 4, 6 or 8.3-inch barrel.

S&W .22 Magnum, Model 53, with .22 L.R. auxiliary cylinder, chamber insert for the standard cylinder, .22 Jet cartridge, and .22 L.R. and Short rounds. Note dual-ignition button on top of hammer.

Kent Bellah reported problems with case setback when firing the .22 Rem. Jet in this revolver. He advised that the chambers should be absolutely dry as well as the cartridge. It is an established fact that lubricated cases and/or chambers do increase chamber pressure. The British use oiled cases in their proof loads to build up chamber pressure. Bellah mentioned that one gun-smith roughened the chambers to cause them to "grasp" the case as it expanded.

S&W .22 L.R. Model 41

The Model 41 is a blowback-operated .22 target pistol. It was introduced in October, 1951, and is S&W's first .22 target automatic. Originally equipped with a 7.3-inch barrel, in 1958 a 5-inch barrel was also introduced. The detachable muzzle-brake is not usable on the 5-inch barrel. There are barrel weights available for the 7.3-inch barrel. The Model 41 has checkered-walnut grips with thumb rests and the wide grooved trigger has adjustable trigger-stop. The micro-click rear sight is mounted on a barrel extension and therefore does not recoil. In 1961 the Model 41 became available in .22 Short for Olympic

S&W .22 Model 41.

and ISU type events. In 1964, the Heavy Barrel model with 5.5-inch barrel appeared. The Heavy Barrel weighs about an ounce more than the standard Model 41 with 7.3-inch barrel. In 1965, a version of the Model 41 Heavy Bar-

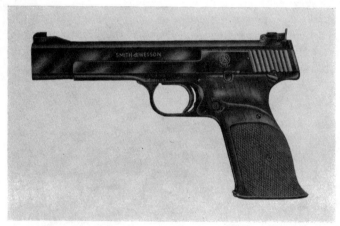

S&W .22 M41 HEAVY BARREL.

rel with extendable front sight was introduced. This pistol has an adjustable sight radius which is obtained by having the front sight mounted on a sliding bar.

The Model 41 series has a button-type magazine release on the left side of the grip and the safety is mounted on the top left rear of the receiver.

S&W .22 L.R. Model 46

The Model 46 is essentially a less-expensive version of the Model 41. It has molded nylon stocks with thumb rests. It does not have a muzzle-brake, checking on the top of the barrel, cocking indicator, adjustable trigger-stop and has a

775

dull blue finish as opposed to the bright blue finish of the Model 41. The Model 46 can be obtained with 5 and 7-inch normal weight barrel or with 5.5-inch heavy barrel. As with the Model 41, the slide-stop holds the slide to the rear after the last shot is fired.

S&W .22 Model 46.

S&W .32 Regulation Police Model 31

Same as pre-WW II revolver, but has ramp-mounted front sight and flat type cylinder-release latch. It is made with 2, 3, and 4-inch barrel and a square butt.

S&W .32 REGULATION POLICE.

S&W .32 Hand Ejector Model 30

The same as the Model 31, but has rounded butt.

S&W .32 K-32 Masterpiece Model 16

Same as K-22 and K-38 except for caliber.

S&W .38 S&W Regulation Police Model 33

The same as the .32 Regulation Police, but has 5-round rather than 6-round cylinder. Made only with 4-inch barrel.

S&W .38 S&W Terrier Model 32

The Terrier, which is made with a 2-inch barrel, has a 5-round cylinder. It has a serrated ramp-type front sight, a low hammer spur, the new flat-type cylinder-release latch and is available in blue or nickel.

S&W 38 TERRIER.

S&W .38 Special Chiefs Special Model 36

The Model 36 was introduced in October 1950. It can be obtained with 2 or 3-inch barrel and has a 5-round cylinder and serrated-ramp front sight. Checkered walnut Magna-type grips are fitted. This was the first of the snub-nose lightweight belly guns of post-war design to appear. In October 1952, the Chiefs Special Airweight Model 37 appeared. Originally fitted with aluminum cylinders, which were not too successful, the Model 37 now uses steel cylinders. These revolvers may be obtained with rounded or square butt and blue or nickel finish.

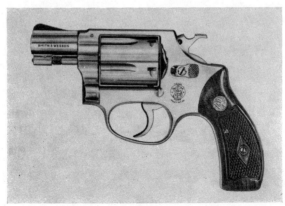

S&W 38 Special CHIEFS SPECIAL STAINLESS.

777

S&W .38 Special Chiefs Special Stainless Model 60

This revolver is the same as the Model 36 with 2-inch barrel, but is made of stainless steel. It appeared in 1966 and has a rounded butt.

S&W .38 Special Bodyguard Airweight Model 38

The Bodyguard Airweight, which was introduced in 1955, has a light-alloy frame, a 5-round cylinder, flat cylinder-release latch and a hammer shroud integral with the frame. The hammer spur can be engaged with the thumb to cock the revolver for single-action fire if so desired. This is a true pocket revolver as it can be withdrawn rapidly from the pocket or fired from the pocket without fear of catching the hammer spur. The Bodyguard can also be obtained in an all-steel construction—the Model 49. Both models are made only with round butt in blue or nickel finish.

S&W .38 Special BODYGUARD AIRWEIGHT.

S&W .38 Special CENTENNIAL.

778

S&W .38 Special Centennial Model 40

The Centennial was put on the market on Smith & Wesson's 100th birthday. It is strongly reminiscent of the old top-break S&W Safety or New Departure model, commonly known as the "lemon squeezer," which was dropped from the line in 1940. The Model 40 is a swing-out cylinder model with 5-round cylinder. The hammer is completely shrouded and a grip safety is fitted. Also made in Airweight—Model 42—which has an aluminum-alloy frame.

S&W .38 Special .38/44 Outdoorsman Model 23

Except for minor changes, identical to the pre-war model; now made with 6-inch barrel. The .38/44 Heavy Duty Model 20 is similar, but does not have micro-adjustable rear sight and ramp-mounted front sight. Model 24 1950 44 Target is the same as the Outdoorsman, but is chambered for the .44 Special cartridge. Model 21 1950 .44 Military is the same as the Heavy Duty, but is also chambered for the .44 Special.

S&W .38 Military & Police Model 10

Same as pre-war revolver, but now made with Magna-type grips, short hammer action, wider hammer spur, and serrated-ramp front sight. Obtainable with 2, 4, 5 or 6-inch barrel and round or square butt. The Military and Police is made in a heavy-barrel model with 4-inch barrel and square butt; this model is 4 ounces heavier than the standard Military & Police. The Military & Police Airweight—Model 12 is made with 2 and 4-inch barrel, round or square butt, flat cylinder-release latch, and aluminum-alloy frame. All the Military and Police models are made in blue and nickel finish. These revolvers use the K-frame and have 6-round cylinders. Over 2,500,000 Military & Police model revolvers had been made by August 1959.

S&W .38 Special MILITARY & POLICE AIRWEIGHT.

S&W .38 Special K-38 Masterpiece Model No. 14

Same as K-22 and K-32; is fitted with barrel rib, micro-adjustable rear sight and Magna stocks. A fine target gun in its class which has been copied on a

779

world-wide basis. It is made with a 6-inch barrel and since 1959 with an 8.3-inch barrel. By 1952, S&W had the weight of all three models adjusted so that all of the Masterpiece revolvers with 6-inch barrels weigh the same—2.3 pounds with 5 rounds in their 6-round cylinders. In the early 1950s about 200 K-38s were made for the .38 S&W cartridge for export to Canada and Great Britain.

S&W K-38 MASTERPIECE with target hammer, trigger and stocks.

In 1961, the K-38 Masterpiece Single Action Model 14 was introduced. The short action of this revolver has been further shortened by 1/8th-inch, giving faster lock time. Improving the revolver for target use, S&W supplied kits with target hammer, grooved target trigger assembly, trigger stop and rebound slide spring for conversion of the standard double-action K-38 Masterpiece by gunsmiths. The factory will also do this conversion.

S&W K-38 MASTERPIECE SINGLE ACTION, Model 14, showing standard short action has been shortened about ⅛" more for faster lock time.

S&W .38 Special Combat Masterpiece Model 15

This is a modification of the K-38 which was introduced in October, 1949. Originally the Model 15 was fitted only with 4-inch barrel, but is now made with a 2-inch barrel as well. It has a Baughman "quick-draw" front sight, but is otherwise much the same as the K-38 Masterpiece Model 14.

S&W .38 Special COMBAT MASTERPIECE.

S&W .357 Magnum Combat Magnum Model 19

Introduced in January, 1956, the Model 19 uses the K-frame and is therefore comparatively light for a revolver of this caliber. Originally produced with 4-inch barrel only, a 6-inch barrel version appeared in 1964 and a 2.5-inch barrel version with round butt and Magna grips came out in 1966. The 4 and 6-inch barrel versions have a square butt with target grips. The front sight is of the Baughman "quick-draw" type and the K-frame size micrometer rear sight are fitted. All versions are available with either blue or nickel finish.

S&W .375 COMBAT MAGNUM.

S&W .357 Magnum Model 27

This revolver, with N-type frame, introduced the .357 Magnum cartridge in 1935. With the exception of the short action, new-design hammer spur and other minor improvements, it is the same as the pre-WW II production. This is possibly the finest type revolver made by Smith & Wesson, and is now obtainable with 3.5, 5, 6, 6.5 and 8.3-inch barrels. It is available with bright blue or nickel finish.

S&W .357 Magnum Highway Patrolman Model 28

A lower-priced version of the Model 27 made with 4 or 6-inch barrel, the Model 28 was introduced in 1954. Available only with standard blue finish which is not as highly polished as that of the Model 27.

S&W 357 Magnum HIGHWAY PATROLMAN.

S&W .41 Magnum Military & Police Model 58

The Model 58 has a 4-inch barrel on the heavy N-frame and is similar to the Model 20 Heavy Duty. It has fixed sights and a square butt. This revolver was apparently developed with the law-enforcement trade in mind. This is a larger revolver than the Model 10 Military & Police which has a K-type frame.

S&W .41 MILITARY & POLICE.

S&W .41 Magnum Model 57

This beautifully-finished revolver introduced the Remington-developed .41 Magnum cartridge in April 1964. It is identical to the .44 Magnum Model 29 which in turn is basically the same as the .357 Magnum Model 27. The Model 57 has oversized target grips, a "red" ramp with a 4, 6 or 8.3-inch barrel. It is available with bright blue or nickel finish.

S&W .44 Magnum Model 29

The Model 29 introduced the powerful .44 Magnum cartridge, developed by Remington in November, 1955. This is one of the world's most powerful handguns and certainly one of the best made and beautifully finished. This is a heavy gun—3.2 pounds with 8.3-inch barrel—but the weight is appreciated when firing the .44 Magnum cartridge which has over three times the muzzle-energy of the .45 Automatic. Firing this cartridge in a light gun or a gun with an awkward grip can be a very unpleasant experience. The Model 29 has over-size target grips. The .44 Special and .44 Russian cartridge can also be used in the Model 29.

S&W .44 Magnum Model 29.

S&W .45 ACP Model 1950 Target Model 26

The Model 26, which was made with 6.5-inch barrel, is basically the same as the .38/44 Outdoorsman. It is no longer carried in the S&W catalog.

S&W .45 ACP 1950 Army Model 22

This is an updated version of the Model 1917 Army. It has a notch rear sight and blade front sight, Magna grips, a square butt and a 5.5-inch barrel. The Model 22, as the other Smith & Wesson .45 ACP revolvers, uses the .45 ACP with three-round clips that grip the rim of the .45 Auto Rim cartridge.

S&W .45 ACP 1955 TARGET.

S&W .45 ACP 1955 .45 Target Model 25

The Model 25 has a heavy 6.5-inch ribbed barrel, target grips, target hammer, target trigger and target sights. It is the best target-grade double-action revolver available for the .45 Automatic cartridge. It is not quite as nicely finished as the Model 27, 29, or 57, but is still a very handsome piece.

S&W 9mm Parabellum Model 39

The Model 39 was put in full production in November, 1954. It is a double-action, recoil-operated automatic with aluminum-alloy receiver and mainspring housing. The pistol has a manual safety on the left rear side of the frame which drops the hammer on a steel hammer block when put on *Safe*. There is also a magazine safety which prevents discharge when the magazine is removed. The Model 39 has an inertia-type firing pin. The barrel of the Model 39 which has one locking rib, tips to unlock.

S&W 9mm Parabellum Model 39.

A single-action version, the Model 44, of this pistol was made in limited quantities. The Model 39 has a button-type magazine release on the left side of the receiver behind the trigger guard. It can be obtained with a blue or nickel finish.

Field-Stripping. The Model 39 is relatively easy to field-strip. Remove magazine and clear the pistol by pulling slide to the rear. Release slide and put safety in the upper (fire) position. Press the slide stop from the right side and draw slide to the rear until the cut-out in the lower left of the slide aligns with the slide stop. Withdraw the slide stop and pull slide forward off the frame. Turn slide upside down; compress recoil spring and remove recoil spring and recoil-spring guide. Remove barrel bushing by rotating and pulling forward. To reassemble, reverse the above steps—the ejector and sear-release lever must be depressed to move the slide to the rear over them.

S&W .38 Special Model 52

This recoil-operated automatic is chambered for the .38 S&W Special Midrange wad-cutter cartridge. It is basically the same as the Model 39, but has an adjustable trigger stop, an improved micrometer-click sight which adjusts ½-inch for windage and 1-inch for elevation at 50 yards, and a target front sight with 1/8th-inch blade.

The Model 52 can be used strictly as a single-action automatic—like the .45 Colt Model 1911A1. It can be used as a double-action by turning the double-action screw in the receiver downwards with an Allen wrench. The Model 52 was introduced in 1961 after Smith & Wesson had produced a limited number of these pistols for the Army Advanced Marksmanship Unit (AAMU) chambered for the .38 AMU cartridge. This is a semi-rim cartridge made in limited quantity

S&W .38 Special Model 52.

for the AAMU by Western and Remington, having the same characteristics as the .38 Special cartridge except for its extractor groove.

This is a tipping-barrel design with one locking rib on the barrel which engages a mating recess in the receiver. The barrel bushing is screwed into the end of the receiver and the portion of the barrel which engages the bushing is enlarged and rounded and acts like a ball bearing in the locking and unlocking process, i.e., it rotates up and down. This bushing and barrel design tend to cut down barrel bushing/barrel wear which, especially if uneven, is one of the primary causes of accuracy loss in tipping-barrel automatic pistols of the basic or modified Browning design. The S&W design eventually wears, as will any similar arrangement, but wear should be even, i.e., the same on top, bottom, and sides. The bushing, of course, must be kept tight or uneven wear will result. Uneven wear of the barrel bushing of tipping barrels usually results in shifts in the center of bullet impact—a condition which is, basically, more distressing than encountering an even enlargement in the gun's grouping.

785

TYPICAL POST-WW II SMITH & WESSON PISTOLS AND REVOLVERS

	Model 41 [1]	Model 46 [2]	Model 18	Model 53	Model 39
Caliber:	.22 L.R. or .22 Short.	.22 L.R.	.22 S, L or L.R.	.22 Rem. Jet; .22 S, L or L.R.	9mm Parabellum.
System of Operation:	Blowback, semi-automatic.	Blowback, semi-automatic.	Double-action revolver.	Double-action revolver.	Double-action recoil-operated semi-automatic.
Length Overall:	9", 12"	8.6", 10.6"	9.1"	9.25", 11.25", 13.25"	7.4"
Barrel Length:	5", 7.3"	5", 7"	4"	4", 6", 8.3"	4"
Feed Device:	10-round, in-line detachable box magazine.	10-round, in-line detachable box magazine.	6-round cylinder.	6-round cylinder.	8-round, in-line detachable box magazine.
Sights:	Undercut blade front; notched-bar rear fully adjustable.	Undercut blade front; notched-bar rear fully adjustable.	Front blade on ramp; notched-bar rear fully adjustable.	Front blade on ramp; notched-bar rear fully adjustable.	Blade front; notched-bar rear fully adjustable.
Weight:	2.7 lb. w/7.3"-barrel.	2.6 lb. w/7"-barrel.	2.3 lb.	2.5 lb. w/ 6"-barrel.	1.6 lb.

[1] Model 41 Heavy barrel as above, but has 5.5"-barrel and weighs 1 oz. more.
[2] Model 46 Heavy barrel as above, but has 5.5"-barrel and weighs 5 oz. more.

TYPICAL POST-WW II SMITH AND WESSON PISTOLS AND REVOLVERS

	Model 52	Model 38 [1]	Model 40 [2]	Model 32	Model 36 [3]
Caliber:	.38 Special.	.38 Special.	.38 Special.	.38 S&W.	.38 Special.
System of Operation:	Double-action recoil-operated semi-automatic.	Double-action revolver.	Double-action revolver.	Double-action revolver.	Double-action revolver.
Length Overall:	8.6"	6.3"	6.5"	6.25"	6.5", 7.5"
Barrel Length:	5"	2"	2"	2"	2", 3"
Feed Device:	5-round, in-line detachable box magazine.	5-round cylinder.	5-round cylinder.	5-round cylinder.	5-round cylinder.
Sights:	Front blade on ramp; notched-bar rear fully adjustable.	Blade and notch.	Blade and notch.	Blade and notch.	Blade and notch.
Weight:	2.6 lb.	.93 lb.	1.2 lb	1.1 lb.	1.2 lb.

[1] Model 49 all-steel version of Model 38 weighs 1.3 lb.
[2] Model 42 is the same as Model 40 but is Airweight—.8 lb.
[3] Model 37 is the same as Model 36, but is Airweight—.9 lb.

TYPICAL SMITH AND WESSON POST-WW II DOUBLE-ACTION REVOLVERS

	Model 60	Model 15	Model 19	Model 28
Caliber:	.38 Special.	.38 Special.	.357 Magnum.	.357 Magnum
Length Overall:	6.5"	7.1", 9.1"	7.5", 9.5", 11.5"	9.25", 11.25"
Barrel Length:	2"	2", 4"	2.5", 4", 6"	4", 6"
Cylinder Capacity:	5 rounds.	6 rounds.	6 rounds.	6 rounds.
Sights:	Blade and notch.	Front blade on ramp; notched-bar rear fully adjustable.	Front blade on ramp; notched-bar rear fully adjustable.	Front blade on ramp; notched-bar rear fully adjustable.
Weight:	1.2 lb.	1.9 lb. and 2.1 lb.	1.9 lb. in short barrel.	2.6 lb. and 2.7 lb.

	Model 57	Model 58	Model 29	Model 25
Caliber:	.41 Magnum.	.41 Magnum.	.44 Magnum.	.45 ACP.
Length Overall:	9.3", 11.3", 13.6"	9.25"	9.3", 11.8", 13.6"	11.8"
Barrel Length:	4", 6", 8.3"	4"	4", 6.5", 8.3"	6.5"
Sights:	Front blade on ramp; notched-bar rear fully adjustable.	Blade and notch.	Front blade on ramp; notched-bar rear fully adjustable.	Front blade on ramp; notched-bar rear fully adjustable.
Weight:	W/6"-barrel, 3 lb.	2.6 lb.	2.7 lb., 2.9 lb., 3.2 lb.	2.8 lb.

S&W FACTORY DESIGNATIONS

In late 1957, S&W simplified identification and ordering by assigning weapons a *Catalog Model Number,* stamped on the frame, visible behind the yoke. Some people confuse these with the serial number. The arms also have a *factory designation,* which is listed for information, rather than to confuse. It is not stamped on the guns.

Factory Designation	Model Number	Factory Designation	Model Number	Factory Designation	Model Number
NT-430	29	KA-38	12	JA-38	37
NT-357	27	KT-32	16	JAC-38	38
NTM-357	28	KT-22	17 & 18	JSA-38	42
N-38	20	KT-22M	48	22 Auto	41
NT-38	23	JAT-22	43	9mm	39 & 44
N-44	21	IT-22	34 & 35	AM22L	46
NT-44	24	I-38 Reg.	32 & 33	JTM-22	51
N-45	22	I-32	30 & 31	KTC22R	53
KT-357	19	J-38	36	N-410	58
K-38	10	JS-38	40	NT-410	57
KT-38 Spec.	14 & 15				

THOMPSON

The Thompson Center Arms Co. is a division of the K. W. Thompson Tool Co. which is located at Rochester, New Hampshire. The Thompson Tool Co. has been manufacturing components for the arms industry for many years and started production of a pistol of their own design in 1967. Design of this pistol, the Contender, started in 1954.

Thompson Center Contender

The Contender is a single-shot, break-open type target pistol which can be obtained with 8.75 inch or 10-inch barrel chambered for the .22 S., L., or L.R., .22 WMR., .22 Hornet, .22 Remington Jet, .38 Special or .357 Magnum. Barrels separately chambered for each of the calibers listed are interchangeable and can be purchased for any of the mentioned cartridges.

The Contender breaks open like a shotgun by squeezing up on the tang of the triggerguard. The fired cases are removed by hand. There are two firing pins—one for center-fire, one for rimfire—mounted in the frame. In the face of the hammer is an offset screw which is rotated to strike the desired firing pin. All metal parts of the Contender are steel and most exposed parts have a polished blue finish. The top of the barrel and sights have a dull matte finish to cut down glare. The grips both have a thumb rest and are, as is the forend, made of checkered walnut. The front sight is a Partridge-type blade mounted on a ramp and the rear sight, which is mounted on the octagonal barrel, is adjustable for elevation and windage. Barrels are tapped for scope mounting. The pistol cannot be fired when the action is open, a safety bar blocks the single-action hammer when the triggerguard tang is pushed up and it remains in place until the action is locked.

THOMPSON CENTER CONTENDER.

To remove the barrel, pull forend down and away from the frame, move up trigger and remove large pin from the frame, then lift off barrel. Trigger pull can be adjusted when the barrel is removed by turning the trigger-pull adjustment screw, located in the left rear of the frame, with an Allen wrench. The Contender is 12.5-inches long and weighs 2.5 pounds with 8.75-inch barrel. It is 13.5-inches long and weighs 2.7 pounds with 10-inch barrel. This is a finely-made pistol which is capable of very creditable performance.

TINGLE

The Tingle Mfg. Co. of Shelbyville, Indiana introduced the Tingle Black Powder Magnum in 1960. The pistol had to be re-named since the term "Magnum," in this context, is a Smith & Wesson registered trade-mark.

Tingle Black Powder Model 1960

Unlike many of the black-powder replicas which are copies or near copies of older arms long out of production, the Tingle is an original design. It is a cap-and-ball single-shot pistol using a .400-inch round ball for which Tingle

TINGLE .40 cal. black-powder pistol.

supplies moulds. The pistol should be used with FFFFg or FFFg black powder, NEVER with smokeless powder. A charge of 27 grains, wadded with .015 bed-ticking for a patch, is recommended.

An 8-inch barrel is standard; longer barrels can be obtained on special order. The Tingle is 11.75 inches long and weighs 2.2 pounds. It has a ramp-mounted blade front sight and an adjustable rear sight. The one-piece grip is made of walnut. A detachable shoulder-stock can also be obtained for this pistol; as a muzzle-loading black-powder weapon, it is exempt from registration with the Alcohol Tax Unit of the IRS, U. S. Treasury.

WHITNEY

The Whitney Wolverine which entered production in 1955 was designed by Robert Hillberg of West Cheshire, Conn.

Whitney .22 L.R. Wolverine

The Wolverine has an outer shell of duraluminum—1955-58 "218 aluminum-alloy," 1958-65, "380 aluminum-alloy"—which contains all the working parts. This single-piece outer shell or frame takes the place of the normal slide and receiver or grip-frame found in most automatics. The Wolverine is blowback-operated with reciprocating semi-circular bolt. The operating tube, a semi-cicular piece which covers the top of the bolt and the greater part of the barrel within the shell, is pinned to the bolt. The tube has a lip at its forward end which lays in front of the barrel-mounted operating spring.

The tube is driven to the rear with the bolt when a cartridge is fired and compresses the operating spring. The spring then pulls the tube and bolt back into firing position. The safety is mounted on the left rear of the frame and is engaged by pushing it down. With the hammer cocked, engagement of the safety blocks the sear and disconnects the trigger from the action.

The Wolverine has a ten round, in-line, detachable box magazine. It has a

WHITNEY WOLVERINE .22 automatic pistol.

4.6-inch barrel, is 9-inches long overall, and weighs 1.4 pounds. All of the operating parts of the Whitney which receive pressure are made of steel. There is very little strain on the duraluminum shell frame.

791

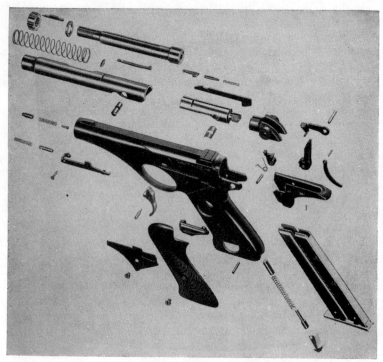

A WHITNEY pistol disassembled.

In 1965 improvements were proposed in the design of the cocking piece, the safety was relocated, a bolt-holding-open device was added, an adjustable rear sight was developed, the firing-pin lock and the barrel-seat washer were eliminated and the shell/frame was redesigned to accept a scope mount. Nothing ever came of this, however, as the Wolverine passed out of production in 1963.

The Wolverine had many good points, but could not compete with the Ruger Standard and the economy .22 automatics put out by Colt and High Standard. Making guns is a tough, competitive business and casualties are many, unfortunately, even among those who have a basically good product.

Field-Stripping. To field-strip the Wolverine, push in the locking plunger located under the barrel nut at the front of the frame and unscrew the barrel nut in a counterclockwise direction. With the hammer at full-cock position, draw the operating tube assembly out of the frame to the rear by pulling back on the cocking piece. The cocking piece is screwed to the bolt and held in place by a pin. Pull forward on the barrel to relieve the operating spring tension on the bolt and punch out the pin which holds the bolt to the operating tube. The bolt, barrel and operating spring can now be removed from the operating tube. No further disassembly is recommended.

U.S.S.R.

The Soviet Union has adopted two new military pistols since WW II, both chambered for a new 9mm cartridge. The 7.62mm Tokarev Model 1933, still in use in some of the satellite countries, is no longer in service in the U.S.S.R.

9mm Makarov (PM)

The PM is quite similar in appearance to the Walther PP, but the PM is somewhat larger. The PM is loaded, fired and field-stripped basically the same as is the Walther.

Differences, PM and Walther PP. The "PM" differs in many ways from the Walther. The PM does not have a loaded-chamber indicating pin. The PM uses a leaf-type mainspring; the Walther uses a coil spring. The trigger-sear linkage of the PM is considerably different than that of the Walther, as is the

SOVIET 9mm Makarov (PM).

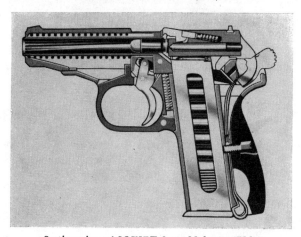

Section view of SOVIET 9mm Makarov (PM).

793

disconnector which moves laterally on the PM. The magazine catch of the Makarov is at the bottom rear of the grip; the Walther has a button-type magazine catch mounted on the left side of the receiver. The PM has an externally-mounted slide stop; the Walther slide stop is completely enclosed within the pistol and is released by drawing back on the slide and allowing the slide to run forward. The ejector of the PM is the back end of the slide-stop bar. The safety of the PM is pushed up to put it on *safe* and pushed down to put on *fire*, which is opposite to that of the Walther. The safety of the PM lays a bar in front of the hammer and has a lug which positions itself in front of the rear shoulder of the receiver, thereby locking the slide to the receiver and preventing the hammer from being cocked. The advantage of this system is questionable.

9mm Stechkin Machine Pistol (APS)

The APS is a blowback-operated weapon capable of automatic as well as semi-automatic fire. It has a detachable shoulder-stock holster similar to that of the Mauser and the Spanish Star Model MM. On both of these counts it, if privately acquired in the United States, requires registration with the Firearms Branch, Alcohol Tax Unit, U. S. Internal Revenue Service. The APS has apparently not been made in as large quantities as the PM since it is not frequently seen in service. The possibility exists that the pistol has been retired from service by the Soviets; in any event, it is a comparatively rare item.

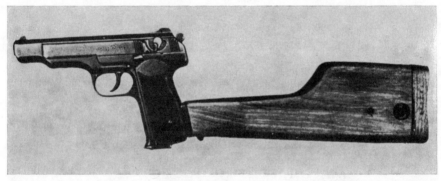

SOVIET 9mm Stechkin (APS) MACHINE PISTOL with shoulder-stock holster attached.

The value of full-automatic pistols with shoulder-stock holsters in the hands of the average man is somewhat dubious. It should be noted, however, that specially-trained personnel can do relatively well with such weapons. Weapons training specialists at the U. S. Army, John F. Kennedy Special Warfare Training Center, Fort Bragg, North Carolina, have turned in creditable performance with the 7.63mm M1932 Mauser machine pistol in automatic fire at ranges up to 100 meters and in semi-automatic fire at ranges of 200 meters. The APS being chambered for the Soviet 9mm cartridge, which has considerably less muzzle energy than the 7.63mm Mauser, probably performs equally well in the hands of specially-trained personnel.

The APS has an interesting disconnecting method for automatic fire. The disconnector, in automatic fire, is pressed down in close contact with the sear/ sear lever when the selector/safety, which is mounted on the left rear of the slide, is set in the automatic-fire position. The other—forward—end of the disconnector rests on the top of a spring-loaded plunger which is mounted in a tube behind the magazine well in the grip. When the slide returns to the battery poistion after a shot is fired, the disconnector is cammed down and exerts sudden sharp pressure on the spring-loaded plunger. The plunger pushes down against the spring, compressing it, and the spring then pushes the plunger back against the disconnector which pivots upward at the rear and downward at the front, causing the sear/sear lever to disengage from the hammer and causing another shot to be fired. This type of disconnection helps to reduce the cyclic rate of fire. The mainspring does double duty in the APS; it also serves as the magazine catch spring.

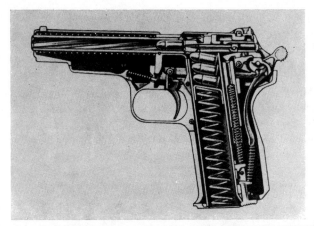

Section view of SOVIET 9mm Stechkin (APS) MACHINE PISTOL.

The APS is disassembled, loaded and fired in a manner similar to the PM excepting its automatic-fire selector. To set the pistol to produce automatic fire, set the safety selector at the point marked "ABT." The rear sight is adjustable by knurled rings to 25, 50, 100 and 150 meters.

SOVIET TARGET PISTOLS

The U.S.S.R. has produced a respectable number of high-quality target pistols since WW II. These have been offered for sale abroad and have turned in very creditable performances at international shooting events in the past fifteen or so years. Some of these pistols have been sold in the United States, but current regulations forbid the import of arms and ammunition from Communist countries.

The first target pistol in the U.S.S.R. used a signal-pistol frame and was developed near the end of the 1920s by Bersenev, a gunsmith at the Izhesky plant. Another designer—M. Blum—developed a self-ejecting .22 target pistol in the early thirties. R-4, a .22 pistol based on the Tokarev M1933 design, was developed by Sevryugin, prior to WW II.

795

MARGOLIN

Mikhail Margolin is probably the best known, in the West at least, of the Soviet target-pistol designers. Margolin produced a number of designs prior to WW II, but his best-known designs have been produced since that period. The most remarkable fact about this highly-talented designer is that he is blind and was so prior to the time he started designing pistols. Margolin's first post-war design, the Model 1949, has had widespread distribution throughout the Communist world. At this point, it should be noted that Soviet model designations for their sporting pistols are sometimes somewhat confusing. Some pistols apparently have several model designations—a date designation and an arbitrary model designation. Some Soviet publications will use the one designation and others will use the other. The date designations, i.e., Model 1948, etc., is rarely used in advertising literature intended for the export market.

Margolin .22 L.R. Model 1949

The Model 1949 is a blowback-operated target pistol and was the first of a series of Margolin pistols all of which vary from each other principally in minor details. The Margolins, with one exception, are all typified by non-recoiling rear sights which are mounted on a bridge over the slide. The bridge is fastened to the receiver. They all also have rear sights adjustable for elevation and are all dismounted in the same fashion. The Margolin has a locking bar which goes through the front part of the slide and prevents the slide from being blown rearward off the receiver, in a manner similar to that used in the early Colt/Browning automatics and the Model 12 Steyr.

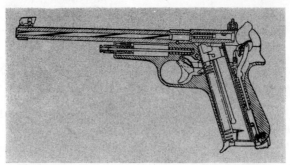

Section view of .22 L.R. MARGOLIN Model 1949.

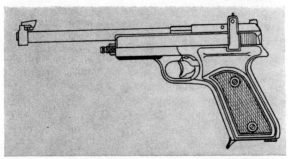

MARGOLIN .22 L.R. Model 1949.

Margolin .22 L.R. Model 1955

This pistol is basically the same as the Model 1949, but has a muzzle-brake/compensator which serves as a barrel weight, target-type grips with hand rest and a different front sight. There are .22 Short versions of this model with shorter barrel and long, heavy compensator/muzzle-brakes which also serve as barrel weights.

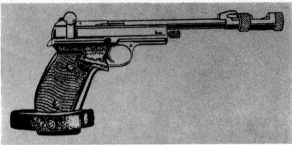

MARGOLIN .22 L.R. Model 1955.

Margolin .22 Short Model MTsZ-1

This is a very unusual .22 Short match pistol which created quite a stir at the Melbourne Olympics in 1956. This blowback-operated pistol is upside down, i.e., the pistol receiver with action, slide and barrel are below the level of the top of the shooter's hand. They are supported by a flat rib which, running from the top of the grip out to a point beyond the barrel, also serves as the mounting point for the front and rear sights. The 5-round magazine is loaded from the top. The pistol has an external hammer as do all the Margolins; ejection is to the right and downward.

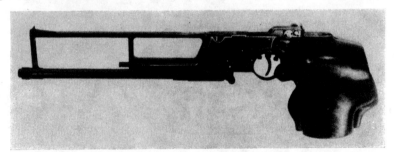

MARGOLIN .22 Short Model MTsZ-1.

As a result of the introduction of this pistol, the Olympic rules on the rapid-fire pistol event were changed to read that all pistols used in the event would have to fit into a box 30-centimeters long, 15-centimeters high and 10-centimeters deep, thereby eliminating this pistol.

Margolin .22 L.R. Model MTs

This is the current production version of the Margolin in .22 L.R. It has a heavy muzzle-brake/compensator and attachable barrel weights of 1.8 and

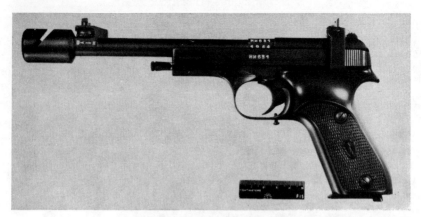

MARGOLIN .22 L.R. Model MTs.

3.5 oz. There is a screw through the bottom of the triggerguard serving as a trigger stop. The safety catch, which locks the sear also serves as a slide stop. The MTs has a removable hand rest. It is supplied with spare front sights of varying thickness and rear sight bars with varying size notches.

MARGOLIN Model MTs field-stripped.

Margolin .22 Short Model MTsU

This is a .22 Short version of the MTs. It has a shorter barrel than the MTs and has, in addition to a detachable hand rest, a projecting hand stop at the top of the grip.

798

OTHER SOVIET TARGET PISTOLS
.22 L.R. Model MTs-2-3

The MTs-2-3 was developed at Tula from the MTs-2 which appeared in 1952. It is a single-shot bolt-action Olympic Free pistol. It has a double-set pin-type trigger. The trigger is set by depressing the triggerguard spur by approximately .4-inch. Weight of pull can be reduced to about 1/8th-ounce. The locking lugs on the bolt are placed about midway on the bolt body. The heel-plate-type hand rest can be locked at the desired setting by use of the large plastic knurled knob protruding from the left grip. The rear sight is adjustable for windage and elevation; as with other Soviet target pistols, three interchangeable sight blades of varying thickness and rear sight bars with varying size notches are supplied. The trigger mechanism has a built-in shock absorber system.

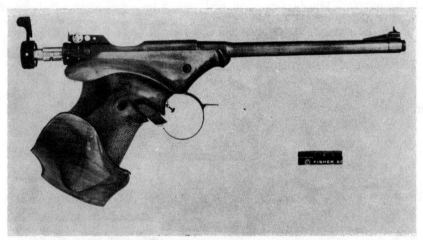

SOVIET .22 L.R. Model MTs-2-3 Free pistol, bolt open.

.22 L.R. Model IZh-1

The IZh-1 is also a single-shot Olympic Free pistol. The pistol has a Martini-type drop block which is operated by a lever on the left side of the grip. Rear-

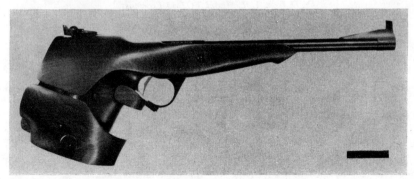

SOVIET .22 L.R. Model IZh-3 Free pistol.

ward movement of the lever drops the block exposing the chamber, cocks the firing pin, and extracts the empty case. Upward movement locks the breech and releases the firing pin from the safe position. The IZh-1 has a rear sight adjustable for windage and elevation. The trigger pull is adjustable as is the hand rest. This pistol was developed at Izhevsky by A. Lobanov and B. Pletskiy, and appeared in 1962. A modification of the IZh-1, the IZh-3, has a rear sight adjustable for elevation and windage and a differently-shaped forend and rear stock which completely covers the top of the hand on the right side of the grip.

.22 L.R. Model TOZ-35

The TOZ-35, sometimes called the Vostok, was developed by Y. Khaydurov and appeared in 1963. It is a single-shot Olympic Free pistol with Martini-type breech mechanism. The breech is opened and closed by a lever which projects from the base of the grip. The set-trigger is cocked by applying pressure downwards on a lever mounted on the left side of the receiver. Weight of trigger pull can be adjusted from 2/5ths-ounce to 3 ounces by turning clockwise a screw in the forend strap forward of the trigger. Creep can be adjusted by a screw directly behind the trigger. The sights are mounted higher than on other Soviet Free pistols. The rear sight is adjustable for windage and elevation; the front sight is mounted on a ramp.

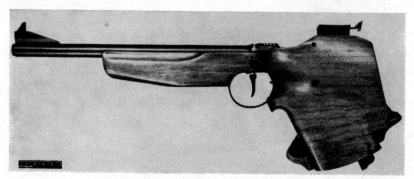

SOVIET .22 L.R. Model TOZ-35 Free pistol.

.22 L.R. SOVIET POST-WW II PISTOLS

	MTs-2-3	IZh-1	TOZ-35 (Vostok)
System of Operation:	Manually-operated bolt.	Manually-operated drop-block.	Manually-operated drop-block.
Length Overall:	Approx. 17"	Approx. 17"	17.25"
Barrel Length:	11.6"	11.5" (Approx.)	11.8"
Weight:	2.53 to 3.3 lb.	2.6 lb.	2.8 lb.

Note: These are all single-shot pistols equipped with changeable-blade front sight and changeable rear notched bars adjustable for windage and elevation.

SOVIET POST-WW II PISTOLS

	Makarov (PM)	Stechkin (APS)	Margolin MTs	Margolin MTsU
Caliber:	9mm (Makarov).	9mm (Makarov).	.22 L.R.	.22 Short.
System of Operation:	Blowback, semi-automatic.	Blowback, semi and full[1] automatic.	Blowback, semi-automatic.	Blowback, semi-automatic.
Length Overall:	6.34"	W/o shoulder stock, 8.85"; w/shoulder stock, 21.25".	12.25"	11"
Barrel Length:	3.83"	5".	6.3"	5.1"
Feed Device:	8-round, in-line detachable box magazine.	20-round, staggered row detachable box magazine.	6-round, in-line detachable box magazine.	6-round, in-line detachable box magazine.
Sights:	Blade and square notch.	Blade front; rear notch adjustable to 25, 50, 100 and 150 meters.	Front blade adjustable for E; notched-bar rear adjustable for W.	Front blade adjustable for E; notched-bar rear adjustable for W.
Weight:	1.56 lb.	1.7 lb. w/o shoulder stock holster; 3.92 lb. with.	2.3 to 2.6 lb.	2.2 to 2.4 lb.

[1] Cyclic rate: 750 rounds per minute.

801

YUGOSLAVIA

Yugoslavia has used a wide variety of pistols as Service arms. Prior to WW II, the Austrian 9mm Model 1912 Steyr and the .380 ACP FN Browning M1922 pistols were widely issued. At the close of WW II, a large number of 9mm Parabellum 08 Lugers and P38 Walthers seized from the Germans were used for a while.

In 1957 the Yugoslavs officially adopted the Soviet 7.62mm Tokarev M1933 which they manufacture at Kragujevac. The Yugoslav-made pistol is called the Model 57; Soviet-made 7.62mm Tokarevs are also used by the Yugoslavs.

YUGOSLAV 7.62mm Model 57.

Section Two
Post-World War II Pistol and Revolver Ammunition

There has been only one new military pistol cartridge introduced into service since WW II—the Soviet 9mm Makarov. By "military cartridge," the general Service cartridge intended primarily for normal military operations such as the U. S. caliber .45 Model 1911 cartridge, is meant. There have been and will be a number of adaptations of standard cartridges or specific cartridges made for limited purposes, i.e., match shooting, special operations, etc. Since the use and manufacture of these cartridges is limited in scope and quantity, it is not felt that they belong in this book. They and similar commercial cartridges, i.e., "wildcats," more properly belong in a book which addresses itself specifically to cartridges and/or handloading of cartridges. We concern ourselves here only with cartridges which have an extensive distribution and use and which are likely to come to the notice of or be used by the average pistol collector/ shooter.

MAKAROV
Soviet 9mm Makarov

This cartridge appears to be modeled on the German 9mm Ultra cartridge which was in a developmental stage at the end of WW II. The Ultra was intended for an enlarged version of the Walther PP and was under development for the Luftwaffe. The Makarov cartridge is intermediate in size and power to the .380 ACP and the 9mm Parabellum. It is used in the Makarov (PM) pistol and the Stechkin Machine Pistol (APS), and is used by East Germany, Poland, Rumania, Bulgaria and Hungary in addition to the U.S.S.R. Characteristics are given in the tabulations accompanying this section.

SOVIET 9mm Makarov pistol cartridge.

There have been a number of commercial cartridges designed for or used in handguns, introduced in the United States since WW II, ranging in caliber from .22 to .44. Important ones will be covered individually.

803

WINCHESTER

.22 Winchester Magnum Rimfire

Usually called the .22 WMR, this cartridge is an enlarged and higher-powered version of the old .22 WRF. Winchester introduced this rimfire in 1959 as a cartridge suitable for varmint shooting. It is advertised as having a muzzle velocity of 2,000 feet per second in a rifle with 24-inch barrel; in a 6.5-inch barrel pistol this is about 1550 feet per second. These velocities are with 40-grain jacketed hollow-point bullet.

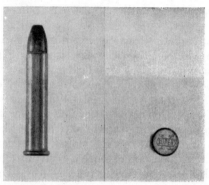

.22 WINCHESTER MAGNUM RIMFIRE cartridge.

It would be somewhat less than honest to say that there have been no problems with this cartridge. To a great extent this is probably due to the fact that many arms manufacturers have been rather slack in their headspace tolerances for the .22 rimfire cartridges. This practice is not bad for the low pressured .22 Short, Long or Long Rifle, but with the higher-pressured Winchester Magnum, which has a relatively light case head, it is a horse of a different color. Pressure is 24,000 p.s.i.

.256 Magnum

This cartridge was developed by Winchester in 1960 by necking down the .357 Magnum to .25 caliber using a 60-grain .25-20 bullet. Prototype revolvers

Experimental .256 WINCHESTER MAGNUM, right, uses necked-down .357 case with .25-20 bullet.

were made by Colt, Ruger and S&W, but none were successful. Ruger solved the problem of case setback experienced in revolvers by developing the Hawkeye, a single-shot on the Blackhawk frame. It is no longer made by Ruger. Universal Firearms makes a rifle—the Ferret—chambered for this cartridge.

REMINGTON

.22 Remington Jet

This cartridge was developed by necking down the .357 Magnum case to .22 and was probably inspired by the Harvey Kay-Chuk, a wildcat round. Kent Bellah reported that the original velocity figure given on this round—2460 feet per second with 40-grain bullet—was greatly exaggerated. Current book velocity is 2100 feet per second with 8.3-inch barrel. Bellah got pressures as high as 45,400 p.s.i. with early loads, and 36,800 p.s.i. with early revised loads. He also reported problems with case setback causing locking of the cylinder. There have been two revisions of this round since it first appeared. The revised rounds use improved soft-point bullets and have lower velocities and less pressure.

The .22 Jet has a very loud report. The use of ear plugs when firing this round, is recommended.

Headstamp of original R-P .22 REM. CFM and improved .22 REM. JET, as currently produced for the S&W .22 Magnum revolver.

Original REMINGTON .22 MAGNUM round (left), and current round with improved bullet, headstamped R-P .22 REM. JET. Note the much greater expansion of the new bullet fired in moist sand (far right).

.221 Remington Fireball

The Fireball was developed for the Remington XP-100 and was introduced early in 1963. The case is a shortened version of the .222 rifle cartridge. This is a high-pressure cartridge and is suitable only for strong actions.

.41 Remington Magnum

This cartridge was introduced in 1963 with the Smith & Wesson Model 57 revolver. Bellah reported that actual velocity with 210-grain soft-point load in a 4-inch barrel is 1250 feet per second, not the listed 1500 feet per second. Accuracy is very good with this cartridge, but recoil is heavy.

Left, .41 REM. MAGNUM, S.P.; Center, RELOAD with Bellah's copy of 1904 Wilder bullet design; Right, wildcat .403 CLAY with same H&G Bellah bullet. All are powerful loads. (Photo courtesy GUNS MAGAZINE).

It is difficult to visualize what role this cartridge was designed to play that cannot be played by the .357 Magnum or the .44 Magnum.

.44 Remington Magnum

This cartridge was developed by Remington and introduced in 1955. The Smith & Wesson Model 29 was the first gun chambered for the .44 Magnum. This cartridge has a higher muzzle energy than any other pistol cartridge in the world, 38% more than the Remington High Speed .357 Magnum Soft Point cartridge. This cartridge is also used in rifles and has more potential than .44-40 rifle loads.

POST-WW II PISTOL AND REVOLVER CARTRIDGES OF NOTE

	9mm Makarov	22 WMR	22 Rem. JET	221 Rem. FIREBALL
Overall Length:	.97"	1.35"	1.65"	1.8"
Case Type:	Rimless, parallel-walled.	Rimmed, parallel-wall.	Rimmed, tapered bottleneck.	Rimless, bottle-necked.
Case Length:	.71"	1.95"	1.28"	1.40"
Case Head Diameter:	.389"	.242"	.375"	.375"
Case Base Diameter:	.389"	.294"	.439"	.378"
Bullet Weight:	94-gr.	40-gr.	40-gr.	50-gr.
Bullet Diameter:	.362"	.224"	.222"	.224"
*Muzzle Velocity:**	1070 fps w/3.8"-barrel.	1550 fps w/6.5"-barrel.	2100 fps w/8.3"-barrel.	2650 fps w/10.5"-barrel.

* Velocities given are the conventional "book" figures.

POST-WW II PISTOL AND REVOLVER CARTRIDGES OF NOTE (Continued)

	.256 Win. Magnum	.41 Rem. Magnum	.44 Rem. Magnum
Overall Length:	1.59"	1.59"	1.61"
Case Type:	Rimmed, bottle-necked.	Rimmed, slightly tapered.	Rimmed, slightly tapered.
Case Length:	1.28"	1.29"	1.28"
Case Head Diameter:	.379"	.435"	.457"
Case Base Diameter:	.440"	.492"	.514"
Bullet Weight:	60-gr.	210-gr.	240-gr.
Bullet Diameter:	.257"	.434" (soft-point) .411" (lead bullet)	.432"
*Muzzle Velocity:**	2350 fps w/8.5"-barrel.	1500 fps (soft-point) and 1050 fps (lead) in 8.3"-barrel.	1470 fps w/6.5"-barrel.

* Velocities given are the conventional "book" figures.

Index